PRISON LIVES

PRISON LIVES

ALMANAC

Prisoner Education Guide

2018 Edition

If today's date is after September 1, 2018, there is an updated version of this publication.

Educational opportunities for prisoners change frequently.
Don't rely on old information!

Order the newly updated 2019 Edition of the *Prison Lives Almanac: Prisoner Education Guide* today!

PRISON LIVES

PO Box 842, Exeter, CA 93221

www.PrisonLives.com

Prison Lives Almanac: Prisoner Education Guide– 2018 Edition

Published by Prison Lives
PO Box 842, Exeter, California, 93221
info@PrisonLives.com
www.PrisonLives.com

Registered Copyright © 2017 by Prison Lives

ISBN-

Special Sales: For information on using *Prison Lives Almanacs* at prison institutions or special prices for bulk quantities, please contact our sales department at: info@PrisonLives.com

To purchase an additional copy of this book, please make your payment of $25 by:

- money order or facility check mailed to *Prison Lives.*
- MoneyGram
- Credit/Debit card at: *www.PrisonLives.com* or by email at *info@prisonlives.com*
- PayPal™ payment sent direct to *info@PrisonLives.com*.

For further information, please contact:

PRISON LIVES
PO Box 842, Exeter, California, 93221
www.PrisonLives.com
info@PrisonLives.com (Corrlinks registered)

Prison Lives is a 501(c)(3) nonprofit organization that educates and enables prisoners to be productive individuals while incarcerated and to prepare them and their families for a positive existence both inside and outside of prison life.

Printed in the United States

Contents

INTRODUCTION

If there's one positive to be drawn from having to live life behind bars it may be that the *time* spent standing still forces a pause in the hectic nature of life beyond the prison walls. This pause allows prisoners the advantage of being able to reflect on their journey up to this point, to take stock of their lives, to possibly reconsider past choices, and to see where they might have taken a different course.

Oftentimes, this reflection leads prisoners down a path of recognition of opportunities they missed along the way, frequently causing them to wish for a do-over, to go back and decide differently so that they would not find themselves staring at four walls... one made of bars.

A common realization that prisoners discover along this reflective journey is that they wished they had taken their education more seriously. The unfortunate statistical reality is that a large chunk of those locked up in America never made it past a 6th grade education. It's a well-known fact that the more education a person has, the likelier that person is to avoid having to live an incarcerated life. Think about it, how many college educated people do you know who have served time?

There is an obvious direct correlation between education and freedom. Those who regret their past education choices are heartened knowing that it's not too late to get that education. The more schooling a prisoner has, *regardless of where or when he got it*, the less likely that prisoner is to ever see the inside of a prison again.

If you have picked up this book, you probably realize that simple fact. However, you also probably realize that the act of getting an education while you live in a prison can be a quite the challenge, to put it rather mildly.

Prison today is not intended to be a school. While the stated purpose of prison used to be to rehabilitate, which certainly encompassed educating prisoners, the modern reality is that prison is designed for punishment, retribution, and keeping offenders from opportunities that are afforded to free members of society. Even though it is proven that education drastically reduces recidivism, which has a positive cascading effect on society, the prison society over the past couple of decades has moved away from education. Between this and the high costs of learning any other way, it has been exceedingly difficult for prisoners who have recognized what additional schooling can do for

> The higher the educational level of the prisoner, the lower the likelihood they will ever come back to prison again.
>
>
>
> ### RECIDIVISM RATES FOR THE EDUCATED
>
> Prisoners with:
>
> **high school** diploma, or equivalent:
> **55%** likely to return to prison
>
> **vocational training**:
> **30%** likely to return to prison
>
> **associate's degree**:
> **13.7%** likely to return to prison
>
> **bachelor's degree**:
> **5.6%** likely to return to prison
>
> **master's degree**:
> **0%** likely to return to prison
>
> Source: Robert Alan, *"An Economic Analysis of Prison Education Programs and Recidivism"* Emory University, Department of Economics, (2006)

them and who would like to begin a path towards becoming better educated.

Fortunately, there appears to be a shift in the works. The tide that has been receding away from prisoner education is now coming back.

Recent attitudes and moves in legislation are focusing on bringing educational opportunities back to prisoners and making it easier for those who would like learn to afford the ability to do so. If you are interested in obtaining an education while incarcerated, which may be the most important action you can take during your imprisoned life, NOW is the perfect time to consider your options.

The road of self-education is by no means an easy one for prisoners. Prisons, although beginning to recognize the importance of providing educational opportunities, still present the biggest challenges to learning. Additionally, and perhaps a greater challenge for many, is the fact that education remains a very expensive prospect, even though some financial aid for prisoners is currently being discussed in congress.

Prison Lives was established as a bridge to all of the information you need to get you started down your path to education, despite your circumstances. Our aim is to provide you with the ultimate tool to access the resources you need to successfully navigate the scholastic world outside of your confined space so that you can make the best use of your time inside.

The **_Prison Lives Almanac: Prisoner Education Guide_** is the only true current prisoner education guide that comprehensively provides all of the information that prisoner-students desire in such a guide.

School make changes annually. Therefore it's important to keep up with these changes as they occur, specifically as they affect prisoners. Information that we track includes available prisoner-friendly print courses, tuition rates, payment options, testing opportunities, and more.

Access to information is never easy for prisoners. We know how much prisoners desire as much detail as possible to be able to make educated choices. We provide this detail in ways you won't find elsewhere, such as through course descriptions, course availability and specific restrictions affecting prisoners.

Prisoners typically don't have the resources to afford upper-level education on their own. Financing options to help prisoners pay for school is the among the most requested information from prisoner-students. We provide the latest in financial aid for prisoners, including information on the latest scholarship opportunities, Pell Grants, tax credits and any additional helpful tools we can find to lower education costs for prisoners.

Prison Lives is dedicated to providing the most comprehensive up-to-date prisoner-focused resources and information to prisoners. We are proud to be able to do so in such a vital area as prisoner education and we look forward to doing so for years to come.

Life doesn't have to end or even stall with a prison sentence. There is an entire world available to empower prisoners. There is no reason for you not to be a part of it.

Education = Freedom
This is your annual guide to discovery of that freedom.

How This Book is Structured

Prison Lives Almanacs are *full* of prisoner resources. So many resources, in fact, that it can be easy to get lost. Therefore, our Almanacs are organized to make it easy for you to pick it up when the need arises and quickly find exactly what you are looking for with just a flip of the pages.

DISTINCT SECTIONS

Instead of listing all of the resources in alphabetical order, we've clearly listed each resource under subject headings, which can be found at the top of each odd-numbered page.

INFORMATION BOXES

> INFORMATION BOXES let you know of highlighted facts that may be important in helping you make decisions on the matters being discussed.

HIGHLIGHTED LISTINGS

Because schools and resources come with varying degrees of reliability, we've highlighted several listings in the following manner to let you know that prisoners have found these listings to be especially reliable resources. If you know of schools or resources that you would recommend, please let us know by telling how they were especially useful to you so that we can highlight them in our next edition.

> **PRISON LIVES**
>
> PO Box 842, Exeter, CA 93221
> *WWW.PRISONLIVES.COM*
> *INFO@PRISONLIVES.COM* (Corrlinks registered)
> Prison Lives is the nation's largest provider of prisoner resources and information. Through up-to-date and reliable publications, they provide prisoners with the most useful tools to make the best use of their time despite their confines.

Thank you for letting *Prison Lives* help you discover your path to freedom! If you find something particularly useful, or if you would like to suggest an edit or change, please feel free to contact us.

In the meantime, enjoy your *Prison Lives Almanac: Prisoner Education Guide,* and check out our other products, including the *Prison Lives Almanac: Prisoner Resource Guide,* full of thousands of current resources prisoners need most, and our *Prison Lives Almanac: Prisoner Entertainment Guide,* your one-stop seasonal guide to enhance your entertainment options.

Part 1 Going to School Behind Bars

The decision to go back to school, regardless of your current age, can be a stressful one. If your just now considering obtaining a formal education while behind bars, there are likely a number of questions pinballing around in your head.

This part provides answers to many of the initial questions that prisoners encounter to help you begin deciding whether this is a path you want to take as well as to begin understanding what's involved with such a step from such a confined place.

Will it really help me after I get out?

Do I really need an education?

What if I'm not getting out?

I HATED school. Why would I want to go back?

A BRIEF HISTORY OF PRISON EDUCATION

The benefits of prison education have been recognized almost since the birth of formal incarceration in this country. In 1791, coincidentally when the Bill of Rights was enacted, the Quakers, a Protestant religion devoted to peaceful principles, formed the first prison in the U.S. The Pennsylvania prison was established to ensure public safety, to reform prisoners, and, according to the original founders of the prison, to bring "humanity toward those unhappy members of society." The Quakers, being one of peace, and known for their philanthropy, hoped to be able to rehabilitate those they locked up, to bring them back as productive members of their society. They soon realized that one of the more effective means to accomplishing that was to educate their prisoners. Therefore, seven years after opening the prison, they added a school.

The very first prison in this country offered educational opportunities.

For nearly 220 years, Americans have known that offering education to prisoners brings positive benefits to society. However, at times prisons were more recognized for their ability to produce manpower. Prison labor trumped most other considerations regarding prisoners beginning in the late 19th century. Prisons soon became an industrial complex of its own where prisoners were forced to spend their days performing the tasks that other Americans would rather not do. During those times, prison administration believed that anything that distracted from the labor services that prisoners provided was a bad idea. Sadly, education certainly fell into that category.

Fortunately, however, by the early 20th century, society was again realizing that rehabilitation was an important aspect of prison time. Since prisoners would eventually be released, it made more sense to at least try to ensure that they came out better than they went in. Education was reintroduced into prison society.

Initially, schooling only involved the most basic learning, which was often heavily religiously bent However, the realization soon came that vocational training was a beneficial way to help prisoners develop useful skills that would not only be of assistance in occupying prisoners time, but would more importantly increase the chances of successful reentry into the world. Prisons, such as Sing Sing, began offering vocational training through correspondence courses.

The U.S. penal system seemed poised to head down a path towards improving the lives of those under their watch, providing actual measures that could serve to reform prisoners. Incarceration rates were relatively low back then, roughly 60 people per 100,000, and looking as though they would only get better.

And Then the Great Depression Happened

Once again, now the late 1920s, prisons were thrust into being used as glorified labor camps. The need for survival closed school books along with any drive for prison education. Incarceration rates doubled over the next decade, topping 131 per 100,000 by the end of the Great Depression. It would be another decade before prison education would get a toe-hold.

The books began to slowly re-open in the early 1950s, generally through the grace of volunteer groups and limited correspondence opportunities. However, it wasn't until 1965 that prison education really got its jump-start. In that year, Congress officially recognized the benefits that education behind bars could do for society and passed *Title IV* of the *Higher Education Act*. This, for the first time in U.S. history, enabled prisoners to receive government funding for education. This financial assistance from the U.S. government, known as *Pell Grants*, made it possible for qualified prisoners to take college level classes while behind bars.

Prison education opportunities skyrocketed. With the help of government aid, college programs were suddenly offered in virtually every state. Prisoners were able to go to actual classes established in prison by local colleges. For the first time, prisoners were earning college degrees, regardless of their crimes or where they happened to be housed.

"Rehabilitation" was again on the lips of prison authorities, and the imprisonment rates began reflecting it. By 1970, the imprisonment rate reflected a significant drop for the first time since the end of the Great Depression, (now 96 per 100,000, down from 117 per 100,000.)

By 1973, there were over 150 education programs in U.S. prisons. By 1980, there were more than twice that many. More than 25,000 prisoners, roughly 8 percent of the prison population, were receiving education behind bars, primarily through in-prison programs. (Only about 13 percent of the education options were through correspondence courses.)

And Then the War on Drugs Began

Prison education was about to experience a devastating blow. Throughout the 80s, violent crime was on the rise. Drugs were blamed. To quell the increases, harsher reforms in sentencing laws incarcerated large amounts of non-violent offenders, leading to much greater imprisonment rates (1980: 138 per 100,000. 1990: 296 per 100,000.) This made it difficult to tell the impact that the proliferation of prison education had on rehabilitation and reentry. Nevertheless, it was widely accepted that without the education options of the 70s and 80s, the recidivism rates – the rate of prisoners that re-offended – would have been much higher.

At the same time, following the lead of notorious conservative senator Jesse Helms of North Carolina, legislators on both sides of the party line began seeking to bar prisoners from receiving federal Pell Grants. They argued that prisoners' ability to get Pell Grants deprived law-abiding students from gaining the financial aid to go to college. Even *Dateline NBC* reported on students ineligible for the grants struggling to pay for college, contrasting them with crime victims who were unhappy that the people who had wronged them had access to college.

In reality, funding never took away from aid opportunities of students on the free side of the wall. The program was need-based, so anyone eligible to receive the grant could receive it. But the public, and some politicians, were misled to believe otherwise. At the time, only .6 percent of Pell Grants overall were going to prisoners. Yet, unreasonable opponents criticized educational institutions for participating in prisoner education and pressured powerful political components who passed the appropriate bills through Congress.

In 1994, with the stroke of then President Bill Clinton's pen, federal education funding for prisoners was withdrawn. Through the *Violent Crime Control and Law Enforcement Act of 1994* and the *Higher Education Reauthorization Act* in that same year, prisoners were suddenly no longer eligible to receive Pell Grants, nor any other student aid. States began following the federal government's lead, dropping their state tuition assistance programs, effectively ending prison education across the nation. Almost immediately every education program in the U.S. turned to dust.

The rest of the 90s and the birth of the new Millennium saw very little restoration of prison education programs. Prisoners were generally left to their own devices to seek out learning opportunities, which, with the already built-in challenges that come with life behind bars, was an uphill battle. Typically, only fortunate prisoners with a tremendous amount of support, and access to a decent amount of financial resources, have been able to earn a quality education from their cells. Of the thousands of educational institutions out there, only a tiny percentage offered options that prisoners were able to partake in. Prisons did very little to make taking such options, or finding other opportunities, an easy prospect. Therefore, getting an education became a fight.

Help Arrives?

At the end of the first decade of this 21st century, prisoner advocacy groups started to feel for the prisoner's plight. Knowing the benefits that such education could bring to prisoners and society, began taking up the fight on their behalf. Many organizations that were keenly aware of what prisoners can accomplish with a little learning took up the banner, petitioning Congress to change their collective minds about financing for student prisoners. Groups like the NAACP urged the courts to make education a condition of parole and probation, noting the positive impact it has on recidivism rates. Higher learning institutions started to go to bat for the cause, asking the political arena to reverse their course on Pell Grants. Even upper levels of the government – from then-Attorney Generals to the then-President of the United States – began voicing their opinion that now was the time to reconsider the importance of prisoner education. They began calling on reforms to allow prisoners to once again have the opportunity to rehabilitate themselves and bring something positive from a place that was, in part, originally designed for precisely that.

Now, thanks to powerful allies, including Bill Gates, George Soros, Warren Buffet, Barack Obama... to drop a few names, prison education is being given another chance. Despite the Pell-Grants-for-prisoners' ban of the 90s, in 2016, the Obama administration got the ball rolling by instituting a pilot program, known as the Second Chance Pell Grant Program, to explore the interest and viability of reinstating the eligibility for prisoners to take advantage of the Pell Grant program. Implemented mid-year 2016, it offered roughly 12,000 Pell Grants for incarcerated students around the country at some 141 state and federal correctional institutions. The $5,815 per student grant could be used to pursue a two- or four-year degree from one of 68 approved colleges and universities.

And Then Trump Arrived

Obama's polices of 2016 are continually being rescinded by the Trump White House. With a tough-on-crime and light-on-education administration, it remains to be seen whether recent changes for the benefit of prisoner-students will be rolled back or expanded.

Throughout these last two centuries, education has played an important role in the rehabilitation of prisoners. There is little doubt of the positives that prison education provides for the educating prisoner, for the prison system they reside in, for their families who want them to do something positive from their circumstances, and for the communities they'll be returning to. It is hoped that we're about to enter into a new era that appreciates the role that educating prisoners can have on the future of this country.

THE FUTURE OF PRISON EDUCATION IS BEING WRITTEN RIGHT NOW. IF YOU TAKE ADVANTAGE OF IT, YOURS IS TOO.

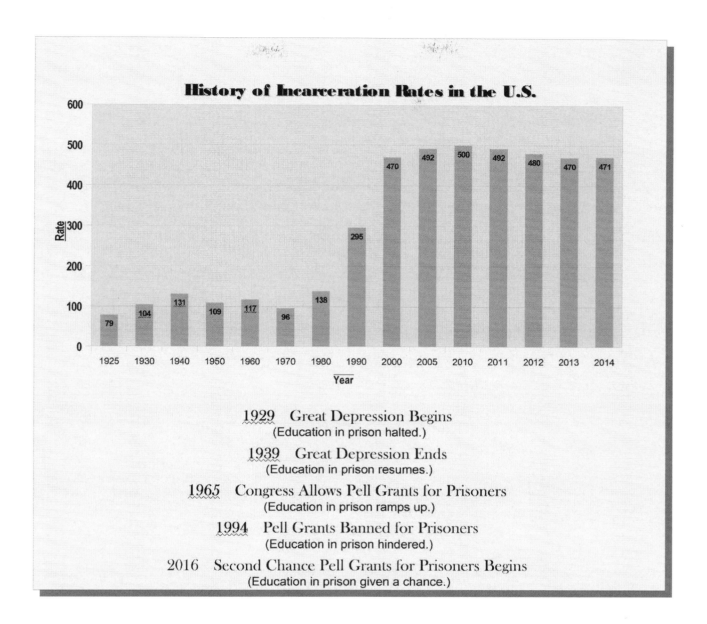

History of Incarceration Rates in the U.S.

Year	Rate
1925	79
1930	104
1940	131
1950	109
1960	117
1970	96
1980	138
1990	295
2000	470
2005	492
2010	500
2011	492
2012	480
2013	470
2014	471

1929   Great Depression Begins
(Education in prison halted.)

1939   Great Depression Ends
(Education in prison resumes.)

1965   Congress Allows Pell Grants for Prisoners
(Education in prison ramps up.)

1994   Pell Grants Banned for Prisoners
(Education in prison hindered.)

2016   Second Chance Pell Grants for Prisoners Begins
(Education in prison given a chance.)

GET AN EDUCATION?

WHY Should I Get an Education?

Why are you in prison? No, we're not asking what you were convicted of. What is the underlying reason that you're here? Is this your first time here? Second, or third? Why?

Did you know that the number one reason why prisoners find themselves in prison, or back in prison again, is that they can't find adequate or steady employment? Was that your unspoken response to the questions above? Or was your response more along the lines of 'I'm just a screw up'? Isn't that just another way of saying that you just weren't smart enough?

Whatever your reason for being here, by accident, offending, or offending again, even if it was just a 'wrong place, wrong time' scenario, or even if you didn't actually do anything to land you here, how would you respond to the question: Do you want another chance?

> "Prisoners who participated in *any* educational opportunities while behind bars were **43% less likely to return to prison** within 3 years than prisoners who did not participate."
> Source: RAND Corporation, 2013

That's what education provides, another chance at life.

If you're picking up this book, you at least have a curiosity about educational opportunities, despite living behind bars. Without a doubt, the most positive thing that you can do while incarcerated is learn something. After all, NOT learning may have been the single greatest factor that landed you in prison in the first place. It only makes sense then to reverse that trend by educating yourself so that you can make better decisions from this day forward.

A 2013 RAND Corporation study found that prisoners who participated in *any* form of educational opportunity while behind bars were 43% less likely to return to prison within three years than prisoners who did not participate. Other studies resoundingly support this claim. The Bard Prison Initiative, which operates in six medium- and maximum-security prisons in New York State, enrolls 300 prisoners in college programs. Formerly incarcerated individuals who have participated in the program return to prison at a rate of LESS THAN 2 PERCENT! In California, the Prison University Project, housed at San Quentin, reports a 17 percent recidivism rate with no violent offenses among their graduates – compared with a national average of 65 percent.

If you don't have your high-school diploma or GED yet, get a high-school education, or take your GED. If you are a high school graduate or hold a GED, learn a skill by taking a vocational course. If you want something more when you get out, to be competitive in the job market, to combat the stigma that will come with being an ex-convict, earn a college education in the field that you're interested in pursuing. And if you really want to set yourself apart from even most educated people in the outside world, study to obtain a master's or doctorate degree from the comfort of your cell!

It cannot be reiterated enough, if you don't want to come back to prison, get an education! Education makes you smarter, no matter how much you already know. The better the education you get, the less likely you are to ever return to prison. It's a proven fact:

EDUCATION = SUCCESS

Education isn't only key to reducing recidivism, it's also the central component to improving chances of post-release employment. According to the RAND Corporation study, people who participate in correctional education programs are 13 percent more likely to be employed following their release.

WHAT IF I'M NOT GETTING OUT?

Over 95 percent of prisoners will one day be released. But even if you are among the 5 percent who are forced to spend the rest of your life in prison, education can reap undeniable benefits for you too.

Among the loudest complaints of prisoners with life sentences are that life is monotonous, boring, a waste of time, and meaningless. While some of those bound to spend the rest of their lives in prison are perfectly content watching TV or playing the same card game day after day, year after year, many lifers want something more. If you are a lifer, and you are reading this right now, we are guessing you are one of them.

Do you desire a different sort of challenge? Do you crave a life that matters in a way that perhaps you had not thought was possible? How many of those around you are trying to better educate themselves? Do you have friends or families that want you to be the best person you can be, despite your confines?

Education can have the effect of living a life outside of the daily grind of your current prison setting.

Getting an education can demonstrate to those who care about you, to those you care about beyond the walls, that you are doing something immensely positive with your life.

Getting an education can even provide you with pathways towards making amends, allowing privileges you never knew were possible, presenting options to assist others in their education ambitions. As an educated prisoner, you can become a useful person in prison generally, such as becoming a point-person on proposals, a commentator to rule changes, or a key source of respected ideas that enhance living conditions for you and others in your facility. You can enjoy any number of other benefits that you would never have otherwise, if not for becoming a better-educated person.

An educated prisoner, regardless of how much time he or she has to serve, is a prisoner who maximizes the amount of opportunities they have in life inside or beyond prison walls. You might be amazed at how many doors open in direct relation with the opening of your mind. But perhaps most importantly, how you view yourself, how others view you, and your entire outlook of the future may be forever changed for the positive.

If this book is in your hands, you have the best tool you can have, besides your brain, to begin taking educational opportunities seriously and quite possibly to begin experiencing a much more productive life than you have been able to prior to this moment.

Education may not be your *Get-Out-of-Jail-Free* card, but it certainly has the capability of being your *Stay-Out-of-Prison-Forever* one. Education is your card to level the playing field. Going to school during your prison stay will certainly keep you busy. Time will pass more quickly. Concentrating on something besides prison life will certainly help to avoid the more negative aspects of prison. With a mind released from the daily monotony of life behind bars, a freedom sets in that you might not have thought possible during a prison stay. Education has the power of discovery, change, focus, drive, and an endless number of other benefits. But most vitally, especially for prisoners, education is freedom.

HOW Do I Get an Education...?

So you want to make positive use of your time by getting a better education while behind bars. If you've gotten this far, you've likely discovered, or soon will, that the path can be challenging. But even though your prison may not be the most accommodating place for those who want to go back to school, it is by no means a closed road with no way through to your goal.

With prison education just beginning to make a comeback in prisons throughout the U.S. Prison administrators are just beginning to recognize the benefits of providing in-prison schooling opportunities. Many are making it easier for prisoners to reach outside of the prison walls through correspondence options. Because each prison system is different, the route to gaining an education from any given prison is a very much like any given city undergoing an annoying amount of road construction.

Some prison systems are progressive and have established a variety of programs to make education an easy option.

> **Before you get started on your path to learning, contact your prison's education coordinator!**
>
> Prison education coordinators exist to assist prisoners with education. While the level of help they actually give you will vary from not-at-all to extraordinarily helpful, they will provide you enough information to determine your next steps. You never know, they may have the perfect path for you ready to walk down.
>
> Find the subheadings below that best match your education goals to determine precisely what questions to ask.

They have a newly blacktopped main road with clearly defined lines to guide you to where you want to go. Their education departments are well staffed with knowledgeable professionals who understand the unique needs of prisoners and the challenges they face with education. They are there to walk you down the road to learning like an experienced tour guide, showing you all of the different paths that you can take, which are likewise newly paved and awaiting your footsteps.

Several prisons across the country are already working with established colleges and universities to provide education opportunities in prison. For example, as of July 2017, prisoners in the state of Washington now have access to state-funded associate degree programs and an expanded slate of vocational certificates. Now every Washington prisoner – with the exception of those on death row or those who already have four-year degrees – are eligible to participate in degree programs provided by the prison system in coordination with local colleges and universities.

In upstate New York, six different prisons currently provide liberal arts instruction to nearly 300 incarcerated students through the Bard Prison Initiative. It is administered by Bard College, allowing prisoners to earn associate's and bachelor's degrees from a prestigious school. More than 20 other colleges and universities – including well-known schools as Vassar, Columbia and Cornell – are likewise offering in-prison education options in New York alone.

New York is not alone. Opportunities are cropping up all over the country. *Goucher College* is now offering Bachelor of Arts degrees in American studies throughout Maryland prisons. Prisoners in Virginia State prisons can now receive college credit for several different classes, including Business Software Applications, Digital Print Reproduction, Commercial Arts and Design, and Computer-Aided Drafting. Oregon regularly offers prisoners for-credit course option through the University of Oregon, often in writing or other prison-friendly fields. Washington just passed a bill enabling most of its prison population to now take in-prison courses to earn various degrees, free of charge.

Unfortunately, however, most prison systems are not quite that far ahead in their road construction projects. There are potholes everywhere, roads that seem impassible, construction equipment in the way, detour signs, people with flags waving you down the wrong road... The path to education can be frustrating. Just when you think you are making progress down a part of the road that seems like you finally might be getting somewhere, there's a "Road Closed" sign that crops up out of nowhere. But as impossible as it might seem, there IS a route you can take to get there. Prisons may make it difficult with their poorly maintained roads, but they do all have streets that lead to the where you want to be. It just takes some patience, more gas in your tank than you may have thought you needed before you set out on this journey, and perseverance to know that you will get there. As annoying as it may be, it is a navigable road system. You can get there... which is why this book exists, to show you the way. To be your tour guide, regardless of how bad the roads are.

> ## Heading in the Right Direction: University of California, Berkeley's Underground Scholars
>
> The Underground Scholars Initiative (USI) was created to support all prospective and current University of California, Berkeley (UC Berkeley) students impacted by imprisonment.
>
> USI helps currently or just-released prisoners transition into the culture of campus by providing them with peer counseling, scholarship information, and other resources; establishing advocates in the campus community on their behalf, building networks with other university organizations to mitigate the effects of incarceration, and helping prisoner-students and their families find alternatives to incarceration with the empowering effects of higher education.

So let us get started. How do you get an education from where you are sitting right now? First, you must consider your starting point and what you want to get out of an education. Look at the following subtitles and decide which one best describes your circumstances and your immediate learning goals.

WHAT do you want to accomplish?

I Just Want to Learn Something

Getting an education does not mean earning a piece of paper that proves that you learned it. It means that you have acquired knowledge in a subject that you didn't know beforehand. You have improved your brain, and perhaps your life, by learning. Granted, that piece of paper has its benefits. It can advantage you in everything from the parole board hearing to finding a better job on the outside, or even in further educational opportunities. But it's not necessary if all you want to do is learn something.

There are wide varieties of options out there if simply learning is your goal, most of which are easily afforded. Chances are that your prison offers some, and likely for free. While most of these types of education are designed to make you a better person, courses such as anger management, substance abuse, and parenting, there are often learning opportunities in areas that may surprise you. Would you like to learn more about birds? How about being an entrepreneur? Maybe meditation, physical fitness, or nutrition? There are free or reasonably priced courses for all of those and many more.

If it's a religious education you want, you've hit the jackpot of learning possibilities! There are almost endless options for religious studies, many specifically designed with prisoners in mind. Just about every major religion offers prisoners free spiritual educational opportunities. All you have to do is ask.

Several opportunities are available to prisoners who just want to learn, which can be found right now in the *Personal Enrichment* and *Religious Studies* portions of our *Find a School* section.

> **If you would like to find out about opportunities for the sake of learning within your prison right now, write to, or visit, your prison's education coordinator and ask the following:**
>
> I'm interested in using my time to learn something while I'm here. What classes are currently being offered for the sake of learning or personal enrichment at this prison?

I Want to Finish My High School Education

If you do not already have your high-school diploma, your first goal may be to gain at least the equivalency of a high-school education. A high-school education, or equivalent options, gets you to the next steps in life, whether your next goals are a better job once you get out (and oftentimes in-prison work opportunities), or to further your education through college-level options. But you don't have to actually get a formal high-school diploma to obtain this equivalent education.

A *General Educational Development* (GED) certificate can provide the majority of the benefits as a high-school diploma. Getting a GED certificate says that you have passed examinations that are considered equivalent to the completion of high school. Even better, most prison systems offer GED education programs freely to all prisoners.

The U.S. government and prison administrations recognize the importance of prisoners having the opportunity to at least achieve the equivalent of a high school education. Therefore, GED instruction and testing is available in every state and in nearly every prison institution across the nation. In fact, this level of education is vital enough that all prisons within the Federal Bureau of Prisons *require* non-high school educated prisoners either to spend 240 hours in educational classes, or to earn their GED. Failure to do so may affect their good time credits, equating to

Getting Your GED

As of 2014, GED exams are no longer administered using print materials. They are now computer based.

The GED examination tests your intellectual ability such as evaluating, analyzing, drawing conclusions, and the ability to understand and apply information and concepts in five areas of study: Writing, Social studies, Science, Interpreting literature and arts, and Math.

You can study in advance through materials provided by your institution, or you can gain an advantage by ordering:

The Complete Idiots Guide to the GED: A 5-subject crash course

available now through *Prison Lives*.

$18.95 FREE shipping & handling.

a loss of about a week of days from the 54 good time days available to federal prisoners per year.

GED vs. High-School Diploma?

Even though a GED is accepted as an official alternative to an actual high-school diploma, it will never provide the quality of education you can get with four years of high school. Where GED classes will teach you the basics of math, science and English, and a few other essentials, high-school classes will delve much deeper into these topics while providing you access to MANY more options in dozens of topics that a GED will never touch. In high school, you can choose the types of math, science or English you would prefer to learn, and add on language, art, or music classes, among others. If you want to see what you're missing by taking a GED, keep your thumb on this page and take a peek at the *High School Studies* course offerings in our *Find a School* section.

Additionally, you have the option through many correspondence high schools to take courses that will better prepare you for quality collegiate education, advanced placement courses, and education that better prepares you for quality employment outside of prison.

If you have already had some high-school education, you are already part way to your actual diploma. The high school you have had thus far counts. You can apply the credits you have already earned and pick up right where you left off.

Seeing as how not coming back to prison is a major benefit of education, you will want to get the best education you can. An actual high-school education will provide you with the best foundation to succeed in whatever you decide to do next, be that more education or life in the outside world. If you are currently at this level of education and want to take learning seriously, you would be wise to seriously consider getting a proper high-school education. Many schools currently offer correspondence high-school education to prisoners, which can also be found in the *High School Studies* portion of our *Find a School* section.

If you would like to get a high-school education or a GED certificate, first see what your prison offers. Write to, or visit, your prison's education coordinator and ask the following:

I would like to look into earning my high school diploma or something comparable. Can you please provide information on what this prison offers for this type of education, and what I have to do to get started? If I would like to pursue correspondence school options, what does the prison require of me?

If you would like to get more information on GEDs or find a local testing center outside of prison, write to:

American Council on Education | GED Testing Service

One DuPont Circle NW, Suite 250, Washington, D.C. 20036
(800) 626-9433
www.acenet.edu   www.gedtest.org

I Want to Learn a Job Skill

Most people who decide to pursue education beyond high school do so for one reason: to get a higher paying job! College is a very involved process, and worse, very expensive. Fortunately, if you have your high-school diploma or GED, you do not have to go to college to learn your way to a better career.

Vocational training and technical schools are a far more economical way of achieving a job skill that you can carry with you beyond prison walls to provide the support you need to make a living and stay out of prison. They also take much less time to complete than college programs. What's more, vocational training is a direct path to getting the education you desire, without having to take a seemingly endless stream of courses that have very little to do with the skill you're working to attain, and without the supervision that colleges require.

Many prisons offer such technical training through apprenticeship programs in plumbing, electrical, construction, HVAC, computer-aided drafting, and more. But even if your prison doesn't currently offer such programs, vocational schools all over the country do. You might be surprised by what's available to you. If you want to become a personal trainer or a paralegal, get into hospitality management or electrical engineering, or if you want to learn video game design, these and many other options are available to you, even as a prisoner. Some of these schools even offer job placement assistance when you get out of prison.

If you have career in mind and would like to know if it's something you can learn through correspondence courses, go to the Vocational studies portion of our *Find a School* section. But don't forget to check to see if your prison is currently offering any vocational options.

> **If you would like to see what your prison offers, write to, or visit, your prison's education coordinator and ask the following:**
>
> I would like to look into vocational education options. Can you please provide information on any such opportunities are currently available in this prison, and what I have to do to get started? If I would like to pursue correspondence options, what does the prison require of me?

I Want to go to College

Your expectations for college-level learning depend largely on your college education goals. Do you care about college credit? Are you just wanting to gain a higher level of knowledge? Are you looking to earn a degree? Associate's or bachelor's... maybe even a graduate degree?

LEARNING FOR KNOWLEDGE

If you just hope to increase your base of knowledge, your options are endless. Virtually every course is at your disposal for purposes of learning. Most of the schools in the book will permit you to take any of the courses without having to commit to a degree program. If you would like to take one course or twenty, you can. You can typically choose to earn college credit, in the event that you later decide that you would like to earn a degree. But if you choose not to earn credit (known as a *non-matriculating student*), many schools will provide tuition discounts and not require that you take proctored exams.

Get a college degree

If you are looking to get a college degree, you must meet certain qualifications before the school will admit you into a program. The following are the general admission requirements for students wishing to attend college at an accredited school. (See discussion on *Accreditation* in upcoming chapter.)

Associate Degree Program

Students must:

> Possess a high school diploma or its equivalent.

> Have access to and provide transcripts of all high school and/or undergraduate work, typically showing a grade point average of 2.1 or greater on a 4.0 scale (schools vary on this requirement), or equivalent from an accredited college or university.

Bachelor Degree Program

Students must:

> Possess a high school diploma or its equivalent.

> Have access to and provide transcripts of all high school and/or undergraduate work, typically showing a grade point average of 2.1 or greater on a 4.0 scale (schools vary on this requirement), or equivalent from an accredited college or university.

Master's Degree Program

Students must:

> Possess a bachelor degree (or its foreign equivalent) from an accredited college of university.

> Have access to and provide transcripts of all high school and/or undergraduate work, typically showing a grade point average of 2.1 or greater on a 4.0 scale (schools vary on this requirement), or equivalent from an accredited college or university.

> Provide transcripts of any graduate courses, typically showing a grade of B or higher (3.0 on a 4.0 scale) or its equivalent from an accredited college or university.

Doctoral Program

Students must:

> Possess a master's degree (or its foreign equivalent) from an accredited college of university.

> Have access to and provide transcripts of all high school and/or undergraduate work, typically showing a grade point average of 3.0 or greater on a 4.0 scale (schools vary on this requirement), or equivalent from an accredited college or university.

> Provide a professional resume.

If you intend to earn a college degree, you will be required to earn a specific number of credits.

Typical credit requirements:

° Associate's degree = 60 credits
° Bachelor's degree = 120 credits

Both types of degrees require that you earn a minimum number of general education credits, which can be earned from any accredited school and then transferred to the school from which you would like to gain your primary education.

General education requirements will typically be between 37 and 40 credits and are earned in the following areas:

° Arts & Humanities (6 to 9 credits)
° Communications (6 to 9 credits)
° Mathematics (3 credits)

° Social & Cultural Sciences (9 to 12 credits)
° History (3 to 6 credits)
° Sciences (6 to 8 credits)

Once you have earned your general education credits you can begin the degree program of your choosing. You will be required to earn approximately 20 additional credits for an associate's degree and another 80 credits per bachelor's degree. The courses you take will depend on the *emphasis* or *major* you choose. Each emphasis or major has a core set of required courses, with the remaining credits earned through electives, or courses of your choosing.

WANT MORE INFO ON COLLEGE EDUCATION?

You can find additional information on obtaining a college education by heading straight to our *Find a School* section under *College Studies*.

Get Involved!

For more than 20 years, prisoners have been barred from receiving funding from the government for education purposes.

The *Second Chance Pell Grant* program is the first step to reversing that policy. In an effort to officially change the law back to allow prisoners to become officially eligible to receive Pell Grant funding, there is a House Bill under consideration this year that addresses this possibility.

Known as the REAL Act of 2017, House Bill 254 amends Title IV (Student Aid) of the Higher Education Act of 1965 to eliminate the provision that prohibits Pell Grant eligibility for individuals incarcerated in federal or state penal institutions.

Contact those considering the bill in Congress to voice your support.

U.S. House of Representatives Committee on Education and Workforce
2181 Rayburn House Office Building
Washington, DC 20515

Friends and family can also get involved by going to:
www.congressmerge.com/onlineDB

Part 2   Challenges You'll Face

There's no doubt about it, getting an education while incarcerated is challenging. But then again, so is virtually everything behind bars.

This part will help you be prepared for the most substantial difficulties every prisoner student faces and must overcome.

Yeah right, it's so noisy in my prison I can't think straight... and I'm suppose to learn in this environment?

How will I ever pay for it?

I have trouble getting a book through the mail room. Is it even possible to get what I need for a formal education?

CHALLENGE #1: THE PRISON

If you were, right now, on the free side of the wall, in the time it took you to read this sentence you would be able to log onto your computer, find one of the dozens of educational institutions out there that offer college-level schooling free of charge, and sign up for a class in just about any subject. Five minutes later, you could be listening to a lecture in your subject of choice, getting your class assignment, and already be fast on your way to gaining an education. And not just any education either. Established and notable colleges all over the world are now offering free online courses. schools like Harvard, MIT, and Berkeley, to name just a few. Colleges and universities worldwide are essentially competing to see who can offer the most and best free educational opportunities to virtually anyone… that is anyone but prisoners.

Despite the technologies that exist in the outside world, education behind bars seems to be stuck in the Stone Age. While internet access and email communication are the norm beyond the walls, most prisoners are stuck with having to communicate by what most schools consider to be outdated methods. Unless a school has intentionally decided that it will continue to supply courses in a way that even the most under-privileged citizens can access, they will have moved beyond the snail-mail option that prisoners must rely on. Unfortunately, out of the thousands of schools in the U.S., only a tiny fraction are prisoner-friendly. Therefore, the options for prisoners who want to continue to learn are extremely limited.

Because there are so few opportunities for prisoners to go to school while they are incarcerated, the options that do exist tend to be terribly expensive and difficult for prisoners to afford. But perhaps the most difficult challenge for hopeful prisoner-students is that the very place that they must depend on to facilitate their learning efforts, the prison they live in, seems to be opposed to the idea of those behind its bars furthering their education.

Every prison in the U.S. will say that they offer educational opportunities for prisoners in their system. It is true! Most prisons do offer *some* form of education. The better reality is that prisons in the U.S. are currently trending towards offering even more educational opportunities. The unfortunate reality, however, is that for every new path of opportunity for prisoners there are a hundred bureaucratic steps to take to get there. On top of that, just about every prison in America suffers from the same illnesses that work against positive initiatives of the prison administration. These illnesses include:

➢ **Not enough funding**

➢ **Lack of properly trained staff to effectively administer education programs**

➢ **Prison staff's inability to adequately deal with the variety of learning disabilities common in prison populations**

➢ **Overcrowded prisons, limiting available spots for prisoner participation**

➢ **The need for security, which inevitably influences every prison program**

Even for prisoners who can afford to pay for outside schooling, the prison still presents a variety of challenges. The lack of cooperation from staff is one of the bigger hurdles. This can be due to an overzealousness for security concerns, resentment over a prisoner having the nerve to better themselves through education, or a selection of other unknowable reasons. This can lead to "lost" class materials, delayed correspondence between prisoner and school, unnecessary conflicts that result in loss of privileges, and more.

Another challenge unique to prison life is the inability to maintain the external communication that formal education requires. Most school advisors will not accept collect calls or go through the necessary setup requirements for prison calling, making obtaining answers to questions or getting education advice a difficult proposition. Even coordinating education with the help of family of other support systems can be a test of a prisoner's patience.

Additionally, learning from the isolation of a prison setting can present several psychological trials. Without the traditional classroom interactions, where like-minded students share the pressures and joys of the courses taken, it is a lonely undertaking. There is a dynamic that comes with conventional schooling that is missing with distance education, one that is far more pronounced when your classroom is a cell. Furthermore, without neighbors who can relate to the education experience, it is a persevering effort that some prisoners struggle to conquer.

Then there is the noise. Toilets flushing neighbors, shouting, doors slamming, officer radios blaring... the inability of finding enough quiet time to concentrate can be maddening. If noise bothers you at all, noise while trying to focus on studies can feel as if it is coming from an air-raid siren.

And finally, there are the ordinary prison restrictions that will tax your reserves of composure. From the limits on the number of books you can have in your cell to the inability to receive some course materials due to spiral binding or other basic supplies, what often seems like unnecessary limitations from the prison will seem more pronounced and unnecessary than ever.

So What Can I Do?

While the challenges that the prison presents can seem insurmountable in the moments they are experienced, these challenges have the distinct ability to be completely manageable.

There are sympathetic authorities within the prison who want you to succeed, generally in the form of the prison education coordinators. These will help you overcome many of the potential potholes the prison presents. Perhaps more vitally, the upper level administration in your prison system, the ones who are working to establish better in-prison education programs, easily see the benefits of higher learning.

In a prison setting, you can have no higher advocate than the prison's administration. It is likely that you will encounter some, if not several, of the prison challenges mentioned. But overcoming them is a lesson that you've likely been learning since your first day in prison.

If you've achieved a maturity that considering educational opportunities require, you will likely be able to relatively easily navigate whatever bumps may occur in your road to successful learning. None of these should discourage you from pursuing higher learning.

CHALLENGE #2: THE COST

The greatest challenge for most prisoners who want to gain a thorough education while trapped behind bars is the ability to finance it. If you think canteen prices are high, wait until you see the tuition price for one college-level course. On the lower end of the tuition spectrum, a single course will cost a few hundred dollars. Add up the 20 classes or so that it'll take to compile enough credits for an associate's degree and you're quickly running up a $10,000 bill. A bachelor's degree from an accredited school can easily cost up to $30,000, and often more. How can a prisoner afford that?!

Without someone to support their scholastic ambitions, chances are that most prisoners will not be able to afford a quality college education. That does not mean that it's impossible. It just means that it is important to have some form of support. If you want an education badly enough, you can find a way.

So What Can I Do?

There is no doubt about it, getting an education can be very expensive, especially on a prisoner's budget. There are, however, economical educational options out there that will allow prisoners on a budget to still be able to gain an education. For instance, as discussed previously, many prisons themselves offer educational opportunities, possibly within the very institution you are housed in right now. Several of these courses are free, but most are at least extremely cheap, often just covering the basic costs of administration and materials. Some of these in-prison options even offer college credit that can be used towards further advancement of your schooling goals.

Another avenue that can be far easier to afford than traditional schooling is through personal enrichment courses. These offer opportunities to learn a specific field of study without having to go through one of the more formal, pricey options. They are limiting, however. There are very few personal enrichment courses from which to choose. The courses that are available are not generally from accredited schools, and are therefore of little use when trying to further your education later through more formal options. However, if you just want to learn something, and if there are courses available that interest you, this may be a great economical option for you. (See *Personal Enrichment Studies* section.)

Religious education is another route that is often extremely easy on any budget. In fact, many religious education options out there are completely FREE to prisoners, including any course materials and Certificates of Completion. Most of these courses are intended as bible studies and will not really be of much advantage to future scholastic achievement. But if you're simply to looking to occupy your time on a positive course of study, religious education may be for you. (See *Religious Studies* section.)

Don't forget. You don't have to go full-scale. All the way to earning a college degree. You can still get a quality, formal education, only more on an a-la carte plan. Most of the schools in this guide allow you to just take the courses you desire without the need for all the ones you don't. If gaining the knowledge and skills is more important than all other considerations, this may be a fantastic and reasonable economical option for you.

The reality, however, is that if you want a college degree through an accredited school, it is going to be expensive. For many it will be prohibitively so. But don't lose hope, there are options out there. They are not necessarily *easy* options, but if you sincerely want formal education, then they are definitely options that are worth pursuing.

Pell Grants or Other Federal Student Aid?

In the past, getting an education from behind bars was not all that difficult, relatively speaking. The government supported such prisoner ambitions by actually funding it. Prisoner-students could apply to the government for federal student aid, and more often than not actually receive it. It opened the door for prison themselves to offer extensive options and excellent ways for prisoners to earn a degree through the offerings within their own prison. However, as discussed in the *History of Prison Education* portion of this book, these opportunities dried up due to the public's misunderstanding that such opportunities for prisoners were taking away from aid opportunities of students on the free side of the wall. In the early 1990s, educational institutions were criticized for participating in prisoner education and powerful political components were pressured into passing the appropriate bills through Congress, which then president, Bill Clinton, signed. Almost immediately, every ounce of student aid for prisoners evaporated and education programs in the U.S. turned to dust.

In 2015, however, efforts were made to bring some of these opportunities back to prisoners. President Obama got the ball rolling by instituting a pilot program for prisoners, known as the *Second Chance Pell Grant Program*. This program was established to explore the interest and viability of reinstating the eligibility for prisoners to take advantage of the Pell Grant federal student aid program. It is currently a very limited program, only available to prisoners who are due to be released within the next 5 years. But it's a start.

Second Chance Pell Grant

T he government's Pell Grant program provides need-based grants to low-income undergraduate and certain post-baccalaureate students to promote access to post-secondary education. However, the *Higher Education Act* (HEA), which controls the use of Pell Grants, stipulates that students who are incarcerated in a Federal or State penal institution are not eligible to participate in the Federal Pell Grant program. This restriction prevents many otherwise eligible incarcerated individuals from accessing financial aid and benefiting from post-secondary education and training.

All is not lost.

On August 3, 2015, the Department of Education released a Federal Register notice inviting institutions of higher education (IHEs) to apply to participate in a new institutionally-based initiative under the Experimental Sites Initiative (ESI), which tests the effectiveness of statutory and regulatory flexibility for IHEs that disburse Federal student aid. This initiative allowed participating IHEs, in partnership with one or more Federal or State correctional institutions, to provide Federal Pell Grant funding to otherwise eligible students who are incarcerated and who are eligible for release back into the community, particularly those who are likely to be released within five years of enrollment in the program.

WHAT IS THE PURPOSE OF THIS INITIATIVE?

This initiative was established to test whether participation in high-quality educational opportunities increases after access to financial aid for incarcerated adults is expanded and examine how waiving the restriction on providing Pell Grants to individuals incarcerated in Federal or State penal institutions influences academic and life outcomes.

According to a Department of Justice-funded 2014 study from the RAND Corporation mentioned previously, incarcerated individuals who participated in high-quality correctional education — including post-secondary correctional education —were 43 percent less likely to return to prison within three years than prisoners who didn't participate in any correctional education programs. Furthermore, it is estimated that for every dollar invested in correctional education programs, four to five dollars are saved on three-year re-incarceration costs. Thus, through this initiative, the Department of Education aims to support the successful transition of justice-involved individuals out of prison and back into the classroom or the workforce.

Known as the *Second Chance Pell Grant Pilot Program*, this initiative may provide you with the educational funding you need to get your quality education. Each grant provides up to $5,815 per student to be used to pursue a two- or four-year degree from one of 68 approved colleges and universities. It is a great opportunity, but there are several catches.

In order to qualify for a *Second Chance Pell Grant*, you must meet the following criteria:

1) **You must be housed in a participating prison.**

   There are currently less than 150 state and federal prisons participating in the program. If the initiative proves successful, it is likely that more prisons will be added. But for now it is only available in roughly 10 percent of the nation's prisons.

2) **You must participate in the program offered by your institution.**

   If you want to study creative writing but your prison isn't offering that course or anything close to it, the *Second Chance Pell Grant* program won't really help you. The participating local college decides through the prison what course of study they will be offering to your particular prison. Some will offer an associate's degree track, while some will offer a bachelor's degree option. But they will likely be within very specific fields that may not match the field that you were hoping to study.

3) You must be within 5 years of being released from prison.

The program is primarily designed to assist prisoners by giving them an education that will help them to succeed after release from prison. Since this is a pilot program, the U.S. Education Department needs to be able to gauge whether this program is working. Therefore, they are currently limiting it to those who are about to get out of prison.

4) You cannot have a drug distribution conviction.

The original Pell Grant opportunities offered to non-prisoners restricts participation from those who have been convicted of distributing drugs. This was part of the tough-on-crime initiatives of the 90s and was included in the Higher Education Act (HEA). Therefore, this rule has been carried over.

5) You must have a high-school diploma or its equivalent.

This is the case with any education grant program.

If you meet all of these criteria, you may be eligible for the program. If you are eligible, and are interested in obtaining a quality education, this is a tremendous opportunity for to take advantage of.

The following pages provide a current listing of schools participating in this year's *Second Chance Pell Grant Pilot Program.* These are the ONLY schools that can offer prisoners Pell Grants under this year's program.

Most of the participating colleges do not offer *correspondence* opportunities for prisoners, but rather work with specific prison systems to offer classes directly within the prisons themselves.

Check with your prison's education coordinator to see if your prison is partnering with any of these schools. If so, and if you meet the program's eligibility requirements, request more information on the classes offered to see if these will assist you in reaching your education goals.

Pell Grant Eligible Schools

STATE	SCHOOL NAME	CORRECTIONAL INSTITUTIONS	SCHOOL TYPE	NEW OR EXISTING PROGRAM	EDUCATION OPTIONS	# ACCEPTED
ALABAMA	Auburn University	Alabama DOC	Public - Four Year	New	Bachelor's Degree	20
	Calhoun Community College	Limestone	Public - Two Year	Existing	Certificate	110
	Ingram State Technical College	Donaldson, Draper, Elmore, Staton and Frank Lee Work Release Center, Tutwiler Prison for Women	Public - Two Year	Existing	Certificate	426
ARKANSAS	Arkansas State University - Newport	McPherson Unit	Public - Two Year	Existing	Certificate, Associates Degree	150
	Shorter College	Arkansas Community Corrections – Texarkana, West Memphis, Ouachita Unit, Pine Bluff Complex,	Private, Nonprofit - Two Year	New	Certificate	250
CALIFORNIA	California State University Los Angeles	California State Prison, Los Angeles County	Public - Four Year	Existing	Bachelor's Degree	30
	Chaffey Community College	California Institution for Women	Public - Two Year	Existing	Certificate, Associates Degree	167
	Columbia College	Sierra Conservation Camp	Public - Two Year	Existing	Certificate, Associates Degree	95
	Cuesta College	CMC San Luis Obispo	Public - Two Year	Existing	Associates Degree	265
	Southwestern Community College District	Richard J. Donovan Correctional Facility	Public - Two Year	Existing	Certificate, Associates Degree	25
CONNECTICUT	Asnuntuck Community College	Osborn, Robinson, Willard-Cybulski	Public - Two Year	New	Certificate	540
	Middlesex Community College	Cheshire and York Correctional Institutions	Public - Two Year	New	Associates Degree	51
	Quinebaug Valley Community College	Brooklyn Correctional	Public - Two Year	New	Certificate, Associates Degree	60
	Three Rivers Community College	York and Corrigan/Radgowski Correctional Institutions	Public - Two Year	New	Certificate	150
FLORIDA	Florida Gateway College	Florida Department of Corrections	Public - Four Year	New	Associates Degree	50
IOWA	Iowa Central Community College	Fort Dodge and North Central Correctional	Public - Two Year	New	Certificate	314

Pell Grant Eligible Schools

STATE	SCHOOL NAME	CORRECTIONAL INSTITUTIONS	SCHOOL TYPE	NEW OR EXISTING PROGRAM	EDUCATION OPTIONS	# ACCEPTED
ILLINOIS	North Park University	Sheridan Correctional Center	Private, Nonprofit - Four Year	New	Bachelor's Degree	16
ILLINOIS	Roosevelt University	Taylorsville	Private, Nonprofit - Four Year	New	Bachelor's Degree	70
INDIANA	Holy Cross College	Indiana Women's Prison Westville Correction Facility (WCF)	Private, Nonprofit - Four Year	Existing	Associates Degree, Bachelor's Degree	100
MASSACHUSETTS	Mount Wachusett Community College	Federal Medical Center, Devens, Massachusetts Correctional Institute – Shirley, and North Central Correctional Facility – Gardner	Public - Two Year	New	Certificate	72
MARYLAND	Anne Arundel Community College	Jessup	Public - Two Year	Existing	Certificate	24
MARYLAND	Goucher College	Maryland Correctional Institution for Women and Maryland Correctional Institution Jessup	Private, Nonprofit - Four Year	Existing	Bachelor's Degree	100
MARYLAND	University of Baltimore	Jessup	Public - Four Year	New	Bachelor's Degree	25
MARYLAND	Wor-Wic Community College	Eastern Correctional	Public - Two Year	New	Certificate	60
MAINE	University of Maine - Augusta	Maine State Prison	Public - Four Year	Existing	Associates Degree	25
MICHIGAN	Delta College	Saginaw Correctional	Public - Two Year	New	Certificate, Associates Degree	15
MICHIGAN	Jackson College	Bellamy Creek, Carson City, Central Michigan, Chippewa, Cotton, Detroit Reentry Center, Gus Harrison, Handlon, Macomb, Marquette, Milan Federal, Muskegon, Newberry, Parnall, West Shoreline, Women's Huron Valley	Public - Four Year	Existing	Certificate, Associates Degree	1305
MICHIGAN	Mott Community College	Thumb Correctional	Public - Two Year	New	Certificate, Associates Degree	155

CHALLENGE #2: THE COST | 37

Pell Grant Eligible Schools

STATE	SCHOOL NAME	CORRECTIONAL INSTITUTIONS	SCHOOL TYPE	NEW OR EXISTING PROGRAM	EDUCATION OPTIONS	# ACCEPTED
MINNESOTA	Fond du Lac Tribal & Community College	Minnesota Corrections Facility-Shakopee	Public - Two Year	Existing	Associates Degree	45
	Pine Technical and Community College	Minnesota Department of Corrections: Rush City, Moose Lake, Willow River	Public - Two Year	Existing	Certificate	30
	South Central College	Minnesota Correctional Facility – Faribault	Public - Two Year	Existing	Certificate	25
NEBRASKA	Metropolitan Community College	Omaha Correctional	Public - Two Year	Existing	Certificate	30
NEW JERSEY	Rutgers, the State University of New Jersey and Raritan Valley Community College	Seven Correctional Facilities: Albert C. Wagner Youth Correctional Facility, East Jersey State Prison, Edna Mahan Correctional Facility for Women, Garden State Youth Correctional Facility, Mountainview Youth Correctional Facility, Northern State Prison, South Woods State Prison	Public - Four Year	Existing	Associates Degree, Bachelor's Degree	598
NEW YORK	Bard College	Coxsackie, Eastern NY, Fishkill, Green Haven, Taconic, Woodbourne	Private, Nonprofit - Four Year	Existing	Associates Degree, Bachelor's Degree	228
	CUNY Hostos Community College	Otisville and Queensboro	Public - Two Year	Existing	Associates Degree	435
	CUNY LaGuardia Community College		Public - Two Year	Existing	Associates Degree	
	CUNY John Jay College of Criminal Justice		Public - Four Year	Existing	Certificate, Associates Degree	
	Marymount Manhattan College	Bedford Hills Correctional	Private, Nonprofit - Four Year	Existing	Associates Degree, Bachelor's Degree	98
	Mercy College	Sing Sing and Taconic	Private, Nonprofit - Four Year	Existing	Associates Degree, Bachelor's Degree	115
	North Country Community College	Federal Correctional Institution, Ray Brook, NY NYSDOCCS Adriondack, Ray Brook, Bare Hill, Malone, and Franklin	Public - Two Year	New	Associates Degree	129
	Nyack College	Taconic & Fishkill	Private,	Existing	Associates Degree,	105

Pell Grant Eligible Schools

STATE	SCHOOL NAME	CORRECTIONAL INSTITUTIONS	SCHOOL TYPE	NEW OR EXISTING PROGRAM	EDUCATION OPTIONS	# ACCEPTED
			Nonprofit - Four Year		Bachelor's Degree	
Ohio	Ashland University	Richland, Grafton, Chillicothe, Allen Correction, Avoyelles, B.B. Ryburn, David Wade, Dixon, Elayn Hunt, Louisiana, Louisiana State Penitentiary, Ohio Reformatory for Women, Belmont, Noble, Mt. Olive, Huttonsville, Lakin, and St. Mary's	Private, Nonprofit - Four Year	Existing	Certificate, Associates Degree, Bachelor's Degree	1040
Oklahoma	Connors State College	Jess Dunn and Eddie Warrior	Public - Two Year	Existing	Associates Degree	225
Oklahoma	Langston University	Oklahoma penal institutions	Public - Four Year	New	Bachelor's Degree	10
Oklahoma	Tulsa Community College	Dick Conner Correctional and Turley Women's Residential Center	Public - Two Year	Existing	Certificate, Associates Degree	44
Oregon	Chemeketa Community College	Oregon State Correctional Institution, Oregon State Penitentiary, Santiam Correctional Institution	Public - Two Year	Existing	Certificate, Associates Degree	186
Pennsylvania	Bloomsburg University of Pennsylvania	PA State Correctional Institution at Mahonoy and Muncy	Public - Four Year	Existing	Certificate	30
Pennsylvania	Indiana University of Pennsylvania	State Correctional Institutions at Houtzdale and Pine Grove	Public - Four Year	New	Associates Degree	30
Pennsylvania	Lehigh Carbon Community College	SCI Frackville and Mahanoy	Public - Two Year	New	Associates Degree	30
Pennsylvania	Villanova University	PA State Correctional Institution at Graterford	Private, Nonprofit - Four Year	Existing	Associates Degree, Bachelor's Degree	25
South Carolina	Northeastern Technical College	Evans Correctional, Federal Correction Institution -Bennettsville	Public - Two Year	New	Associates Degree	180
	Alvin Community College	Clemens, Darrington, Jester 3, Ramsey 1, Stringfellow, Terrell, Wayne Scott	Public - Two Year	Existing	Certificate, Associates Degree	380

Pell Grant Eligible Schools

STATE	SCHOOL NAME	CORRECTIONAL INSTITUTIONS	SCHOOL TYPE	NEW OR EXISTING PROGRAM	EDUCATION OPTIONS	# ACCEPTED
TEXAS	Cedar Valley College	Sanders Estes Unit - Texas Department of Justice	Public - Two Year	New	Certificate	120
	Clarendon College	Rufe Jordan Unit and T L Roach Unit, Texas Department of Criminal Justice	Public - Two Year	Existing	Associates Degree	100
	Lamar State College - Port Arthur	Federal Correctional Complex- Beaumont, Texas Stiles Unit of the Texas Department of Criminal Justice	Public - Two Year	Existing	Certificate, Associates Degree	243
	Lee College	Texas Department of Criminal Justice Eastham, Ellis, Ferguson, Luther, Huntsville, Luther, and Wynne Units	Public - Two Year	Existing	Certificate, Associates Degree	1134
	Mountain View College	Sanders Estes Unit - Texas Department of Justice	Public - Two Year	New	Certificate	40
	Southwest Texas Junior College	Briscoe Unit	Public - Two Year	New	Certificate, Associates Degree	142
	University of Houston - Clear Lake	Ramsey 1	Public - Four Year	Existing	Bachelor's Degree	85
	Wiley College	Madison Parish Detention Center, Louisiana Corrections Women at St. Gabriel, and Winnfield Correctional Center	Private, Nonprofit - Four Year	New	Associates Degree, Bachelor's Degree	300
VIRGINIA	Danville Community College	Green Rock Correctional Center	Public - Two Year	New	Certificate, Associates Degree	138
	Rappahannock Community College	Haynesville Correctional	Public - Two Year	Existing	Associates Degree	49
VERMONT	Bennington College	Great Meadow	Private, Nonprofit - Four Year	Existing	Associates Degree	56
WASHINGTON	Centralia College	Cedar Creek	Public - Four Year	Existing	Associates Degree	12
	Seattle Central Community College	Monroe Correctional	Public - Four Year	Existing	Associates Degree	63
	Tacoma Community College	Washington Corrections Center For Women and Mission Creek Corrections Center For Women	Public - Two Year	Existing	Associates Degree	60

Pell Grant Eligible Schools

STATE	SCHOOL NAME	CORRECTIONAL INSTITUTIONS	SCHOOL TYPE	NEW OR EXISTING PROGRAM	EDUCATION OPTIONS	# ACCEPTED
WISCONSIN	Milwaukee Area Technical College	Wisconsin Department of Corrections	Public - Two Year	Existing	Certificate, Associates Degree	250
WEST VIRGINIA	Glenville State College	FCI-Gilmer, West Virginia Department of Corrections – Huttonsville Correction Center	Public – Four Year	Existing	Associates Degree, Bachelors Degree	215

In-Prison Programs

The following are just some of the many in-prison programs around the country that are **not** participants in the Second Chance Pell Grant program.

STATE	INSTITUTION	PROGRAM	SCHOOL	PROGRAM DESCRIPTION	EDUCATION OPTION
Alabama	9 Alabama facilities	Alabama Prison Arts & Education Project (APEAP)	Auburn University	Provides access to quality educational experiences in the arts and humanities ,taught by a pool of 80 writers, artists, scholars and other visiting teachers.	CEU Credits
Arizona	Florence State Prison & Eyman State Prison	Prison English Program	Arizona State University I Temple	Provides creative writing coaching and English courses, as well as the study of Shakespeare, ESL, linguistics, philosophy, drama and Chinese.	Noncredit/ no degrees
California	California State Prison I Solano	Solano College in Prison Project	Solano Community College	Offers humanities and business classes.	Certificate
California	California Rehabilitation Center	Claremont Colleges Inside-Out Prison Exchange Program	Pitzer College	Offers a variety of college-level for-credit educational opportunities.	For-Credit
Georgia	Arrendale State Prison	The Chillon Project	Life University	Offers full associate and bachelor degree programs, including a degree program in Positive Human Development and Social Change (PHDSC)	Associate & Bachelor degrees
Georgia	Phillips State Prison	Common Good Atlanta	Georgia Tech & Georgia State University	Offers a variety of college-level for-credit educational opportunities.	For-Credit
Illinois	Stateville Prison	Prison + Neighborhood Arts Program	A coalition of Chicago-area colleges	Offers a variety of arts and humanities classes.	Some degrees

STATE	INSTITUTION	PROGRAM	SCHOOL	PROGRAM DESCRIPTION	EDUCATION OPTION
Indiana	Westville Correctional Facility	Westville Education Initiative	Holy Cross College & Notre Dame	Offers full Associate of Arts and Bachelor of Arts degree programs.	Associate & Bachelor degrees
Kansas	Ellsworth Correctional Facility & Learned Correctional Mental Health Facility	Barton Prison Initiative	Barton Community College	Adult basic education and certifications, including carpentry, welding, plumbing, manufacturing, Microsoft Office Specialist, IC3 Certification, and NCCER Core Certificate.	Certificates
Massachusetts	Numerous Massachusetts facilities and several other states	Changing Lives Through Literature	University of Massachusetts Dartmouth	Brings carefully selected literary world to assist in gaining life insights and transformation.	Noncredit/ no degrees
Michigan	Macomb Correctional Facility & Parnell Correctional Facility	Vera's Pathways	Jackson College & Kalamazoo Valley Community College	Offers a variety of college-level for-credit and degree educational opportunities. Vera's Pathways is a multi-state initiative to bring education to institutions across the country.	Associate & Bachelor degrees
	7 state prisons	Prison Education Initiative	Jackson College	Offers a variety of certificate options as well as Associate's degrees in General Studies and Arts.	Certificates & Associate degrees
Missouri	Women's Eastern Reception, Diagnostic & Correctional Center (WERDCC) & Missouri Eastern Correctional Center (MECC)	Prison Performing Arts	Coalition	Places nationally-known playwrights to produce and develops theatrical productions inside the prisons, which prisoners perform.	Noncredit/ no degrees
New Jersey	6 state prisons	NJ STEP	Princeton, Rutgers and Drew University & several community colleges	The New Jersey Scholarship & Transformative Education in Prisons Consortium (NJ-STEP) offers a number of for-credit course options leading to Associate and Bachelor of Arts degrees.	Associate & Bachelor degrees
New Mexico	Penitentiary of New Mexico	Prison English Program	Arizona State University	Temple	Provides creative writing coaching and English courses, as well as the study of Shakespeare, ESL, linguistics, philosophy, drama and Chinese.	Noncredit no degrees
New York	Wallkill Correctional Facility	NYU's Prison Education Program	New York University	Offers educational programming leading to an Associate of Arts in Liberal Studies.	Associate degree
	6 medium-security prisons	Prison Reentry Institute	John Jay College of Criminal Justice (CUNY)	Provides college readiness classes and a variety of for-credit college courses.	For-credit courses
North Carolina	Medium security prisons	Higher Education in Prisons Program	Guilford College	Offers ten college courses and an employment certification option.	For-credit courses
	Southern Correctional Institution, Piedmont Correctional Institution & Dan River Work Farm	Wiser Justice	Guilford College	Offers a variety of liberal arts course options, enough to earn up to 30 college credits. Also offers the nation's only in-prison Leadership in Energy Environmental Design (LEED) certification.	For-credit courses & certificate

STATE	INSTITUTION	PROGRAM	SCHOOL	PROGRAM DESCRIPTION	EDUCATION OPTION
Ohio	All Ohio prisons	Correctional Education	Ashland University	Several courses, including Financial Literacy, Conflict Resolution, Facilitating At-Risk Student Learning, Fundamentals of Correctional Education and Fundamentals of Effective Problem Solving.	Noncredit no degrees
Oregon	Oregon State Penitentiary	Inside Out	University of Oregon	Offers a rotating variety of classes, often for-credit – currently Creative Writing.	Some For-credit classes
Pennsylvania	FCI McKean	University of Pittsburgh @ Bradford Prison Education Program (UPBPEP)	University of Pittsburgh	Variety of for-credit college courses.	For-credit courses
Pennsylvania	SCI Graterford	Villanova Undergraduate Program	Villanova University	Offers educational programming leading to an Associate of Arts in Liberal Studies.	Associate degree
Utah	Draper State Prison	INSPIRE	University of Utah	Offers a variety of science courses and workshops.	Noncredit no degrees
Washington	Airway Heights Correction Center	AHCC Corrections Education	Spokane Community College	Adult basic education, I-Best Aerospace Composites, college readiness, general business, bookkeeping, upholstery and CAD.	Certificates & diplomas
Washington	Washington Correctional Center for Women	Freedom Education Project Puget Sound	Tacoma Community College	Offers educational programming leading to an Associate of Arts degree.	Associate degree

Other Potential Sources of Education Financing

Charitable Foundations

Are you part of a minority? Are you part of a classification of people that are supported by outside organizations to ensure that equality is afforded?

Some prisoner-students have had success in finding funding through various charitable organizations and corporations that were established for certain groups to give individuals the same opportunities as the masses. Most of these opportunities provide scholarships, internships, and fellowships to individuals based on ethnic or social backgrounds, among other criteria. If you are African American, Asian, American Indian, Hispanic, Alaskan-Native, or part of some other similar minority, it is very possible that you can gain some measure of support through organizations that were established just for you.

Below is a small list of some of these organizations, which you can write to see what opportunities may currently be available to you. Bear in mind that the majority of the programs that these organizations offer are focused towards those applicants who show the most academic promise and the greatest level of need.

The next section, Scholarships, provides a lot more detail on specific scholarships currently being offered by these organizations and many others.

AMERICAN INDIAN COLLEGE FUND

8333 Greenwood Boulevard, Denver, CO 80221
(303) 426-8900
www.collegefund.org
The American Indian College Fund awards scholarships to American Indian and Alaskan-Native who demonstrate that they are academically gifted and are in financial need. They typically award scholarships to approximately 5,000 students annually.

ASIAN & PACIFIC ISLANDER AMERICAN SCHOLARSHIP FUND

2025 M St. NW, Suite 610, Washington, DC 20036
(202) 986-6892
www.apisf.org
The Asian & Pacific Islander American Scholarship Fund awards scholarships to Asian and Pacific Islander students who can demonstrate academic achievement. They have awarded roughly $75 million to such students since 2003.

GATES MILLENNIUM SCHOLARS PROGRAM

PO Box 10500, Fairfax, VA 22031
(877) 690-4677
www.gmsp.org

The Gates Millennium Scholars Program awards scholarships to African-American, American Indian/Alaskan-Native, Asia-Pacific Islander-American, and Hispanic-American students who are, or intend to be, full-time students at a degree-granting college. They look for applicants who can demonstrate high academic achievement, leadership skills, and a financial need.

HISPANIC SCHOLARSHIP FUND

1411 West 190th St., Suite 700, Gardena, CA 90248
(877) 473-4636
www.hsf.net
The Hispanic Scholarship Fund awards scholarships to Hispanic-American, Mexican-American, and Puerto Rican students who are enrolling in a full-time degree-granting college. Students must demonstrate high academic achievement and a financial need.

UNITED NEGRO COLLEGE FUND

1805 7th St. NW, Washington, DC 20001
(800) 331-2244
www.uncf.org
The United Negro College Fund awards scholarships to African American students from low-to-moderate income families. They award 10,000 scholarships or internships annually. Applicants must demonstrate that they are high academic achievement.

2018 Scholarships

Just because you're in prison does not mean that you are not eligible to receive scholarships to help for your education. Prisoners, however, may not be the most obvious choice for organizations that grant scholarships, making getting them a challenge. But if you have decided to bravely go down the path of gaining an education while behind bars, you are likely up for that challenge.

To help you on your path to finding scholarship money, we've provided some things you should know about the process of applying for scholarships, some strategies to follow, and some places to begin looking for the funding that help you realize your ambitions for a formal education, despite your confines.

THE SCHOLARSHIP PROCESS

The process of applying for a scholarship is fairly straightforward.

1. Locate scholarships you want to apply for.

2. Apply for the scholarships

3. Wait to hear back from the scholarship organization

Getting a scholarship, while straightforward, is not quite as simplistic. There is an art to it, which is why there are entire books written about how to get a scholarship.

Once you have located a scholarship you would like to apply for, you will receive a scholarship application to fill out. Once you receive it, you'll quickly discover that it looks pretty simple, like maybe something you could knock out in an hour or so before lunch. Don't let it fool you! The application is one of the most vital parts of winning any scholarship. This is your introduction, your first impression, and there is no re-do to make this first impression. You'll want to put your best foot forward, which requires that you take this step very seriously.

Generally, all organizations will require potential students to meet certain criteria and obligations, including:

- a high school diploma or equivalent, either already earned in in the process

- at least a 2.5 GPA

- letters of recommendation

- an essay regarding the students eligibility and goals

There are a number of books that dive directly into this process that you would be well-served to look into. A number of them can be found in the *Appendix* section of this book. But as you consider your scholarship options, you may want to get a better idea of what kinds of things scholarship-granting organizations are looking for in those they offer such financial opportunities.

The following pages will introduce you to a wealth of scholarship opportunities.

Scholarships Specifically for Prisoners

Scholarship opportunities specifically for prisoners come and go. The following scholarships are the most current as of the publication of this book.

NOTE: Many organizations limit their scholarships offerings to prisoners housed within they state they are based. We have clearly marked which organizations offer their scholarships regionally and/or nationally. If an organization listed below does not offer scholarships nationally or specifically in your region do not attempt to apply for them. You are wasting your time and theirs.

SCHOLARSHIPS FOR PRISONERS | NATIONALLY

COMMITMENT TO CHANGE COLLEGE SCHOLARSHIP | JEREMY GORDON – ATTORNEY AT LAW

PO Box 2275, Mansfield, TX 76063
(972) 483-4865
www.gordondefense.com

Purpose: The Jeremy Gordon law firm, a criminal defense firm, offers scholarships four times each year through their *Commitment to Change College Scholarship* for prisoners would like to take classes from Adams State University. Applicants cannot already hold a bachelor's degree.

Amount: Tuition and books for one course at Adams State University.

PRISON EDUCATION FOUNDATION

4031 Colonel Glen Highway, Beavercreek, OH 45431
(877) 361-1725
www.prisonedu.org   info@prisonedu.org

Purpose: Assists with education funding for serious students. The foundation prefers that the recipient enroll in two classes totaling up to eight credit hours and personally be willing to pay one-half of the tuition, although one class may be taken with the foundation paying the entire tuition. Applicants must be within seven years of a scheduled release date and have no serious disciplinary incidents within the past 12 months.

Amount: Varies, but generally the cost of one course, up to four credit hours.

PRISON SCHOLAR FUND

1752 NW Market St. #953. Seattle, WA 98107
psf.azurewebsites.net

Purpose: Opens access to post-secondary education opportunities to incarcerated students with support and mentoring, and helps them reintegrate back into society with transition support that includes job readiness and placement. They will typically award a scholarship for one course at a time until the applicant proves they are able to complete the course and meet academic performance standards. Once a track record is established, the applicant will be considered a "Prison Scholar" and provided latitude to enroll in more than one course at a time.

Amount: Varies, but generally the cost of one course at an accredited school.

BRAIN ZIEGER SCHOLARSHIP ESSAY CONTEST | THE ZIEGER FIRM

1500 John F. Kennedy Blvd., Suite 620A, Philadelphia, PA 19102
(215) 546-0340
www.brianzieger.com   info@brianzieger.com

Purpose: *The Zieger Firm* is a Philadelphia criminal defense attorney firm that understands the benefits of education for prisoners and non-prisoners. They offer the biannual *Brain Zieger Scholarship,* which is administered through an essay contest. Students are asked to submit a 500-word essay answering a question.

Amount: Up to $1,000.

SCHOLARSHIPS FOR PRISONERS | REGIONALLY

TRANSCENDING THROUGH EDUCATION FOUNDATION | TTEF

5 Grant Court, Newport, RI 02840
www.transcendingthrougheducation.org

Purpose: To provide resources and support for **Rhode Island** prisoners to obtain higher education. They offer two types of scholarships: one to current prisoners and one to an ex-offender who will be pursuing their education upon release from prison. Must be a Rhode Island prisoner with a high school diploma or GED.

Amount: Varies, but generally up to $1,000.

OTHER PRISONER-RELATED SCHOLARSHIPS

CHARLES W. COLSON SCHOLARSHIP | INSTITUTE FOR PRISON MINISTRIES (IPM)

500 College Ave., Whaeaton, IL 60187
(630) 752-5727
www.wheaton.edu/BGCE/Initaitives/Institute-for-Prison-Ministries/IPM/Colson-Scholarship

Purpose: The *Colson Scholarship Program* is administered by IPM and named in honor of Chuck Colson for his valuable service to the field of prison ministry. They award scholarships to ex-offenders who are looking to attend Wheaton College upon release from prison and to progress to a life of Christian leadership.

Amount: Varies.

Other Scholarships Prisoners Can Apply For

There are literally millions of scholarships made available to students every year. Most of them do not apply specifically to prisoner-students. Therefore, we have scoured nearly 2 million of the 2017 scholarships to pull out ones that prisoners may find useful. There is no guarantee that all of the following will allow prisoners to apply. Even if there is no restriction against prisoners, remember that you are going up against outside world students that these organizations more traditionally tend to grant scholarships to. Make sure to read previous sections of this book to see how you can use this to your advantage.

CULTURAL SCHOLARSHIPS

AFRICAN-AMERICAN (FIND MORE UNDER "MULTI-CULTURAL")

CATHERINE W. PIERCE SCHOLARSHIPS

United Negro College Fund (UNCF) 1805 7th Street NW, Washington, DC, 20001
(800) 331-2244
www.uncf.org
Purpose: To help African American students majoring in art or history.
Amount: Up to $5,000.

CITIGROUP FELLOWS PROGRAM

United Negro College Fund (UNCF) 1805 7th Street NW, Washington, DC, 20001
www.uncf.org
Purpose: To assist sophomores at United Negro College Fund (UNCF) member colleges and universities who plan to pursue business careers.
Amount: $6,400.

CONGRESSIONAL BLACK CAUCUS SPOUSES EDUCATION SCHOLARSHIP

1720 Massachusetts Ave. NW, Washington, DC 20036
(202) 263-2800
www.cbcfinc.org
Purpose: To support African American students who are pursuing undergraduate of graduate degrees.
Amount: Varies.

CONGRESSIONAL BLACK CAUCUS SPOUSES EDUCATION SCHOLARSHIP

1720 Massachusetts Ave. NW, Washington, DC 20036
(202) 263-2800
www.cbcfinc.org
Purpose: To support African American students who are pursuing careers in visual arts.
Amount: Up to $3,000.

HERBERT LEHMAN SCHOLARSHIPS

NAACP Legal Defense and Educational Fund
40 Rector St., 40th Floor, New York, NY 10006
(212) 965-2200
www.naacpldf.org   mbagley@naacpldf.org
Purpose: To support African American students who are attending college for the first time.
Amount: $2,000

HUBERTUS W.V. WELLEMS SCHOLARSHIP FOR MALE STUDENTS

NAACP | The United Negro College Fund
8260 Willow Oaks Corporate Dr., Fairfax, VA 22031
(800) 331-2244
www.naacp.org
Purpose: To aid male students who are studying certain math and science subjects at the undergraduate and graduate levels.
Amount: $3,000

NATIONAL ASSOCIATION OF BLACK ACCOUNTANTS NATIONAL SCHOLARSHIP PROGRAM

National Association of Black Accountants
7249-A Hanover Pkwy., Greenbelt, MD 20770
(301) 474-NABA
www.nabainc.org
Purpose: To support African Americans and other minorities in the accounting and finance professions.
Amount: $1,000-$10,000.

NATIONAL ASSOCIATION OF BLACK JOURNALISTS SCHOLARSHIP PROGRAM

National Association of Black Journalists
1100 Knight Hall, Suite 3100, College Park, MD 20742
(301) 405-7520
www.nabj.org
Purpose: To support African-American students who are planning to pursue careers in journalism.
Amount: Up to $2,500.

ROBERT A. CATLIN/DAVID W. LONG MEMORIAL SCHOLARSHIPS

American Planning Association
205 N. Michigan Ave., Suite 1200, Chicago, IL 60601
(312) 431-9100
www.planning.org   pbcd.policy@gmail.com
Purpose: To encourage African-American students to pursue graduate studies in urban planning.
Amount: $1,500.

JULIANNE MALVEAUX SCHOLARSHIP | NATIONAL ASSN. OF NEGRO BUSINESS AND PROFESSIONAL WOMEN'S CLUBS

1806 New Hampshire Ave. NW, Washington, DC 20009-3298
(202) 483-4206
www.nanbpwc.org   info@nanbpwc.org

Purpose: To award scholarships to college students majoring in journalism, economics or a related field.
Amount: Varies.

ARMENIAN

ASA SCHOLARSHIPS | ARMENIAN STUDENTS' ASSOCIATION OF AMERICA

333 Atlantic Avenue, Warwick, RI, 02888
(401) 461-6114
www.asainc.org asa@asainc.org
Purpose: To provide scholarships for students of Armenian descent.
Amount: Varies.

EREMIAN SCHOLARSHIPS | ARMENIAN RELIEF SOCIETY OF NORTH AMERICA INC.

80 Bigelow Avenue, Watertown, MA, 02472
(617) 926-5892
www.ars1910.org ars1910@aol.com
Purpose: To provide merit and need-based scholarships for students of Armenian ancestry.
Amount: Varies

ASIAN/ISLANDER

ASIAN AND PACIFIC ISLANDERS AMERICAN SCHOLARSHIPS

2025 M Street NW, Suite 610, Washington, DC, 20036
(202) 986-6892
Purpose: To provide financial assistance to Asian and Pacific Island Americans. Applicants must be of Asian or Pacific Island ethnicity as defined by the U.S. Census, and they must be legal citizens, nationals or permanent residents of the United States.
Amount: $2,500-$15,000.

ASIAN WOMEN IN BUSINESS SCHOLARSHIPS

Asian Women in Business 42 Broadway, Suite 1748, New York, NY, 10004
(212) 868-1368
www.awb.org info@awib.org
Purpose: To recognize Asian women who have demonstrated scholarship, leadership or commitment to community. Applicants must be women of Asian or Pacific Islander descent.
Amount: Up to $5,000.

IDA M. POPE MEMORIAL SCHOLARSHIP | HAWAII COMMUNITY FOUNDATION | SCHOLARSHIPS

827 Fort Street Mall, Honolulu, HI 96813
(888) 731-3863
www.hawaiicommunityfoundation.org
scholarships@hawaiicommunityfoundation.org
Purpose: To assist female students of Hawaiian ancestry in obtaining higher education.

Amount: Varies.

KOREAN ANCESTRY GRANT

William Orr Dingwall Foundation
PO Box 57088, Washington, DC 20037
www.dingwallfoundation.org
Purpose: To aid students of Asian ancestry.

Amount: Up to $10,000

MINE & GONSAKULTO SCHOLARSHIP

Far West Athletic Trainers' Association | District 8
www.fwatad8.org   nhbergerr@gmail.com
Purpose: To aid students of Asian descent in California, Nevada and Hawaii who are pursuing higher education in athletic training.

Amount: Varies.

TAIWANESE AMERICAN SCHOLARSHIP FUND

Asian Pacific Community Fund
1145 Wilshire Blvd., First Floor, Los Angeles, CA 90017
(213) 624-6400
www.apcf.org   scholarships@apcf.org
Purpose: To assist Taiwanese-American students with education expenses.

Amount: $2,500.

UPS HALLMARK SCHOLARSHIPS | U.S. PAN ASIAN AMERICAN CHAMBER OF COMMERCE

1329 18th St. NW, Washington, DC 20036
(800) 696-7818
www.uspaacc.com/scholarships/overview
Purpose: To provide financial assistance to Asian-American students.

Amount: Varies.

GREEK

HELLENIC TIMES SCHOLARSHIP FUND

823 Eleventh Ave., New York, NY 10019
www.htsfund.org   htsfund@aol.com
Purpose: To financially help Greek American students.

Amount: $2,000

NATIONAL AND DISTRICT SCHOLARSHIPS | AMERICAN HELLENIC EDUCATION PROGRESSIVE ASSN. (AHEPA)

1909 Q. St. NW, Suite 500, Washington, DC 20009
(202) 232-6300
www.ahepa.org
Purpose: To support projects furthering the goals of AHEPA: studies concerning Hellenism, Hellenic culture or Greek-American life.

Amount: Up to $2,000

P.A. MARGARONIS SCHOLARSHIP | AMERICAN HELLENIC EDUCATION PROGRESSIVE ASSN.

1909 Q St. NW, Suite 500, Washington, DC 20009
(202) 232-6300
www.ahepa.org   ahepa@ahepa.org
Purpose: To support students of Greek descent.

Amount: Up to $2,500.

HISPANIC (FIND MORE UNDER 'MULTI-CULTURAL'.)

BECA #TRADUCTOR | SPANISHDICT

1400 Key Blvd., Suite 1200, Arlington, VA 22209
(305) 505-4667
www.spanishdict.com/tranductor
Purpose: To reward students who are literate in both Spanish and English.

Amount: $1,000.

CONGRESSIONAL HISPANIC CAUCUS INSTITUTE SCHOLARSHIP AWARD

300 M Street SE, 5th Floor, Suite 510, Washington, DC, 2003
(202) 543-1771
Purpose: To reward Latino students for public service activities in their communities.

Amount: $1,000-$5,000.

HISPANIC SCHOLARSHIP FUND (HSF) | ASSOCIATION OF LATINO PROFESSIONALS IN FINANCE AND ACCOUNTING (ALPFA) SCHOLARSHIP PROGRAM

1411 W. 190th St., Suite 325, Los Angeles, CA 90248
(877) 473-4636
www.hsf.net   scholar1@hsf.net
Purpose: To aid outstanding Latino students who are majoring in finance, accounting, economic, business administration or management.

Amount: $2,000-$10,000

HISPANIC SCHOLARSHIP FUND (HSF) | GENERAL COLLEGE SCHOLARSHIP PROGRAM

1411 W. 190th St., Suite 325, Los Angeles, CA 90248
(877) 473-4636
www.hsf.net   scholar1@hsf.net
Purpose: To support students of Hispanic heritage.
Amount: $500-$5,000

HISPANIC SCHOLARSHIP FUND (HSF) | VERIZON FOUNDATION SCHOLARSHIP PROGRAM

1411 W. 190th St., Suite 325, Los Angeles, CA 90248
(877) 473-4636
www.hsf.net   scholar1@hsf.net
Purpose: To aid outstanding Latino undergraduates.
Amount: Varies.

HISPANIC SCHOLARSHIP FUND (HSF) | WELLS FARGO SCHOLARSHIP PROGRAM

1411 W. 190th St., Suite 325, Los Angeles, CA 90248
(877) 473-4636
www.hsf.net   scholar1@hsf.net
Purpose: To aid Hispanic undergraduates who are attending or transferring to a four-year college.
Amount: $2,500

LULAC GENERAL & HONORS AWARDS | LEAGUE OF UNION LATIN AMERICAN CITIZENS

1133 19th St.. NW, Suite 1000, Washington, DC 20036
(202) 835-9646
Purpose: To provide assistance to Latino students of all levels of education.
Amount: $250-$5,000

MARIA ELENA SALINAS SCHOLARSHIP PROGRAM | NATIONAL ASSN. OF HISPANIC JOURNALISTS SCHOLARSHIP COMMITTEE

1050 Connecticut Ave. NW, 10th Floor, Washington, DC 20036
www.nahj.org   ntita@nahj.org
Purpose: To support Spanish-speaking students who plan to become broadcast journalists.
Amount: Up to $5,000.

MAS FAMILY SCHOLARSHIPS | JORGE MAS CANOSA FREEDOM FOUNDATION

PO Box 14-1898, Miami, FL 33114
(305) 529-0075
www.masscholarships.org

Purpose: To aid undergraduate and graduate students of Cuban descent who are studying selected subjects.
Amount: Up to $8,000.

NATIONAL HISPANIC HEALTH PROFESSIONAL STUDENT SCHOLARSHIP

1216 Fifth Ave., Room 457, New York, NY 10029
(212) 419-3686
www.nhmafoundation.org
Purpose: To support Hispanic students who are planning to pursue careers in health care.
Amount: $2,000-$5,000.

QUE LLUEVA CAFE SCHOLARSHIPSCHICANO | ORGANIZING AND RESEARCH IN EDUCATIONAL

PO Box 160144, Sacramento, CA 95816
www.ccore.org
Purpose: To aid undocumented Latino students who wish to attend college.
Amount: Varies.

IRISH

IRISH CULTURAL AND EDUCATIONAL GRANT | IRISH FESTIVALS, INC.

1532 Wauwatosa Ave., Milwaukee, WI 53213
(414) 476-3378
www.irishfest.com
Purpose: To support students wishing to study Irish culture.
Amount: Varies.

ITALIAN

NATIONAL ITALIAN AMERICAN FOUNDATION SCHOLARSHIP

1860 19th St. NW, Washington, DC 20009
(202) 387-0600
www.niaf.org   scholarships@niaf.org
Purpose: To support Italian-American students.
Amount: $2,500-$12,000.

LGBTQ

HORIZONS FOUNDATION

550 Montgomery St., Suite 700, San Francisco, CA 94111
(415) 398-2333

www.horizonsfoundation.org *info@horizonsfoundation.org*

Purpose: To assist Bay area gay, lesbian, bisexual and transgender Asian and Pacific Islander students.

Amount: Up to $1,000

HOWARD COUNTY PFLAG ACADEMIC SCHOLARSHIPS |

PO Box 1479, Columbia, MD 21044
(410) 290-8292
www.pflagmd.org
Purpose: To support outstanding gay, lesbian, bisexual and transgendered students and their straight allies.

Amount: $2,000.

PARENTS, FAMILIES AND FRIENDS OF LESBIANS & GAYS GENERAL SCHOLARSHIPS

1828 L St. NW, Washington, DC 20036
(202) 467-8180
www.pflag.org
Purpose: To provide educational opportunities for the LGBTQ community.

Amount: Varies.

LITHUANIAN

KNIGHTS OF LITHUANIA SCHOLARSHIP PROGRAM

14 Pine Ave., Johnstown, NY 12095
(518) 705-1165
www.knightsoflithuania.com
Purpose: To assist Lithuanian Americans in obtaining higher education. Must have been a member of Knights of Lithuania for at least two years.

Amount: Varies.

MULTI-CULTURAL

ACTUARIAL DIVERSITY SCHOLARSHIPS | ACTUARIAL FOUNDATION

475 N. Martingale Road, Suite 600, Schaumberg, II, 60173-2226
(847) 706-3581
www.beanactuary.org *scholarship@actfund.org*
Purpose: To promote diversity through an annual scholarship program for African American, Hispanic and Native American Indian students and encourage academic achievements by awarding scholarships to full-time undergraduate students pursuing a degree in actuarial profession.

Amount: $1,000-$4,000.

AICPA SCHOLARSHIP FOR MINORITY ACCOUNTING STUDENTS | AMERICAN INSTITUTE OF CERTIFIED PUBLIC ACCOUNTANTS

220 Leigh Farm Road, Durham, NC, 27707
(919) 402-4500
Purpose: To encourage minority students to become certified public accountants (CPAs). Applicants must be African-American, Native American, Latino or Asian American students who are majoring in accounting.

Amount: Up to $5,000.

AMERICAN CHEMICAL SOCIETY SCHOLARS PROGRAM

1155 Sixteenth Street, NW, Washington, DC, 20036
(800) 227-5558
www.acs.org *crobinson@rubber.org*
Purpose: To encourage minority students to pursue careers in the sciences and to help them acquire the skills necessary for success in these fields. Applicants must be African American, Hispanic/Latino or American Indian.

Amount: Up to $5,000.

AMERICAN SOCIETY OF CRIMINOLOGY FELLOWSHIPS FOR ETHNIC MINORITIES | AMERICAN SOCIETY OF CRIMINOLOGY DEPARTMENT OF SOCIOLOGY AND CRIMINAL JUSTICE

1314 Kinnear Rd., Suite 212, Columbus, OH 43212-1156
www.arc41.com *roner@udel.edu*
Purpose: To encourage minorities to study criminology or criminal justice. Applicants must be African American, Asian American, Latino or Native American.

Amount: $6,000.

GATES MILLENNIUM SCHOLARS FOUNDATION | GATES FOUNDATION

PO Box 10500, Fairfax, VA 22031
(877) 690-4677
www.gmsp.org
Purpose: To provide outstanding minority students with opportunities to complete their undergraduate college educations.

Amount: Varies.

NATIONAL CONSORTIUM FOR GRADUATE DEGREES FOR MINORITIES IN ENGINEERING AND SCIENCE (GEM)

1430 Duke St., Alexandria, VA 22314
(703) 562-3646

www.gemfellowship.org *info@gemfellowship.org*
Purpose: To provide fellowships for minority engineering and computer science students pursuing master's degrees.

Amount: Varies.

HISPANIC SCHOLARSHIP FUND (HSF) | MARATHON OIL CORPORATION COLLEGE SCHOLARSHIP PROGRAM

1411 W. 190th St., Suite 325, Los Angeles, CA 90248
(877) 473-4636
www.hsf.net *scholar1@hsf.net*
Purpose: To aid minority undergraduates who are studying selected subjects. Applicants must be U.S. Citizens or legal; permanent residents who are African-American, Native American, Asian, Pacific Islanders or Alaska Natives.

Amount: Up to $15,000

MINORITY SCHOLARSHIPS | NATIONAL STRENGTH & CONDITIONING ASSOCIATION (NSCA)

1885 Bob Johnson Dr., Colorado Springs, CO 80906
(800) 815-6826
www.nsca.com/foundation
Purpose: To encourage minorities to enter the field of strength and conditioning. Applicants must be African-American, Hispanic, Asian-American or Native-American students working toward a graduate degree related to strength and conditioning.

MINORITY SCHOLARSHIP AWARD FOR PHYSICAL THERAPY STUDENTS | AMERICAN PHYSICAL THERAPY ASSOCIATION

1111 N. Fairfax St., Alexandria, VA 22314
(703) 684-2782
www.apta.org *minority@apta.org*
Purpose: To aid minority physical therapy students. Applicants must be legal permanent residents or U.S. Citizens who are African-American, Hispanic, Native American, Pacific Islander, Native Hawaiian or Alaska Native.

Amount: Varies.

MUTUAL OF OMAHA ACTUARIAL SCHOLARSHIP FOR MINORITY STUDENTS

Mutual of Omaha Plaza, Omaha, NE 68175
(402) 351-3300
www.mutualofomaha.com
Purpose: To support undergraduate students who are preparing for actuarial careers. Applicants must be legal permanent residents or U.S. Citizens who are African-American, Hispanic, Native American, Asian American or from another underrepresented minority group.

Amount: $5,000

PUBLIC RELATIONS STUDENT SOCIETY OF AMERICA | DIVERSITY MULTICULTURAL SCHOLARSHIPS

33 Maiden Lane, 11th Floor, New York, NY 10038
(212) 460-1474
www.prssa.org *prssa@prssa.org*
Purpose: To aid minority communications students. Applicants must be of African-American, Latino, Asian, Native American, Alaska Native or Pacific Islander descent.

Amount: $1,500.

SCHOLARSHIPS FOR SOCIAL JUSTICE | HIGHER EDUCATION CONSORTIUM FOR URBAN AFFAIRS

2233 University Ave. W, Suite 210, St. Paul, MN 55114
(651) 646-8832
www.hecua.org *info@hecua.org*
Purpose: To support students from low-income families, students from ethnic minorities and students who are the first in their family to go to college.

Amount: $1,500.

MINORITY CORPORATION COUNSEL ASSOCIATION (MCCA) | LLOYD M. JOHNSON, JR. SCHOLARSHIP PROGRAM

111 Pennsylvania Ave. NW, Washington, DC 20004
(855) 670-ISTS
www.mcca.com *contactus@mcca.com*
Purpose: To support first-year entering law students.

Amount: $10,000

MARICIA SILVERMAN MINORITY STUDENT AWARD | PUBLIC RELATIONS STUDENT SOCIETY OF AMERICA

33 Maiden Lane, 11th Floor, New York, NY 10038
(212) 460-1474
www.prssa.org *prssa@prssa.org*
Purpose: To aid minority students who are preparing for careers in public relations.

Amount: $5,000

TRAILBLAZER SCHOLARSHIP | CONFERENCE OF MINORITY TRANSPORTATION OFFICIALS

100 M St. SE, Suite 917, Washington, DC 20003
(202) 857-8065
www.comto.org
Purpose: To support minority students in the field of transportation.

Amount: $2,500.

NATIVE AMERICAN

A.T. ANDERSON MEMORIAL SCHOLARSHIPS | AMERICAN INDIAN SCIENCE AND ENGINEERING SOCIETY

2305 Renard Place, Albuquerque, NM 87106
(505) 765-1052
www.aises.org
Purpose: To provide scholarships for Native Americans and Alaskan Native students majoring in science, engineering, medicine, natural resources, math and technology.

Amount: $1,000-$2,000.

ADOLPH VAN PELT SCHOLARSHIPS | ASSOCIATION OF AMERICAN INDIAN AFFAIRS

Lisa Wyzlic, Director of Scholarship Programs, 966 Hungerford Drive, Suite 12-B, Rockville, MD, 20850
(240) 314- 7155
www.indian-affairs.org lw.aia@indian-affairs.org
Purpose: To assist Native American/Alaskan Native undergraduate students based on merit and financial need.

Amount: $1,500.

ALLOGAN SLAGLE MEMORIAL SCHOLARSHIPS | ASSOCIATION ON AMERICAN INDIAN AFFAIRS

Lisa Wyzlic, Director of Scholarship programs 966 Hungerford Drive, Suite 12-B, Rockville, MD, 20850
(240) 314-7155
www.indian-affairs.org lw.aaia@indian-affairs.org
Purpose: To assist Native American/Alaska Native undergraduate and graduate students from tribes that are not recognized by the federal government.

Amount: $1,500.

AMERICAN INDIAN SCHOLARSHIPS | NATIONAL SOCIETY DAUGHTERS OF THE AMERICAN REVOLUTION COMMITTEE SERVICE OFFICE

Attn.:Scholarships 1776 D Street NW, Washington, DC, 20006-5303
(202) 628-1776
www.dar.org
Purpose: To assist Native American students.

Amount: $4,000.

CHEROKEE NATION DIRECTED STUDIES SCHOLARSHIPS | CHEROKEE NATION UNDERGRADUATE SCHOLARSHIP PROGRAM

P.O. Box 948, Tahlequash, OK, 74465
(918) 453-5000
www.Cherokee.org collegeresources@cherokee.org

Purpose: To aid Cherokee college students.

Amount: Full tuition, books and fees.

CHEROKEE NATION REGISTERED NURSING SCHOLARSHIPS | CHEROKEE NATION UNDERGRADUATE PROGRAMS

P.O. Box 948 Tahlequah, OK, 74465
(918) 453-5000
www.cherokee.org collegeresources@cherokeee.org
Purpose: To aid Cherokee students who are pursuing degrees in registered nursing.

Amount: Varies.

CHEROKEE NATION SCHOLARSHIP GRADUATE | UNDERGRADUATE SCHOLARSHIP PROGRAMS

P.O. Box 948 Tahlequash, OK, 74465
(918) 453-5000
www.cherokee.org collegeresources@cherokee.org
Purpose: To aid graduate students who are members of the Cherokee Nation.

Amount: Varies.

CHICKASAW NATION EDUCATION FOUNDATION PROGRAM

P.O. Box 1726, Ada, OK, 74821
(580) 421-9031
www.Chickasaw.net
Purpose: To assist Chickasaw students who demonstrate academic excellence, community service, dedication to learning and commitment to Native Americans.

Amount: Varies.

CHIEF MANUELLO SCHOLARSHIP PROGRAM | OFFICE OF NAVAJO NATION SCHOLARSHIP AND FINANCIAL ASSISTANCE

P.O. Box 1870, Window Rock, AZ, 86515
(928) 871-7444
www.onnsfa.org
Purpose: The scholarship was created to help high-achieving Navajo students.

Amount: $7,000

CITIZEN POTAWATAMI NATION TRIBAL ROLLS SCHOLARSHIPS

1601 S. Gordon Cooper Drive, Shawnee, OK, 74801
(405) 275-3121
www.potawatomi.org lcapps@potawatomi.org
Purpose: To assist Citizen Potawatomi Nation tribal members who are pursuing higher education.

Amount: Up to $2,000.

DISPLACED HOMEMAKER SCHOLARSHIPS | ASSOCIATION ON AMERICAN INDIAN AFFAIRS

Lisa Wyzlic, Director of Scholarship Programs
966 Hungerford Drive, Suite 12-B, Rockville, MD, 20850
(240) 314- 7155
www.indian-affairs.org lw.aia@indian-affairs.org
Purpose: To provide assistance to Native American/Alaska Native undergraduate men and women in any curriculum who would be unable to complete college due to family responsibilities.

Amount: $1,500.

ELIZABETH AND SHERMAN ASCHE MEMORIAL SCHOLARSHIPS | ASSOCIATION ON AMERICAN INDIAN AFFAIRS

Lisa Wyzlic, Director of Scholarship Programs 966 Hungerford Drive, Suite 12-B, Rockville, MD, 20850
(240) 314-7155
www.indian-affairs.org lw.aaia@indian-affairs.org
Purpose: To provide financial assistance to American Indians who are seeking undergraduate degrees in public health or science.

Amount: $1,500.

EMILIE HESENMEYER MEMORIAL SCHOLARSHIPS | ASSOCIATION ON AMERICAN INDIAN AFFAIRS

Lisa Wyzlic, Director of Scholarship Programs 966 Hungerford Drive, Suite 12-B, Rockville, MD, 20850
(240) 314-7155
www.indian-affairs.org lw.aaia@indian-affairs.org
Purpose: To provide financial assistance to Native Americans, especially those who are studying education.

Amount: Varies.

FLORENCE YOUNG MEMORIAL SCHOLARSHIPS | ASSOCIATION OF AMERICAN INDIAN AFFAIRS

966 Hungerford Dr., Suite 12-B, Rockville, MD 20850
(240) 314-7155
www.indian-affairs.org
Purpose: To provide financial assistance to Native Americans who are working toward a master's degree in art, public health or law.

Amount: Varies.

FOUNDATION SCHOLARSHIPS | CIRI FOUNDATION

3600 San Jeronimo Dr., Suite 256, Anchorage, AK 99508-2870
(800) 764-3382
www.thecirifoundation.org tcf@thecirifoundation.org
Purpose: To provide financial aid for Alaska Natives.

Amount: Up to $20,000

HOPI SCHOLARSHIPS | HOPI TRIBE GRANTS AND SCHOLARSHIP PROGRAM

PO Box 123, Kykotsmovi, AZ 86039
(800) 762-9630
www.hopieducationfund.org heef@hopieducationfund.org
Purpose: To help Hopi students with academic achievement.

Amount: $4,000

JEAN CHARLEY-CALL NURSING SCHOLARSHIP | HOPI TRIBE GRANTS AND SCHOLARSHIP PROGRAM

PO Box 123, Kykotsmovi, AZ 86039
(800) 762-9630
www.hopieducationfund.org heef@hopieducationfind.org
Purpose: To aid Hopi Indian nursing students.

Amount: $1,000

MESBEC PROGRAM | CATCHING THE DREAM | SCHOLARSHIP AFFAIRS OFFICE

8200 Mountain Rd. NE, Suite 203, Albuquerque. NM 87110
(505) 262-2351
www.catchingthedream.org
Purpose: To provide scholarships to high-achieving American Indians in the fields of math, engineering, science, business, education and computers.

Amount: $500-$5000

MORRIS K. UDDALL SCHOLARSHIP | MORRIS K. UDDALL FOUNDATION

130 S. Scott Ave., Tucson, AZ 85701-1922
(520) 901-8500
www.udall.gov info@udall.gov
Purpose: To aid students committed to careers related to the environment, tribal policy or Native American health care.

Amount: Up to $5,000

NATIONAL AMERICAN JOURNALISTS ASSOCIATION | UNIVERSITY OF OKLAHOMA AT GAYLORD COLLEGE

395 W. Lindsey St., Norman, OK 73019-4201
(605) 677-5282
www.naja.com info@naja.com
Purpose: To assist Native American students pursuing journalism degrees.

Amount: $500-$3,000.

NATIVE AMERICAN EDUCATION GRANT | PRESBYTERIAN CHURCH (USA)

100 Witherspoon St., Louisville, KY 40202
(888) 728-7228 ext. 5776
www.pcusa.org
Purpose: To aid Alaska Natives and Native Americans pursuing full-time post-secondary education.

Amount: Up to $1,500.

NATIVE AMERICAN LEADERSHIP EDUCATIONAL | CATCHING THE DREAM

Scholarship Affairs Office, 8200 Mountain Rd. NE, Suite 203, Albuquerque, NM 97110
(505) 262-2351
www.catchingthedream.org
Purpose: To increase the number of American Indian teachers in American Indian schools.

Amount: $500-$5,000.

NORWEIGIAN

GENERAL HERITAGE & CULTURE GRANTS | SONS OF NORWAY FOUNDATION

1455 W. Lake St., Minneapolis, MN 55408
(800) 945-8851
www.sofn.com   *foundation@sofn.com*
Purpose: To preserve the Norwegian heritage.

Amount: $1,500

GEORGE CHOY MEMORIAL GAY ASIAN PACIFIC ALLIANCE (GAPA) SCHOLARSHIPS | HEALTH PROFESSIONS PRE-GRADUATE SCHOLARSHIP PROGRAM

Indian Health Service | Scholarship Program Office
5600 Fishers Lane, MS: OHR (11E53A), Rockville, MD 20857
(301) 443-6197
www.ihs.gov
Purpose: To aid Native Americans and Alaska Natives who are enrolled in selected health-related pre-professional degree programs.

Amount: Full tuition and fees.

HIGHER EDUCATION GRANT | BUREAU OF INDIAN AFFAIRS

1849 C St. NW, MS-3512 MIB, Washington, DC 20240-0001
(202) 208-6123
www.bia.gov
Purpose: To assist American Indian and Alaska Native students obtaining their undergraduate degrees.

Amount: Varies.

POLISH

POLISH NATIONAL ALLIANCE SCHOLARSHIP | EDUCATIONAL DEPARTMENT

6100 Cicero Ave., Chicago, IL 60646
(800) 621-3723
www.pnaznp.org   *pna@pnaznp.org*
Purpose: To assist members of the Polish National Alliance with their undergraduate studies.

Amount: Varies.

SCOTTISH

ST. ANDREWS SOCIETY OF WASHINGTON, DC SCHOLARSHIPS

PO Box 7849, Washington, DC 20044
www.saintandrewsociety.com
Purpose: To assist students of Scottish birth or descent.

Amount: Varies.

UKRAINIAN

EUGENE & ELINOR KOTUR SCHOLARSHIP TRUST FUND | UKRAINIAN FRATERNAL ASSOCIATION

371 N. 9th Ave., Scranton, PA 18504-2005
(570) 342-0937
www.members.tripod.com/~ufa_home
Purpose: To support Ukrainian students.

Amount: At least $1,000.

WOMEN

AAUW EDUCATIONAL FOUNDATION CAREER DEVELOPMENTAL GRANTS | AMERICAN ASSOCIATION OF UNIVERSITY WOMEN (AAUW)

Educational Foundation Dept. 60, 301 ACT Drive, Iowa City, IA, 52243-4030
(319) 337-1716 x60
www.aauw.org   *aauw@act.org*
Purpose: To support college-educated women who need additional training to advance their careers, re-enter the workforce or change careers.

Amount: $2,000-$12,000.

AGNES MISSIRIAN SCHOLARSHIPS | ARMENIAN INTERNATIONAL WOMEN'S ASSOCIATION

65 Main Street #34, Watertown, MA, 02472
(617) 926-0171
www.aiwainternational.org aiwain@aol.com
Purpose: To honor the memory of Professor Agnes Missirian and assist Armenian women in obtaining higher education.

Amount: $2,000

EMERGE SCHOLARSHIPS

3555 Peachtree Road, suite 520-121, Atlanta, GA, 30326
(770) 905-5175
www.emergescholarships.com
info@emergescholarships.org
Purpose: To provide financial assistance to women who are returning to school to change or further their careers and to stay-at-home moms who need additional training.

Amount: $2,000-$5,000.

ENTERTAINMENT SOFTWARE ASSOCIATION FOUNDATION | FOUNDATION SCHOLARSHIP PROGRAM

575 7th St. NW   Suite 300, Washington, DC 20004
(202) 223-2400
www.esafoundation.org
Purpose: To support female and minority students working on degrees toward a career in computer and video game arts.

Amount: $3,000

GLAMOUR'S TOP TEN COLLEGE WOMEN COMPETITION | CONDE NASTE PUBLICATIONS

4 Times Square, New York, NY 10036
(800) 244-4526
www.glamour.com/about/top-10-college-women
ttcw@glamour.com
Purpose: To recognize outstanding female college students.

Amount: $3,750-$20,750

JEANNETTE RANKIN WOMEN'S SCHOLARSHIP FUND

1 Huntington Rd., Suite 701, Athens, GA 30606
(706) 208-1211
www.rankinfoundation.org info@rankinfoundation.org
Purpose: To support the education of low-income women over 35 years of age or older.

Amount: Varies.

LIVE YOUR DREAM AWARDS PROGRAM | SOROPTIMIST INTERNATIONAL OF THE AMERICAS

1709 Spruce St., Philadelphia, PA 19103
(215) 893-9000

www.soroptimist.org siahq@soroptimist.org
Purpose: To assist women who are entering or re-entering the workforce with educational and skills training support.

Amount: Up to $10,000

MARGARET McNAMARA MEMORIAL FUND FELLOWSHIPS

1818 H St. NW, MSN H2-204, Washington, DC 20433
(202) 473-8751
www.mmmf-grants.org familynetwork@worldbank.org
Purpose: To provide financial assistance to women from developing countries who are currently studying to earn college degrees in the U.S., Canada, or developing countries in Africa.

Amount: $4,000-$12,000

P.E.O. PROGRAM FOR CONTINUING EDUCATIONAL | PEO INTERNATIONAL

3700 Grand Ave., Des Moines, IA 50312
(515) 255-3153
www.peointernational.org
Purpose: To assist women whose education has been interrupted.

Amount: Up to $3,000.

SHARON B. BANLS MEMORIAL UNDERGRADUATE SCHOLARSHIPS | WOMEN'S TRANSPORTATION SEMINAR (WTS) INTERNATIONAL

1701 K St. NW., Suite 800, Washington, DC 20006
(202) 955-5085
www.wsiinternational.org
Purpose: To help women pursuing transportation careers with their higher education expenses.

Amount: $5,000.

FOSTER FAMILIES

CALIFORNIA CHAFEE GRANT FOR FOSTER YOUTH | CALIFORNIA STUDENT AID COMMISSION

P.O. Box 419026, Rancho Cordova, CA, 95741-9026
(888) 224-7268
www.csac.ca.gov studentsupport@csac.ca.gov
Purpose: To provide educational assistance for students who have been in foster care in California. Applicants must be current or former foster youth who are under 22 years of age.

Amount: Up to $5,000.

DISABILITY / ILLNESS

The following organizations provide scholarships for students with the following disabilities, illnesses or conditions.

ADHD

SHIRE ADHD SCHOLARSHIP PROGRAM

PO Box 562, Chestertown, MD 21620
www.shireadhdscholarship.org
Amount: $2,000.

BLINDNESS

AMERICAN COUNCIL OF THE BLIND | SCHOLARSHIP PROGRAM

1703 N. Beauregard St., Suite 420, Alexandria, VA 22311
(202) 467-5081
www.acb.org   info@acb.org
Amount: $1,000-$2,500.

AMERICAN FOUNDATION FOR THE BLIND SCHOLARSHIP COMMITTEE

1000 Fifth Ave., Suite 350, Huntington, WV 25701
www.afb.org
Amount: $2,500

ASSOCIATION FOR EDUCATION AND REHABILITATION OF THE BLIND AND VISUALLY IMPAIRED

1703 N. Beauregard St., Suite 440, Alexandria, VA 22311
(202) 467-5081
www.aerbvi.org
Amount: $750

NATIONAL FEDERATION OF MUSIC CLUBS | HINDA HONIGMAN AWARD FOR THE BLIND

2400 Coronado Dr., Hoover, AL 35226
(205) 822-6117
www.nfmc-music.org
Purpose: Provides aid to blind instrumentalists/vocalists.
Amount: $450-$800

CANCER

MARILYN YETSO MEMORIAL SCHOLARSHIP | ULMAN CENTER

1215 E. Fort Ave., Suite 104, Baltimore, MD 21230
(410) 964-0202
www.ulmanfund.org
Purpose: To support students who have cancer or have lost a parent to cancer.
Amount: $2,500

NATIONAL COLLEGIATE CANCER FOUNDATION

4858 Battery Lane, #216, Bethesda, MD 20814
www.collegiatecancer.org
Purpose: Provides aid for those affected by cancer.
Amount: $1,000.

PATIENT ADVOCATE FOUNDATION

700 Thimble Shoals Blvd., Suite 200, Newport News, VA 23606
www.patientadvocate.org
Purpose: Provides aid to those who have been diagnosed with cancer or another life-threatening illness.
Amount: $3,000.

ORANGE COUNTY COMMUNITY FOUNDATION | MICHAEL A. HUNTER MEMORIAL SCHOLARSHIPS

30 Corporate Park, Suite 410, Irvine, CA 92606
www.oc-cf.org
Purpose: Provides support for those affected by leukemia.
Amount: $2,000-$3,000

ULMAN CANCER FUND FOR YOUNG ADULTS

1215 E. Fort Ave., Suite 104, Baltimore, MD 21230
(410) 964-0202
www.ulmanfund.org
Purpose: To support students who have cancer or have lost a parent to cancer.
Amount: $2,500

CYSTIC FIBROSIS

BOOMER ESIASON FOUNDATION

483 10th Ave., Suite 300, New York, NY 10018
(646) 292-7930
www.esiason.org
Amount: $500-$2,500.

CYSTIC FIBROSIS SCHOLARSHIP FOUNDATION (CFSF)

1555 Sherman Ave. #116, Evanston, IL 60201
www.cfscholarship.org
Amount: $1,000.

DEAF/HEARING IMPAIRED

ALEXANDER GRAHAM BELL ASSOCIATION FOR THE DEAF AND HARD OF HEARING

3417 Volta Place NW, Washington, DC 20007
www.agbell.org
Amount: $1,000-$10,000.

COCHLEAR AMERICAS

13059 E. Peakview Ave., Centennial, CO 80111
www.cochlearamericas.com
Purpose: Supports cochlear implant recipients.
Amount: $2,000.

SERTOMA INTERNATIONAL

1912 E. Meyer Blvd., Kansas City, MO 64132
www.sertoma.org
Amount: $1,000

TPA SCHOLARSHIP TRUST FOR THE DEAF AND NEAR DEAF

2041 Exchange Dr., St. Charles, MO 63033
(314) 371-0533
www.tpahq.org
Purpose: To support student who are deaf or hearing impaired who would like to attend college.
Amount: Varies.

EPILEPSY

HUDSON MEDICAL COMMUNICATIONS | UCB FAMILY EPILEPSY SCHOLARSHIPS

120 White Plains Rd., Tarrytown, NY 10591
(866) 825-10591
www.ucb.com
Purpose: To support students with epilepsy.
Amount: Up to $5,000

HEMOPHILIA/BLOOD DISORDER

ACCREDO'S HEMOPHILIA HEALTH SERVICES

201 Great Circle Rd., Nashville, TN 37228
www.hemophiliahealth.com   contactus@applyists.com
Amount: At least $1,500.

NUFACTOR | ERIC DOSTIE MEMORIAL COLLEGE SCHOLARSHIPS

41093 County Center Dr., Temecula, CA 92591
www.kellycom.com
Amount: $1,000

SOOZIE COURTER HEMOPHILIA SCHOLARSHIP PROGRAM | PFIZER

225 E. 42nd St., New York, NY 10017
(888) 999-2349
www.hemophiliavillage.com
Amount: $2,500-$4,000.

HIV-POSITIVE

HIV-POSITIVE SCHOLARSHIP | STDCHECK.COM

(800) 456-2323
www.stdcheck.com
Purpose: To support students who are HIV-Positive.
Amount: $250-$5,000.

IMMUNE DEFICIENCY

IMMUNE DEFICIENCY FOUNDATION | ERIC MARDER SCHOLARSHIPS

110 West Rd., Suite 300, Towson, MD 21204
(800) 296-4433
www.primaryimmune.org
Purpose: To support students with a primary immune deficiency disease..
Amount: Varies.

MENTAL ILLNESS

DISABLED STUDENT SCHOLARSHIP | DISABILITY CARE CENTER

2875 S. Orange Ave. #500, Orlando, FL 32806
(888) 504-0035
www.disabilitycarecenter.org/giving-back/scholarships
Purpose: To support students who have physical or mental impairment who are pursuing college education.
Amount: $500.

PROMISES SCHOLARSHIP | PROMISES MALIBU

20723 Rockcroft Dr., Malibu, CA 90265
(310) 695-1708
www.promises.com/scholarship

Purpose: To support students who have been affected in some way by mental illness.

Amount: $1,000-$6,000.

MULTIPLE SCLEROSIS

NATIONAL MULTIPLE SCLEROSIS SOCIETY

733 Third Ave., New York, NY 10017
www.nationalmssociety.org
Amount: $1,000-$3,000.

SCHIZOPHRENIA & RELATED DISORDERS

CENTER FOR REINTEGRATION | BAER REINTEGRATION SCHOLARSHIP

PO Box 259, Lafayette Hill, PA 19444
(800) 809-8202
www.reintegration .com/scholarship-program
Purpose: Provides aid to students with schizophrenia, schizophreniform, schizoeffective disorder or bipolar disorder.
Amount: Varies.

CENTER FOR REINTEGRATION | LILLY REINTEGRATION SCHOLARSHIPS

PO Box 259, Lafayette Hill, PA 19444
(800) 809-8202
www.reintegration.com/scholarship-program
Purpose: Provides aid to students with schizophrenia, schizophreniform, schizoeffective disorder or bipolar disorder.
Amount: Varies.

OTHER

FLICKER OF HOPE FOUNDATION

8624 Janet Lane., Vienna, VA 22180
www.flickerofhope.org
Purpose: Provides aid to burn survivors.
Amount: Varies.

LITTLE PEOPLE OF AMERICA

250 El Camino Real, Suite 201, Tustin, CA 92780
www.lpaonline.org
Purpose: Provides aid to those affected by dwarfism.
Amount: $250-$1,000

GENERAL/MISCELLANEOUS

AAU KARATE

PO Box 22409, Lake Buena Vista, FL 32830
www.aaukarate.org
Purpose: To reward a young adult who participated in AAU karate for at least four years.
Amount: $1,000

ALPHA KAPPA ALPHA EDUCATIONAL FOUNDATION

5656 S. Stony Island Ave., Chicago, IL 60637
(800) 653-6528
www.akaeaf.net   akaeaf@akaeaf.net
Purpose: To assist students who have overcome hardship to achieve educational goals.
Amount: Varies

APARTMENT LIST SCHOLARSHIP

500 3rd St., Suite 555, San Francisco, CA 94107
www.apartmentlist.com/scholarship
Purpose: To support students who exemplify one or more Apartments List's core values of forever learning, driven by data, making an impact, bold while pragmatic, endlessly helpful and succeeding together. Essays on the topic required.
Amount: $2,500.

BANKMOBILE FINANCIAL LITERACY SCHOLARSHIP

401 Park Ave. S, New York, NY 10016
(917) 941-4704
www.bankmobile.com/the-annual-bank-mobile-financial-literacy-scholarship
Purpose: To support student financial literacy.
Amount: $1,500.

BIG PICTURE PURPOSE CONTEST | TEMPLETON PRESS

300 Conshohocken State Rd., Suite 665, West Conshohocken, PA 19428
(484) 531-8380
www.thebigpicture.life/contest
Purpose: To reward students who are focused on a purpose or goal.
Amount: $500.

COLEMAN ENTREPRENEURIAL SCHOLARSHIPS | NETWORK FOR TEACHING ENTREPRENEURSHIP

120 Wall Street, 18th Floor, New York, NY, 1005
(212) 232-3333

www.nfte.com
Purpose: To support students majoring or concentrating in entrepreneurship.
Amount: $5,000.

CONCORD SCHOLARSHIP

2989 West Maple Loop, Suite 200, Lehi, UT 84043
www.concordnow.com/scholarship
Purpose: To support students while providing valuable information about contracts.
Amount: $1,000.

CREATE REAL IMPACT | IMPACT TEEN DRIVERS

Attn: Create Real Impact Contest P.O. Box 161209 Sacramento, CA, 95816
(916) 733-7432
www.createrealimpact.com info@impactteendrivers.org
Purpose: To raise awareness of the dangers of distracted driving and poor decision making.
Amount: $500-$1,500.

CREATIVE WORKFORCE TRANSITION SCHOLARSHIP | CRAFT RESUMES

3422 Old Capitol Trail, Suite 700, Wilmington, DE 19808
(888) 385-3312
www.craftresumes.com/scholarship
Purpose: To facilitate a successful transition from college to career. Students must submit a vision of how to facilitate this transition.
Amount: $1,000.

DELETE CYBERBULLYING SCHOLARSHIP AWARD

2261 Market Street #291, San Francisco, CA, 94114
www.deletecyberbullying.org help@deletecyberbullying.org
Purpose: To get students committed to the cause of deleting cyberbullying.
Amount: $1,000.

DON'T TEXT AND DRIVE SCHOLARSHIPS | DIGITAL RESPONSIBILITY

3561 Homestead Road #113, Santa Clara, CA, 95051
www.digitalresponsibility.org
scholarship@digitalresponsibility.org
Purpose: To help students understand the risks of texting while driving.
Amount: $1,000.

HIT THE BOOKS SCHOLARSHIPS | COFFEEFORLESS.COM

250 South 18th Street, Suite 802, Philadelphia, PA, 19103
(800) 261-2859

www.coffeeforless.com/scholarship/ info@coffeeforless.com
Purpose: To support college students between 18 and 25 years of age with college expenses through an essay contest that includes their passion for coffee in the content.
Amount: $500.

HITCHED WEDDING SCHOLARSHIP

Unit 7 Stanhope Gate, Stanhope Rd., Chamberly, UK GU15 3DW
www.hitched.co.uk/wedding-scholarship
Purpose: To reward creative excellence among students. Must submit blog on a wedding topic.
Amount: $1,000.

INTERNATIONAL ASSOCIATION OF FIRE CHIEFS FOUNDATION (IAFC) FOUNDATION SCHOLARSHIPS

1325 West Walnut Hill Lane, PO Box 152225, Irving, TX 75015-2225
(855) 806-9992
www.exploring.org
Purpose: To assist students in fire sciences or related academic programs.
Amount: $500.

INTERNATIONAL ASSOCIATION OF PLUMBING AND MECHANICAL OFFICIALS (IAPMO) | ESSAY SCHOLARSHIP CONTEST

4755 E. Philadelphia Street, Ontario, CA, 91761
(909) 472-4100
Purpose: To share the "importance the plumbing and mechanical industry plays in our everyday lives."
Amount: $500-$1,000.

INTERNATIONAL ASSOCIATION OF FIRE CHIEFS FOUNDATION FIRE EXPLORER SCHOLARSHIPS

200 Explorers Learning for Life, P.O. Box 15225, Irving, TX, 75015-2225
(972) 580-2433
www.learningforlife.org/exploring pchestnu@lflmail.org
Purpose: To support students who are pursuing careers in fire sciences.
Amount: $500.

INVERTERS R US POWER SCHOLARSHIPS

5544 Tappan Dr., Reno, NV 89523
(866) 419-2616
www.invertersrus.com
Purpose: To support students who have an interest in alternative power.
Amount: $1,000.

LA TUTORS INNOVATION IN EDUCATION SCHOLARSHIP

9454 Wilshire Blvd., Suite 600, Beverley Hills, CA 90212
(424) 335-0067
www.latutors123.com/scholarship
Purpose: To reward innovation. Applicants will have developed an innovative project that has made a difference in lives.
Amount: $500.

LIBERTY SCHOLARSHIP AND LEADERSHIP PROGRAM | NATIONAL LIBERTY MUSEUM

321 Chestnut St., Philadelphia, PA 19106
(888) 667-6150
www.libertyscholars.libertymuseum.org
Purpose: To encourage future leaders who are committed to fostering good character, civic responsibility and respect for all people.
Amount: $500-$7,500.

LIVE MAS SCHOLARSHIP | TACO BELL FOUNDATION

www.livemasscholarship.com
Purpose: To support students who are innovative and creative dreamers.
Amount: $2,500-$25,000.

MARY CHURCH TERRELL & MEDGAR EVARS AWARD | NATIONAL ASSN. OF BLACKS IN CRIMINAL JUSTICE

1801 Fayetteville St., 106 Whiting Criminal Justice Building, PO Box 20011-C, Durham, NC 27707
(919) 683-1801
www.nabcj.org
Purpose: MCT rewards activism for positive change in criminal justice on city and state levels. ME rewards efforts to ensure that all people, including those in institutions receive equal justice under the law.
Amount: Varies.

NATIONAL VETERANS STIPEND | INSTITUTE OF SCRAP RECYCLING INDUSTRIES

1615 L St., Suite 600, Washington, DC 20036
(202) 662-8500
www.isri.org
Purpose: To support veterans who are seeking higher education.
Amount: $2,000.

NEW LOOK LASER TATTOO REMOVAL SCHOLARSHIPS

19 Briar Hollow, Suite 115, Houston, TX 77027
(713) 783-2000
www.newlookhouston.com
scholarship@newlookhouston.com
Purpose: To educate students about laser tattoo removal. Students must be pursuing a degree with an emphasis in either nursing, medicine, engineering, or natural or applied sciences.
Amount: $1,000.

OUT-OF-THE-BOX THINKING SCHOLARSHIP | LITTER-ROBOT

2900 Auburn Ct., Auburn Hills, MI 48236
(877) 250-7729
www.litter-robot.com/blog/outside-of-the-box-thinking-scholarship/
Purpose: To support students who have a passion for pets and innovative ideas for pet care.
Amount: $500-$1,500.

SECOND CHANCE SCHOLARSHIP CONTEST | AMERICAN FIRE SPRINKLER ASSOCIATION

12750 Merit Dr., Suite 350, Dallas, TX 75251
(214) 349-5965
www.afsascholarship.org
Purpose: To help students pay for higher education.
NOTE: SELECTION IS MADE BY RANDOM DRAWING FROM THE POOL OF ENTRANTS.
Amount: $1,000

TECHNOLOGY ADDICTION AWARENESS SCHOLARSHIPS | DIGITAL RESPONSIBILITY

3561 Homestead Rd. #113, Santa Clara, CA 95051
www.digitalresponsibility.org
scholarship@digitalresponsibility.org
Purpose: To help students understand the negative effect of too much screen time.
Amount: $1000.

WOMEN DIVERS HALL OF FAME | SCHOLARSHIPS & GRANTS

43 Mackey Ave., Port Washington, NY 10050
www.wdhof.org   scholarships@wdhof.org
Purpose: To support those of all ages who are pursuing careers in diving.
Amount: Up to $2,000

ZALE PARRY SCHOLARSHIPS | ACADEMY OF UNDERWATER ARTS AND SCIENCES

27 W. Anapuma St., #317, Santa Barbara, CA 93101
(919) 369-0583
www.auas-nogi.org
Purpose: To support students pursuing a career in ocean exploration, diving equipment technology, hyperbaric research and marine conservation.
Amount: $6,000

ARTS

ARTISTS (BROADLY)

ELIZABETH GREENSHIELDS FOUNDATION GRANTS

1814 Sherbrooke St. West, Suite 1, Quebec, Canada H3H 1E4
www.elizabethgreenshieldfoundation.org
Purpose: To promote appreciation of painting, drawing, sculpture and the graphic arts by supporting students, artists and sculptors.
Amount: CAD $15,000-$18-000

IRENE RYAN ACTING SCHOLARSHIPS | JOHN F. KENNEDY CENTER FOR THE PERFORMING ARTS

2700 F St. NW, Washington, DC 20566
(800) 444-1424
web.kennedy-center.org/education
Purpose: To aid outstanding student performers. Must be nominated by their school and be able to audition, which may be done by video, if your institution allows it.
Amount: Up to $2,500.

JOHN F. AND ANNA LEE STACEY SCHOLARSHIP FUND FOR ART AND EDUCATIONAL

1700 NE 63rd St., Oklahoma City, OK 73111
(405) 478-2250
www.nationalcowboymuseum.org/education/staceyfund
Purpose: To support students wishing to enter the art profession.
Amount: $5,000.

COMPOSER

ASCAP FOUNDATION MORTON GOULD YOUNG COMPOSER AWARDS

One Lincoln Plaza, New York, NY 10023
(212) 621-6219
www.ascapfoundation.org
Purpose: To encourage young composers early in their careers.
Amount: Varies.

COPY EDITORS

AMERICAN COPY EDITOR'S SOCIETY | COPY EDITING SCHOLARSHIPS

3909 N. Meridian St., Indianapolis, IN 46208
www.copydesk.org
Purpose: To support students interested in copy editing.
Amount: $1,000-$2,500

GRAPHIC ARTISTS

CORPORATE LEADERSHIP & RESOURCE CENTER SCHOLARSHIPS | 19 GRAVURE EDUCATION FOUNDATION

PO Box 25617, Rochester, NY 14625
(315) 589-8879
www.gaa.org/gravure-education-foundation
Purpose: To provide aid for students pursuing degrees in printing or graphic arts. (NOTE: Murray State students – a prisoner-friendly correspondence school – are eligible for 'Resource Center Scholarships' from this foundation.)
Amount: $1,000-$1,500

ILLUSTRATORS

ILLUSTRATORS OF THE FUTURE | RON HUBBARD'S WRITERS OF THE FUTURE CONTEST

7051 Hollywood Blvd., Los Angeles, CA 90028
(323) 466-3310
www.writersofthefuture.com
Purpose: To discover deserving amateur aspiring illustrators.
Amount: $1,500-$5,000

PLAYWRIGHTS

CLAUDER COMPETITION PRIZE | PORTLAND STAGE COMPANY

PO Box 1458, Portland, ME 04104

www.portlandstage.com

Purpose: To support playwrights. (Must live in one of the New England states or have previously lived in one and written material relevant to the region.)

Amount: Up to $2,500

NATIONAL TEN MINUTE PLAY CONTEST | ACTORS THEATRE OF LOUISVILLE

316 W. Main St., Louisville, KY 40202-4218
(502) 584-1265
www.actorstheatre.org
Purpose: To identify emerging playwrights.

Amount: $1,000

POETS

POETRY POWER

295 E. 8th St., Suite 3W, New York, NY 10009
(347) 460-6741
www.poetrypower.org
Purpose: To reward students who write slam poetry or poetry about education.

Amount: $1,000

RUTH LILLY & DOROTHY SARGENT ROSENBERG POETRY FELLOWSHIP PROGRAM | POETRY MAGAZINE

444 N. Michigan Ave., Suite 1850, Chicago, IL 60611-4034
www.poetryfoundation.org
Purpose: To encourage the study of writing and poetry.

Amount: $15,000-$25,800.

PUBLIC SPEAKERS

BECA #TRADUCTOR | SPANISHDICT

1400 Key Blvd., Suite 1200, Arlington, VA 22209
(305) 505-4667
www.spanishdict.com/tranductor
Purpose: To reward students who are literate in both Spanish and English.

Amount: $1,000.

BILL GROVE SCHOLARSHIP & CAVETT ROBERT SCHOLARSHIPS | NATIONAL SPEAKERS ASSN.

Attn: Scholarship Committee, 1500 S. Priest Dr., Tempe, AZ 85281
(480) 968-2552
www.nsaspeaker.org

Purpose: Top encourage study in the filed of professional speaking.

Amount: $5,000

SOCIAL SCIENCES

AALL EDUCATIONAL SCHOLARSHIPS | AMERICAN ASSOCIATION OF LAW LIBRARIES

105 W. Adams, Suite 3300, Chicago, IL, 60603
(312) 939-4764
www.aallnet.org *scholarship@aall.org*
Purpose: To encourage students to pursue careers as law librarians.

Amount: Varies.

ACCOUNTING STUDENT SCHOLARSHIP PROGRAM | WILEY EFFICIENT LEARNING

PO Box 4223, Sedona, AZ 86340
(888) 884-5669
www.efficientlearning.com
Purpose: To support students who are taking accounting courses.

Amount: $1,000.

AMERICAN EXPRESS SCHOLARSHIP COMPETITION | AMERICAN HOTEL AND LODGING EDUCATIONAL FOUNDATION (AH&LEF)

1250 I Street NW, Suite 1100, Washington, DC, 20005-3931
(202) 289-3188
www.ahlef.org *chammond@ahlef.org*
Purpose: To provide financial assistance to students pursuing a degree in hospitality management.

Amount: Up to $2,000

AMERICAN RADIO RELAY LEAGUE FOUNDATION | BILL, W2ONV & ANN SALERNO MEMORIAL

225 Main St., Newington, CT 06111-1494
(860) 594-0384
www.arrl.org/the-arrl-foundation
Purpose: To provide financial assistance to amateur radio operators with high Academic achievement.

Amount: $1,000.

ASSOCIATION OF EQUIPMENT MANAGEMENT PROFESSIONALS FOUNDATION SCHOLARSHIPS |

P.O. Box 1368, Glenwood Springs, CO, 81602
(970) 384-0510
www.aemp.org *stan@aemp.org*
Purpose: To support students interested in the field of heavy equipment management.

Amount: Up to $2,000.

COSMETOLOGY SCHOLARSHIP | SALON SUPPLY STORE

350 Hiatt Dr., Palm Beach Gardens, FL 33418
(800) 617-0525
www.salonsupplystore.com/[pages/beauty-school-scholarship
Purpose: To assist cosmetology students.
Amount: $1,000.

DAVIS PUTTER SCHOLARSHIP

PO Box 7307, New York, NY 10167-7307
davisputter@davisputter.org
Purpose: To support students interested in the field of peace and justice studies.
Amount: Varies.

EXPERT INSTITUTE | LEGAL BLOG WRITING CONTEST

75 Maiden Lane, Suite 704, New York, NY 10038
(888) 858-9511
www.theexpertinstitute.com/writing-contest
Purpose: To support law students. Must submit a 1,000-2,500-word blog article on the use of expert witnesses in litigation.
Amount: $200-$500.

HEATING AND REFRIGERATION INSTITUTE CLIFFORD H. "TED" REES, JR. SCHOLARSHIP FOUNDATION

2111 Wilson Boulevard, Suite 500, Arlington, VA, 22201
(703) 524-8800
Purpose: To support students preparing for careers in heating, ventilation, air-conditioning and refrigeration (HVAC) technology.
Amount: Up to $2,000.

FRANK M. CODA SCHOLARSHIPS | AMERICAN SOCIETY OF HEATING, REFRIGERATING AND AIR-CONDITIONING ENGINEERS (ASHRAE)

1791 Tullie Circle, NE, Atlanta, GA, 30329
(404) 636-8400
www.ashrae.org ibenedict@ashrae.org
Purpose: To support undergraduate students who are preparing for careers in the heating, ventilation, air-conditioning and refrigeration industry.
Amount: $5,000.

GEORGE A. STRAIT MINORITY SCHOLARSHIPS | AMERICAN ASSOCIATION OF LAW LIBRARIES

105 W. Adams, Suite 3300, Chicago,IL, 60603
(312) 939-4764
Purpose: To encourage minorities to enter careers as law librarians.
Amount: Varies.

GOLDEN GATE RESTAURANT ASSOCIATION SCHOLARSHIPS

220 Montgomery Street, Suite 990, San Francisco, CA, 94104
(415) 781-5348
www.ggra.org ggra@ggra.org
Purpose: To provide scholarships for college students who wish to pursue a career in the restaurant/food service industry.
Amount: Varies.

INTERNATIONAL FOOD SERVICE EXECUTIVES ASSOCIATION WORTHY GOAL SCHOLARSHIPS

c/o Joseph Quagliano, 8824 Stancrest Drive, Las Vegas, NV, 89134
(502) 589-3602
www.ifsea.com
Purpose: To help students receive food service management training beyond the high school level.
Amount: $250-$1,500.

JOE FRANCIS HAIRCARE SCHOLARSHIP PROGRAM

P.O. Box 50625, Minneapolis, MN, 55405
(651) 769-1757
www.joefrancis.com
Purpose: To provide barber and cosmetology students with financial aid.
Amount: $1,200.

L.B. CEBIK, W4RNL & JEAN CEBIK, N4TZP MEMORIAL SCHOLARSHIP | AMERICAN RADIO RELAY LEAGUE FOUNDATION

225 Main St., Newington, CT 06111-1494
(860) 594-0384
www.arrl.org/the-arrl-foundation
Purpose: To provide financial assistance to amateur radio operators with high Academic achievement.
Amount: $1,000.

LEXISNEXIS/JOHN R. JOHNSON MEMORIAL SCHOLARSHIP ENDOWMENT | AMERICAN ASSOCIATION OF LAW LIBRARIES

105 W. Adams, Suite 3300, Chicago, IL, 60603
(312) 939-4764
www.aallnet.org scholarship@aall.org

Purpose: To encourage current and future law librarians in memory of John Johnson, a prominent law librarian.

Amount: Varies.

OFFICE SUPPLY SCHOLARSHIP | BULKOFFICESUPPLY.COM

1614 Hereford Rd., Hewlett, NY 11557
(800) 658-1488
www.bulkofficesupply.com
Purpose: To support students pursuing teach, art or who are planning on owning their own business.

Amount: $1,000.

PROJECTMANAGER.COM'S INNOVATION SCHOLARSHIP

3420 Executive Center Dr., Suite 160, Austin, TX 78731
(800) 765-2495
www.projectmanager.com/scholarship
Purpose: To support students who have a passion for the project management field.

Amount: $1,000.

PUBLISHING PROFESSIONALS NETWORK | SCHOLARSHIP FOR BOOK AND COVER DESIGN

c/o Postal Annex, 274 Redwood Shores Pkwy., Box 129, Redwood City, CA 94065-1173
(916) 320-0638
www.pubpronetwork.org/scholarship-program/
operation@pubpronetwork.org
Purpose: To support students pursuing careers in book design.

Amount: $1,000.

REHABMART.COM SCHOLARSHIP

1353 Athens Hwy., Elberton, GA 30635
(800) 827-8283
www.rehabmart.com/scholarship
Purpose: To support students with disabilities, health science students or students majoring in special needs education.

Amount: $250-$2,500.

TECHCHECKS BUSINESS LEAADERSHIP SCHOLARSHIP

138 Daniel Dr., Lakewood, NJ 08701
(866) 527-3758
Purpose: To reward students pursuing a degree that emphasizes business or marketing.

Amount: $1,000.

TIMOTHY S.Y. LAM FOUNDATION EDUCATION SCHOLARSHIPS

PO Box 98141. Las Vegas, NV 89193-8141
(702) 900-7584
www.timothysylam.org
Purpose: To support students pursuing a career in the hospitality industry.

Amount: Up to $2,000.

ULTIMATE PROMOTION SCHOLARSHIP | SLANT MARKETING

150 N. Wacker Dr., Suite 1220, Chicago, IL 60606
(312) 929-3789
www.slantmarketing.com/the-ultimate-promotion-scholarship
Purpose: To support students who create an ultimate promotional experience for a product.

Amount: $1,500.

Scholarships for Your Children

Since you are considering education opportunities for a better future for yourself, it is likely that you recognize the importance of these opportunities for your children as well.

As it is perhaps the children of the incarcerated who suffer most greatly, combined with the fact that children are our greatest resource, several organizations have stepped up to assist these young ones to thrive despite their adversity. The following organizations all offer education scholarship opportunities to the children of those impacted by incarceration.

As with any scholarship opportunity, potential students are expected to meet certain criteria and obligations, including a high school diploma or equivalent, either already earned in in the process, at least a 2.5 GPA, letters of recommendation, and an essay regarding the students eligibility and goals. In the case of the following, organizations will require the student to provide proof of eligibility that the student has been affected by incarceration.

Many organizations a re state-specific. If your child is not living in one of the state-specific regions, there is no need to apply.

SCHOLARSHIPS FOR YOUR CHILDREN | NATIONALLY

CREATIVE CORRECTIONS EDUCATION FOUNDATION (CCEF)

6546 Calder Ave., Beaumont, TX 77706
(409) 861-2536
www.creativecorrectionseducationfoundation.org
Purpose: Provides educational opportunites for young adults between the ages of 18 and 27, who have an incarcerated or paroled parent. They offer several scholarships annually for enrollment to college or trade schools nationwide. They also offer specific programs to children of the incarcerated in the Milwaukee, WI and Beaumont, TX areas.
Amount: $1,000 - $5,000

WRITEAPRISONER.COM SCHOLARSHIP PROGRAM

PO Box 10-S, Edgewater, FL 32132
Purpose: Biannual scholarships for children of prisoners and children victims. Must be submitted between March 1 and June 1. Submissions outside of this range will not be accepted.
Amount: Varies, beginning with $250 toward a two or four-year educational institution.

SCHOLARSHIPS FOR CHILDREN | REGIONALLY

AVA'S GRACE SCHOLARSHIP FOUNDATION

(636) 940-8027
www.avasgrace.org *avasgrace@connecttionstosuccess.org*
Purpose: Ava's Grace awards annual scholarships to children of the incarcerated who live in **MISSOURI**, **KANSAS**, or **ILLINOIS**.
Amount: $3,000 - $5,000.

ScholarCHIPS

PO Box 56404, Washington, D.C. 20040
www.scholarchipsfund.org

Purpose: Annual scholarships for children with incarcerated parents who live in the **DISTRICT of COLUMBIA**, **MARYLAND** or **VIRGINIA**. If awarded, students may renew the scholarships for up to 3 years of undergraduate education. They also provide mentoring and offer students opportunities to attend plays and other vents at no charge.

Amount: $2,500 scholarships and $250 book awards.

WILLY THE PLUMBER SCHOLARSHIP

www.willytheplumberscholarship.net

Purpose: Annual scholarship program for children of prisoners who live in **UTAH**. Priority is given to students with the most troubled parents, such as if both parents are incarcerated or if the child is a victim of an abusive parent that are now incarcerated. Applications must be received by April 15.

Amount: Up to $1,000.

Every edition of the *Prison Lives Prisoner Education Guide* will bring all the latest scholarship opportunities and other financial aid options prisoners can use to gain a higher education!

Military/Veteran Education Benefits

If you are a veteran, even though you are now incarcerated, you may be eligible for veteran education benefits. The Department of Veterans Affairs (VA) offers several education benefit options that most colleges accept. Below are a few highlights of some of these programs. If you would like more information, be sure to contact the addresses at the bottom of this section.

POST-9/11 GI BILL   (NOTE: TIME LIMIT OF 15 YEARS FROM LAST DISCHARGE OF SEPARATION.)

The Post-9/11 GI Bill provides education benefits for service members who have served on active duty for 90 or more days since September 10, 2001. These benefits are tiered based on the number of days served on active duty, but generally, if you enroll in a state college or university you will receive a percentage of your "in-state" tuition and fees (100 percent for service of 3 years or more, tiered down in increments of 10 percent for every 6 less months served, i.e. 30 months = 90 percent, 24 months = 80 percent, and so on, down to 90 days, which awards 40 percent.) If you enroll in a privately operated college or university you will get up to $17,500 per year toward tuition and fees.

Additional benefits included:

- monthly housing stipend of up to $2,800 per month (housing stipends are even provided for distance education);
- book and supplies stipend of up to $1,000 per year;
- funding for licensing, certifications, college placement tests, work study, apprenticeship programs and more.

MONTGOMERY GI BILL   (NOTE: TIME LIMIT OF 10 YEARS FROM LAST DISCHARGE OF SEPARATION.)

The Montgomery GI Bill (MGIB) is the most commonly used VA education benefit.

You're eligible if:

- you entered service on or after July 1, 1985, and you did not decline this benefit at your initial entry into service, OR

- you entered the service before January 1, 1977, and you have educational assistance entitlement, OR

- you were voluntarily separated under the Voluntary Separation Incentive (VSI), or Special Separation Benefit (SSB) programs and had your military pay reduced by $1,200, OR

- you were involuntarily separated from active duty after February 2, 1991, OR

- you were on active duty and a participant in the Post-Vietnam Era Veterans' Educational Assistance Program (VEAP) on or before October 9, 1996, or you first entered the National Guard under title 32, between July 1, 1985 and November 28, 1989, and you elected chapter 30 benefits between October 9, 1996 and October 8, 1997, and you paid $1,200, OR

- you were on active duty and eligible for VEAP benefits on October 9, 1996, you elected chapter 3 benefits between November 1, 2000 and October 31, 2001, and you paid $2,700.

OTHER VA EDUCATIONAL PROGRAMS

° **Montgomery GI Bill - Selected Reserve (MGIB-SR)** (NOTE: Eligibility expires on the date of separation from the Selected Reserves.)

° **Reserve Educational Assistance Program (REAP)** (NOTE: No time limit as long as you rmain on the same level of the Ready Reserve from which called to active duty.)

° **Post-Vietnam Era Veterans' Educational Assistance Program (VEAP)**

IMPORTANT NOTE:

Being incarcerated, the government will likely reduce, but not restrict, your VA educational benefits.

Remember, in addition to accepting education benefits, most colleges will give credit for military courses, programs, and certifications that you have previously taken as a member of the armed forces. They typically will grant this credit at no charge to you. These credits can generally be applied to degree programs for up to 75 percent of the required credits per desired degree. That means that if you have enough military training, you may only have to earn another 30 credits to get a bachelor's degree.

Contact your regional VA office to learn more about the education benefits that apply to you:

VETERANS AFFAIRS EASTERN REGION	VETERANS AFFAIRS CENTRAL REGION
PO Box 4616, Buffalo, New York 14240-4616	PO Box 66830, St. Louis, Missouri 63166-6830
VETERANS AFFAIRS SOUTHERN REGION	VETERANS AFFAIRS WESTERN REGION
PO Box 100022, Decatur, Alabama 30031-7022	PO Box 8888, Muskogee, Oklahoma 74402-8888

Calculate your education benefits eligibility at: *www.military.com/gi-bill-calculator/*

Learn more and obtain benefits applications at: *www.va.benefits.gov/gibill/*

Tax Credits!

Maybe you haven't thought much about tax benefits since you've been incarcerated, perhaps assuming that they could not be of any real benefit to you from inside your cell.

But when it comes to your education, tax benefits are definitely worthy of consideration. Since the U.S. government does not currently have any programs to financially assist prisoners with education, and while the reintroduction of the Pell Grants for prisoners is still in the *pilot program* stage, tax benefits are the only sure way for prisoners to get any money from the government to help pay for schooling.

Tax benefits are available for American citizens who pay taxes. They are typically designed as incentives to encourage Americans to utilize goods and services that enhance American ideals. For instance, education is obviously a positive thing for Americans to pursue. Therefore, the government lends some assistance in pursuing it by way of tax credits.

There are two tax credits currently available that can help you or your families offset the cost of college education, which includes, tuition, books, supplies, and equipment. They are the *American opportunity credit* and the *lifetime learning credit*. Both are established as "credits," meaning that they reduce the amount of overall taxes you pay. If you spend money on education, you can get at least some, if not all, of it back at tax time. As with most tax credits, they must be claimed either by yourself, your spouse, or by someone who can claim you as a dependent. And there are specific restrictions that must be adhered to, some that particularly effect prisoners. But generally, prisoners are eligible to receive these credits, and would be foolish for not claiming them.

AMERICAN OPPORTUNITY CREDIT

The *American opportunity credit* lets students or their families claim a credit of up to $2,500 per year on money they spent on education. This credit can be claimed every year for up to four years. This means that over the course of four years, the government will issue tax credit totaling $10,000. With planning, ten thousand dollars can completely pay for an entire bachelor's degree education program.

It has another advantage in that forty percent of it is refundable, meaning that the government will directly reimburse you that amount if the education credit amounts to more than the tax you owe. If you spend $2,500 on education, and what you owe on your taxes is less than your tax credit, the government will issue you a check for up to $1,000 per filing year. For prisoners who generally make very little income, and thus have to pay very few, if any, taxes, this is can be a huge benefit.

On the negative side, as far as prisoners are concerned, if you have been convicted of a federal or state felony for possessing or distributing a controlled substance, you, or your family, will not be eligible to receive this tax credit.

Other Requirements:

° The one claiming the credit cannot make more than $90,000 per year if single or head of household; or no more than $180,000 if married and filing jointly.

° You must be pursuing a degree program, or other recognized education credential, not just individual courses, and be enrolled for at least one half of an academic period workload.

° The school you are taking classes from must be accredited.

LIFETIME LEARNING CREDIT

The *lifetime learning credit* lets students and their families claim up to $2,000 per year on money they spent for education. The reason this tax credit is known as a 'lifetime' credit is because, unlike the American opportunity credit, this credit can be claimed every year that you are paying for an education.

There are some other important distinctions between the two credits, some good, some not so much for prisoners. For instance, on the negative side, the lifetime learning credit is a nonrefundable credit, meaning that if your credit exceeds the tax you owe, the government will not issue you a check for the difference. Additionally, while all of the same education expenses are eligible, you can only receive credit for them if the fees were paid directly to the school, as opposed to buying books or other materials from outside sources.

On the positive side, especially for prisoners, there are no restrictions for students with felony drug convictions. If you have a felony possession or distribution conviction, you are still eligible for this credit. Also, you do not have to be pursuing a degree program. You can just take one course at a time if you'd prefer. Additionally, you are not required to go to an accredited school, although, the school must be eligible to participate in a student aid program by the U.S. Department of Education.

If you are considering an education, these tax credits can be a valuable tool in helping you afford it. It's well worth planning your budget with these credits in mind. Where you may not have thought it was feasible to pay for an education, these credits may allow you to reevaluate that.

If your family is going to ultimately be footing the bill for your schooling, these credits can drastically help reduce their financial burden. Just bear in mind that they must be able to claim you as a dependent before they can take advantage of these credits.

For more information on education tax credits, contact the following:

Internal Revenue Service
Tax Forms and Publications*

1111 Constitution Avenue NW, IR-6526
Washington, DC 20224
www.irs.gov/formspubs

*Request Publication 970 'Tax Benefits for Education' and Form 8863.

California Community Colleges Board of Governors Fee Waiver

If you are a California prisoner/resident, you have a particularly useful financial advantage at your disposal. The *California Community Colleges Board of Governors Fee Waiver* covers tuition for community college students who are California residents. This means that your entire tuition would be **free** if you qualify. Each waiver lasts for an entire school year and you can apply for additional school years as you advance through your education. The fee waiver does not cover the cost of textbooks, but getting your tuition paid for is by far the hardest part.

Eligible Recipients:

- California residents

- Non-California residents on active duty in the military who are stationed in California

- Dependents of active military personnel stationed in California

- Students who attended a California high school for a minimum of 3 years, graduated from a California high school of an equivalency degree in the state of California

- Non-California residents who can prove that they are victim's of trafficking, domestic violence, or other serious crimes

In order to maintain your *Board of Governors Fee Waiver* you must meet the following standards:

- You must maintain at least a 2.0 GPA

- You must satisfactorily complete more than 50% of all classwork attempted

If you fail to meet these criteria, you will lose your *Board of Governors Fee Waiver,* unless you have extenuating circumstances, such as accidents, illness, evidence of an inability to obtain essential support services, or if you were a former foster youth (who is now 24 years or younger) or a veteran.

For more information on *California Community Colleges Board of Governors Fee Waiver*, contact the following:

California Community Colleges | Chancellor's Office

1102 Q Street, 4th Floor, Sacramento, CA 95814

(800) 987-ICAN

icanaffordcollege.com

Part 3 The Language of Education

Before you get started, it will be helpful to know the education terminology – what the various terms in this guide and everything you see on formal education mean.

This part will assist you in gaining a better understanding of each of these terms and assist you in knowing what to look for as you begin your education journey.

NOTE: There is also a glossary in the back of this guide, which provides a brief synopsis of further education-related terms.

Credit Hours?
Credits by Examination?

Accreditation?

CEUs?

Experiential Learning?

ACCREDITATION: WHAT DOES IT MEAN?

Before you invest a lot of time or money into something, it is wise to know what you are getting and that it is worth the investment. One of the ways to ensure that in terms of education is through the use of this book. But a more formal method in determining whether a particular school is worthwhile is through *accreditation*.

Accreditation is the quality control of the education community. It is the stamp of approval by one or more accrediting organizations, which by a process review schools, colleges, universities, and other educational institutions to judge the quality of their education. If the review process goes well, the institution is awarded with an "accredited" status.

An accredited institution is one that meets or exceeds the educational standards set forth by the accrediting organization, which typically assures that the school has in place quality course instruction, student support, and other services necessary to ensure that students can achieve their educational goals.

As a school, getting accredited is a stringent and lengthy process. Schools apply through the accrediting agency of choice. The accrediting organization then sends out a team of evaluators who visit the school, weighing several aspects, including, but not limited to, the following.

Does the School...

✓ have quality educational services?

✓ have a clearly defined mission, goals, and objectives?

✓ have up-to-date course offerings and curriculum?

✓ has adequate facilities, equipment, record protection, and student services?

✓ have qualified faculty, staff, and administrators?

✓ have fair admission policies, adequate enrollment agreements, and equitable tuition refund policies?

✓ have honest advertising practices?

✓ prove that they are financially able to deliver quality educational services?

✓ conduct continuous research to assure improvement in all of the above?

Even if all of that is in accordance with the organization's quality standards, they still won't give their accreditation. Instead, they observe the school for years to ensure that the level of quality was not just temporary. After a couple of successful quality years, the school still is not accredited. At this point they merely earn the distinction as being a "candidate" for accreditation. It can take a decade or more for a school to achieve the status of *accredited*. Even then, the school is inspected and reviewed periodically – typically every 3 to 5 years – to make sure that their standards are maintained.

So if you see that a school is accredited, you know that the school has voluntarily undergone a comprehensive review process and it has been determined that you can get a quality education from that institution.

There are a number of accrediting organizations across the nation, some of which, unfortunately, are not actually credible themselves. Therefore, you do have to be careful to look beyond the statement by a school that says they are "accredited." However, it's relatively easy to determine if an accrediting organization is legitimate. Simply compare the accrediting organization with the list in our book (which is located in our *Resource Center.)*

Or you can write to the *U.S. Department of Education* or the *Council of Higher Education* to determine if the accrediting agency in question is approved by them.

U.S. Department of Education (USDE) | Accrediting Agency Evaluation Branch

1990 K Street NW, Washington, D.C. 20006
(202) 502-7765
www.ed.gov

Council for Higher Education Accreditation (CHEA)

One Dupont Circle NW, Suite 510, Washington, D.C. 20036-1136
(202) 955-6126
www.chea.org   chea@chea.org

Below is the short-list of accrediting organizations whose accreditations **can** be counted on. You will find their names mentioned frequently throughout our school listings.

If you would like more information on these or other accrediting agencies, be sure to check out our *Resource Center.*

Some Trustworthy Accrediting Agencies

Distance Education Accrediting Commission (DEAC)

Accredits distance education institutions

Middle States Association of Colleges and Schools | Commission on Higher Education (MSCHE)

Accredits East Coast states south of New England

New England Association of Schools and Colleges | Commission on Institutions of Higher Education (NEASC-CIHE)

Accredits New England states

North Central Association of Colleges and Schools | The Higher Learning (NCA-HLC)

Accredits central states

Northwest Commission on Colleges and Universities (NWCCU)

Accredits northwestern states

Southern Association of Colleges & Schools | Commission on Colleges (SACS-COC)

Accredits southern states

Western Association of Schools and Colleges | Accrediting Commission for Senior Colleges and Universities (WASC-ACSCU)

Accredits institutions that offer more than two-year programs

Western Association of Schools and Colleges | Accrediting Commission for Community and Junior Colleges (WASC-ACCJC)

Accredits Community Colleges and Junior Colleges

Accrediting Council for Independent Colleges and Schools (ACICS)

Accredits vocational schools

AdvancED

AdvancED is a combination of the North Central Association of Colleges and Schools Commission on Accreditation & School Improvement (NCA-CASI) and the Southern Association of Colleges and Schools Council on Accreditation & School Improvement (SACS-CASI), accrediting central and southern states.

UN-Trustworthy Accrediting Agencies

Below is a current list of accrediting organizations whose accreditation **cannot** be counted on if you are looking to transfer credits from a school accredited by them to a reputable college or university.

NOTE: None of the following accrediting agencies are recognized as college ac creditors in the U.S. By either the Council on Higher Education Accreditation or the U.S. Department of Education. Take courses from them with great caution and the understanding that degrees from schools announcing accreditation by any of these may not be valid for continuing education or many employment opportunities.

If you would like more information on these or other accrediting agencies, be sure to check out our *Resource Center.*

American Association for Adult & Continuing Education (AAACE)

American Association for Higher education & Accreditation (AAHEA)

Accreditation Council for Distance Education (ACTDE)

Accreditation Council for Online Acedemia (ACOHE)

Accreditation Panel for Online Colleges & Universities (APTEC)

Accrediting Commission International (ACI)

American Accrediting Association of Theological Institutions

American Council of Private Colleges and Universities

American Association of Drugless Practitioners (ADP)

Association of Accredited Bible Schools

Association of Distance Learning Programs (ADLP)

Association of Private Colleges and Universities

Association for Online Academic Accreditation

Association for Online Excellence

Association for Online Academic Excellence

Board of Online Universities Accreditation (BOUA)

Central American Council of Accreditation

Council for Distance Education

Council of Online Higher Education

Central States Consortium of Colleges & Schools

Distance and Online Universities Accreditation Council (DOUAC)

Distance Learning International Accreditation Association (DEIAA)

Distance Learning Quality Assurance Agency (DLQAA)

European Accreditation Board of Higher Education (EABHE)

Global Accreditation Bureau (GAB)

Global Accredited Council for Business Education (GACBA)

Global Accreditation Council for Business Education (GACBE)

Global Accreditation Commission for Distance Education (GACDE)

Global Global Accredited Council for Online Academia

International Commission for Higher Education

International Accreditation Agency for Online Universities (IAAOU)

International Accreditation Association for Online Education (IAAFOE)

International Accreditation Commission (IAC)

International Association Council for Engineering Professionals (IACEP)

International Accreditation Commission for Online Universities (IACOU) (Kingston)

International Accreditation Commission for Online Educational Institutions (IACOEI)

International Accreditation Organization (IAO)

International Education Ministry Accreditation Association

International Higher Learning Commission

International Online Education Accrediting Board (IOEAB)

North American Distance Learning Association (NADLA)

National Academic Higher Education Agency (NACHE)

National Academy of Higher Education

National Accreditation and Certification Board (NACB)

National Board of Education (NBOE)

National College Accreditation Council (NCAC)

National Commission of Accredited Schools (NCAS)

National Distance Learning Accreditation Council (NDLAC)

New Millennium Accrediting Partnership for Educators Worldwide

Organization for Online Learning Accreditation (OKOLA)

Transworld Accrediting Commission International (TAC)

United Christian College Accreditation Association (UCCAA) (Divine Heart)

United Nations Council

United States Distance Education & Training Council **of Nevada**[1]

Universal Accreditation Council (UAC)

Universal Council for Online Education Accreditation (UCOEA)

World Association for Online Education (WAOE)[2]

World Association of Universities and Colleges (WAUC)

World Online Accrediting Commission (WOEAC)

Worldwide Accrediting Commission of Christian Educational Institutions (WWAC)

Worldwide Higher Education Accreditation Society (WHEAS)

---

[1] Not to be confused with the Distance Education Accrediting Commission (DEAC), which is a legitimate accrediting agency that is recognized by the U.S Department of Education.

[2] WAOE is a legitimate and esteemed professional agency for educators. It is a discussion group of teachers who are experimenting with computer-mediated methods of teaching in schools around the world. They are not, however, an accrediting agency and do not condone the use of its name for accreditation purposes by any school.

CREDITS: WHAT ARE THEY?

Credit Hours

Credit hours are the units by which colleges measure how much college-level education you have had. Typically, one college-level course will be worth 3 or 4 credit hours. The typical associate's degree will require roughly 60 credit hours to achieve, while a bachelor's degree will generally require about 120 credit hours.

Credit-By-Examination

There are two primary phases of formal education. There is the class work, which includes studying, completing assignments, and any quizzes along the way. And then there is the big exam to make sure that you learned everything that you needed to learn to gain a mastery of the subject matter studied. Credit-by-examination, for the most part, lets you skip the first phase and go straight to taking the exam.

Of course you must have an acquired knowledge of the subject matter before you take the test or you will fail it. But if you have that knowledge already, perhaps through prior work experience, personal interests or activities, or by taking a crash course on the subject, taking advantage of credit-by-examination options can save a noticeable amount of time, and in many cases – and most vitally for prisoners – save a substantial amount of money.

Another benefit of credit-by-exams is that you don't necessarily have to enroll at any school to start earning credit. Not having to enroll means that you are not obligated to pay for expensive courses to gain the credit you need for the academic path you've decided on. But you also are not obligated to the course time limits that can make going to college while behind bars a stressful prospect. You can begin earning credit-by-examination right now.

In order to succeed on credit-by-examination tests you need specific knowledge of the subject. Even previous background in the subject is no guarantee that you can simply take and pass the exam. **Adequate test preparation is critical**.

Fortunately, since these exams are equivalent to the comprehensive end-of-course exams given in most course studies, the materials you need are available. Further, most providers of these exams offer an examination guide when you apply for the test. These typically provide an outline of the subject covered by the exam and list recommended texts for study, which are invaluable in helping you prepare for the subject. Some even provide practice tests which you can take to discover areas where you may be weak and will need to study harder. It is wise to bear in mind that credit-by-exams tests are generalized and are not based solely on one particular textbook. Therefore, you'll want to review two or more textbooks per subject when preparing for your tests.

Credit-by-Examination Program Overviews

There are many options for those who want to take advantage of credit-by-examination programs. Unfortunately, however, as with most things that are convenient in the outside world, they are not always accessible to prisoners. The following will show you what credit-by-examination options exist in the off-chance that your prison provides a way to take advantage of them. But it will focus primarily on what is most useful for prisoners.

COLLEGE-LEVEL EXAMINATION PROGRAM (CLEP)

CLEP is the most widely used equivalency testing service. This is because it is also the most widely accepted by education institutions, recognized by nearly 3000 colleges and universities in North America.

CLEP tests are offered in 34 subjects, with exams formatted in multiple choice and each 90-minutes in duration. Each exam costs $120. This may seem excessive, until you consider that taking the courses through your chosen school will often cost a considerable amount more, in both money and time. Therefore, it is likely that whatever school you're hoping to seek a degree from will accept credits you have earned through CLEP testing.

However, as of December 31, 2011, due to decreasing test-taker volume and increases in program maintenance costs, CLEP exams are no longer available through paper-and-pencil testing. This means that they are typically unavailable to prisoners who cannot go to a CLEP testing center. However, some institutions have begun allowing prisoners to take their CLEPs through their education departments. Check with your facility to see if this is an option for you.

If you have taken CLEPs in the past, this credit will likely still be usable for credit at most schools.

For further information, contact:

COLLEGE-LEVEL EXAMINATION BOARD | COLLEGE-LEVEL EXAMINATION PROGRAM (CLEP)

45 Columbus Ave., New York, NY 10023
(800) 257-9558, (212) 713-8000
www.collegeboard.org

DANTES SUBJECT STANDARDIZED TESTS (DSST)

The *Defense Activity for Non-Traditional Education Support* (DANTES) is a testing service that was originally developed for military personnel by the Educational Testing Service. Now, however, they offer the *DANTES Subject Standardized Tests* (DSSTs) to anyone, military or civilian. Similar to CLEPS and Excelsior exams, these tests cover a variety of topics that are designed to be equivalent to the final exams of college courses that you would otherwise have to spend a full course fee and a semester studying. Earned credits will be transferrable to most schools.

DSSTs are the most inexpensive method for earning college credit, at $80 for each three-credit-hour course. Tests are offered in approximately 40 subjects in the general areas of applied technology, business, humanities, math, science, social sciences, and education. They have no time limit.

As with CLEPS, taking these tests can be a challenge for prisoners. They require the tester to go to a testing center, of which there are approximately 600 across the nation, very few of which are located in prisons. You will need to ask your prison education coordinator whether this option is available to you.

For more information on DSSTs, contact the following:

DANTES PROGRAM

PO Box 6604, Princeton, NJ 08541
(877) 471-9860, (609) 720-6740
www.getcollegecredit.com

EXCELSIOR COLLEGE EXAMS

Excelsior College offers approximately 60 exam options covering six areas of study, including arts and sciences, business, education, health sciences and nursing. Formerly known as the *Regents College Examinations*, these exams are of special interest to those pursuing a medical profession, as nearly half of their exam options are related to this field, including over 20 exams in the field of nursing.

While other exam programs are geared towards introductory-level college courses, Excelsior exams are unique in that they offer a selection of intermediate to upper-level (3rd and 4th year) subjects, as well as graduate studies, worth 3 to 8 credits each. They are, unfortunately, also a pricier option, costing as much as the credit-hour rates of many colleges (up to $400 per test).

On the positive side, many of these exams are offered in print-based format and can be administered by the education department at your prison. Additionally, Excelsior exam credits are accepted by most colleges.

For more information on Excelsior College Exams, contact the following:

EXCELSIOR COLLEGE TEST ADMINISTRATION

7 Columbia Circle
Albany, New York 12203-5159
(888) 647-2388
www.excelsior.edu

or write to:

REGISTRY OF CREDIT ADMINISTRATION | AMERICAN COUNCIL ON EDUCATION

One Dupont Circle NW, Suite 250
Washington, DC 20036-1193

Experiential Learning Credit

"The only source of knowledge is experience." - Albert Einstein.

Everyone has life experience that has provided some degree of knowledge in one or many fields. Perhaps some of that knowledge has even been learned through experiences had while behind bars. Did you know that you may actually be able to use this experience to get college credit?

Many schools at the college level understand the importance of life experience and offer a process by which they can assess your real-life experience to determine if yours are worthy of college credit without actually having to take any classes to earn that credit. In a nutshell, college credit is given for what you know, regardless of how, when, or where you learned it.

You might think that because you do not have any specific technical training you're unlikely to qualify for such an option, but you may be surprised by the sorts of life activities that may make you eligible. With thousands of courses covering every subject imaginable in schools around the country, it is more likely than not that something you know is worth college credit right now.

What is your Experience?

The following are just a handful of activities that may be eligible for Experiential Credit. This is by no means an exhaustive list, but it gives you a good idea of the possibilities, which you can use to assess whether something in your past, or even a current hobby or activity might be of some benefit in gaining college credit. Ask yourself if you have done or are proficient at any of the following:

Lived or spent time in a foreign country
Speak another language or sign language
Remodeled a home, built a deck, etc.
Written a book
Designed web pages or computer programs
Typing and other office skills
Taught Sunday School or led a Bible study
Given or prepared speeches
Map reading
Inventory control
Military strategy
Played an instrument
Participated in church activities
Raised animals
Worked on a farm
Built furniture
Bodybuilding
Repaired a car

Frequented a museum
Learned yoga
Sold Real Estate
Studied first aid or CPR
Written for a local newspaper
Visited National Parks
Sang in a choir, band, or orchestra
Volunteered for a political campaign
Attended seminars
Landscaping
Researched your family history
Acted in plays or other productions
Meal planning and nutrition
Set up a business or marketing plan
Learned a trade in prison
Extensive reading of any subject
Attended a convention
Been a Dungeon master

As you can see, there are many ways that you may have gained experience, some you may have even forgotten about. It is well worth the effort taken to remember and catalog these experiences. Doing so, and presenting them properly to the school you are hoping to earn college credit from, may provide you with a valuable opportunity to earn credit in the fastest and most economical way.

HOW IT WORKS

Gaining the experience was perhaps more straightforward then getting credit for it. Unfortunately, there is no standard way that all colleges convert this experience. There's no catalog that you can look at that will tell you definitively what your experience is worth, at least not one that is universally accepted by every school.

There are a handful of publications out there that some schools use to determine credit evaluation for life experience, such as:

- National Guide to Educational Training Programs, by ACE/Oryx Press.
- Guide to the Evaluation of Educational Experiences in the Armed Forces, by Oryx Press.
- Portfolio Development and Adult Learning: Purposes and Strategies

However, students cannot rely on these as definitive sources of what to expect when trying to gain credit.

Instead, colleges typically make a determination of your life-experience credit worth by performing what they call a *portfolio assessment*. An experiential learning portfolio is essentially a resume on steroids. It is a cataloging of what you know. How you assemble this portfolio is vital and could mean the difference between successfully gaining credit or not.

Typically, the school you are trying to earn credit from will have very specific guidelines to follow, but here are some universal steps that you can take to prepare for a portfolio assessment.

> ### Step One: List what you know.

Think back on your life, year by year, and make an inventory of as many learning experiences as you can recall. Create an outline of what you learned and think about how that learning may correspond with college-level education.

> ### Step Two: Find courses similar to what you already know.

Browse the school courses and their descriptions in this book and through school materials. It is likely that you'll discover courses you didn't know existed that you are already knowledgeable in. Pay special attention to the course descriptions. These are key in building and forming the narrative for your portfolio.

Note: The courses and descriptions in this book are only the print-based course offerings from each school. Many of these schools offer many other courses that are not feasible for prisoners to take. However, these courses may be useful in determining if you have enough experience to earn credit in them, since you will not actually need to take the class. If you are interested in experiential credit options offered by a school, make sure to write them for their entire course list.

> ### Step Three: Contact the school's portfolio advisor.

Schools that offer experiential learning credit will have an advisor who can walk you through their program and offer valuable input to ensure that you have the information necessary and the best possible chance at earning the credit you seek. It is what they are there for.

> ### Step Four: Start building your portfolio.

A portfolio consists of four primary parts:

1) a cover sheet explaining your desire;

2) a table of contents showing what's inside, including a list of attachments;

3) a narrative explaining your relevant learning experiences, detailing what you have learned from these, specific points that authenticate your experience, a demonstration of your understanding of the topic, and why this information is important to you; and

4) evidence of your learning, including certificates, samples of your work, or any other proof such as photos, news clippings, letters from supervisors, artwork, licenses, graded tests, and much more.

> ### Step Five: Submit your portfolio.

Once completed, submit your portfolio for evaluation. This can be a lengthy process, taking up to a few months.

Note: Portfolio assessment is not free. Typically, a school will charge a fee for each credit earned. Others, like Ohio University, will require that you take an *experiential learning portfolio development course*, worth credit itself. If you are hoping to earn large amounts of credit for your experience, such a course may be advisable to increase your chances at earning the most credit for that experience.

Experiential learning can be a fast track towards earning your way to a degree. In addition to gaining the credit, you will have done so with a portfolio of real-life experience, thus bolstering your chances at finding the career you desire.

When combined with other options such as credit by exams, DSSTs, and other examinations, you can earn substantial amounts

> ### Recommended College Portfolio Assessment Programs
>
> The following schools offer comprehensive portfolio assessment programs, as well as work with prisoners. You will find their contact information and many course descriptions in the *Find a School* section.
>
> **Ohio University**
>
> **Thomas Edison State University**
>
> **Thompson Rivers University**
>
> **Upper Iowa University**

of credit without ever taking a class. Keep in mind that several colleges limit the amount of credits that can be earned through these methods. However, the amount permitted is typically well worth the consideration.

THOMAS EDISON COLLEGE EXAMINATION PROGRAM (TECEP)

TECEPs may currently be the best option for prisoners. This is for two reasons: 1) all TECEPs come in pen and paper format. Prisoners can actually take them. And, 2) they are reasonably priced.

If you are enrolled at Thomas Edison State University, which is a prisoner-accessible school with extensive course and degree options in this book, you can take the TECEP examinations for $38 per credit. For non-enrolled students (non-matriculated), the cost is $52 per credit. Since most TECEPs earn three credits, it will cost you either $114 or $156, depending on your enrollment status. To take the same course at Thomas Edison State University, earning the same amount of credit, it will currently cost you $499 per credit, or just shy of $1,500. For a tenth of the tuition cost, and roughly half of even the most economically-priced college, you can earn the credits.

TECEPs consist of mostly multiple-choice questions, although some have short-answer or essay questions. They are administered through a proctor at your institution, so you will need to arrange for proctoring through your prison's education department. TECEPs are graded as either Credit (CR) – which is awarded at what would be equivalent to a letter grade of C or better – or No Credit (NC). These do not affect the grade point average (GPA). This means that an official transcript from the school will not show a numeric score or a letter grade. It will only reflect the exams successfully completed and the number of credits earned.

If you do not pass the exam, you are allowed to take it one additional time. However, to do so, you must re-register and pay another test fee.

TECEP test options can be found under the listing for Thomas Edison State University in the College Studies section of this book.

For further information, contact:

THOMAS EDISON STATE UNIVERSITY | OFFICE OF TEST ADMINISTRATION

111 West State Street, Trenton, NJ 08608
(888) 442-8372, (609) 633-9242
www.tesc.edu *testing@tesc.edu*

CEU Credits

Also known as Continuing Education Units, CEUs are earned from various schools for a variety of courses. Once earned, they can be used for college credits at colleges that receive them. Typically, each CEU is equal to roughly ¼ of a credit hour at most schools. More specifically, 3.2 to 4.8 CEUs are equal to 1 undergraduate credit and 5.0 to 6.4 CEUs are equal to 1 graduate credit, depending on the whether the chosen school uses semester or quarter hours.

A few things to bear in mind while considering taking a credit-by-examination:

You cannot bluff your way through these exams. You must have a comprehensive understanding of the exam subject.

Make sure you know which exam services your school of choice accepts for credit.

Part 4 Find a School!

So you've decided you want to proceed with getting an education. Now the fun part begins, getting to go through all of the education options available to you to take you on a path to a better future.

This part will let you see all of the current courses available to prisoners, including their description, prices, requirements, and more. It is broken down by levels of education. Simply flip to the level you are looking to get started in and have fun exploring.

College and Graduate Studies?

High School?

Personal Enrichment Studies?

Vocational Training?

PERSONAL ENRICHMENT STUDIES

If you are not sure where to begin with your education journey, you've found the right spot.

The entire point of education is to gain knowledge and to better yourself. You do not have to pay thousands of dollars to accomplish this. In many cases, you do not have to pay anything at all. You can simply pick up a book and gain a measure of knowledge you did not have prior to opening those pages. But for the aspiring student, a structured course in a specific field of study is what works best, such as the structure provided through personal enrichment studies.

BENEFITS OF PERSONAL ENRICHMENT STUDIES

If you are just starting out and trying to decide what direction you want to take, a personal enrichment course may be precisely what you are looking for. These courses provide the structure of formal education without the stress of time limitations, grades, or accumulation of credits.

- **There is no pressure.** You simply pay for the course materials and study at your own pace, in your own time.

- **It is relatively cheap**. The course costs tend to be far more reasonable than any other upper-level education option. Where individual courses will run you into the hundreds of dollars for vocational and college-level classes, personal enrichment courses typically require just a nominal fee, and are sometimes FREE.

- **You will obtain proof of learning.** With every course completion, you'll typically receive a *Certificate of Completion* as proof of what you've learned. Not only does this provide you with the satisfaction of accomplishment, it also demonstrates to others, such as family, friends, or the parole board, that you have been using your incarcerated time wisely and beneficially.

NEGATIVES OF PERSONAL ENRICHMENT STUDIES

The difference between taking a personal enrichment course and a college course is that they do not typically provide benefits that you can use beyond the knowledge they provide. In other words, they generally offer very little in the way of assistance towards college-level studies or job-specific qualifications.

- **They are not typically accredited.** While most institutions that offer personal enrichment studies provide quality education, since many of these courses are not accredited by outside organizations, there is no way to ensure that the course will be a quality one. The general rule of thumb, if this if your concern, is to chooses a course from a school that is accredited for other levels of studies, such as a recognized university.

- **They do not offer college credit.** Personal enrichment courses do not count for college credit. While you may be able to use some of your gained knowledge to earn credit through knowledge-based college exams, these courses will typically not provide quite the level of knowledge necessary to qualify.

o **This is not job training.** These courses are typically designed to give the student knowledge in fields that are usually outside the scope of what you would learn in vocational or college studies. Therefore, while they may help you gain knowledge in areas you need in your life, such as general life skills, religion, or some low-level academics, they will generally not advance you towards a career.

Personal enrichment studies provide value to anyone who wants to learn.

They are a good place to start to see if you have what it takes to go further down an educational path. If you take one of these courses and decide that you do not like it, you will quickly find that taking an even more formal education path may not be for you. But if you discover that you enjoy learning, or at least the benefits learning comes with, personal enrichment courses may be just what you've needed all along to thrust you into becoming a prisoner-student and attaining educational or career knowledge that you never thought possible from a prison setting.

Personal Enrichment School Recommendations

Schools, and what you want out of them, vary in so many ways the it is impossible to make an overall recommendation. Therefore, we leave that up to the accrediting agencies. However, one common interest among all prisoners is the quality of the communication between the outside world and your cell.

When researching schools. We send requests to each one as if we are prisoners. We want to know how they respond to your requests, which is a great guide in determining how well the school will work with you should you decide to enroll.

The following schools are recommended as institutions who stood out from the rest in how well they communicated, how accommodating they were to our requests for information, how comprehensive their sent information was, and how willing they were to work with prisoners. Starred "*" listings are exceptional in meeting the above criteria, proving that they have a good understanding of the unique challenges that prisoners face.

American Bible Academy (religious studies)
ECS Ministries (religious studies)
Global University (religious studies)
Gospel Echoes (religious studies)
Lamp & Light Publishers (religious studies)
PASS Program (enrichment studies)

SCHOOL LISTING LAYOUT

CONTACT INFORMATION

This is the school's address and where you can go for more information on that school. There is always more information than we can provide concerning each school. We encourage you to contact every school you are interested in.

DESCRIPTION

Key details are provided about each school so that you are aware of information of note that may impact you as a prisoner-student.

ACCREDITATION

The following schools are all accredited by a variety of agencies, which are marked under each entry. As you've learned, accreditation is vital in determining the quality of a learning institution. But not all accrediting agencies are created equal. Therefore, you should exercise caution when selecting a school. (For a complete discussion on this topic, see section on *Accreditation* early in this book.)

AVAILABLE TO PRISONERS

This will keep you informed of what you can earn from this school, such as diplomas, degrees, and certificates. School offerings change regularly, which is why we update this book annually.

TUITION

This is the fee the school charges for courses, course credits, grade levels, and other programs.

PAYMENT PLANS

Many schools offer payment plans to make programs more affordable during study. Even if a payment plan is not listed, a school may be willing to work with you to develop an affordable plan that will work with your circumstances.

CREDIT TRANSFER/EXAM OPTIONS

If you have previously earned credits from another school, this section will tell you if this school may allow you to transfer those credits in. It will also let you know if they have credit-by-exam options.

TIME LIMITS

Schools generally place limits on how long you have to take a course. If you cannot complete your course in time, many schools offer extensions, often for a fee.

PROCTOR REQUIRED?

This area will tell you if a school require their examinations to be proctored (supervised by an impartial person.)

CANCELLATION POLICY

If you are unhappy with the school, or you determine that the courses you purchased are just not going to work for you, this section will tell you about the schools course refund policy.

AVAILABLE COURSES

This section provides information on the courses offered by the school, including courses available, descriptions, and prerequisites.

Personal Enrichment Studies | General

American Community Corrections Institute | Lifeskills

PO Box 1910
Orem, Utah 84059-1910
(435) 633-2100
www.inmatelifeskills.com   info@inmatelifeskills.com

American Community Corrections Institute offers life skills studies, specifically designed for prisoners, in the form of story format workbooks. Each completed course comes with a Certificate of Completion, which may be useful in demonstrating a path to rehabilitation.

Accreditation: None

Available for Prisoners

Certificates of Completion in a variety of self-directed life skills studies

Tuition Rates:	**$45 per course for prisoners** ($85 for others)
Payment Plan:	None
Textbooks:	Included in tuition
Time Limit:	None

ACCI Lifeskills
Available Courses

Anger Management | W 111
Instead of managing anger, this course teaches students to avoid it. The more that can be learned to avoid anger, the more productive life becomes.

Cognitive Awareness | W 118
This course is primarily designed for offenders but can be used by therapists and others where a strong cognitive component is needed. It is written as historical fiction as it follows real people solving real problems.

Contentious Relationships | W 116
Primarily used by civil courts to help couples resolve their difference and reduce potential damage to children. The curriculum uses cognitive restructuring models that have been proven to help individuals overcome negative thoughts, feelings and emotions.

Domestic Violence | W 129
This course was designed for both the abuser and the victim, for abusers because of their self-defeating behaviors, and for victims because of their lack of cognition and propensity for revictimization.

Driving Under the Influence | W 128
A strong cognitive restructuring course that challenges the faulty thinking that leads to driving under the influences.

Employment | W 124
This course follows two fictional characters on their way to finding employment through corrections in behavior and thought pattern.

Offender Corrections | W 112
This program was designed for repeat offenders. It guides students through the thinking errors which result in criminal activity, discussing how their self-defeating thoughts and behaviors continue recycling.

Offender Responsibility | W 119
This course demonstrates the consequences of denial, justification and other self-defeating thoughts and offers solutions.

Parenting | W 117
This course teaches parents important cognitive skills to help them to parent in a way that avoids abuse and neglect.

Theft/Shoplifting | W 121
This course helps students to recognize the cause of their theft and shoplifting behavior and how to overcome these.

Substance Abuse | W 114
This course follows the lives of two family groups, one chemically free, the other saturated with substance abuse. It follows their victories and defeats as they confront the addictions.

Cornell Lab of Ornithology

159 Sapsucker Woods Road
Ithaca, New York 14850-1999
(607) 254-2452
www.birds.cornell.edu/homestudy

The *Cornell Lab of Ornithology* offers an ornithology course (the scientific study of birds). This is written at an introductory college level and includes bird behavior, migration, ecology, conservation, and other bird-related subjects. Some schools have accepted completion of this course as 3 credits hours.

Accreditation: None

Available for Prisoners

Certificate of Completion in Ornithology, and possible credit consideration

Tuition Rates:	**$200 for entire course**
Payment Plans:	None
Textbooks:	Not included in tuition. (Requires the Handbook of Bird Biology, Third Edition retails for $130)
Time Limit:	None

This course is currently not available and will be re-released later in the fall of 2017. It is not clear at this point whether the course will still be available in a print-based format or only online.

Getting Out by Going In | GOGI

PO Box 88969
Los Angeles, California 90009
www.gettingoutbygoingin.org *coach@gettingoutbygoingin.org*

GOGI was created by prisoners for prisoners. The GOGI Anger Management courses are their latest offering, helping prisoners build options beyond the usual responses to life's irritations. The course is a 6-week course that requires as little as 5 to 10 minutes each day. They use real-life stories in the course, asking students to make suggestions as to how the prisoners in the story might best handle the situation.

GOGI offers several study guides, including *Increasing Your Peace: Anger Management the GOGI Way, Teach Me to GOGI: The Ultimate GOGI Group Study Guide, GOGI Tools for Positive Decision Making,* and others. They are available through the mail or printable through their website.

Accreditation: None

Available for Prisoners

Certificate of Completion in Anger Management

Tuition:	$50
Payment Plan:	None
Textbooks:	Included with tuition
Time Limit:	None

Prisoner Assistance Scholastic Service

PASS PROGRAM

PO Box 2009
San Francisco, California 94126
(888) 670-7277
www.passprogram.org   passprogram@passprogram.org

The *Prisoner Assistance Scholastic Service* (PASS) offers a comprehensive self-help based course of study for prisoners. It is designed specifically to assist prisoners in life skills that may help rehabilitation efforts, improve prospects of successful parole board hearings and reduce individual recidivism.

The program is divided into two semesters of five courses (10 total).

Accreditation: None

Available for Prisoners

Personal Psychological Development degree

Certificate of Completion

Tuition Rates:	$500 for entire program
Payment Plans:	None
Textbooks:	Included in tuition
Time Limit:	None (average completion time: 6 to 12 months)

PASS Program
Available Courses

The following courses are designed to complement one another and therefore cannot be purchased individually. Student will receive the first five courses for the first semester, followed by an exam. Once the semester has been successfully completed, student will receive certificates of completion for each course followed by the next five courses and exam. Once remaining courses are successfully completed, students will receive certificates of completion for remaining courses and their diploma.

FIRST SEMESTER	SECOND SEMESTER
1. Victim Awareness	6. Parenting
2. Anger Management	7. Non-Violent Communication
3. Addiction & Substance Abuse	8. Conflict Resolution
4. Domestic Violence & Crimes Against Women	9. Living with Purpose
5. Gang Diversion	10. Re-entry into Society

Rio Salado College

2323 West 14th Street
Tempe, Arizona 85281-6950
(877) 517-8345, (480) 517-8345
www.riosalado.edu   incarcerated.reentr@riosalado.edu

Rio Salado College offers a reentry program specifically designed for prisoners that can be used for personal enrichment. To take these courses will be a pricey option, but the courses are quality and provide a good preview of what college-level education is like for those who are considering further education. These courses are good for college credit. They also offer a number of other certificate and associate degree options. (See the *College Studies*.)

Courses can be taken as certificate programs in groups or as individual courses.

Accreditation: North Central Association of Colleges and Schools, The Higher Learning Commission

AVAILABLE TO PRISONERS

Workforce Development & Community Reentry Certificate Program
Various personal enrichment courses

Tuition Rates:	**$216 per credit for nonresidents** **$81 per credit for Arizona residents**
Payment Plan:	None
Textbook Fees:	Not included in tuition. They offer a book buy-back program.
Additional Fees:	**Registration fee: $15** **Materials fee: $15 per course**
Cancellation Policy:	Full refund within 9 days of enrollment; Other percentages based on percentage of course completion.
Transfer/Exam Options:	Not applicable
Time Limits:	12 to 16 weeks
Proctor required?	No, unless you want college credit.

Rio Salado College
Certificate Programs

These certificate programs are designed to meet the needs of students who are interested in a specific professional specialization, and which may be helpful toward parole board consideration and reentry planning.

These are groups of courses that provide a concentration in a particular study area, without the need to take the general education courses of degree programs. They are more economical options than a full degree track.

Once completed, each of the following certificate earns college credit as marked, which can be used towards future learning.

COURSE	CREDIT
Personal Skill Development	WFR110	3
Family Reunification	WFR112	3
Social Skill Development	WFR114	1
Substance Abuse Education	WFR116	1
Job Readiness	WFR118	3
Job Retention	WFR120	3
Total Credits	**13**
Total Cost	**$2,795 plus fees**

Rio Salado College
Personal Enrichment Courses

WORKFORCE RE-ENTRY

Re-entry Skills: Personal Skill Development | WFR110 (3 credits)
Personal skill development necessary for transition from incarceration to community. Includes development of a personal value system and decision-making strategies as well as a conflict management. Also covers time and money management. Also covers time and money management, goal setting, and the basics for everyday life.

Re-entry Skills: Family Reunification | WFR112 (3 credits)
Reunification procedures for the incarcerated person's effective transition. Includes building and maintaining self-esteem and effective communication for healthy families or support systems. Also covers family and networking culture, discipline, and expectations, for release.   Prerequisites: Permission of Department or Division.

Re-entry Skills: Social Skills Development | WFR114 No Exams (1credit)
Re-entry Skills: Substance Abuse Education | WFR116 At-Home MD/FN 1credit.

Re-entry Skills: Job Readiness | WFR118 No Exams (3 credits)
Preparing the incarcerated person for release into the working world. Includes education, skills assessment, and work experience. Also covers job search skills such as resume writing, applications, and interviewing.

Re-entry Skills: Job Retention | WFR120 No Exams (2 credits)
Job retention procedures and techniques for incarcerated persons in transition. Includes workplace protocol, job performance, and employer-employee interaction. Also covers stress management and communication skills as well as interpersonal relationships in the work place.

Syda Foundation | Siddha Yoga Meditation Prison Project

PO Box 99140
Emeryville, California 94662
(510) 893-4648
www.siddhayoga.org   prisonproject@siddhayoga.com

The *Syda Foundation* Prison Project is dedicated to disseminating the siddha yoga teachings and practice to incarcerated individuals. They offer prisoners a free monthly newsletter and home study course. Over 5,000 students in 1,500 prisons are currently enrolled.

The Siddha Yoga Study Course contains the teachings of *Hurumayi Chidvilasananda*, a spiritual master who teaches how to live life as true human beings. Students learn that within each of us, behind mind, body and ego, is a divine power called the Self. They learn how to apply the ancient teachings on the Self in practical ways.

The course, if taken without a pause, lasts seventeen years. The introductory package comes with a full explanation of the course, an example of the lessons, a Sanskrit Glossary and advanced Sanskrit Pronunciation Guide.

After six months of successive study, you can request pictures of the related Gurus, and after a year they will send yoga books and magazines.

Course is available in English and Spanish.

Accreditation: None

<u>Available for Prisoners</u>

Siddha Yoga Study Course

The Erika Project

425 Knollcrest Lane
Charlevoix, MI 49720
(269) 355-3585
www.vocationnavigator.com

The Erika Project has developed a program called *Vocation Navigator*. It is currently comprised of three workbooks for three different levels of learning, including the original *Student Edition* geared towards Juniors in High School, the *Seminar Edition*, useful for those working in street ministries helping people find jobs, and *A New Beginning* designed for prisoners.

A New Beginning is a 100-page lesson that helps those who are about to get out. The program presents job seeking using practical sensibility in an easy-to-follow, no-nonsense way. Through exercises, it assists students to apply the knowledge in ways that will that will have a lasting benefit upon reentry.

Accreditation: None

Available for Prisoners

A New Beginning workbook

Cost: FREE

Personal Enrichment Studies | Religious

> NOTE: The following personal enrichment studies opportunities are all religious in nature. They are broken down into two sections:
>
> **Fee-based Religious Studies**
>
> **Free Religious Studies**
>
> These organizations do not typically accept transfer credits or grants for study, and they do not typically offer credits to transfer to other institutions. If you would like to earn college credit for religious courses taken, go to our *Vocational* Studies and *College Studies* sections to find out which religious education institutions are eligible for credits.
>
> The following courses award a *Certificate of Completion* or Diploma in the course of study, unless otherwise noted. These are good prep options if you are considering taking more advanced religious studies in the future.

Fee-based Religious Studies

Full Gospel Bible Institute

3018 East Lincoln Highway, PO Box 337
Parkesburg, Pennsylvania 19365
(610) 857-2357

Full Gospel Bible Institute (FBGI) offers the Christian Workers Course program to prisoners at a reduced rate, and sometimes without charge. The program consists of ten subjects with 16 units of study.

Applicants are asked to make a donation towards supplies and shipping costs. Actual incurred costs of the course have been set at $280, but they will process a prisoner's application with a donation of $10.

Courses:	Christian Workers Course
Tuition Rates:	Students are asked to make donations towards the cost of the course. No sponsorship costs set at $280 per program; Partial scholarship cost set at $160; FREE tuition when available for prisoner students (There is usually a waiting list.)

Available Courses

Personal Evangelism	New Testament Survey I, II, and III
Prayer and Fasting	Life of Christ I and II
The Holy Spirit	Divine Healing I and II
The Gifts of the Spirit	Dispensational Truth
Tithing	Course Thesis Paper
The Trinity I & II	

Moody Bible Institute

820 N. La Salle Boulevard
Chicago, Illinois 60610
(800) 758-6352, (312) 329-4000
www.moody.edu   mdlc@moody.edu

Tuition Rates:	**$49 per course; $367.50 per certificate program. Scofield courses: $200 per course, $585 per certificate program.** **Certificate fee: $5.**
Additional Fees:	**Shipping: $12 per course, $2 for each additional course in the same order; $28 shipping on Certificate program courses**
Time Limits:	6 months per course; 18 months per Scofield course; 4 years per certificate program

Moody Bible Institute
Personal Enrichment Certificate Programs

The following certificate programs are ideal if you want to gain proficiency in a specific area. You have the option of receiving a certificate of completion at the end of each course (for a $5 fee), but you will receive a series certificate of completion after completion of all ten courses in a series (free of charge), as well as ten (10) CEUs per series.

Bible Studies Certificate

Course	CEUs
Old Testament Survey I | BI0001	1
Old Testament Survey II | BI0002	1
Survey of the New Testament | BI0005	1
James | BI0070	1
Bible Prophecy | BI0091	1
How to Understand the Bible | BI0099	1
The Doctrine of the Holy Spirit | TH0004	1
Basic Christian Doctrine | TH0012	1
Plus two Electives	1
Total CEUs	**10**
Total Cost	**$367.50**

New Testament Studies Certificate

Course	CEUs
Matthew | BI0051	1
John | BI0054	1
Acts | BI0055	1
Romans | BI0056	1
Ephesians | BI0064	1
Hebrews | BI0069	1
Revelation | BI0077	1
Life of Christ | BI0090	1
Plus two Electives	2
Total CEUs	**10**
Total Cost	**$367.50**

Old Testament Studies Certificate

Course	CEUs
Genesis | BI0011	1
Exodus | BI0012	1
Joshua | BI0017	1
Judges & Ruth | BI0018	1
Psalms | BI0029	1
Proverbs | BI0030	1
Isaiah | BI0033	1
Daniel | BI0037	1
Plus two Electives	2
Total CEUs	**10**
Total Cost	**$367.50**

Personal Ministry & Leadership Series

Course	CEUs
Teaching with Results | ED0001	1
Keys to Happy Family Life | ED0002	1
Successful Soul Winning | ED0002	1
The Cults Exposed | ED0006	1
A Holy Life & How to Live it | TH0009	1
First Steps in Christian Faith | TH0016	1
God's Will for your Life | TH0017	1
Plus two Electives	2
Total CEUs	**10**
Total Cost	**$367.50**

Electives

Micah | BI0009	1 CEU
1 Samuel | BI0014	1 CEU
2 Samuel | BI0016	1 CEU
1 Kings | BI0016	1 CEU
2 Kings | BI0023	1 CEU
1 Corinthians | BI0057	1 CEU
Galatians | BI0062	1 CEU
1 and 2 Peter | BI0072	1 CEU
How to Manage Money | ED0036	1 CEU
Biblical Basis of Missions | MI0001	1 CEU
Memorize the Word | PS0030	1 CEU
The Good News | TH0018	1 CEU

Scofield Bible Studies Certificate

Each of the following Scofield courses earn 9 CEUs. They can be taken individually or together (for a total of 27 CEUs).

Course	CEUs

Scofield Bible Doctrine	TH0097	9
Scofield New Testament	BI0098	9
Scofield Old Testament	BI0097	9
Total CEUs		**27**
Total Cost		**$540**

Scofield Plus Three Certificate

Course	CEUs

Scofield Bible Doctrine	TH0097	9
Scofield New Testament	BI0098	9
Scofield Old Testament	BI0097	9
Teaching with Results	ED0001	1
Successful Soul Winning	ED0002	1
The Biblical Basis of Missions	MI0001	1
Total CEUs		**30**
Total Cost		**$585**

Moody Bible Institute
Available Courses

BIBLICAL STUDIES

Old Testament Survey I | BI0001
Old Testament Survey II | BI0002
Survey of the New Testament | BI0005
Genesis | BI0011
Exodus | BI0012
Joshua | BI0017
Judges & Ruth | BI0018
1 Samuel | BI0014
2 Samuel | BI0016
1 Kings | BI0016
2 Kings | BI0023
Psalms | BI0029
Proverbs | BI0030
Isaiah | BI0033
Daniel | BI0037
Matthew | BI0051
John | BI0054
Acts | BI0055
Romans | BI0056
1 Corinthians | BI0057
Galatians | BI0062
Ephesians | BI0064
Hebrews | BI0069
James | BI0070
1 and 2 Peter | BI0072
Revelation | BI0077
Life of Christ | BI0090
Bible Prophecy | BI0091
How to Understand the Bible |

MINISTRY STUDIES

Teaching with Results | ED0001
Keys to Happy Family Living | ED0002

Building Successful Sunday School | ED0003
Understanding Students | ED0031
How to Manage your Money | ED0036
Successful Soul Winning | ED0002
The Cults Exposed | ED0006
The Biblical Basis of Missions | MI0001
Memorize the Word | PS0030

THEOLOGICAL STUDIES

The Doctrine of the Holy Spirit | TH0004
A Holy Life & How to Live it | TH0009
Basic Christian Doctrine | TH0012
First Steps in the Faith | TH0016
God's Will for your Life | TH0017
The Good News | TH0018

RHEMA Correspondence Bible School

PO Box 50220
Tulsa, Oklahoma 74150-0220
(866) 481-7227, (918) 258-1588 ext. 2216
www.rhema.org/rbcs

RHEMA Correspondence Bible School offers a Certificate of Completion for each unit completed. Once you have completed all units, you will receive an RCBS Diploma.

Courses: *Certificates* in Dynamics in Faith (5 lessons), Healing Truth (7 lessons), Life of Prayer (4 lessons), The Christian Life (7 lessons), Charismatic Truths (6 lessons), and Covenant Truths (6 lessons).

Tuition Rates: **$35 per lesson. (Full prisoner scholarships available, for which you'll be placed on a waiting list.)**

Additional Fees: $25 one-time fee (RHEMA *Diploma* awarded upon completion of all certification programs.)

Phrear School of Theology | International Maranatha Institute

Central Campus for Distance Learning
PO Box 337, Parkesburg, PA 19365

Courses: The Comforter – The Holy Spirit, Understanding Prayer and Fasting, The Trinity, Dispensational Truth, Christ Jesus – His Life, New Testament Books, Spiritual Gifts, Scriptural Principles of Giving, Personal Witnessing, and Divine Healing

Tuition Rates: **$ 25 Registration Fee PLUS $29 per course.**

Seminary Extension

901 Commerce St., Suite 500
Nashville, Tennessee 37203-3631
(800) 229-4612, (615) 242-2453
www.seminaryextension.org sa@seminaryextension.org

Courses: *Certificates* in Bi-Vocational Ministry, Lay Ministry, and Women's Ministry. *Diplomas* in Biblical Studies, Educational Ministries, Ministries/Pastoral Education, and Theological Foundation.

Tuition Rates: **2-Credit Courses: $136   3-Credit Courses: $169**

(Textbooks not included)

Additional Fees **Transcript Fee: $10; Course Extension Fee: $35 (courses expire after 6 months); Course Reactivation Fee: $50**

CERTIFICATE PROGRAMS

CERTIFICATE IN BIVOCATIONAL MINISTRY STUDIES

This certificate is designed for individuals currently serving as or thinking about serving as a small church or bivocational minister.

CERTIFICATE IN LAY MINISTRY TRAINING

This certificate is designed for individuals currently serving as or thinking about serving in lay or volunteer ministry positions.

CERTIFICATE IN WOMEN'S MINISTRY

This certificate is designed for individuals currently serving as or thinking about serving in positions of women's leadership or ministry.

DIPLOMA PROGRAMS

DIPLOMA IN BIBLICAL STUDIES

The Diploma in Biblical Studies provides an opportunity of in-depth study for individuals seeking to fulfill their call to Christian ministry where biblical study is their main focus, whether vocational or avocational.

DIPLOMA IN EDUCATIONAL MINISTRIES

The Diploma in Educational Ministries provides an opportunity of in-depth study for individuals seeking to fulfill their call to educational church ministry, whether vocational or avocational.

DIPLOMA IN MINISTRIES/PASTORAL EDUCATION

The Diploma in Ministries/Pastoral Education provides an opportunity of in-depth study for individuals seeking to fulfill their call to Pastoral ministry, whether full-time, bivocational or as an avocational volunteer.

DIPLOMA IN THEOLOGICAL FOUNDATION

Seminary Extension offers this program to encourage continued Christian education. In order to earn this diploma, students must already have a diploma from Seminary Extension or must have completed a program that is equivalent to or greater than our diploma program.

BIBLICAL STUDIES CURRICULUM

Studying in the Biblical Studies area will do the following:

- Seek with growing interest and devotion to understand God through His Word, and to respond in faith, love, and obedience
- Gain increasing understanding of the facts and truths recorded in the bible, and then to recognize the relationship of these facts and truths to each other in light of the total biblical revelation
- Develop a sound understanding of and appreciation for the nature of the Bible and the ways in which an infinite God used finite human beings to record His Word
- Develop understanding and skills needed to interpret the Bible in light of sound biblical scholarship
- Learn to select, and use effectively in Bible study, resource materials such as lexicons, concordances, dictionaries, encyclopedias, and commentaries

Biblical Backgrounds | BB2102	2 credits	Philippians, Colossians, and Philemon | NT2179	2 credits
How To Understand The Bible | BB3100	3 credits	1 & 2 Thessalonians | NT2181	2 credits
Nehemiah | OT2133	2 credits	1 & 2 Timothy | NT2182	2 credits
Genesis, Part 1 | Ot2206	2 credits	Hebrews | NT2185	2 credits
Old Testament Survey, Part 1 | OT3103	3 credits	James | NT2187	2 credits

Old Testament Survey, Part 2 | OT3104	3 credits	1,2, & 3 John | NT2189	2 credits
Isaiah | OT3125	3 credits	Revelation | NT2190	2 credits
Amos | OT3132	3 credits	Matthew | NT2270	2 credits
Exodus | OT3207	3 credits	John | NT2273	2 credits
Jeremiah | Ot3226	3 credits	Acts | NT2274	2 credits
Mark | NT2171	2 credits	New Testament Survey, Part 1 | NT3166	3 credits
Romans | NT2175	2 credits	New Testament, Part 2 | NT3167	3 credits
Corinthians | NT2176	2 credits	Luke | NT3172	3 credits
Galatians | NT2177	2 credits		

Ethics-History-Theology Curriculum

Objectives for courses listed in this area are listed below. These courses will help students to:

- Develop a valid system of personal beliefs about God and His relationship to mankind
- Gain increasing ability, with God's help, to demonstrate in daily life the meaning and reality of professional theological truths
- Express genuine Christian love for persons who have religious beliefs different from one's own and to gain some understanding and appropriate appreciation for the religious beliefs of others
- Discover appropriate meanings and values in Christian history
- Understand ways in which God has worked in human history and continues to work today
- Gain increasing understanding of important personalities, events, and movements which have influenced the course of Christian history
- Learn to test Christian principles and practices in the light of past and current events
- Learn to evaluate contemporary problems and issues in the light of their historical settings and biblical insights

Introduction To Christian Ethics | CE3231	3 credits	Formation For Ministry | GM2500	2 credits
Southern Baptist Heritage | CH2313	3 credits	Disciplines Of Disciplineship | GM2501	2 credits
History Of Christianity | CH3211	3 credits	The Bivocational Pastor | GM2565	2 credits
History Of Christian Thought | CH3212	3 credits	Public Worship | PM2254	2 credits
Survey Of Baptist Missions | MS2222	3 credits	Evangelism | PM2255	2 credits
Contemporary World Religions | MS3223	3 credits	Pastoral Leadership In A Small Church | PM2258	2 credits
Philosophy Of Religion | TH2302	2 credits	Contemporary Christian Preaching | PM3257	3 credits
Systematic Theology | TH3200	3 credits	Pastoral Ministry | PM3259	3 credits
New Testament Theology | TH3201	3 credits	Pastoral Care | PM3351	3 credits
Principles Of Church Administration	3 credits	Childhood Education In The Church |	2 credits

CA3281		RE2262	
Marriage And Family | CE2232	2 credits	Working With Youth In The Church | RE2265	2 credits
Women Leading Women | CE2233	2 credits	Educational Ministry In The Church | RE3260	3 credits
How To Plant A Church | CD2390	2 credits	Dynamics Of Teaching | RE3264	3 credits
Leading A Music Ministry In A Small Church | CM2271	2 credits		

FREE Religious Studies

> NOTE: The following courses are all FREE and largely designed with prisoners in mind and come recommended by prisoners. There are various levels of study and degrees of difficulty. The more advanced studies are marked as such.
>
> All offer *Certificates of Completion* or *Diplomas*, unless marked otherwise.

FREE CHRISTIAN COURSES

Amazing Facts, Inc.

PO Box 909, Roseville, California 95678
(916) 434-3880
www.amazingfacts.org

Amazing Facts provides easy lessons, tracts and magazines covering a variety of topics. They have recently updated their offerings, which now consist of 27 study guides.

After completing all 27 guides, they do provide a certificate of completion.

Courses: See below
Difficulty: Easy

Available Courses

The following courses are the first 14 of the 27 available study guides available. You will receive the first one with your requests and up to four at a time after each completion.

STUDY GUIDES

- #1 Is There Anything Left You Can Trust?
- #2 Did God Create the Devil?
- #3 Saved From Certain Death
- #4 A Colossal City in Space
- #5 Keys for a Happy Marriage
- #6 Written in Stone!
- #7 The Lost Day of History
- #8 Ultimate Deliverance
- #9 Purity & Power!
- #10 Are the Dead Really Dead?
- #11 Is the Devil in Charge of Hell?
- #12 1,000 Years of Peace
- #13 God's Free Health Plan
- #14 Is Obedience Legalism?

ONE-ISSUE MAGAZINES (NO SUBSCRIPTIONS)

Amazing Health Facts
Benefits of Belief
8 Secrets to Better Health
Great Controversy, The
Hidden Truth
Living Longer & Feeling Better
Lose Weight, Feel Great
Our Amazing Universe
Rest of Your Life
Secrets of Daniel & Revelation
Spiritualism & the Occult
When Life is Unfair
Why Be a Vegetarian

American Bible Academy

PO Box 1627, Joplin, Missouri 64802
(417) 781-9100
www.arm.org *info@arm.org*

American Bible Academy (ARM) is one of the largest prison-focused bible correspondence programs in the country. They offer some of the highest quality and more challenging courses, which consist of 120-page commercial quality textbooks.

Several courses are also available in Spanish.

They also provide FREE downloads of other bible textbooks, commentaries, courses, tracts, and other Christian Resources.

Courses: See below
Difficulty: Advanced

Available Courses

The following courses are available in the order listed. Each course is 120 pages long and includes three exams, which must be completed with a 70% grade average before the next course is shipped.

ARM will also mail these courses to your spouse so that you can study the courses at the same time.

Courses are available in English or Spanish. They are each worth 1 credit unless noted otherwise, which may be accepted for elective credits by other schools.

Gospel of John (Intro - non-credit)
Christian Doctrine | Volume One
Christian Doctrine | Volume Two
Christian Doctine | Volume Three
Book of Acts | Volume One

Book of Acts | Volume Two
Gospel of Mark
Galatians/Philippians
Christian Doctrine | Volume Three

Bible Correspondence Course

PO Box 3328, Sugar Land, Texas 77487-3328
(281) 498-0465

Bible Correspondence Course offers a series of basic courses, which are each awarded a certificate of completion. Postage is paid both ways.

Courses: Numerous series. (First lesson of a seven lesson series: Is This All There Is?)
Difficulty: Easy

Bible Correspondence Fellowship

PO Box 2300, Port Orchard, WA 98366
www.biblecorrespondence.org

Bible Correspondence Fellowship offers 27 basic and intermediate Bible education courses for adult prisoners, all prepared by *Prison Mission Association* to help answer common question about the Bible and Christian life.

Available Courses

Can God save me even after the things I have done?	How do I deal with temptations in my life?	...Crime and Justice?
Can I know with certainty that I am saved?	How can I purify my thoughts?	...Debt?
Can I lose my salvation?	How can I control my anger?	...Honesty?
Must I be water baptized in order to be saved?	How can I overcome hatred, bitterness and resentment?	Communicating with the dead?
If I am saved, should I be able to speak in tongues?	How do I pray?	What does the Bible teach us about alcohol and drug abuse?
Will Christians go through the tribulation?	**What does the Bible say about...**	How can I know God's will for my life?
Is there an unpardonable sin?	...Divorce & remarriage?	Should a Christian marry an unbeliever even if they love each other?
How can I have victory over sin?	...Sex outside of marriage?	Can I live as I choose?
	...Homosexuality?	Why does a loving God allow innocent people to suffer?
	...Wealth?	
	...Work?	

Bible Studies by Mail

PO Box 2077, Las Cruces, New México 88004

Bible Studies by Mail offers 18 basic courses for adult prisoners.

Courses: See below. All courses come from Mailbox Club International Series.
Difficulty: Easy

Available Courses

Understanding True Love	My New Life in Christ III	Fishers of Men
A Country Called Heaven	Practical Christian Living	The Spirit World
My New Life in Christ I	God's Great Salvation	John
God's Word: The Bible	Basic Bible Truths	Mark
Know & Grow	Winning the Race of Life	Acts
My New Life in Christ II	Light of the Old Testament	Galatians

Catholic Home Study

PO Box 363, Perryville, MO 63775
www.catholichomestudy.org

Catholic Home Study offers nine basic study options to teach those who are new to the Catholic faith the fundamentals of Catholicism.

Courses: We Believe: A Survey for the Catholic Faith, The Catholic Guide to the Bible, The Catholic Catechism Book, We Pray: Living in God's Presence, We Live: To Know, Love and Serve God, We Worship: A Guide to the Catholic Mass, Christ's Mother and Ours: A Catholic Guide to Mary, The Privilege of Being Catholic, The Search for Happiness
Difficulty: Easy to moderate

Christ for Me | Mailbox Ministry

PO Box 1694, Tahlequah, OK 74465
www.christforme.org   cfm@christforme.org

Christ for Me offers a comprehensive selection of bible studies, ranging from child-level easy to college-level difficulty, all part of the *Mailbox Club International* series. They will provide a bible to any student in need. If course is too easy or difficult, they will send you a study on your level.

Courses: Over 75 courses. 4 of their courses are college level (see below)
Difficulty: Easy to difficult.

Available Courses

BASIC KNOWLEDGE

A Country Called Heaven
My New Life in Christ I
My New Life in Christ II
My New Life in Christ III

INTERMEDIATE KNOWLEDGE

Practical Christian Living
Love, Dating and Marriage
Basic Bible Truths
Fishers of Men
Winning the Race of Life
Romans
God's Great Salvation
Basic Bible Doctrine
The Lordship of Christ
Study in the Book of Ephesians
A Study in Exodus
The Gospel of John
The Revelation of Jesus Christian

The Three Epistles of John
The Epistle to the Hebrews
Developing a Devotional Lifestyle

ADVANCED COURSES

Journey of a Lifetime
Journey Through the Tabernacle
Journey to the Cross
Journey into the Heavenlies
Journey From the Beginning
Journey Into Spirit-filled Living
Journey Into Discipleship
Journey to a Faithful Finish
Journey to a Practical Faith
Journey from Tragedy to Triumph
Journey to a Bold Obedience
Journey to Your Spiritual Gift
Journey Into Assurance
Journey Into Knowing God
Journey Into Hope
Journey Into Success
Deepening Your Spiritual Roots

Journey Into Pleasing God
Journey From Confusion to Celebration
Journey Into Kingdom Secrets
Journey Into Better Relationships
Journey Into God's Applause
Journey Into Intimacy With God
Journey Into Joy
Journey Into Knowing What God Wants You To Be
Journey From Religion to Relationships
Journey Into Renewal
Journey Into Christlikeness
Journey Into the Spirit World
Journey Into Servanthood

COLLEGE LEVEL COURSES

A Passion for God's Word
Essential Truths 1 : Living With God
Essential Truths 2: Walking With God
Essential Truths 3: Working With God

Crossroad Prison Ministries

PO Box 900, Grand Rapids, MI 49509-0900
(800) 668-2450, (616) 530-1300
www.crossroadbibleinstitute.org

Crossroads Bible Institute connects students with mentors who help you study the Bible. They offer more than a dozen different correspondence Bible study courses that each contain up to 14 lessons. A bible is provided upon request. Courses are available in Spanish.

Courses: Over a dozen course options.
Difficulty: Moderate.
These in-depth courses take, on average, 4 to 6 years to complete them in their entirety.

Discover Bible School

PO Box 308, Georgetown, TN 37336

Discover Bible School provides printed bible studies to prisoners. They offer 27 small lessons designed to discover answers to hundreds of Bible questions.

Courses: 27 lessons containing Christian and bible-themed subjects.
Difficulty: Easy

Emmaus Correspondence School | ECS Prison Ministries

PO Box 1028. Dubuque, IA 52004-1028
(563) 585-2070
www.ecsministries.org   ecsorders@ecsministries.org

ECS Prison Ministries is one of the largest correspondence ministry schools in the country. They offer courses in more than 120 languages to over 100 countries. Their prison correspondence courses are available in over 70 courses in both English and Spanish. But they can provide other language materials if needed.

A bible is awarded upon completion and grades over 90 are eligible for college credit that can be used at *Louisiana Baptist University*.

Courses: Over 70 courses containing Christian and bible-themed subjects.
Difficulty: Moderate. These are in-depth courses.

Exodus Prison Ministry

PO Box 6363, Lubbock, TX 79493
(806) 791-3673
www.exodusprisonministry.org

Exodus Prison Ministry is a non-denominational Christian ministry. They offer 35 studies, which are mailed one to three at a time with additional reading materials. They provide postage-paid envelopes for return of answer sheets.

Courses: 35 study books from various authors containing Christian and bible-themed subjects.
Difficulty: Moderate. These are in-depth courses.

Available Courses

A Life That's Real	Galatians
How To Study Your Bible	Our Nearest Kinsman
Winning Your War Against Satan	Elisha
John: An Eyewitness Report	God Unveils The Future
Christians On The Move	The All-Sufficient Christ: Colossians
The Art Of Personal Witnessing	Esther
Major Bible Doctrines	Philippians
Checkpoints Of The Christian Life (John 1)	Ephesians (2 books)
Necessity Of Prayer	Jonah Speaks Today
Genesis I	Why Christians Suffer?
Genesis II	Joseph
Genesis III	Job (2 books)
Portraits Of Christ In Tabernacle, Vol I	Elijah (2 books)
Portraits of Christ In Tabernacle, Vol II	Proverbs (2 books)
Discovering The Will Of God	Present Labor, Future Rewards
Romans I	Revelations I
Romans II	Revelations II
The Holy Spirit And The Believer	

Global University | School for Evangelism & Discipleship

1211 South Glenstone Avenue
Springfield, Missouri 65804-0315
(800) 433-0315, (417) 862-9533
www.globaluniversity.edu   berean@globaluniversity.edu

Global University School for Evangelism and Discipleship presents a very high quality basic understanding of the gospel for those seeking to know God's Word. They help new believers explore foundational topics on Christian living, including prayer, Bible study, and worship. Certificates and diplomas are offered upon request.

These courses are available in over 100 languages; however, they are only FREE in English & Spanish.

Tuition Rates:	These courses are FREE for prisoners. (Typically, these courses are priced from $5 to $10 each, and $5 shipping per book.)
Time Limits:	None

Global University School for Evangelism and Discipleship
Available Courses

Request one at a time, beginning with the first course in each series. Upon completion the next course will be mailed to you.

THE GOAL OF THIS SERIES IS TO INTRODUCE JESUS CHRIST AS THE SAVIOR FOR ALL PEOPLE.

The Great Questions of Life

Highlights in the Life of Christ

Pathways for Turbulent Times

Challenge to Encounter

We Hear the Prophets

THIS SERIES IS WRITTEN FOR THOSE SEEKING ANSWERS ABOUT GOD BASED ON DIFFERENT WORLDVIEWS, SUCH AS ISLAM, SPIRITISM, MATERIALISM, POSTMODERNISM, EASTERN MYSTICISM, AND CATHOLICISM.

Is Jesus God?

The Right Path

The Greatest Miracle

Searching for Answers

I Am God

The Spirit World

Freedom from Karma

Absolutes or Not

The Counterfeit Wealth

Global University School for Evangelism and Discipleship
Discipleship Courses

Designed to personally engage new believers in how to grow in their relationship with Christ and fellow Christians. There are two series developed for discipleship. The Christian Life Series, designed to equip believers to reach their communities with the gospel and prepare for further studies in Christian Service, and the 21st-Century Discipleship Series, created as a devotional.

THIS SERIES CONSISTS OF THREE BOOKS WITH SIX LESSONS EACH. STUDENTS WHO STUDY ONE LESSON PER WEEK WILL FINISH THE SERIES IN EIGHTEEN WEEKS.

UNIT ONE	UNIT TWO	UNIT THREE
Your New Life	When You Pray	God's Design – Your Choice
Your Bible	How to Study the Bible	John's Gospel
Who Jesus Is	Your Helpful Friend	We Believe
The Church	Christian Worship	What Churches Do
Personal Evangelism	Christian Workers	The Teaching Ministry
Bible Ethics	Marriage and the Home	The Christian in the Community

THIS SERIES CONSISTS OF THREE BOOKS WITH THIRTEEN LESSONS EACH. STUDENTS WHO STUDY ONE LESSON PER WEEK WILL FINISH THE SERIES IN THIRTY-NINE WEEKS.

Book One: Getting Started
Book Two: Facing Issues
Book Three: Making a Difference

Global University School for Evangelism and Discipleship
Training | Christian Service Series

Students can earn a Christian Service Diploma by completing all eighteen courses.

UNIT ONE	UNIT TWO	UNIT THREE
Christian Maturity	Prayer and Worship	The Responsible Christian
Kingdom, Power, and Glory	Tents, Temples, and Palaces	Understanding the Bible
Cornerstones of Truth	Alive in Christ	Counselor, Teacher, and Guide
The Christian Church in Ministry	Starting New Churches	Helping Christians Grow
Spiritual Gifts	Preaching and Teaching	Sharing the Good News
Solving Life's Problems	People, Tasks, and Goals	Abundant Living

Gospel Echoes Team Association

PO Box 255, Goshen, Indiana 46527-0555
(675) 533-0221
www.gospelechoes.com   info@gospelechoes.com

Gospel Echoes is an organized nationwide group of teams that offer a moderately easy bible correspondence study course. At the end of the courses, prisoners receive a personalized bible with their name engraved on the cover.

They also offer scripture address booklets, a simplified New Testament study bible, as well as other support services to prison chaplains.

Courses: 8-Series, 99 lesson Christian-themed course: God's Great Love; Growing in the Christian Life; Sharing Your Christian Faith; Growing Toward Maturity; The Christian Way in Marriage; Growing Through Bible Study; Good News About Jesus; and The Acts of the Apostles
Difficulty: Easy

Gospel Express Ministries

PO Box 217, Lynn, NC 28750

Gospel Express Ministries is a Christian prison ministry that offers two different courses of study. The first one is based on the book of Romans and includes five books. After completing the first four courses, you can choose from between two books as a reward. The second course of study, called *The Touch of His Hand,* has three books and is a more basic study about the Lord's Prayer

Courses: Easy to moderate. First course covers the book of Romans, which consists of five study books. Once you complete the course, you can select
Difficulty: Easy. Courses take 2-5 years to complete in their entirety.

Lamp and Light Publishers

26 Road 5577, Farmington, NM 87401-1436
(505) 632-3521

Lamp and Light Publishers offer a number of courses to prisoners for free that would normal require a fee. The first course will arrive with your inquiry.

They provide a certificate of completion after each course and will reward you with a book as your studies progress.

Lessons are available in English, Spanish, French, German, and Portuguese.

Courses: 14 courses containing over 140 lessons on Christianity (see below)
Difficulty: Easy. Courses take 2-5 years to complete in their entirety.

Available Courses

The First Step	Studying His Word
Steppingstones to God	Praying to Him
Footprints of Christ	Committed to Him
Seven Steps too Obedience	Managing His Money
In Step with the Prince of Peace	Christian Brotherhood
The Faith Worth Dying For	Worshiping Him
Rewards of the Faithful	Fasting for His Glory
The Heavenly Pilgrimage	Discerning His Will
Building Christian Homes	Witnessing for Him
The Life of Christian Stewardship	Shepherding the Sheep
In the Beginning	Bearing Fruit for His Glory
So Were the Churches Established	

Loved Ones of Prisoners | LOOPs

PO Box 14953, Odessa, TX 79768
(432) 580-5667
www.loopsministries.com

LOOPs is a non-profit, non-denominational Christian corporation created for the support of prison inmates and their families. Their sole purpose is "Mending broken hearts through Jesus Christ" by application of God's word to physical, mental, social and spiritual problems. They offer several Bible correspondence courses as well as a monthly newsletter.

Courses: 19 courses on Christianity (see below)
Difficulty: Easy

Available Courses

Keys to Bible Study
Biblical Truth and How to Find It
Book of Acts
Book of Colossians
Book of 1st Corinthians
Book of 2nd Corinthians
Book of Ephesians
Essential Bible Truths
Book of Exodus
Book of Genesis
Book of Hebrews
Book of Job
Book of Philippians
Book of John
Book of Matthew
Book of Revelation (You must complete one other course before requesting the Book of Revelation.)
Book of Romans
Book of 1st Timothy
Book of 2nd Timothy

Lighthouse Ministries

PO Box 537
Copperhill, Tennessee 37317
(423) 496-7116
lighthouseminist@yahoo.com

Lighthouse Ministries offers prisoners and their family members a complete Bible Study consisting of 37 study booklets. They send Sunday School books and other gospel literature with each study lesson, and provide a *King James Version* of the Bible upon request.

Students who complete the course are encouraged to further their studies through a more intensive fee-based course through the *Landmark Bible Institute*, through which you can earn an English Bible Diploma (see separate listing in the *College Studies | Unaccredited* section).

Courses are available in English and Spanish.

Courses: 37-part Bible Study
Difficulty: Easy

Mount Hope Prison Ministry

25 Summit Avenue, PO Box 1511
Hagerstown, Maryland 21741-1511

Mount Hope Prison Ministry offers a 9-course Bible Study Program for prisoners and their families. The lessons are intended to be used with the *King James Version* of the Bible.

Courses: Basic Bible Beliefs; Walk the Talk; Gospel of John; Seeking and Searching; Through the Bible; Acts of the Apostles; Romans; Revelation; Genesis
Difficulty: Easy

Mount Zion Bible Institute

2603 West Wright Street, Pensacola, Florida 32505
(850) 438-1037
www.mountzion.org   school@mountzion.com

Mount Zion Bible Institute (MZBI) offers prisoners more than 60 courses, based mostly on Christian classics from prior centuries. No particular denomination is emphasized; the courses are designed to focus the student on the Bible as the Word of God. Certificates awarded upon completion of each course.

They offer a wide variety of FREE and fee-based literature in both English and Spanish. Free Bible upon request.

Courses: 60+ courses in five main areas of study (see next page)
Difficulty: Easy to advanced

Mount Zion Bible Institute
Available Courses

SALVATION	PRACTICAL WALK	GENERAL STUDY	
What is a Biblical Christian	Freedom from Bitterness	The Life of Jesus Christ	Baptism
Forgiveness	Divine Guidance	Joy in the Gospel of John	Infallible Word of God
Man's Ruin – God's Redemption	A Call to Prayer	Fundamentals of the Faith	Bible Doctrines Simply Explained
All of Grace	Spiritual Warfare	New Testament Survey	God's Astounding Grace
Biblical Repentance	At the Altar of Sexual Idolatry	The Church in History	God Reigns Over All
The True Gospel vs. the False Gospel	Thoughts for Young Men	Methods of Bible Study	Divinely Inspired Word
Look to Jesus	Profiting from the Word	Mark's Sketchbook of Christ	Sinners in God's Hand
Decisional Regeneration	Holiness	Story of the Puritans	Deity of Christ
Saving Faith: It's Meaning	Set Apart for Christ	Guide to Bible Study	Doctrines of Grace in John
	Biblical View of Self-Esteem	Old Testament Survey	London Confession of Faith
	Altar of Sexual Idolatry	Church Officers	Justification in Law
	Hidden Life of Prayer	Biblical Eldership	Sovereignty of God
	In the Footprints of the Lamb		
	The Walk of Repentance	**DOCTRINE**	**FOUNDATIONAL DOCTRINE**
	Minister's Self Watch	The Pilgrim's Progress	Gospel
	Spiritual Foundations of Ministry	Attributes of God	Justification
	To Preach Christ	The Holy Spirit	Substitution
		The Cross	Repentance
			Conversion
			Imputed Righteousness
			Doctrine of Sanctification

PMI Center for Biblical Studies | PMI Bible Institute

PO Box 177
Battle Creek, Michigan 49016-0177
(269) 282-9381

PMI Center for Biblical Studies offers a variety of courses that apply to basic Christian living. Every student begins with an 8-lesson study project called *Foundations of Faith*. They do NOT award a Certificate of Completion.

Courses: Knowing You Are Saved, Everyday Living, Understanding God, The Lordship of Jesus, Fellowship and Church, Giving and Tithing, Praying with Power, Victorious Christian Living
Difficulty: Easy

Prisoners for Christ Outreach Ministries

Bible Study Correspondence School
PO Box 1530, Woodinville, WA 98072-1530

Prisoners for Christ Outreach Ministries offers 130 Bible-based lessons, which are divided into two groups: Basic and Advanced curricula. Basic lessons are structured around gaining an understanding of Jesus and applying his teachings. Advanced lessons studies books of the New Testament with more depth.

A certificate of completion is awarded after each completed unit.

Courses: BASIC: Basic Beliefs, Parables of Jesus I/II, Study on Prayer, Sharing Your Faith, Men of the Bible I/II, Women of the Bible. ADVANCED: I/II Corinthians, Galatians, Ephesians, James, I/II/III John, Gospel of John, Philippians, Colossians.

Difficulty: Easy to intermediate

Rock of Ages Ministries | College of Biblical Studies

PO Box 4419
Dalton, GA 30719
(706) 459-3233
www.roapm.com   roacobs@gmail.com

The *Rock of Ages College of Biblical Studies and Theological Seminary* has been offering religious education since 1996. Until recently, they offered their college level studies to prisoners, but canceled them due to too many issues with prison policies. They now only offer prisoners Discipleship lessons, which are designed to take the student through the New Testament and some of the Old Testament. A Certificate of Completion is awarded with each lesson.

Courses: One course for each book of the New Testament and some Old Testament.

Difficulty: Moderate

Salvation Army | Continuing Education Center

1032 Metropolitan Parkway SW
Atlanta, Georgia 30310
www.salvationarmysouth.org/sce/biblecourses.html

The Salvation Army offers a wide range of quality bible study correspondence courses that engage the prisoner through question and answer format. The courses they provide for FREE are ones that other providers charge for.

Courses: Over 20 Christian and bible-themed courses

Difficulty: Easy to difficult. Courses are very in-depth.

Set Free Prison Ministries

PO Box 5440, Riverside, CA 92517
www.spiritualfreedom-setfree.org

Set Free Prison Ministries provides a number of Bible-themed correspondence opportunities for prisoners. They also distribute high-quality religious newsletters and magazines from *Moody Global Ministries* (see separate listing for Moody Bible Institute in the *College Studies* section.) Even if not interested in their course study, you can request to be placed on their mailing list for additional religious materials, including the monthly *Today in the Word* magazine.

Courses are available in English and Spanish

Courses: Several bible-themed courses.
Difficulty: Easy

Source of Light Ministries International

1011 Mission Road
Madison, Georgia 30650
(706) 342-0397
www.sourcelight.org   slm@sourcelight.org

Source of Light Ministries offers a wide variety of beginner bible-themed courses that provide a solid foundation for further religious study. Many of their courses offered for FREE are offered by other organizations for a fee.

Courses are offered in a variety of languages including Creole, French, Hungarian, Korean, Portuguese, Romanian, Russian, Spanish, and Tagalog.

They will provide a bible to any who need one and do provide a Certificate of Completion.

Courses: Over 18- lessons on Christianity and the bible (see below)
Difficulty: Easy

Available Courses

My New Life in Christ I	The Spirit World
My New Life in Christ II	God's Word – The Bible
My New Life in Christ III	Light from the Old Testament
Practical Christian Living	Mark
God's Great Salvation	John
Winning the Race of Life	Acts
Basic Bible Truths	Galatians
Fishers of Men	Know and Grow

Steinkamp Bible Study | Water of Life Community Church

14418 Miller Suite K, Fontana, CA 92336

Steinkamp Bible Study offers ten Bible lessons that are useful in gaining a basic understanding of bible principles and answers to commonly asked biblical questions.

They award a Certificate of Completion.

Courses: Ten lesson study: Learn How to Lead Others to Jesus, Learn How to Begin Your Life Anew, Learn the 4 Spiritual Laws, Study the Old Testament, Study the Nerw Testament, Easy Reading & Understanding, Learn Bible Facts, Non-Denominational, Are We Forgiven for Our Sins, and Bible, Tracts, Life-Changing Books and Certificates
Difficulty: Easy

United Prison Ministries International

890 County Road 93, PO Box 8, Verdana, Alabama 36091
(205) 755-4744
www.upmi.org   daphne.hunter@gmail.com

United Prison Ministries International provides spiritual literature that can be used for bible study and education. These are useful in gaining a basic understanding of bible principles and answers to commonly asked biblical questions.

They do NOT award a Certificate of Completion.

Courses: Bible Questions Answered (also available in Spanish); Bible Answers; Desire of Ages; Keys to Happiness; Bible Lessons: What the Bible Says.
Difficulty: Easy

FREE Buddhism Courses

Asian Classics Institute

7055 Juniper Drive, Colorado Springs, CO 80908
(212) 475-7752
www.world-view.org   aci@world-view.org

Asian Classics Institute offers prisoners with core studies in the teachings of Buddha, a condensed version of the Six Great Books of Buddhism. 15 formal study courses are offered one at a time, which include an audio tape or CD. Certificate of Proficiency offered upon completion.

Courses: 18 study courses covering the fundamentals of Buddhism
Difficulty: Easy to moderate

Available Courses

The following correspondence courses on the teachings of Buddha are free to prisoners. However, they will not be sent if you do not have access to a tape or CD player, since written materials will not make much sense without the tape/CD. You may need to go through the prison's chaplain services to receive these if your mail room is likely to reject them without a special arrangement.

Request one course at a time following each completion.

Course One | The Principle Teachings of Buddhism
Course Two | Buddhist Refuge
Course Three | Applied Meditation
Course Four | The Proof of Future Lives
Course Five | How Karma Works
Course Six | The Diamond-Cutter Sutra
Course Seven | The Bodhisattva Vows
Course Eight | Death & the Realms of Existence

Course Nine | The Ethical Life
Course Ten | A Guide to the Bodhisattva's Way of Life I
Course Eleven | A Guide to the Bodhisattva's Way of Life II
Course Twelve | A Guide to the Bodhisattva's Way of Life III
Course Thirteen | The Art of Reasoning
Course Fourteen | Lojong, Developing the Good Heart
Course Fifteen | What the Buddha Really Meant

Dharma Companions

PO Box 9254, Santa Rosa, California 95405-1254
www.dharmacompanions.wordpress.com

Courses: Variety of Buddhism-themed courses.

Kadampa Buddhism | Sarah Buddhist Center

PO Box 12037, San Francisco, CA 94112
www.kadampas.org

Courses: The teachings of a Geshe (Doctor of Theology).

FREE HINDU COURSES

American Gita Society, The

511 Lowell Place, Fremont, CA 94536
www.gita-society.com

The American Gita Society will provide a Bhagavad Gita for use with their studies.

Courses: Various studies on Gita.

International Pure Bhakti Yoga Society | IPBYS

PO Box 52724, Durham, NC 27717
www.prisonseva.org

IPBYS offers a bhakti-yoga (linking God through devotion) course based on spiritual life. They also offer a bi-monthly newsletter and various books, free of charge, based on the philosophy of bhakti yoga.

Courses: Monthly course called *Journey to Prema*, written by a prisoner on spiritual enlightenment.

Syda Yoga | Prison Project

PO Box 99140, Emeryville, CA 94662
(510) 428-1836
www.siddhayoga.org

NOTE: See separate listing in main Personal Enrichment Studies section.

Courses: 17-year Siddha yoga course

FREE Islam Courses

Islamic Education Center

2551 Massachusetts Ave. NW, Washington, D.C. 20008
(202) 332-8343
www.theislamiccenter.org

The Islamic Education Center will provide a Koran for use with studies.

Courses: Islamic study guides
Difficulty: Easy to difficult.

FREE Jewish Courses

Aleph Institute, The

9540 Collins Ave., Surfside, FL 33154
(305) 864-5553
www.alephinstitute.org

Courses: Jewish faith studies.

FREE Rosicrucian/Western Wisdom Courses

Rosicrucian Fellowship

International Headquarters
2222 Mission Avenue, Oceanside, California 92058
(760) 757-6600
www.rosicrucianfellowship.org   *rf@rosicrucianfellowship.org*

The Rosicrucian Fellowship offers the Western Wisdom Bible course, which begins by teaching the Rosicrucian Philosophy, a mystical belief involving spiritual astrology. Once you've completed the twelve lessons in the part of the course, you are become a member of the Fellowship and become a 'regular student', when you will begin receiving bi-monthly lessons. The course is free, however to take the course, students must purchase the textbook: The Rosicrucian Cosmo Concept for $25.

Course: Western Wisdom Bible course; Esoteric Christian Philosophy, Spiritual Astrology, Deeper Biblical Truths
Difficulty: Intermediate

HIGH SCHOOL STUDIES

If you have never gone to high school or if you dropped out of high school somewhere along the way, completing your high school education may be your first step toward getting a good education. While it is likely that your institution offers a program by which you can earn a GED, earning your high school diploma will provide a much higher quality education, one which will best prepare you for future educational opportunities, or just a future. You can attend college classes with only having earned a GED, but a high school education may drastically increase the odds of your success and enjoyment of the college or life experience. Fortunately, every prisoner is eligible to earn a high school diploma right from the comfort of their cell.

What to Expect from Correspondence High School

Correspondence high school education has been around since before our grandparents attended high school. Millions of students across the nation have received a home-schooled high school education from the same programs listed in this section. While many schools are now moving to internet-based learning, there is still enough interest in older home-school methods to encourage schools to continue offering high school diplomas in a way that happens to work for prisoners.

ACCREDITATION

As with any reliable and quality education, school accreditation is important. In the case of high school education, it is vital if you ever intend to further your learning through college-level studies. Colleges are not likely to accept your high school credentials for enrollment into their programs if the school you earned them from is not accredited. Therefore, most of the high schools listed in this section are regionally accredited and thus offer you quality educational opportunities.

Schools listed here that are not regionally accredited, such as Stratford Career Institute, may be useful if you are just looking to gain a better education beyond what a GED or self-study methods may provide. Just know that by enrolling in these high school diploma programs you are not actually gaining a high school diploma in the eyes of other education facilities or most employers.

HOW MUCH HIGH SCHOOL DO I NEED?

How many courses you need to take to earn you high school diploma depends on how much high school education you already have. If you went to high school but dropped out, it is likely that you have already earned some of the credits necessary to graduate. If you have not passed any high school classes in the past, you will likely have to start at the beginning, at ninth grade.

To earn a high school diploma, students are typically required to complete 18 units of credit, of which 13 are required courses and five are electives. Some schools require you to earn 21 to 24 credits to obtain a diploma. For college preparatory high school diploma programs, students likewise must earn 18 credits; however, only 3 of them are elective courses.

Each high school course counts for HALF a credit because each course takes roughly one semester of the two semesters required for each school year. That means that you will need to take between 36 and 48 classes for a complete high school education, depending on the school you choose.

Each school has different required courses, which typically includes variations of the following:

- ° Writing
- ° English
- ° Literature (American and World)
- ° Speech
- ° Science (Biology/Environmental)

- ° U.S. History
- ° Health/Physiology
- ° Social Civics (Government)
- ° Psychology

➤ To get a rough estimate of how many credits you still need, assume that you will need six credits for each year you did not go to high school.

For example, if you finished you freshmen year, you still have three years of high school left and will likely need to make up around 18 credits, or 36 classes.

Typical High School course requirements:

English: 4 Credits (8 courses)

Science: 3 Credits (6 courses)

Math: 3 Credits (6 courses)

Social Studies: 4 Credits (8 courses)

Health: 2 Credits (4 courses)

Electives: 5 Credits (10 courses)

NOTE: Requirements vary by school. Some schools will have more of less requirements in each or other subjects.

THE FOLLOWING IS A SAMPLE BREAKDOWN OF THE STANDARD HIGH SCHOOL CURRICULUM:

NINTH GRADE

2 English (i.e. Effective Reading Skills & Writing)
2 Math (i.e. Basic Math I & II)
2 Science (i.e. Health & Nutrition)
2 Social Studies (i.e. World Geography I & II)
Electives

TENTH GRADE

2 English
2 Math (i.e. Pre-Algebra I & II)
2 Science (i.e. Physical/Earth Sciences I & II)
2 Social Studies (i.e. World History I & II)
Electives

ELEVENTH GRADE

2 English
2 Math (i.e. Algebra I & II)
2 Science (i.e. Biology I & II)
2 Career Planning (i.e. Entrepreneurship I & II)
2 Social Studies (i.e. American History I & II)
Electives

TWELFTH GRADE

2 English (i.e. American Lit & Effective Speech)
2 Math (i.e. Geometry I & II)
2 Social Studies (i.e. American Government & World Cultures)
2 Financial Skills (i.e. Personal Finance & Econ)
Electives

PROGRAMS OF STUDY

Many high schools offer two or more programs of study that you can take, depending on your learning ambition. Typically, these include a general studies program and a college preparatory program.

General studies diploma programs are designed for students who intend to enter the job market or a community or technical college soon after graduation. It consists of fundamental courses taught at a basic high school level.

College preparatory diploma programs are designed for students who intend to go to college after graduation. The course of study consists of more challenging courses, especially in math and science. They will prepare students for the ACT and SAT exams, and for a four-year college education.

WHAT ARE AP COURSES?

Many schools offer Advanced Placement, or AP courses. AP courses are college-level courses taken as part of your high school curriculum. They typically require that you take prerequisite classes and, since they are intended to prepare you for college, are more difficult than the standard high school courses. In fact, by successfully completing these courses and the AP exams, you are eligible for college credit, which can be transferred to your college of choice when you continue your education beyond high school. AP courses provide a great means to get a jump-start on your next level of learning, your college education.

NOTE: While a few of the high schools listed in this section offer AP courses, most of these require some online access and therefore may be difficult to take from your institution. If you are considering AP courses, be sure to first check with your institution's education coordinator and the school to ensure that you will be able to complete these courses under your circumstances.

HOW DO I GET STARTED?

➢ **Go Browsing**

Browse the following schools to see what works best for your circumstances. Consider the tuition costs, additional fees, course offerings, and other information provided.

➢ **Get More Info**

Once you find a school that appeals to you, write to the school to get more information. They will send you everything you need to know to take courses from their school, which will help you make a more informed choice.

➢ **Apply**

After reviewing the program options, apply for admission to the program that best fits your needs and goals.

➢ **Pick Your Classes**

Either at the time of application, or after you apply, you will receive a welcome packet containing the courses available to you with instructions on how to proceed. Choose your courses.

➢ **Pass Your Courses**

Study hard and pass your courses in the time allowed. Typically, you will be allowed to complete the courses you take in as little as five weeks and no more than a full calendar year. A general course of study includes approximately 12 courses per year. However, it's not uncommon for a student to complete a full correspondence high school curriculum in as little as 2 years with dedicated study.

➢ **Graduate**

Complete all of the courses and get your high school diploma.

SCHOOL LISTING LAYOUT

CONTACT INFORMATION

This is the school's address and where you can go for more information on that school. There is always more information than we can provide concerning each school. We encourage you to contact every school you are interested in.

DESCRIPTION

Key details are provided about each school so that you are aware of information of note that may impact you as a prisoner-student.

ACCREDITATION

The following schools are all accredited by a variety of agencies, which are marked under each entry. As you've learned, accreditation is vital in determining the quality of a learning institution. But not all accrediting agencies are created equal. Therefore, you should exercise caution when selecting a school. (For a complete discussion on this topic, see section on *Accreditation* early in this book.)

AVAILABLE TO PRISONERS

This will keep you informed of what you can earn from this school, such as diplomas, degrees, and certificates. School offerings change regularly, which is why we update this book annually.

TUITION

This is the fee the school charges for courses, course credits, grade levels, and other programs.

PAYMENT PLANS

Many schools offer payment plans to make programs more affordable during study. Even if a payment plan is not listed, a school may be willing to work with you to develop an affordable plan that will work with your circumstances.

CREDIT TRANSFER/EXAM OPTIONS

If you have previously earned credits from another school, this section will tell you if this school may allow you to transfer those credits in. It will also let you know if they have credit-by-exam options.

TIME LIMITS

Schools generally place limits on how long you have to take a course. If you cannot complete your course in time, many schools offer extensions, often for a fee.

PROCTOR REQUIRED?

This area will tell you if a school require their examinations to be proctored (supervised by an impartial person.)

CANCELLATION POLICY

If you are unhappy with the school, or you determine that the courses you purchased are just not going to work for you, this section will tell you about the schools course refund policy.

AVAILABLE COURSES

This section provides information on the courses offered by the school, including courses available, descriptions, and prerequisites.

High School Recommendations

Schools, and what you want out of them, vary in so many ways the it is impossible to make an overall recommendation. Therefore, we leave that up to the accrediting agencies. However, one common interest among all prisoners is the quality of the communication between the outside world and your cell.

When researching schools. We send requests to each one as if we are prisoners. We want to know how they respond to your requests, which is a great guide in determining how well the school will work with you should you decide to enroll.

The following schools are recommended as institutions who stood out from the rest in how well they communicated, how accommodating they were to our requests for information, how comprehensive their sent information was, and how willing they were to work with prisoners. Starred "*" listings are exceptional in meeting the above criteria, proving that they have a good understanding of the unique challenges that prisoners face.

American School (not to be confused with American Academy of Pinecrest)
Citizens' High School
* University of Nebraska High School

No longer offering high school courses for prisoners.

The following schools have previously offered high school education options through paper-based courses, but have since converted to an 'online-only' option for their correspondence offerings.

If you do NOT have internet access through your prison, these schools will not be able to help you. If, however, your prison does provide internet access, you may be able to take study through these schools. If so, we've provided their contact info below:

Brigham Young University
120 Morris Center, Provo, UT 84602-0300
(801) 378-2868
elearn.byu.edu   indstudy@byu.edu

Ashworth College
6625 The Corners Parkway, Suite 500
Norcross, GA 30092
(800) 615-8232, (770) 729-8400
education@ashworthcollege.edu

Laurel Springs
302 West El Paseo Rd., Ojai CA 92023

**Texas Tech University |
Independent School District**
15th Street & University Avenue
PO Box 42191
Lubbock, Texas 79401
(806) 742-7101
www.ttuisd.ttu.edu   ttuisd@ttu.edu

American Academy of Pinecrest

Southpark Centre, 12651 South Dixie Highway, Miami, Florida 33156
www.diplomaathome.com

American Academy of Pinecrest offers an accelerated high school diploma program. A high school diploma is awarded – this is not a high school GED.

Although they state that they are accredited, they are not regionally accredited by an agency recognized by the U.S. Department of Education, which may make getting into some colleges difficult. Students who are planning on attending additional schooling after high school would be wise to check with their potential college of choice for acceptance of this high school or consider other options.

Accreditation: National Association for the Legal Support of Alternative Schools (NALSAS) and Accrediting Commission International (this agency is not recognized by the U.S. Department of Education or CHEA.)

AVAILABLE TO PRISONERS

Accelerated High School Diploma Program

Tuition Rates:	**$350.00 for entire course of study**
Payment Plans:	Down payment of $64 and $40 per month.
Textbook Fees:	Included in tuition.
Additional Fees:	Administrative fee: $25; Re-Exam fee: $25 (for students who do not average a 2.0 or higher by end of course.)
Cancellation Policy:	Full refund within 30 days of enrollment, less the administrative fee. No refund after 30 days.
Transfer Options:	N/A
Time Limitations:	None

American Academy of Pinecrest
Course Requirement

All students take a High School Qualifying Exam. In some cases, the exam, combined with credits for prior courses taken and life experience will earn the high school diploma.

Students not receiving credit for prior courses of life experience will take both the Qualifying High School Exam and at least on of the following high school subjects.

English Writing Skills
U.S. Constitution
History of the Bible

American School

2200 E. 170th Street, Lansing, Illinois 60438
(708) 418-2800
www.americanschoolofcorr.com   customerrelations@americanschool.org

American School is one of the largest correspondence high schools in the nation, and are accustomed to working with prisons. If you have a GED, you can apply credits towards the 9th grade portion of studies. They will also make an allowance for previous high school credits earned, with the exception of physical education, driver's education, religion, performing arts (chorus, drama, band, etc.) or ROTC.

Students who complete their high school education here will earn a high school diploma. American School also awards $21,000 annual scholarships to their students.

Accreditation: Middle States Association of Colleges & Schools Commission on Elementary & Secondary Schools (MSA-CESS)

AVAILABLE TO PRISONERS

General High School Diploma

College Preparatory High School Program

Independent Study Program

Tuition Rates:	**$120-240 per course, or by grade level** **Grades 9-12: $2,250** **Grades 10, 11 & 12: $1,800** **Grades 11 & 12: $1,350** **Grade 12 only: $900** **If sending payment in full at time of enrollment, student receives a refund of $50 to $100.**
Payment Plans:	Down payment of $150 to $250, $125 to $200 per month.
Textbook Fees:	Included in tuition.
Additional Fees:	None
Cancellation Policy:	Full refund within 10 days of enrollment. Full refund less $75 from 10 days up to first completed assignment. Additional fees apply depending on level of course completion. $100 reduction per verified credit.
Transfer Options:	Up to 13.5 units/credits may be applied towards either diploma track
Time Limitations:	4 years for full high school program

American School
Available Courses

ENGLISH AND LANGUAGE ARTS

English, Basic Grammar
Students learn the technology and structure of the English language in an easy-to-understand, step-by-step fashion. Parts of speech, sentence structure, choice and use of words, capitalization and punctuation are covered.

English 1
This course introduces three aspects of language arts: literature, grammar and composition. In the literature segments, students read short stories, poetry, folk tales and nonfiction. The emphasis is on enjoying and understanding various types of literature. In the grammar and composition lessons, students deal with parts of speech, characteristics of sentences and paragraph development. The course encourages the development of research and communication skills.

English 1: Understanding
Students review basic approaches to literature and fundamentals of grammar and composition before learning new information about these elements. In the literature lessons, students read short stories, essays, poetry, dramas, and an epic. The grammar and composition lessons help students improve communication abilities, and the course also teaches research skills.

English 2
Students continue to develop their skills in the three aspects of language arts. In the literature segments of the course, students read short stories, poetry, drama and tales of King Arthur and his Knights of the Round Table. In the grammar and composition lessons, students study the parts of speech, basic parts and characteristics of sentences, capitalization and punctuation, research skills and step-by-step development.

English 2: Understanding
Students review before learning new information about the fundamentals of grammar and composition, and the study of literature. In the literature lessons, students read short stories, nonfiction, essays and drama. The course allows students to continue their development of research, written and oral communication skills.

English 3
The historical development of American literature from the colonial period to 1900 is the central theme of this course. Students gain an understanding of the ideas that fostered the growth of the United States and the ways in which its literature became distinctively American. Students develop composition skills by analyzing the literary selections and applying the basic organizational pattern of a good essay. The course also covers modernist prose and poetry, and American nonfiction and drama. Writing is central to the course. Three written projects allow students to explain personal literary interpretations, develop fictional characters, and write creatively.

ALSO OFFERED: PRACTICAL ENGLISH & BUSINESS ENGLISH

Writing I
This course presents the basics of expository writing. Students learn, step-by-step, to write unified, coherent papers. While learning to write, students learn to think in an organized, systematic fashion. They also study effective uses of language, as well as methods of connecting ideas and expanding ideas by means of details and examples.

Writing II
This course is a comprehensive guide to writing. It contains four units, each devoted to trait-ideas, Organization, Sentence Fluency, and Word Choice. The optional trait of Presentation is also discussed. Students take objective assessments to measure their knowledge of the Six Traits and apply these skills in written projects. The course includes non-graded writing assignments that help students develop the graded projects.

Speech: How to Talk More Effectively
This one-semester introduction to public speaking will help students to become aware of such kinds of public speaking as informative and persuasive speaking, and to realize that public speaking involves both formal speeches to an audience and informal discussions with smaller groups of people. Students are also taken through step-by-step process for developing several kinds of formal speeches.

ALSO OFFERED: PUBLIC SPEAKING 1

LITERATURE

American Literature

This course is designed to foster in students the desire to read and the ability to express their ideas about what they read. Students read the books listed as required texts plus two more books they choose from an annotated book list. The themes appeal to the interests and concerns of teenagers. The reading material ranges from beginning to intermediate high school level. Books read include: Rascal; Sounder; The Pearl; To Kill a Mockingbird. and Bearstone.

British Literature

This course will examine literary contributions from many British authors. Students will read a variety of short fiction and essays. The course addresses common human themes, such as heritage and tradition in the British community.

Literature, Classic Adventure

This course is a survey of short fiction containing a sampling of short stories from the nineteenth and twentieth centuries. The course discusses the elements that make up prose fiction in addition to exploring human nature, encouraging philosophical thought, and interpreting social commentary.

Literature 1

This course provides an in-depth exploration of English and American literature. Poetry, short stories, drama, novels, and literary essays are analyzed. In addition to discussing works from each of these literary genres, the course concentrates on helping students to form their own interpretations of literary words.

Literature 2

This course emphasizes writing and literary analysis, teaching students to express their interpretations in written form. Poetry, short stories, novels drama and expository prose are covered.

ALSO OFFERED: LITERATURE 3 & 4 FOR COLLEGE PREPARATORY STUDIES

MATHEMATICS

Mathematics 1: Essential

This course is specifically designed for students who need to develop understanding and skill in using basic arithmetic. After studying the four basic operations (addition, subtraction, multiplication, and division of whole numbers), students learn to solve word problems involving these operations. Interpretation of word problems is covered thoroughly and understandably. Topics such as estimating, rounding and factoring are introduced to provide a foundation for further study in the second semester of basic mathematics.

Mathematics 2: Essential

After reviewing operations with whole numbers, students are introduced to fractions, operations with fractions and decimals, and problems involving money and percentages. Word problems are used extensively in this course to relate concepts to practical situations. Topics covered in the first semester of basic mathematics are thoroughly reviewed before further expansion and clarification. Students practice each concept in a step-by-step manner before moving on to more complex topics.

Business Math

In this course students will develop mathematical skills that apply to common business activities, operations and transactions. The topics include whole numbers, fractions, decimals, percentages, ratios, proportions, rounding, estimation and metric measurement. Business applications such as money records, wages and pay rates, job benefits, commissions, budgeting, and home and transportation costs are studied. Students will also study loans, credit cards, taxes, saving and borrowing money, stocks, bonds, insurance, basic statistics and graphs, and profit and loss. Students focus on developing mathematical skills.

Pre-Algebra 1

The course provides a "bridge" between the skills learned in General Math and those more advanced concepts students will learn in First Year Algebra and Geometry. This course provides an introduction to algebraic expressions and integers, decimals, factors, exponents, fractions, ratios and percentiles. It also provides an introduction to both algebraic concepts and geometry through an exploration of equation solving, inequalities, linear functions, graphing, spatial thinking, data analysis, probability, and nonlinear functions.

Algebra 1

In the first semester of this series, students will become familiar with basic algebraic concepts by using variables, function patterns, graphs, rational numbers to solve equations and inequalities with one or two variables. Students may need to use the equation editor feature or drawing tools in their word processing to complete the projects for electronic submission. Please be aware that students are responsible for learning to use these tools and for completing all parts of the projects prior to submission.

Algebra 2

Students will become familiar with systems of equations and inequalities, exponents and their functions, factoring, polynomials, radical expressions, combinations and permutations. Students may need to use the equation editor feature or drawing tool in their word processing to complete the projects for electronic submission. Please be aware that students are responsible for learning to use these tools and for completing all parts of the projects prior to submission.

Geometry 1

This course is designed to help students develop reasoning skills using geometric terms and processes, concepts of logic, and applied problem solving. Topics covered in this course include patterns, inductive and deductive reasoning, models, points, lines, coordinate plans, paralleled lines, measuring angles, basic constructions, reasoning and proofs, parallel and perpendicular lines, congruent triangles, and relationships within triangles. This course also develops reasoning skills using geometric terms and processes, concepts of logic, and applied problem solving. Topics covered in this course include quadrilaterals, ratios and proportions, right triangles and trigonometry, transformations, areas of polygons and circles, surface area and volume, and tangents, chords and arcs.

Precalculus

This course provides a detailed examination of algebraic and inverse functions, graphs, exponential and logarithmic functions, conic sections, matrices, determinants, complex numbers, and discrete algebra.

Trigonometry

A thorough discussion of trigonometric concepts and applications are presented in this course. Students study proofs of trigonometric identities, solutions, of right and oblique triangles, solutions of trigonometric equations and functions, vector applications and polar coordinates.

NATURAL SCIENCES

Health

In this course, students are introduced to medically accepted means of promoting physical and mental well-being. Among the subjects addressed are skills for living a healthy lifestyle, self-esteem, physical fitness and nutrition, the effects of alcohol and drugs on the human body, and disease prevention.

Earth Science

This course is the first in a two semester series that provides an introduction to the basic principles of physics, chemistry, Earth science, and space science. Students will use mathematics in these areas as well as logical methods and practical applications. Topics covered include the nature of science, motion, forces, Newton's Laws, energy, work and machines, electricity, magnetism, energy sources, waves, light, sound, Earth's internal processes, weather, and climate.

Physical Science

This course is the second in a two-semester series that provides an introduction to the basic principles of physics, chemistry, Earth science, and space science. Students will use basic mathematics in these areas as well as logical methods and practical applications. Topics covered include the properties and classification of matter, solids, liquids, and gases, chemical bonds and reactions, radioactivity and Earth in space, time and seasons, the Moon, the solar system and stars, galaxies and the cosmos. Both hands-on Labs and Virtual Labs that allow students to experience the application of concepts, interactions, and processes are included.

ALSO OFFERED: ENVIRONMENTAL EARTH & FORENSIC EARTH

Biology

Includes a basic understanding of biology, basic chemistry, structure of cells and how they communicate, energy conversions, cell reproduction, genetics, gene expression, genetic engineering, origin of life, changes in organisms, ecosystems and succession, environmental problems and solutions, and the classification of living things. Students will also study fundamental biological concepts as they explore the structure and function of bacteria, viruses, fungi, and plants. They will investigate the diversity and development of invertebrate and vertebrate animals and learn about the anatomy and physiology of the human body.

Chemistry

The course presents an introduction to principles and procedures in chemistry. Students study scientific measurements, chemical names and formulas, states of and changes in matter, numerical relationships in chemical reactions, trends expressed in the periodic table and the behavior of gasses. Students calculate empirical and molecular formulas, write and balance equations, determine mole and mass, interpret chemical equations and gain insight into the various models of the atom. Also focuses on chemical bonding, water and solutions, reaction rates and equilibrium, acids, bases and salts, oxidation-reduction reactions and carbon compounds.

Physics

Physics represents a continuing effort to solve problems and interpret experience in a logical way. This first semester course encourages students to observe and relate physics principles to the world around them and investigate various physical phenomena related to forces, vectors Newton's laws of motion, acceleration, velocity, resistance and projectile motion. They will also learn about gravitational fields, satellite motion, special relativity, momentum, and inertia. Students will explore the world they live in through the properties of matter: elements, solids, liquids, and gases.

Anatomy and Physiology

Anatomy and Physiology is a detailed study of the human body, its parts and structures, and how these function together to create and sustain human life. In this course we will start with an introduction to terminology, human development, and body processes, then move on to the functioning of cells, tissues, and systems. With these basics to build on students will compile an extensive vocabulary of complete understanding of the human body.

ALSO OFFERED: PHYSIOLOGY & HEALTH

SOCIAL STUDIES

Sociology

Sociology is the study of the behavior of people in groups. In this course, students learn about the social development of individuals in a society and consider the effects that culture, language and status have on this development. Special attention is given to mechanisms of social control and to forces of social change. By analyzing social institutions and examining contemporary social problems, students develop an understanding of the characteristics of social interaction in a complex, modern society.

Psychology

This introduction to psychology covers a broad range of topics, including learning processes, the development of personality, mental and emotional problems, the psychology of group behavior and social attitudes. Studying these topics helps students develop an awareness and an understanding of the many forces that influence their behavior.

World Geography

Geography allows people to find the answers to their questions about the world and understand the link between people and places. While studying about physical and human geography of the United States, Canada, Latin America, Europe, Asia, Australia, the island nations of the Pacific, Antarctica and Africa, students will explore the relationships between people and their physical environment, and analyze the interactions between the culture and geography of selected regions. physical features. Students will learn valuable information about the world we inhabit today including how and where people live, and how their lives are changing in response to their physical environment, their governments, and their economic systems.

World History

This course is an introduction to world history that traces human development from ancient times to the beginning of the eighteenth century. Students will learn the facts, concepts, and principles they need to gain a better grasp on the history, culture, political, social, and economic development of many different societies around the globe. Special attention is given to the civilizations that developed in the Middle East, India, China, Africa, and Latin America as well as those in Europe and North America. Finally, this course will examine the global political, social, and economic issues, as well as international relations in today's world.

U.S. History

This course traces the major historical developments in the United States from 1900 to the present. Students examine the causes and effects of the Industrial Revolution, immigration, reform movements, the two world wars and other historical phenomena that have influenced American society since the Civil War. Social history is emphasized throughout.

Social Civics: Government

Students learn about the functions, powers and structures of the three branches of the national government of the United States. They consider the constitutional systems of separation of powers and checks and balances. In addition, students examine the role that the national government plays in the solution of specific foreign and domestic problems.

VISUAL AND PERFORMING ARTS

Art: Drawing Animals
This course provides an introduction to the visual art of drawing animals.

Art: Drawing Landscapes
This course provides an introduction to the visual art of drawing landscapes.

Music Appreciation
Music is often described as a universal language because it exists in all cultures. This course approaches music from a global perspective. Students will learn to notice cultural influences on music while exploring the common human ideas that music addresses. They will analyze the musical traditions of Western Europe, Asia, India, Africa, Latin America, South America and the United States. They will learn about the significance of music from multiple perspectives: as art, a science, and a business.

ALSO OFFERED:

Photography & Digital Photography

WORLD LANGUAGES

French 1
In this first-year course, students are introduced to the basic grammatical concepts necessary to develop reading and writing skills in French. They become acquainted with French culture through a variety of reading and writing skills in French. They become acquainted with French culture through a variety of readings in both French and English. Students can also develop speaking and listening skills by hearing and speaking French themselves. The course covers basic sentence structure of positive and negative statements, commands and questions, and present and future tenses. Audio files are embedded in the online course and are available on an Audio CD for offline use. Textbook: French English/ English French Dictionary.

French 2
This course reinforces and augments the grammatical concepts presented in First Year French. Students build new vocabulary, learn more advanced grammar concepts, increase their reading, writing, and listening skills, and develop their knowledge of many essential parts of speech including the past tense, direct object pronouns, and a number of commonly used French idioms and expressions. Audio files are embedded in the online course and are available on an Audio CD for offline use.

Latin 1
The Latin readings for this course, adapted from ancient history and mythology, deal with the Trojan war and the story of Aeneas and his journey to Italy. Students work intensely on nouns, adjectives and verbs; study first, second and third declension nouns in all cases; and learn to form the six tenses of Latin verbs in the active voice for all four conjugations. Audio files are embedded in the online course and are available on an Audio CD for offline use.

Spanish 1
Through this course students develop a good grasp of Fundamental Spanish grammar that enables them to read simple stories and compose simple paragraphs. Basic sentence structure, parts of speech and regular and irregular verbs in the present tense are covered in this course, and students will develop vocabulary related to clothing, the home, time, weather, the calendar, numbers, and family relationships. Students also develop an understanding of culture and geography of Mexico and other Spanish-speaking areas. Audio files allow the students to listen to words and phrases as they are used in everyday life. Audio files are embedded in the online course and are available on an Audio CD for offline use.

Spanish 2
Students increase their vocabulary, their understanding of grammatical constructions, and their ability to read and write Spanish during this second year course through discussions of such diverse topics as entertainment, food, geography, and travel. Audio files and interactive activities, and the preterit tense. Audio files are embedded in the online course and are available on an Audio CD for offline use.

BUSINESS, CAREER & TECHNICAL

Business Communication
This course will discuss workplace communications, including speeches, presentations, office etiquette, business letters, emails, resumes, job applications, etc. Students will learn how to present themselves effectively in formal situations and learn real-life skills that will help them succeed in the business world.

ALSO OFFERED:

BUSINESS LAW, BUSINESS MATH, COMPUTERS, KEYBOARDING & SOCIAL MEDIA

Consumer Economics
This course provides an overview of how economic systems function and teaches the students about their rights and responsibilities as consumers. Students learn steps for making responsible economic decisions. They also study the basics of personal money management, including the budgeting, saving, investing, credit, housing and transportation costs, and insurance. The course is practical, "real world" guide for consumers in the twenty-first century.

Economics
In this challenging course students gain an understanding of basic economic concepts by examining historical and current examples of economic principles at work. They study the role and workings of the market in modern capitalistic economies and analyze how government controls the market systems in free societies.

Life Management Skills
This course is designed to provide students with hands-on experience in researching careers, making short-term, middle-term, and long-term goals, identifying job opportunities, applying for jobs, and conducting successful interviews. Students will have an opportunity to build a personal portfolio, and they will also learn about workplace relations and personal money management. Students can assess their skills, interests, values, aptitudes, and personalities to determine individual career possibilities.

Office Procedures
This course is designed to help students develop skills in major office functions that will be important in their future careers as either employees or business owners. Students will acquire skills they need to adapt to new office procedures and technologies while becoming aware of their interests, strengths, and weaknesses related to the demands of an office environment. Topics covered include written and oral communications, information, and professional development and career management.

Thinking & Learning Strategies
This course is designed to improve study skills, habits and attitudes through experimentation with new study procedures and through application of established study methods.

Introduction to Technology | TECH 003 256 (0.5 credits/5 hours)

ALSO OFFERED:

Accounting
Automotive Systems
Blueprint Reading
Building Trades
Carpentry
Child Care
Clothing
Drafting
Electricity
Fashion & Interior Design
Food Study
Home Planning & Decorating
Home Repair & Maintenance
Parenting

Citizens' High School

188 College Drive, PO Box 66089
Orange Park, Florida 32065-6089
(904) 276-1700, (800) 736-4723
www.citizenshighschool.com   inforequests@citizenshighschool.com

Citizens' High School offers high-school education. They do not offer as many course options (only 20 courses in 7 subjects) as other correspondence schools, and their courses tend to be on the more basic side. However, they are a cheaper option than most.

Elective courses include Life management and Business options.

They offer a 30-day money back satisfaction guarantee as well as an SAT/ACT Exam Assistance Program.

A certificate of completion is awarded with each course completion.

Accreditation: Distance Education Accrediting Commission (DEAC)

AVAILABLE TO PRISONERS

General Studies High School Diploma

Academic Studies High School Diploma

Independent Study Courses

Tuition Rates:	**$179 per course** **$716 per academic year (4 courses each year)**
Payment Plans:	$179 down payment, $99 to $179 per month (your choice) or $716 down payment, $716 per academic year
Textbook Fees:	Included in tuition
Additional Fees:	**$10 mailing fee per course (or $40 per academic year)**
Cancellation Policy:	Full refund within 30 days of enrollment; 5 days to first lesson submission 80%; other percentages based on number of courses completed
Transfer/Exam Options:	Transfer options are available
Time Limits:	3 years per diploma program, 1 year per individual course; $20 for a 12-month extension

Citizen's High School
Available Courses

ENGLISH

English, Basic Grammar

Students learn the technology and structure of the English language in an easy-to-understand, step-by-step fashion. Parts of speech, sentence structure, choice and use of words, capitalization and punctuation are covered.

English 1

This course introduces three aspects of language arts: literature, grammar and composition. In the literature segments, students read short stories, poetry, folk tales and nonfiction. The emphasis is on enjoying and understanding various types of literature. In the grammar and composition lessons, students deal with parts of speech, characteristics of sentences and paragraph development. The course encourages the development of research and communication skills.

Literature 1

This course provides an in-depth exploration of English and American literature. Poetry, short stories, drama, novels, and literary essays are analyzed. In addition to discussing works from each of these literary genres, the course concentrates on helping students to form their own interpretations of literary words.

Literature 2

This course emphasizes writing and literary analysis, teaching students to express their interpretations in written form. Poetry, short stories, novels drama and expository prose are covered.

MATHEMATICS

Applied Mathematics

This course is specifically designed for students who need to develop understanding and skill in using basic arithmetic. After studying the four basic operations (addition, subtraction, multiplication, and division of whole numbers), students learn to solve word problems involving these operations. Interpretation of word problems is covered thoroughly and understandably. Topics such as estimating, rounding and factoring are introduced to provide a foundation for further study in the second semester of basic mathematics.

Consumer Math

In this course students will develop mathematical skills that apply to consumer activities, operations and transactions. The topics include whole numbers, fractions, decimals, percentages, ratios, proportions, rounding, estimation and metric measurement. Business applications such as money records, wages and pay rates, job benefits, commissions, budgeting, and home and transportation costs are studied. Students will also study loans, credit cards, taxes, saving and borrowing money, stocks, bonds, insurance, basic statistics and graphs, and profit and loss. Students focus on developing mathematical skills.

Algebra 1

In the first semester of this series, students will become familiar with basic algebraic concepts by using variables, function patterns, graphs, rational numbers to solve equations and inequalities with one or two variables. Students may need to use the equation editor feature or drawing tools in their word processing to complete the projects for electronic submission. Please be aware that students are responsible for learning to use these tools and for completing all parts of the projects prior to submission.

Algebra 2

Students will become familiar with systems of equations and inequalities, exponents and their functions, factoring, polynomials, radical expressions, combinations and permutations. Students may need to use the equation editor feature or drawing tool in their word processing to complete the projects for electronic submission. Please be aware that students are responsible for learning to use these tools and for completing all parts of the projects prior to submission.

Geometry

This course is designed to help students develop reasoning skills using geometric terms and processes, concepts of logic, and applied problem solving. Topics covered in this course include patterns, inductive and deductive reasoning, models, points, lines, coordinate plans, paralleled lines, measuring angles, basic constructions, reasoning and proofs, parallel and perpendicular lines, congruent triangles, and relationships within triangles. This course also develops reasoning skills using geometric terms and processes, concepts of logic, and applied problem solving. Topics covered in this course include quadrilaterals, ratios and proportions, right triangles and trigonometry, transformations, areas of polygons and circles, surface area and volume, and tangents, chords and arcs.

HISTORY

U.S. History
This course traces the major historical developments in the United States from 1900 to the present. Students examine the causes and effects of the Industrial Revolution, immigration, reform movements, the two world wars and other historical phenomena that have influenced American society since the Civil War. Social history is emphasized throughout.

Social Civics: Government
Students learn about the functions, powers and structures of the three branches of the national government of the United States. They consider the constitutional systems of separation of powers and checks and balances. In addition, students examine the role that the national government plays in the solution of specific foreign and domestic problems.

World History
This course is an introduction to world history that traces human development from ancient times to the beginning of the eighteenth century. Students will learn the facts, concepts, and principles they need to gain a better grasp on the history, culture, political, social, and economic development of many different societies around the globe. Special attention is given to the civilizations that developed in the Middle East, India, China, Africa, and Latin America as well as those in Europe and North America. Finally, this course will examine the global political, social, and economic issues, as well as international relations in today's world.

SCIENCE

Biology
Includes a basic understanding of biology, basic chemistry, structure of cells and how they communicate, energy conversions, cell reproduction, genetics, gene expression, genetic engineering, origin of life, changes in organisms, ecosystems and succession, environmental problems and solutions, and the classification of living things. Students will also study fundamental biological concepts as they explore the structure and function of bacteria, viruses, fungi, and plants. They will investigate the diversity and development of invertebrate and vertebrate animals and learn about the anatomy and physiology of the human body.

Earth Science
This course is the first in a two semester series that provides an introduction to the basic principles of physics, chemistry, Earth science, and space science. Students will use mathematics in these areas as well as logical methods and practical applications. Topics covered include the nature of science, motion, forces, Newton's Laws, energy, work and machines, electricity, magnetism, energy sources, waves, light, sound, Earth's internal processes, weather, and climate.

Physical Science
This course is the second in a two-semester series that provides an introduction to the basic principles of physics, chemistry, Earth science, and space science. Students will use basic mathematics in these areas as well as logical methods and practical applications. Topics covered include the properties and classification of matter, solids, liquids, and gases, chemical bonds and reactions, radioactivity and Earth in space, time and seasons, the Moon, the solar system and stars, galaxies and the cosmos. Both hands-on Labs and Virtual Labs that allow students to experience the application of concepts, interactions, and processes are included.

FOREIGN LANGUAGES

French
In this first-year course, students are introduced to the basic grammatical concepts necessary to develop reading and writing skills in French. They become acquainted with French culture through a variety of reading and writing skills in French. They become acquainted with French culture through a variety of readings in both French and English. Students can also develop speaking and listening skills by hearing and speaking French themselves. The course covers basic sentence structure of positive and negative statements, commands and questions, and present and future tenses. Audio files are embedded in the online course and are available on an Audio CD for offline use.   Textbook: French English/ English French Dictionary.

Spanish
Through this course students develop a good grasp of Fundamental Spanish grammar that enables them to read simple stories and compose simple paragraphs. Basic sentence structure, parts of speech and regular and irregular verbs in the present tense

are covered in this course, and students will develop vocabulary related to clothing, the home, time, weather, the calendar, numbers, and family relationships. Students also develop an understanding of culture and geography of Mexico and other Spanish-speaking areas. Audio files allow the students to listen to words and phrases as they are used in everyday life. Audio files are embedded in the online course and are available on an Audio CD for offline use.

Cornerstone Christian Correspondence School

15938 U.S. Highway 17
Townsend, GA 31331
(912) 832-3834
cornerstonechristianministry.org *info@cstoneschool.org*

Cornerstone Christian Correspondence School was established in 1996 to help busy adults to obtain their high school diploma through the mail. Students order a series of five tests that cover the main courses of study, which will be taken under the supervision of a proctor (subjects include Language Arts, Writing Skills, Social Studies, Science & Mathematics). If the student passes with a grade of 70 or better, a high school diploma is awarded. If a course snot passed, a study guide will be mailed and the student will retake the test until a passing grade is achieved.

Although they state that they are accredited, they are not regionally accredited by an agency recognized by the U.S. Department of Education, which may make getting into some colleges difficult. Students who are planning on attending additional schooling after high school would be wise to check with their potential college of choice for acceptance of this high school or consider other options.

Accreditation: They claim accreditation by Accrediting Commission International (ACI), but this agency is not recognized by the U.S. Department of Education or CHEA.

AVAILABLE TO PRISONERS

General Studies High School Diploma

Tuition Rates:	$75 for entire program
Payment Plans:	none
Textbook Fees:	none
Additional Fees:	Enrollment fee: $25 Retesting fee: $15
Cancellation Policy:	No refunds
Transfer/Exam Options:	Not applicable
Time Limits:	None

Hadley School for the Blind

700 Elm Street
Winnetka, Illinois 60093-2554
(800) 323-4238, (847) 446-8111
www.hadley.edu   info@hadley.edu

Hadley School for the Blind offers tuition-free high school education to legally blind and the visually impaired and their family members.

Most courses are currently available in English Braille American edition (EBAE). Newly developed courses are transcribed into Unified English Braille (UEB) and audio.

An eye report from your medical provider is required to verify your impairment prior to admission into the school.

Accreditation: Distance Education Accrediting Commission (DEAC), North Central Association of Colleges and Schools | The Higher Learning (NCA-HLC)

AVAILABLE TO PRISONERS

High School Diploma studies for the visually impaired

Tuition Rates:	**Free for those who qualify for admission to the school (visually impaired)**
Payment Plans:	Not applicable
Textbook Fees:	Not applicable
Additional Fees:	Not applicable
Transfer/Exam Options:	Up to 12 units
Time Limits:	4 years per diploma program

Hadley School for the Blind
Available Courses

ENGLISH

Basic English Skills 1 & 2
Elements of Poetry
English Composition
Literature: Drama
Literature: Nonfiction
Literature: Fiction
Punctuation
Spelling: Word Study

MATHEMATICS

Abacus 1 & 2
Practical Math 1 & 2
Pre-Algebra 1 & 2
Algebra 1 & 2

SCIENCE

Life Science
Physical Science
Health
Human Eye 1 & 2
Earth & Space Sciences

SOCIAL STUDIES

American Government
U.S. History: Discovery to the
Jacksonian Era
U.S. History: The Nineteenth Century
U.S. History: World Wars
U.S. History: Post-World War Years
World History

BRAILLE

Braille Literacy 1: Tactile Reading
Braille Literacy 2: Learning the
Alphabet
Braille Literacy 3: Uncontracted Braille
Braille Literacy 4: Contracted Braille
Braille Music Reading
The Essentials of the Nemeth Code
Everyday Reading in UEB

TECHNOLOGY

Internet Concepts
Web Browsing
Typing & Keyboarding

BUSINESS CONCEPTS & SKILLS

Finding Employment
Business Communications
Business Writing
Business Law 1 & 2
Effective Listening

INDEPENDENT LIVING

Diabetes: Toward Self-Management
Independent Living Series
Managing Personal Finances
Personality Psychology
Staying Safe: Emergencies & Disasters
Personal Safety: Self Defense Strategies
Self-Esteem & Adjusting with Blindness
Guide Dogs

PARENTING SERIES

Parenting: Preparation
Parenting: Infancy
Parenting: Early Years

LANGUAGE

Conversational Spanish 1 & 2

RECREATION

Chess for Beginners
Chess: Principles & Strategies
Container Gardening

Keystone High School

920 Central Road
Bloomsburg, Pennsylvania 17815-9982
(800) 255-4937, (570) 784-5220
www.keystoneschoolonline.com   info@keystonehighschool.com

Keystone High School provides quality educational opportunities for prisoners, with a number of elective course options, although on the higher end of the cost spectrum. Unfortunately, most of their college preparatory (advanced placement) courses are only available online.

Accreditation: Middle States Association of Colleges and Schools | Commission on Secondary Schools; AdvancED

AVAILABLE TO PRISONERS

High School Diploma

Tuition Rates:	**$349 per full credit (year-long) course**
	$249 per half credit (semester) course
Payment Plan:	25% Down Payment and either 4, 6, or 9 equal monthly payments for the remainder, depending on total purchase price
Textbook Fees:	Most are included in tuition
Additional Fees:	**Administration Fee: $25 (if using a payment plan); Shipping Fee: $20 per course**
Cancellation Policy:	Full refund within 5 days of enrollment; 5 days to first lesson submission full refund minus $75; other percentages based on the number of courses completed
Transfer/Exam Options:	Transfer/Exam options are allowed
Time Limit:	12 months

Keystone High School
Available Courses

The following courses are all print-based and can be used to earn sufficient credits toward a high school diploma IF you already have some high school credits. Several other courses are offered (mainly languages, electives and AP courses), but they are only available online and therefore cannot be taken by most prisoner students. This may prevent you from being able to earn a full high school diploma solely from this school.

ENGLISH

World Literature
Creative Writing
English I, II, III
Grammar and Composition

WORLD HISTORY

American Government
Civics
U.S. History
Geography
Economics

MATHEMATICS

Algebra I, II
Calculus
Consumer Math
Geometry
Pre-Algebra
Pre-Calculus
Refresher Math
Trigonometry

HEALTH

Health
Lifetime Fitness
Psychology

SCIENCE

Biology
Chemistry
Earth Science
Environmental Science
Life Science
Physical Science
Physics

BUSINESS LAW

Marketing
Working for Success
Skills for Success

ART AND MUSIC APPRECIATION

Fine Art
Art Appreciation
Music Appreciation

Penn Foster Career Center

925 Oak Street
Scranton, Pennsylvania 18515
(570) 342-7701
www.pennfosterhighschool.edu   info@pennfosterhighschool.edu

Penn Foster is one of the largest correspondence schools in the country, offering a large variety of education options, including High School Diplomas

Accreditation: MSCS, Distance Education Accrediting Commission (DEAC)

AVAILABLE TO PRISONERS

High School Diploma

High School Diploma with Health Care Concentration

Tuition Rates:	**$1,295 per program**
Textbooks Fees:	Included in tuition
Additional Fees:	Not applicable
Transfer/Exam Options:	Up to 16 credits may be transferred
Time Limits:	One year, $75 per 6-month extension

Penn Foster Career Center
Available Course Topics

Art	Mathematics
Biology	Music
Career	Nutrition
Chemistry	Orientation
English Literature	Psychology
Geography	Science
History	Social Science
Human Relations	Spanish

Southeastern High School

3241 Executive Way, Suite 400
Miramar, Florida 33025
(800) 285-3514

Southeastern High School, formerly the *Continental Academy*, offers an economical alternative to correspondence High School education, with a money-back guarantee.

Accreditation: Southern Association of Colleges & Schools | Commission on Colleges (SACS-COC)

AVAILABLE TO PRISONERS

High School Proficiency Diploma (not suitable for college, only for employment purposes)

Tuition Rates:	**$350 for whole program**
Payment Plans:	$40 down payment, $40 per month (total $395)
Textbook Fees:	Included in tuition
Additional Fees:	Not applicable
Transfer/Exam Options:	Not applicable
Time Limits:	Not applicable

Earn your High School Proficiency Diploma by taking one 24 credit test!

The test will include: English, Mathematics, Science, Social Studies, General Studies.

Access to a teacher via phone available.

The school supplies you with a study guide.

Multiple-Choice Test is an Open-Book Exam.

Stratford Career Institute

1 Champlain Commons, Unit 3, PO Box 1560
Saint Albans, Vermont 05478
(800) 556-4559
www.sci-careers.com

Stratford Career Institute (SCI) offers diploma and certification programs in a number of areas, including a High School education, but they are not an accredited school.

This diploma will not be accepted by most colleges.

If you're looking for the education without a diploma, this is a relatively economical option. Their tuition fee is all-inclusive with convenient payment plans.

(See Vocational Studies for other SCI offerings.)

Accreditation: NONE

AVAILABLE TO PRISONERS

High School "Diploma"

Tuition Rates:	**$989 for entire program** **(they regularly offer a $300 discount)**
Payment Plans:	$20 down payment, 18 monthly payments of $37.16
Textbook Fees:	Included in tuition
Additional Fees:	None
Cancellation Policy:	Full refund within 5 days of enrollment; 5 days to first lesson submission, 80% refund; other percentages based on the number of courses completed
Transfer/Exam Options:	Not applicable
Time Limits:	Not applicable

Stratford Career Institute
Available Courses

High School Diploma

A comprehensive program that allows adult students to earn their High School Diploma. All required subjects are included in the curriculum: English, Science, Math, History, Government, Social Studies, and electives.

Beware: This institution is not accredited and therefore any diploma will likely not be accepted by most colleges.

Thompson Rivers University

BC Center for Open Learning, 3rd Floor
805 TRU Way
Kamloops, British Columbia, V2C 0C8 Canada
(800) 663-9711, (250) 852-7000
www.truopen.ca   student@tru.ca

Thompson Rivers University is British Columbia, Canada's primary distance education provider. They offer Adult Basic Education (ABE) certificate courses. ABEs are Canada's equivalent of high school education in the U.S. If you are looking to gain the equivalent of a high school education, this may be an option worth considering. However, if you are considering continuing your education beyond high school, beware. Because the school is located in Canada, some post-secondary colleges may not accept their high school equivalency credentials.

Prisoners can call them toll free to discuss options (Monday – Friday 8:00am to 4:40pm (Pacific Standard time))

Accreditation: Association of Universities and Colleges of Canada

AVAILABLE TO PRISONERS

High School equivalent certificates and diplomas, including:
ABE Intermediate Certificate (10th grade equivalency)
ABE Advanced Certificate (11th grade equivalency)
BC Adult Graduation Diploma (High School Diploma equivalency)

Tuition Fees:	**$181 per credit** (Canadian dollars)* (**$143.24** U.S. dollars) **(Most courses will cost $429.73 each** (U.S. dollars)**)**
Payment Plan:	None
Textbook Fees:	Most are included in tuition
Additional Fees:	**Application fee: $24** (U.S. dollars) **Non-resident fee: $24.06 per credit** (U.S. dollars)
Cancellation Policy:	Full refund if canceled within the 5 months of enrollment, void after first assignment submission.
Transfer/Exam Options:	Transfer and assessment exam options are available
Time Limit:	Varies by course

*Tuition Fee based on recent Canadian-to-U.S. Currency exchange rate of $0.79 (as of July 20, 2017)

Thompson Rivers University
Adult Basic Education (ABE) Certificates & Diploma Programs

ABE INTERMEDIATE CERTIFICATE (EQUIVALENT TO A 10TH GRADE EDUCATION)

Reading and Writing English | ENGL 0401
Intermediate Mathematics | MATH 0401
Science (select one):
Consult with Program Advisor
One elective of choice:
Consult with Program Advisor

ABE ADVANCED CERTIFICATE (EQUIVALENT TO AN 11TH GRADE EDUCATION)

Advanced English Skills | ENGL 0501
Advanced Mathematics | MATH 0523
Science (select two):
General Biology | BIOL 0501
Principles of Chemistry | CHEM 0501
Introductory Physics | PHYS 0501

BC ADULT GRADUATION DIPLOMA
(EQUIVALENT TO A 12TH GRADE EDUCATION. WITH INTERMEDIATE & ADVANCED CERTIFICATIONS, STUDENT IS ELIGIBLE FOR A HIGH SCHOOL EQUIVALENT DIPLOMA.)

English (select one):
Introduction to Literature | English 0601
Survey of British Literature | ENGL 0641

Mathematics (select one):
Advanced Mathematics | MATH 0523
Accounting I | ACCT1211 (not recommended if going to college)

Electives (select three):
Provincial Biology | BIOL 0601
Survey of British Literature | ENGL 0641 (if not already taken)
Pre-Calculus | MATH 0633
Senior Physics | PHYS 0601
Others may be available. Consult Program Advisor.

Thompson Rivers University
Available Courses

ACCOUNTING

Accounting I | ACCT1211

Students develop the ability to record business transactions and prepare financial statements for a small business enterprise. Topics include accounting and the business environment; adjusting and closing entries and completing the accounting cycle; merchandising accounting; accounting information systems; internal control and cash; receivables; property, plant and equipment; goodwill and intangible assets; and current liability.

BIOLOGY

General Biology | BIOL 0501

General Biology includes a basic understanding of biology, basic chemistry, structure of cells and how they communicate, energy conversions, cell reproduction, genetics, gene expression, genetic engineering, origin of life, changes in organisms, ecosystems and succession, environmental problems and solutions, and the classification of living things.

Provincial Biology | BIOL 0601

Topics include cell biology, photosynthesis and cellular respiration, human anatomy and physiology, and genetics. The course is concerned primarily with human biology.

CHEMISTRY

Principles of Chemistry | CHEM 0501

The course presents an introduction to principles and procedures in chemistry. Students study scientific measurements, chemical names and formulas, states of and changes in matter, numerical relationships in chemical reactions, trends expressed in the periodic table and the behavior of gasses. Students calculate empirical and molecular formulas, write and balance equations, determine mole and mass, interpret chemical equations and gain insight into the various models of the atom. This course contains both hands-on labs and multimedia activities to provide an in-depth investigation into the subjects presented.

ENGLISH

Reading and Writing English | ENGL 0401

This course presents the basics of reading and writing English. Students learn, step-by-step, to write unified, coherent papers. While learning to write, students learn to think in an organized, systematic fashion. They also study effective uses of language, as well as methods of connecting ideas and expanding ideas by means of details and examples.

Advanced English Skills | ENGL 0501

Students review before learning new information about the fundamentals of grammar and composition, and the study of literature. In the literature lessons, students read short stories, nonfiction, essays and drama. The course allows students to continue their development of research, written and oral communication skills.

Introduction to Literature | English 0601

This course is designed to foster in students the desire to read and the ability to express their ideas about what they read. Students read the books listed as required texts plus two more books they choose from an annotated book list. The themes appeal to the interests and concerns of teenagers. The reading material ranges from beginning to intermediate high school level.

Survey of British Literature | ENGL 0641

In this course, students further their understanding of the historical development of English literature as they read selections by major authors of the Romantic age, the Victorian era and the 20th century. They apply and improve their writing skills as they analyze the many facets of the literary selections they read.

MATHEMATICS

Intermediate Mathematics | MATH 0401

Students develop an understanding of fractions, decimals and percentages, and develop skills using these operations. They learn to handle data through graphs, scientific notation and means of comparison; and they apply their understanding of concepts, operations and data to practical problems in interest, insurance, taxes, banking and budgeting.

Advanced Mathematics | MATH 0523

Advanced Mathematics begins with a review of the number system and the basic operations of addition, subtraction, multiplication, and division. Next students will learn about lines, angles, triangles, and finding volume, surface area, and area of shapes. Lastly, the course will focus on formulas and equations. Students will learn how to solve linear algebraic equations and graphing inequalities.

Pre-Calculus | MATH 0633

This course provides a detailed examination of algebraic and inverse functions, graphs, exponential and logarithmic functions, conic sections, matrices, determinants, complex numbers, and discrete algebra.

PHYSICS

Introductory Physics | PHYS 0501

Physics represents a continuing effort to solve problems and interpret experience in a logical way. This first semester course encourages students to observe and relate physics principles to the world around them and investigate various physical phenomena related to forces, vectors Newton's laws of motion, acceleration, velocity, resistance and projectile motion. They will also learn about gravitational fields, satellite motion, special relativity, momentum, and inertia. Students will explore the world they live in through the properties of matter: elements, solids, liquids, and gases. This course includes both hands-on and virtual lab activities and projects.

Senior Physics | PHYS 0601

Principle topics are kinetics in one and two dimensions; dynamics; energy; momentum and equilibrium; electricity; magnetism; and quantum physics.

University of Nebraska | High School

PO Box 888440
Lincoln, Nebraska 68588-8400
(866) 700-4747   (402) 472-3388
www.highschool.nebraska.edu   highschool@nebraska.edu

The *University of Nebraska* (UNHS) provides extensive quality high school and college preparatory curriculum options for prisoners. Unfortunately, many of their AP courses require online access.

They partner with the University of Nebraska at Omaha (UNO) to offer students the opportunity to earn college credit UNHS courses. By completing approved courses in the program, students receive an official UNO transcript for the course as well as high school credit.

Accreditation: Nebraska Department of Education; AdvancED

AVAILABLE TO PRISONERS

High School Diploma

Tuition Rates:	**$200 per ½ credit (semester) course** **$400 per language course** **Nebraska residents receive a 15% discount**
Payment Plan:	None
Textbook Fees:	Not included in tuition
Additional Fees:	**Administration Fee: $50 per course** **Mail Processing: $15 per course**
Cancellation Policy:	Refunds are allowed up to 30 days after course enrollment, less processing costs of $30 per course and $15 for other fees.
Transfer/Exam Options:	Transfer/Exam Options are allowed. $30 evaluation fee applies.
Time Limit:	12 months. $35 per 3-month extension
Proctor Required?	Yes

University of Nebraska High School
Available Courses

BUSINESS

Winning in the Workplace | BUSH 031 055 (0.5 credits/5 hours)

This course provides an overview of the entire employment experience. It prepares students for a job search, explains the application process, and discusses the situations that workers face. The course stresses both the rights and responsibilities of employees, emphasizing personal money management, workplace safety, insurance, liability, and strategies for investing.

Personal Finance and Economics | BUSH 033 059 (0.5 credits/5 hours)

This course provides an overview of how economic systems function and teaches the students about their rights and responsibilities as consumers. Students learn steps for making responsible economic decisions. They also study the basics of personal money management, including the budgeting, saving, investing, credit, housing and transportation costs, and insurance. The course is practical, "real world" guide for consumers in the twenty-first century.

Economics | Bush 035 060 (0.5 credits/5 hours)

In this challenging course students gain an understanding of basic economic concepts by examining historical and current examples of economic principles at work. They study the role and workings of the market in modern capitalistic economies and analyze how government controls the market systems in free societies.

Entrepreneurship | Bush 037 055 (0.5 credits/5 hours)

This course introduces students to the idea of starting their own business. Students learn about basic economic concepts as they study different types of businesses and learn about what is involved in starting and managing each of them. Main topics include business communication, ethics, marketing, strategies. Activities ask students to create and evaluate original ideas for new businesses and products.

Office Practices | Bush 038 055 (0.5 credits/5 hours)

This course is designed to help students develop skills in major office functions that will be important in their future careers as either employees or business owners. Students will acquire skills they need to adapt to new office procedures and technologies while becoming aware of their interests, strengths, and weaknesses related to the demands of an office environment. Topics covered include written and oral communications, information, and professional development and career management.

Ethics in the Workplace | Bush 039 055 (0.5 credits/5 hours)

In this course, students learn about ethical principles and study ways to apply those principles at work. The course examines interpersonal relations, as well as business practices such as marketing, lending and advertising. Environmental protection and fair employment practices are also discussed. Ethics in the Workplace prepares students to compete in the business world while following standards of honesty, fairness and responsibility.

Business Communications | Bush 043 056 (0.5 credits/5hours)

This course will discuss workplace communications, including speeches, presentations, office etiquette, business letters, emails, resumes, job applications, etc. Students will learn how to present themselves effectively in formal situations and learn real-life skills that will help them succeed in the business world.

CAREER PLANNING

Career Planning: Learning, Earning and Living Skills | CPLH 003 057 (0.5 credits/5 hours)

This course is designed to provide students with hands-on experience in researching careers, making short-term, middle-term, and long-term goals, identifying job opportunities, applying for jobs, and conducting successful interviews. Students will have an opportunity to build a personal portfolio, and they will also learn about workplace relations and personal money management. Students can assess their skills, interests, values, aptitudes, and personalities to determine individual career possibilities.

Everyday Etiquette | FCSH 001 259 (0.5 credits/5 hours)

Everyday Etiquette is designed to help the student deal with the stresses and strains experienced in this technologically advanced, population-dense society. This course provides an introduction to the use of proper etiquette in communications and personal actions at home, in school, in the community, and in the workplace. This course will help the student learn how to respect the viewpoints, cultural styles, and customs of others and behave in ways which promote harmonious relations in all situations.

Study Skills | STSH 001 256 (0.5 credits/5 hours)

This course is designed to improve study skills, habits and attitudes through experimentation with new study procedures and through application of established study methods.

Introduction to Technology | TECH 003 256 (0.5 credits/5 hours)

Technology pervades nearly every aspect of our lives and includes any use of human knowledge to extend our abilities, solve problems, meet needs, or make things easier or more efficient. This course provides an introduction to the history and nature of six general types of technology. Through it students will explore how technology works, including the design process, problem solving, outcomes, and applications. Students will investigate how technology is changing the fields of communication, biotechnology, manufacturing, construction, transportation, and energy and power. They will also explore related careers that are part of these fields.

ENGLISH AND LANGUAGE ARTS

Basic Grammar | ENGH 001 257 (0.5 credits/5 hours)

Students learn the technology and structure of the English language in an easy-to-understand, step-by-step fashion. Parts of speech, sentence structure, choice and use of words, capitalization and punctuation are covered.

Intermediate Grammar | ENGH 002 257 (0.5 credits/5 hours)

This course challenges students with an in depth study of grammar. Students review parts of speech and usage, sentence patterns, basic punctuation and capitalization. They study clauses, phrases and sentence problems; and complex pronoun, verb and adverb forms.

Effective Reader Skills | ENGH 005 059 (0.5 credits/5 hours)

This course helps students become more effective readers by emphasizing strategies that will help improve basic language and literacy skills. They study central themes, main ideas, major and minor details, inferences, fact, opinion, context clues and vocabulary.

American Literature Studies | ENGH 011 056 (0.5 credits/5 hours)

This course is designed to foster in students the desire to read and the ability to express their ideas about what they read. Students read the books listed as required texts plus two more books they choose from an annotated book list. The themes appeal to the interests and concerns of teenagers. The reading material ranges from beginning to intermediate high school level. Books read include: Rascal; Sounder; The Pearl; To Kill a Mockingbird. and Bearstone.

Multicultural Literature | ENGH 015 061 (0.5 credits/5 hours)

This course will examine literary contributions from many cultural groups. Students will read a variety of short fiction and essays. The course addresses common human themes, such as heritage, identity, gender, race, traditions, and community. Students will study the importance of these themes to different groups in society.

Short Stories | ENGH 019 058 (0.5 credits/5 hours)

This course is a survey of short fiction containing a sampling of short stories from the nineteenth and twentieth centuries. The course discusses the elements that make up prose fiction in addition to exploring human nature, encouraging philosophical thought, and interpreting social commentary.

Basic Expository Writing | ENGH 023 056 (0.5 credits/5 hours)

This course presents the basics of expository writing. Students learn, step-by-step, to write unified, coherent papers. While learning to write, students learn to think in an organized, systematic fashion. They also study effective uses of language, as well as methods of connecting ideas and expanding ideas by means of details and examples.

Writing for Success | ENGH 025 056 (0.5 credits/5 hours)

This course is a comprehensive guide to writing, concentrating on the "6+1 Traits" of writing. The course contains six units, each devoted to trait-ideas, Organization, Sentence Fluency, Word Choice, Voice, and Convention. The optional trait of Presentation is also discussed. Students take objective assessments to measure their knowledge of the Six Traits and apply these skills in written projects. The course includes non-graded writing assignments that help students develop the graded projects.

Ninth Grade English 1: Introduction to Language Arts | ENGH 031 059 (0.5 credits/5 hours)

This course introduces three aspects of language arts: literature, grammar and composition. In the literature segments, students read short stories, poetry, folk tales and nonfiction. The emphasis is on enjoying and understanding various types of literature. In the grammar and composition lessons, students deal with parts of speech, characteristics of sentences and paragraph development. The course encourages the development of research and communication skills.

Ninth Grade English 2: Beginning Grammar and Composition | ENGH 032 059 (0.5 credits/5 hours)

Students review basic approaches to literature and fundamentals of grammar and composition before learning new information about these elements. In the literature lessons, students read short stories, essays, poetry, dramas, and an epic. The grammar and composition lessons help students improve communication abilities, and the course also teaches research skills.

Tenth Grade English 1: Intermediate Language Arts | ENGH 035 059 (0.5 credits/5 hours)

Students continue to develop their skills in the three aspects of language arts. In the literature segments of the course, students read short stories, poetry, drama and tales of King Arthur and his Knights of the Round Table. In the grammar and composition lessons, students study the parts of speech, basic parts and characteristics of sentences, capitalization and punctuation, research skills and step-by-step development.

Tenth Grade English 2: Intermediate Grammar & Composition | ENGH 036 059 (0.5 credits/5 hours)

Students review before learning new information about the fundamentals of grammar and composition, and the study of literature. In the literature lessons, students read short stories, nonfiction, essays and drama. The course allows students to continue their development of research, written and oral communication skills.

Eleventh Grade English 1: Early American Literature | ENGH 039 059 (0.5 credits/5 hours)

The historical development of American literature from the colonial period to 1900 is the central theme of this course. Students gain an understanding of the ideas that fostered the growth of the United States and the ways in which its literature became distinctively American. Students develop composition skills by analyzing the literary selections and applying the basic organizational pattern of a good essay.

Eleventh Grade English 2: Modern American Literature | ENGH 040 059 (0.5 credits/5 hours)

The course covers modernist prose and poetry, and American nonfiction and drama. Writing is central to the course. Three written projects allow students to explain personal literary interpretations, develop fictional characters, and write creatively.

Twelfth Grade English 1: Early British Literature | ENGH 043 059 (0.5 credits/5 hours)

Students read many of the great works from the Anglo-Saxon period through the eighteenth century. They gain an understanding of the development of English literature as they study Shakespeare's Macbeth, and selections from Beowulf, The Canterbury Tales, and Paradise Lost. Students work on improving their writing skills by preparing papers that analyze the literary works.

Twelfth Grade English 2: Modern British Literature | ENGH 044 059 (0.5 credits/5 hours)

In this course, students further their understanding of the historical development of English literature as they read selections by major authors of the Romantic age, the Victorian era and the 20th century. They apply and improve their writing skills as they analyze the many facets of the literary selections they read.

Effective Speech Communication | ENGH 047 059 (0.5 credits/5 hours)

This one-semester introduction to public speaking will help students to become aware of such kinds of public speaking as informative and persuasive speaking, and to realize that public speaking involves both formal speeches to an audience and informal discussions with smaller groups of people. Students are also taken through step-by-step process for developing several kinds of formal speeches.

Advanced Placement English Literature and Composition 1 | ENGH 071 056 (0.5 credits/5 hours)

This course provides an in-depth exploration of English and American literature. Poetry, short stories, drama, novels, and literary essays are analyzed. In addition to discussing works from each of these literary genres, the course concentrates on helping students to form their own interpretations of literary words. Advanced Placement Literature and Composition 1 is the first course in a two-course sequence designed to prepare students for the College Board Advanced Placement English Literature and Composition Examination. Accordingly, the written projects in the course emphasize the analysis of literary experts, and the course devotes much time to the use and interpretation of literary devices. While this course helps prepare students for College Board Examination, this examination is NOT required for completion of Advanced Placement Literature and Composition 1. This course has been authorized by College Board. Purchase of the printed course syllabus is recommended for study beyond course completion.

Advanced Placement English Literature and Composition 2 | ENGH 072 056 (0.5 credits/5 hours)

Advanced Placement English Literature and Composition 2 is the second course in a two-course sequence designed to prepare students for the College Board Advanced Placement English Literature and Composition Examination. The course emphasizes writing and literary analysis, teaching students to express their interpretations in written form. Poetry, short stories, novels drama and expository prose are covered. In addition to the graded assignments, the course includes many non-graded activities that will prepare students for the College Board examination. Books read include: Hard Times; On Liberty; The Canterbury Tales.

HEALTH AND PHYSICAL EDUCATION

Health and Wellness | HLTH 001 256 (0.5 credits/5 hours)

There is more to a healthy lifestyle than nutrition and exercise. This course is an in-depth exploration of the basic aspects of health and wellness, including skills for making healthy choices and managing stress. Students will learn the importance of physical fitness and nutrition, investigate the effects that drugs and medicines have on their health, and discover strategies for disease prevention.

Introduction to Health Care | HLTH 025 055 (0.5 credits/5 hours)

Health care services make up one of the largest industries in the United States. The number of possible career jobs in health care is exploding rapidly today, and the need for health care professionals continues to grow. This course will provide you with the knowledge and tools you can use to determine if a career in health care is for you! Whether choosing to work directly with patients, or providing support services, all careers in the health care industry are important, rewarding, and provide benefits to others.

MATHEMATICS

Basic Math 1 | 001 255 (0.5 credits/5 hours)

This course is specifically designed for students who need to develop understanding and skill in using basic arithmetic. After studying the four basic operations (addition, subtraction, multiplication, and division of whole numbers), students learn to solve word problems involving these operations. Interpretation of word problems is covered thoroughly and understandably. Topics such as estimating, rounding and factoring are introduced to provide a foundation for further study in the second semester of basic mathematics.

Basic Mathematics 2 | MTHH 002 255 (0.5 credits/5 hours)

After reviewing operations with whole numbers, students are introduced to fractions, operations with fractions and decimals, and problems involving money and percentages. Word problems are used extensively in this course to relate concepts to practical situations. Topics covered in the first semester of basic mathematics are thoroughly reviewed before further expansion and clarification. Students practice each concept in a step-by-step manner before moving on to more complex topics.

General Mathematics 1 | MTHH 005 256 (0.5 credits/5 hours)

Students develop an understanding of fractions, decimals and percentages, and develop skills using these operations. They learn to handle data through graphs, scientific notation and means of comparison; and they apply their understanding of concepts, operations and data to practical problems in interest, insurance, taxes, banking and budgeting.

General Mathematics 2 | MTHH 006 256 (0.5 credits/5 hours)

General Mathematics 2 begins with a review of the number system and the basic operations of addition, subtraction, multiplication, and division. Next students will learn about lines, angles, triangles, and finding volume, surface area, and area of shapes. Lastly, the course will focus on formulas and equations. Students will learn how to solve linear algebraic equations and graphing inequalities.

Business Math 1 | MTHH (0.5 credits/5 hours)

In this course students will develop mathematical skills that apply to common business activities, operations and transactions. The topics include whole numbers, fractions, decimals, percentages, ratios, proportions, rounding, estimation and metric measurement. Business applications such as money records, wages and pay rates, job benefits, commissions, budgeting, and home and transportation costs are studied.

Students will need access to a scanner to submit the projects for this course electronically.

Business Math 2 | MTHH (0.5 credits/5 hours)

In this course students will study loans, credit cards, taxes, saving and borrowing money, stocks, bonds, insurance, basic statistics and graphs, and profit and loss. Students focus on developing mathematical skills. Case studies are used extensively so that concepts are related to everyday business and personal situations. Any basic-function or business calculator may be used with this course.

Pre-Algebra 1 | MTHH 021 255 (0.5 credits/5 hours)
Pre-Algebra 1 is the first course of a two-semester Pre-Algebra series. The course provides a "bridge" between the skills learned in General Math and those more advanced concepts students will learn in First Year Algebra and Geometry. This course provides an introduction to algebraic expressions and integers, decimals, factors, exponents, fractions, ratios and percentiles. The course is designed to build upon what students already know, and provide them the background and readiness for Algebra and Geometry.

Pre-Algebra 2 | MTHH 022 255 (0.5 credits/5 hours)
In Pre-Algebra 2 students will gain a solid preparation for both algebra and geometry. The second semester of the Pre-Algebra series, this course provides an introduction to both algebraic concepts and geometry through an exploration of equation solving, inequalities, linear functions, graphing, spatial thinking, data analysis, probability, and nonlinear functions. The course is designed to introduce algebraic thinking skills and to connect the concepts to arithmetic skills that students already know. This course provides a "bridge" to First Year Algebra and Geometry by building on the mathematical concepts and skills students need.

First Year Algebra 1 | MTHH 031 060 (0.5 credits/5 hours)
In the first semester of this series, students will become familiar with basic algebraic concepts by using variables, function patterns, graphs, rational numbers to solve equations and inequalities with one or two variables. Students may need to use the equation editor feature or drawing tools in their word processing to complete the projects for electronic submission. Please be aware that students are responsible for learning to use these tools and for completing all parts of the projects prior to submission.

First Year Algebra 2 | MTHH 032 060 (0.5 credits/5 hours)
In the second semester of this algebra series, students will become familiar with systems of equations and inequalities, exponents and their functions, factoring, polynomials, radical expressions, combinations and permutations. Students may need to use the equation editor feature or drawing tool in their word processing to complete the projects for electronic submission. Please be aware that students are responsible for learning to use these tools and for completing all parts of the projects prior to submission.

Geometry 1 | MTHH (0.5 credits/5 hours)
This course is the first of two courses designed to help students develop reasoning skills using geometric terms and processes, concepts of logic, and applied problem solving. Topics covered in this course include patterns, inductive and deductive reasoning, models, points, lines, coordinate plans, paralleled lines, measuring angles, basic constructions, reasoning and proofs, parallel and perpendicular lines, congruent triangles, and relationships within triangles. Frequent skill checks, guided practice sections, and reviews will help ensure that students get the most from this course. Career connections sections in every lesson help students learn more about career choices. This course uses many of the problem solving skills and equations learned in First Year Algebra.

Geometry 2 | MTHH 036 059 (0.5 credits/5 hours)
This course is the second of two courses designed to help students develop reasoning skills using geometric terms and processes, concepts of logic, and applied problem solving. Topics covered in this course include quadrilaterals, ratios and proportions, right triangles and trigonometry, transformations, areas of polygons and circles, surface area and volume, and tangents, chords and arcs. Frequent skill checks, guided practice sections, and reviews will help ensure that students get the most from this course. Career connections sections in every lesson help students learn more about career choices. This course uses many of the problem solving skills and equations learned in First Year Algebra.   Students who have not completed at least one year of algebra may need to review linear and quadratic equations and relationships.

Advanced Algebra 1 (2nd Year Algebra 1) | MTHH 039 058 (0.5 credits/5 hours)

This course is the first in the Advanced Algebra series. It builds and expands on the concepts and tools learned in earlier algebra courses to evaluate and graph functions and equations with two or more variables, differentiate between expressions, equations, inequalities, and absolute values, use the quadratic formula to write and solve quadratic equations and functions, solve radical functions, and work with matrices.

Advanced Algebra 2 (2nd Year Algebra 2) | MTHH 040 058 (0.5 credits/5 hours)

This course is the second in the Advanced Algebra series. It builds on the tools and principles learned in earlier algebra and geometry courses, including solving and graphing exponential and logarithmic functions, simplifying expressions, solving equations, graphing geometric shapes, working with arithmetic and geometric sequences, probabilities, and trigonometric equations. A graphing calculator is required for this course. NOTE: This course is equivalent to Algebra II (2nd semester).

Precalculus 1: Analytic Geometry and Algebra | MTHH 043 059 (0.5 credits/5 hours)

This course provides a detailed examination of algebraic and inverse functions, graphs, exponential and logarithmic functions, conic sections, matrices, determinants, complex numbers, and discrete algebra.

Precalculus 2: Trigonometry | MTHH 044 059 (0.5 credits/5 hours)

A thorough discussion of trigonometric concepts and applications are presented in this course. Students study proofs of trigonometric identities, solutions, of right and oblique triangles, solutions of trigonometric equations and functions, vector applications and polar coordinates.

Statistics and Probability | MYHH 045 058 (0.5 credits/5 hours)

This course will introduce students to the field of statistics, which is important in business, medicine, social studies, athletics, agriculture, and many other areas. The student will learn how to gather, represent, and analyze data, using equations, graphs, tables, estimates, and hypotheses. The course requires a graded project that includes the use of a computer and Microsoft Excel.

Financial Algebra | MTHH 047 055 (0.5 credits/5 hours)

Financial Algebra is a combination of Algebra and finance taught using applications and project based models. Financial Algebra is a course designed for students who are pursuing a stronger knowledge and skill set of Algebra concepts. Financial Algebra combines algebraic and graphical approaches with practical business and personal finance applications, which help to motivate students to explore algebraic thinking patterns and functions in a financial context.

NATURAL SCIENCES

The Science of Health | SCIH 011 055 (0.5 credits/5 hours)

In this course, students are introduced to medically accepted means of promoting physical and mental well-being. Among the subjects addressed are skills for living a healthy lifestyle, self-esteem, physical fitness and nutrition, the effects of alcohol and drugs on the human body, and disease prevention. NOTE: This course can be used for either science or health and physical fitness credit. Students should not take both this course and Health and Wellness. Students may receive credit toward graduation for Health and Wellness or the Science of Health, but not both.

The Science of Nutrition | SCIH 012 056 (0.5 credits/5 hours)

In this course, students will learn what nutrition is and why it is important. This course will give students the knowledge and tools they need to make nutrition choices that will lead to a healthy lifestyle. The course focuses on the impact of nutrition on the human body, weight management, the function of nutrients and the interaction between nutrition and physical activity in maintaining a healthy lifestyle. NOTE: This course can be used for science or health and physical fitness credits.

Physical and Earth Sciences 1 | SCIH 021 059 (0.5 credits/5 hours)

This course is the first in a two semester series that provides an introduction to the basic principles of physics, chemistry, Earth science, and space science. Students will use mathematics in these areas as well as logical methods and practical applications. Topics covered include the nature of science, motion, forces, Newton's Laws, energy, work and machines, electricity, magnetism, energy sources, waves, light, sound, Earth's internal processes, weather, and climate. Both hands-on Labs and Virtual Labs that allow students to experience the application of concepts, interactions, and processes are included.

Physical and Earth Sciences 2 | SCIH 022 059 (0.5 credits/5 hours)

This course is the second in a two-semester series that provides an introduction to the basic principles of physics, chemistry, Earth science, and space science. Students will use basic mathematics in these areas as well as logical methods and practical applications. Topics covered include the properties and classification of matter, solids, liquids, and gases, chemical bonds and reactions, radioactivity and Earth in space, time and seasons, the Moon, the solar system and stars, galaxies and the cosmos. Both hands-on Labs and Virtual Labs that allow students to experience the application of concepts, interactions, and processes are included.

Biology 1 | SCIH 025 061 (0.5 credits/5 hours)

Biology 1 includes a basic understanding of biology, basic chemistry, structure of cells and how they communicate, energy conversions, cell reproduction, genetics, gene expression, genetic engineering, origin of life, changes in organisms, ecosystems and succession, environmental problems and solutions, and the classification of living things.

Biology 2 | SCIH 026 061 (0.5 credits/5 hours)

In this second semester course, students will continue their study of fundamental biological concepts as they explore the structure and function of bacteria, viruses, fungi, and plants. They will investigate the diversity and development of invertebrate and vertebrate animals and learn about the anatomy and physiology of the human body.

Chemistry 1 | SCIH 031 062 (0.5 credits/5 hours)

The course presents an introduction to principles and procedures in chemistry. Students study scientific measurements, chemical names and formulas, states of and changes in matter, numerical relationships in chemical reactions, trends expressed in the periodic table and the behavior of gasses. Students calculate empirical and molecular formulas, write and balance equations, determine mole and mass, interpret chemical equations and gain insight into the various models of the atom. This course contains both hands-on labs and multimedia activities to provide an in-depth investigation into the subjects presented.

Chemistry 2 | SCIH 032 062 (0.5 credits/5 hours)

In this course, students continue their study of the principles and procedures in chemistry. They focus on chemical bonding, water and solutions, reaction rates and equilibrium, acids, bases and salts, oxidation-reduction reactions and carbon compounds. This course contains both hands-on labs and multimedia activities to provide an in-depth investigation into the subjects presented.

Physics 1 | SCIH 035 058 (0.5 credits/5 hours)

Physics represents a continuing effort to solve problems and interpret experience in a logical way. This first semester course encourages students to observe and relate physics principles to the world around them and investigate various physical phenomena related to forces, vectors Newton's laws of motion, acceleration, velocity, resistance and projectile motion. They will also learn about gravitational fields, satellite motion, special relativity, momentum, and inertia. Students will explore the world they live in through the properties of matter: elements, solids, liquids, and gases. This course includes both hands-on and virtual lab activities and projects.

Physics 2 | SCIH (0.5 credits/5 hours)

In this second semester Physics course students will continue their exploration of the world around them through an investigation into heat, phase changes, radiation, thermodynamics, sound and light vibrations and waves, color, reflection and refraction, lenses, electrostatics, electric currents, magnetism, electromagnetism, and finally atomic and nuclear physics. This course includes both hands-on and virtual lab activities and projects.

Ocean Biology | SCIH 039 055 (0.5 credits/5 hours)

This course incorporates several basic themes as it covers the life in our world's oceans. One of the primary themes of this course is the vast diversity, structure, function, and ecology of organisms in the world's oceans. Students will also learn to relate the physical sciences to the study of marine life. Particular attention is paid to the challenges that marine organisms face in changing ecosystems and to the interactions of humans with the marine environment.

Astronomy |SCIH 043 055 (0.5 credits/5 hours)

This course will examine modern day astronomy including topics about the solar system, stars, galaxies, cosmology, and Astrobiology. Students will begin by studying the night sky and progress towards the Solar system, the Milky Way galaxy, through black holes and quasars. The course will wrap up with topics such as using the scientific method to understand how the universe began and is evolving, to how scientists search for life beyond our own solar system.

Anatomy and Physiology | SCIH 045 055 (0.5 credits/5 hours)

Anatomy and Physiology is a detailed study of the human body, its parts and structures, and how these function together to create and sustain human life. In this course we will start with an introduction to terminology, human development, and body processes, then move on to the functioning of cells, tissues, and systems. With these basics to build on students will compile an extensive vocabulary of complete understanding of the human body.

SOCIAL STUDIES

Sociology | SSTH 003 058 (0.5 credits/5 hours)

Sociology is the study of the behavior of people in groups. In this course, students learn about the social development of individuals in a society and consider the effects that culture, language and status have on this development. Special attention is given to mechanisms of social control and to forces of social change. By analyzing social institutions and examining contemporary social problems, students develop an understanding of the characteristics of social interaction in a complex, modern society.

Psychology | SSTH 007 058 (0.5 credits/5 hours)

This introduction to psychology covers a broad range of topics, including learning processes, the development of personality, mental and emotional problems, the psychology of group behavior and social attitudes. Studying these topics helps students develop an awareness and an understanding of the many forces that influence their behavior.

World Geography 1 | SSTH 021 061 (0.5 credits/5 hours)

Geography allows people to find the answers to their questions about the world and understand the link between people and places. While studying about physical and human geography of the United States, Canada, Latin America, and Africa, students will explore the relationships between people and their physical environment, and analyze the interactions between the culture and geography of selected regions. NOTE: World Geography 1 and 2 may be taken in any sequence.

World Geography 2 | SSTH 022 061 (0.5 credits/5 hours)

This course focuses on the people, places, physical features, and unique characteristics of Europe, Asia, Australia, the island nations of the Pacific, and Antarctica. Students will learn valuable information about the world we inhabit today including how and where people live, and how their lives are changing in response to their physical environment, their governments, and their economic systems. Students will learn that Geography is not just the study of our physical world, but also the study of interactions between humans, their land, natural resources, weather, and ecosystems. Throughout the course students use such geographic skills as reading and drawing maps, analyzing charts and diagrams and interpreting technical vocabulary. NOTE: World Geography 1 and 2 may be taken in any sequence.

World History 1 | SSTH 031 060 (0.5 credits/5 hours)

This course is an introduction to world history that traces human development from ancient times to the beginning of the eighteenth century. Students will learn the facts, concepts, and principles they need to gain a better grasp on the history, culture, political, social, and economic development of many different societies around the globe. Special attention is given to the civilizations that developed in the Middle East, India, China, Africa, and Latin America as well as those in Europe and North America.

World History 2 SSTH 032 060 (0.5 credits/5hours)

This course focuses on the history of nations and regions around the globe from about 1700 to the present. Students begin by examining the main figures and political views of the Enlightenment, the impact of the revolutions around the globe, and the Industrial Revolution. The study of political systems and the growth of Western democracies and global imperialism then help set the stage for understanding the causes and effects of world-wide conflicts in the twentieth century. Finally, this course will examine the global political, social, and economic issues, as well as international relations in today's world.

American History 2 SSTH 034 060 (0.5 credits/5 hours)

This course traces the major historical developments in the United States from 1900 to the present. Students examine the causes and effects of the Industrial Revolution, immigration, reform movements, the two world wars and other historical phenomena that have influenced American society since the Civil War. Social history is emphasized throughout.

American Government: Theories, Policies, and Politics SSTH 037 059

Students analyze the American federal system of government as outlined by the Constitution of the United States. The constitutional rights guaranteed to American citizens, as well as the relationship of citizens to states, are discussed in detail as students study state and local government, and examine the structures of the 50 state governments.

American Government: National Level | STH 038 059 (0.5 credits/5 hours)

Students learn about the functions, powers and structures of the three branches of the national government of the United States. They consider the constitutional systems of separation of powers and checks and balances. In addition, students examine the role that the national government plays in the solution of specific foreign and domestic problems.

International Relations | SSTH 043 057 (0.5 credits/5 hours)

This course provides an overview of international relations. Students will analyze interactions among countries, learning different ways to explain why countries act as they do. Main topics include states, nations, war, peace, trade, alliances, international organizations, non-state groups, and globalization. This course will introduce students to the terms and methods political scientists use when studying international relations and assumes they will have survey-level knowledge of world history.

World Cultures 1: North and South America and Europe | SSTH 053 057 (0.5 credits/5 hours)

This course introduces multicultural studies through the investigation of the physical and human geography, history, and cultures of the continents of North America, South America, and Europe (including Russia). Through this course students will develop an understanding of the interactions between geography and culture that have influenced the lifestyles and challenges faced by various culture groups throughout these regions. This will help students gain a greater understanding of their own culture and realize how diverse cultural traditions affect their lives. It will encourage them to actively participate in the culturally diverse world in which they live.

World Cultures 2: Africa, Asia, Australia, and Oceania | SSTH 054 057 (0.5 credits/5 hours)

This course introduces multicultural studies through the investigation of the physical and human geography, history, and cultures of the continents of Africa, Asia, Australia, and Oceania. Through this course students will develop an understanding of the interactions between geography and culture that have influenced the lifestyles and challenges faced by various culture groups over time throughout these regions. This course will help students gain a greater understanding of their own culture and realize how diverse cultural traditions affect their lives. It will encourage them to actively participate in the culturally diverse world in which they live.

Advanced Placement U.S. History 1 | SSTH 071 057 (0.5 credits/5 hours)

This course is the first half of a two-semester sequence designed to prepare students for the college Board Advanced Placement United States History Examination. Lessons contain discussion of textbook readings, analysis of primary and secondary sources, research activities, chart and map exercises, objective self-check tests and interpretive essays. There are also five unit reviews that help students master College Board's thematic learning objectives, as well as consider historic themes over time. AP U.S. History 1 explores the social, political and economic development of the United States from the Colonial Era until 1877. It covers pre-Columbian America, European colonization, the American Revolution, the formation of the American political system, agricultural and industrial trends, westward expansion, social conditions and the mounting differences between North and South. The course discusses the Civil War and concludes with a survey of the Reconstruction process through which the southern states were readmitted to the Union. This course is authorized by College Board. The College Board Examination is NOT required for completion. Printed course content and Internet access are recommended.

Advanced Placement U.S. History 2 | SSTH 072 057 (0.5 credits/5 hours)

This course is the second half of a two-semester sequence designed to prepare students for the College Board Advanced Placement United States History Examination. Lessons contain discussion of readings, analysis of primary and secondary sources, research activities, chart and map exercises, objective self-check tests and interpretive essays. There are also five unit reviews that help students master College Board's thematic learning objectives, as well as consider historic periodization and interpret primary and secondary sources. Graded projects require students to defend interpretations in historic essays and trace the development of historic themes over time. AP U.S. History 2 explores the social, political and economic development of the United States from 1877 until today. The student will study westward expansion, Native American-White relations, the development of the modern capitalist system, organized labor, urban growth, progressive reform, the Great Depression, the New Deal programs, the relationship between government and private business, civil rights issues, cultural diversity and American foreign relations. This course has been authorized by College Board. While AP U.S. History 2 will help prepare students for the College Board Examination, this examination is NOT required for completion of the course.

Advanced Placement Comparative Government and Politics | SSTH 073 055 (0.5 credits/5 hours)

This course teaches students the tools and methods that political scientists use to analyze governments in different countries. Students apply these techniques while exploring the political systems of Britain, Russia, China, Mexico, Iran, Nigeria, and the United States. While learning about the structures and functions of government in each of these countries, students also evaluate how the trends of globalization, democratization, and marketization are influencing countries around the world. The course will prepare students for the College Board AP Comparative Government and Politics examination and is intended for students who have an in-depth interest in world affairs. Students are NOT required to take the College Board Examination to receive credit for the course from UNHS.

VISUAL AND PERFORMING ARTS

Elements of Drawing | ARTH 003 055 (0.5 credits/5 hours)

This course provides an introduction to the visual arts. It concentrates on the principles of drawing, discussing the roles of an art critic and an art historian. Although unit evaluations and progress tests are objective, graded projects allow students to create original works of art.

Appreciating Art | ARTH 015 255 (0.5 credits/5 hours)

This course introduces students to a wide array of artistic works. It examines painting, sculpture, and architecture from ancient times until the present. The course emphasizes art history and art criticism, rather than the creation of new works. Appreciating Art provides an overview of many different cultures.

Exploring Visual Design | ARTH 017 055 (0.5 credits/5hours)

This course introduces the student to basic elements and principles of design, taking the student on a visual journey that includes an exploration of line, shape, color, space, texture, balance, unity, contrast, emphasis, pattern, and movement and rhythm as they apply to the visual arts, and the ways in which artists use these to achieve a desired effect or outcome. Students will learn to recognize the elements and principles of design in everyday objects, works of art, and architecture from around the world. It is highly suggested that students have internet access so that they can view the artworks in color and access the websites provided to take full advantage of the resources included in this course. There is no kit supplied for this course.

Discovering Music | MUSH (0.5 credits/5 hours)

Music is often described as a universal language because it exists in all cultures. This course approaches music from a global perspective. Students will learn to notice cultural influences on music while exploring the common human ideas that music addresses. They will analyze the musical traditions of Western Europe, Asia, India, Africa, Latin America, South America and the United States. They will learn about the significance of music from multiple perspectives: as art, a science, and a business.

Music Theory | MUSH 031 055 (0.5 credits/5 hours)

Students will increase their understanding and enjoyment of music through the study of the elements of music theory in this course. They will study musical notation, major and minor scales, key signatures, intervals, triads, rhythm, and fundamental terminology. Access to a keyboard or musical instrument is Not required, although it will be helpful. Students who have studied band, orchestra, or voice can succeed in this course, but the course is best suited for those who have studied piano, keyboard or organ.

WORLD LANGUAGES

First Year French | FREH 001 060 (0.5 credits/5 hours)

In this first-year course, students are introduced to the basic grammatical concepts necessary to develop reading and writing skills in French. They become acquainted with French culture through a variety of reading and writing skills in French. They become acquainted with French culture through a variety of readings in both French and English. Students can also develop speaking and listening skills by hearing and speaking French themselves. The course covers basic sentence structure of positive and negative statements, commands and questions, and present and future tenses. Audio files are embedded in the online course and are available on an Audio CD for offline use.   Textbook: French English/ English French Dictionary.

Second Year French | FREH 002 060 (1 credit/10 hours)

This course reinforces and augments the grammatical concepts presented in First Year French. Students build new vocabulary, learn more advanced grammar concepts, increase their reading, writing, and listening skills, and develop their knowledge of many essential parts of speech including the past tense, direct object pronouns, and a number of commonly used French idioms and expressions. Audio files are embedded in the online course and are available on an Audio CD for offline use.

Third Year French | FREH 003 060 (1 credit/10 hours)

In this course, students take an imaginary tour of Paris and examine the United States from this vantage. After reviewing the grammar and the rules presented in First and Second Year French, students study indirect objects; emphatic, interrogative and reflexive pronouns; and verbs in the reflexive voice, the imperfect tense and the conditional mood. Students continue to enhance their reading, writing, speaking, and listening skills. Audio files are embedded in the online course and are available on an Audio CD for offline use.

First Year Latin | LATH 001 059 (1 credit/10hours)

The Latin readings for this course, adapted from ancient history and mythology, deal with the Trojan war and the story of Aeneas and his journey to Italy. Students work intensely on nouns, adjectives and verbs; study first, second and third declension nouns in all cases; and learn to form the six tenses of Latin verbs in the active voice for all four conjugations. Audio files are embedded in the online course and are available on an Audio CD for offline use. The CD contains the audio files for both the First Year Latin course and the Second Year Latin course.   Textbook: Jenny's First Year Latin. Workbook to Jenny's 1st Year Latin. English Grammar for Students of Latin.

Second Year Latin | LATH 002 059 (1 credit/10 hours)

The readings for this course are based on the founding of Rome and its early history as a monarchy and then a republic. The grammar includes pronouns, passive voice of verbs, infinitives, adverbial expressions, participles, deponent verbs and indirect statements. Students are provided with numerous opportunities to practice individual grammar concepts and to use their developing vocabulary skills. By the end of this course, students will have a firm grasp of basic Latin grammar and an extensive Latin vocabulary. The Audio CD is available for offline use and contains the audio files for both the First Year Latin course and the Second Year Latin course.

First Year Spanish | SPNH (1 credit/10 hours)

Through this course students develop a good grasp of Fundamental Spanish grammar that enables them to read simple stories and compose simple paragraphs. Basic sentence structure, parts of speech and regular and irregular verbs in the present tense are covered in this course, and students will develop vocabulary related to clothing, the home, time, weather, the calendar, numbers, and family relationships. Students also develop an understanding of culture and geography of Mexico and other Spanish-speaking areas. Audio files allow the students to listen to words and phrases as they are used in everyday life. Audio files are embedded in the online course and are available on an Audio CD for offline use.

Second Year Spanish | SPNH 002 059 (1 credit/10 hours)

Students increase their vocabulary, their understanding of grammatical constructions, and their ability to read and write Spanish during this second year course through discussions of such diverse topics as entertainment, food, geography, and travel. Audio files and interactive activities, and the preterit tense. Audio files are embedded in the online course and are available on an Audio CD for offline use.

Third Year Spanish | SPNH 003 058 (1 credit/10 hours)

A thorough review of regular, irregular, and stem-changing verbs in the present and preterit tenses in this course leads smoothly and naturally into a study of reflexive verbs and the imperfect, present progressive and present perfect tenses. Students expand their ability to write complex sentences using reflexive verbs, direct objects, and indirect object pronouns. They will increase their knowledge of Hispanic culture as they read and hear about special occasions, holidays, and practices observed by Spanish-speaking people. Third Year Spanish students will increase their ability to read, write, and also speak and understand Spanish using audio files recorded by native speakers. Audio files are embedded in the online course and are available on an Audio CD for offline use

Fourth Year Spanish |SPNH 004 058 (1 credit/10 hours)

Students thoroughly review regular, irregular and stem-changing verbs in the present, preterit and imperfect tenses before beginning a study of the future, conditional, and present subjunctive tenses. Fourth Year Spanish students will increase their ability to read, write, and also speak and understand Spanish using audio files created by native speakers. Listening and recording hardware or software of some type is essential for this course. Audio files are embedded in the online course and are available on an Audio CD in mp3 format for offline use. Students will be required to submit both audio and written components for grading. If students submit recordings by mail, CDs may be used.

VOCATIONAL STUDIES

If you just want to know how to be a paralegal, there's no real necessity for you to learn math beyond what you learned through the equivalent of your high school education. If you want to become a religious minister, there's likely no reason for you to study chemistry. Vocational courses let you pick precisely what you want to learn, allowing you to move more quickly down a career path without the typical heavy load of a college degree track. Without having to take a heavy load of courses, vocational education can end up saving you a considerable amount of money.

Many prisons offer vocational learning opportunities for prisoners, although often with very limited options. Frequently, such educational opportunities come on-the-job, with several prisons offering apprenticeship and employment in fields such as plumbing, electrical, welding, and manufacturing, among others. However, these jobs are among the more competitive forms of employment behind bars, which limits the number of prisoners who can gain such skill sets.

Very few prison systems offer adequate opportunities for prisoners who want to learn a trade. Notably, only a couple of states have made the availability of vocational training a priority. Texas, for instance, works with a number of local colleges and universities to provide vocational opportunities to most Texas prisons in about two dozen different fields. North Carolina has made a science out of providing prisoners with educational options. Upon arrival into their prison system, all prisoners are tested to determine what kind of education is appropriate for their background and goals, vocational training being chief among the options. North Carolina colleges and universities work with the Department of Corrections to provide vocational programs on-site, some through video and web-conferencing. Others offer free correspondence opportunities to in-state prisoners, which would otherwise cost hundreds of dollars for a prisoner to participate.

Most prisons offer some form of education, but it is typically only the most basic of education, such as GED courses or life skills classes. For the majority of the rest of the incarcerated, when it comes to gaining a skill while incarcerated, prisoners are on their own. Fortunately, however, there are a wealth of options in a variety of fields for prisoners to learn a skill through correspondence courses.

THE SCHOOLS

All of the following schools have expressed a willingness to work with prisoners and to meet their specific needs, such as print-based courses, catering to prison requirements, and other accommodations. If a school is not listed here, it is for the following reasons. 1) It is likely that they do not offer a convenient means for prisoners to take courses through their school; or 2) it may be one that offers prisoners educational opportunities but do so only in coordination with specific prison systems. These latter schools are not listed because they are already known within your prison system to anyone seeking to gain an education within those prisons. If you have not already done so, contact your prison education coordinator to find out if there are current educational opportunities being offered to your prison system by schools in your area.

Vocational School Recommendations

Schools, and what you want out of them, vary in so many ways the it is impossible to make an overall recommendation. Therefore, we leave that up to the accrediting agencies. However, one common interest among all prisoners is the quality of the communication between the outside world and your cell.

When researching schools. We send requests to each one as if we are prisoners. We want to know how they respond to your requests, which is a great guide in determining how well the school will work with you should you decide to enroll.

The following schools are recommended as institutions who stood out from the rest in how well they communicated, how accommodating they were to our requests for information, how comprehensive their sent information was, and how willing they were to work with prisoners. Starred "*" listings are exceptional in meeting the above criteria, proving that they have a good understanding of the unique challenges that prisoners face.

* **Adams State University** (paralegal)
* **Blackstone Career Institute** (paralegal)
International Sports Sciences Association
National Tax training School
University of Georgia
University of Wisconsin Disaster Management Center

SCHOOL LISTING LAYOUT

CONTACT INFORMATION

This is the school's address and where you can go for more information on that school. There is always more information than we can provide concerning each school. We encourage you to contact every school you are interested in.

DESCRIPTION

Key details are provided about each school so that you are aware of information of note that may impact you as a prisoner-student.

ACCREDITATION

The following schools are all accredited by a variety of agencies, which are marked under each entry. As you've learned, accreditation is vital in determining the quality of a learning institution. But not all accrediting agencies are created equal. Therefore, you should exercise caution when selecting a school. (For a complete discussion on this topic, see section on *Accreditation* early in this book.)

AVAILABLE TO PRISONERS

This will keep you informed of what you can earn from this school, such as diplomas, degrees, and certificates. School offerings change regularly, which is why we update this book annually.

TUITION

This is the fee the school charges for courses, course credits, grade levels, and other programs.

PAYMENT PLANS

Many schools offer payment plans to make programs more affordable during study. Even if a payment plan is not listed, a school may be willing to work with you to develop an affordable plan that will work with your circumstances.

CREDIT TRANSFER/EXAM OPTIONS

If you have previously earned credits from another school, this section will tell you if this school may allow you to transfer those credits in. It will also let you know if they have credit-by-exam options.

TIME LIMITS

Schools generally place limits on how long you have to take a course. If you cannot complete your course in time, many schools offer extensions, often for a fee.

PROCTOR REQUIRED?

This area will tell you if a school require their examinations to be proctored (supervised by an impartial person.)

CANCELLATION POLICY

If you are unhappy with the school, or you determine that the courses you purchased are just not going to work for you, this section will tell you about the schools course refund policy.

AVAILABLE COURSES

This section provides information on the courses offered by the school, including courses available, descriptions, and prerequisites.

Vocational Schools | What They Offer

SCHOOL	DIPLOMA	CERTIFICATE OF COMPLETION
ADAMS STATE UNIVERSITY		✓
AMERICAN HOTEL & LODGING ASSN. EDUCATIONAL INSTITUTE	✓	✓
BLACKSTONE CAREER INSTITUTE	✓	✓
CLEVELAND INSTITUTE OF ELECTRONICS		✓
GLOBAL UNIVERSITY BEREAN SCHOOL OF THE BIBLE	✓	✓
INTERNATIONAL SPORTS SCIENCES ASSN.		✓
INSTITUTE FOR WRITERS		✓
JOU KUBERT'S WORLD SCHOOL OF CARTOON & GRAPHIC ART		✓
NATIONAL TAX TRAINING SCHOOL		✓
OHIO UNIVERSITY SOUTHERN		✓
OKLAHOMA STATE UNIVERSITY		✓
STRATFORD CAREER INSTITUTE	✓	✓
THE CENTER FOR LEGAL STUDIES		✓
TRUCK MARKETING INSTITUTE		✓
UNIVERSITY OF GEORGIA		✓
UNIVERSITY OF WISCONSIN MANAGEMENT	✓	
U.S. CAREER INSTITUTE		✓

Vocational Studies | General

American Hotel & Lodging | Association Educational Institute

2113 North High Street
Lansing, Michigan 48906
(800) 390-8399, (517) 372-8800
www.ahlei.org/distancelearning *dlearning@ahla.com*

American Hotel & Lodging offers several certificate and diploma opportunities in the hospitality field. Courses are largely paper-based, but require some internet use. Consult with the school to determine if you will be able to complete the courses under your circumstances. NOTE: AM&L is NOT accredited.

Accreditation: None

AVAILABLE TO PRISONERS

Certificates in:
Hospitality Fundamentals; Hospitality Operations

Certificate of Specialization

Diplomas in:
Hospitality Management; Food & Beverage Management

Tuition Rates:	**$245 per course**
	(unless student is a member of the AH&LA, or by taking multiple courses.)
Payment Plan:	None
Textbook Fees:	Included in tuition
Additional Fees:	None
Transfer/Exam Options:	Not applicable
Time Limit:	4 months per course
Proctor Required?	Yes

American Hotel & Lodging
Available Courses

INTRODUCTION TO HOSPITALITY

Hospitality Today: An Introduction (103)
The Lodging and Food Service Industry (100)

ROOMS DIVISION

Managing Technology in the Hospitality Industry (468)
Hospitality Facilities Management and Design (281)
Managing Front Office Operations (333)
Managing Housekeeping Operations (338)
Security and Loss Prevention Management (387)

FOOD & BEVERAGE

Management of Food and Beverage Operations (241)
Planning and Control for Food and Beverage Operations (464)
Managing Service in Food and Beverage Operations (349)
Managing Beverage Operations (346)
Food Safety: Managing with the HACCP System (245)

FINANCE & ACCOUNTING

Hospitality Industry Managerial Accounting Revised (462)
Hospitality Industry Financial Accounting (260)
Hotel and Restaurant Accounting (261)
Accounting for Hospitality Managers (362)

SALES & MARKETING

Convention Management and Service (478)
Hospitality Sales and Marketing (472)
Revenue Management: Maximizing Revenue in Hospitality Operations (374)

HUMAN RESOURCES

Supervision in the Hospitality Industry (250)
Managing Hospitality Human Resources (357)

GENERAL MANAGEMENT

Leadership and Management in the Hospitality Industry (304)
Understanding Hospitality Law (391)
Contemporary Club Management (313)

Cleveland Institute of Electronics

1776 East 17th Street
Cleveland, Ohio 44114
(800) 243-6446, (216) 781-9400
www.cie.wc.edu   monical@cie-wc-edu

The *Cleveland Institute of Electronics* offers a wide array of electronics and computer technology-related courses. Prisoner students are free to take several of the courses, as many are through textbook learning and other printed materials. However, to take the exams, which are required for graduation, students will need access to the internet. If you have no access to the internet through the prison education department or through friends/family, you will not be able to obtain a certificate of completion.

Accreditation: None, but licensed by the State of Ohio, Board of Career Colleges and Schools

AVAILABLE TO PRISONERS

Professional Certificates in Electronics Technologies

Tuition Rates:	**$1054 - $2892 per course** (see below)
Payment Plan:	$10 down and $50 to $100 per month
Textbook Fees:	Not included in tuition. Book buy-back program offered.
Additional Fees:	**Shipping: $10 per course**
Cancellation options:	Full refund within 5 business days of signing Enrollment Agreement. 15% fee before completion of first course. Other refunds based on the percentage of the courses that have been completed.
Transfer/Exam Options:	Not applicable
Time Limits:	8 to 42 months, depending on course taken
Proctor required?	Yes

Cleveland Institute of Electronics
Available Courses

Electronics Technology with FCC License Preparation | Course 1A $1,580

Designed to help students obtain the General Radiotelephone Operator License (GROL) and gain a thorough education in electronics. The GROL is required to adjust, maintain, or internally repair any FCC licensed radiotelephone transmitters in the aviation, maritime, and international fixed public radio services. It is issued for the lifetime of the holder.

Broadcast Engineering | Course 2 $1,580

Designed to provide the specialized knowledge required for a career as a broadcast engineering technician at a radio or TV station. It is also valuable for the cable technician who must maintain and repair studio equipment. Learn about electronics along with emerging mobile media technologies and post-production techniques.

A+ Certification & Computer Technology | Course 2C $1,140

Designed to train students with little or no computer experience about computer technology, troubleshooting and preparing them to pass the recently updated CompTIA A+ Certification exam. This is the starting point for a career in IT. The exam covers maintenance of PCs, networking, mobile devices, laptops, operating systems, printers, security, and troubleshooting. This course does not include the certification exam, rather it prepares the student to take it directly from CompTIA.

CompTIA Network+ Certification & Computer Technology | Course 3C $1,140

Designed to train individuals with little or no computer networking background about computer technology and prepare them to pass the recently updated CompTIA Network+ Certification exam. This course does not include the network certification exam, rather it prepares the student to take it directly from CompTIA.

Wireless & Electronics Communications | Course 4 $1,580

Designed to provide a thorough understanding of Wireless and Personal Communications along with providing a solid core of instruction in electronics. Explores important theories and principles related specifically to communication. Best suited for students who already have some previous education or practical experience in electronics.

Electronics Engineering | Course 6 $2,892

An advanced-level course designed for technicians and engineers who want a deeper understanding of electronic circuits and advanced mathematics. Requires at least one year of high school algebra or geometry.

Computer Security Specialist | Course 6C $1,140

Learn how to design, install and manage security systems. Designed to provide the specialized knowledge required for a career in Cyber Security. Master computer security techniques in an easy-to-understand format.

IT Security | Course 7C $1,580

Learn to create, install and maintain IT Security systems. This course expands on the knowledge learned in Course 6C to include lessons on Network Defense and Countermeasures, Security Techniques, and Ethics. Provides essential troubleshooting techniques necessary to repair and secure a wide array of computer networks and electronic devices.

Intro to Game Development & Mobile Apps | Course 8C $1,140

Designed to gives students with no prior computer experience the skills and confidence needed to develop games for mobile devices and other platforms. Learn how to develop apps on today's Smartphone platforms, apply programming experience to build a game for iOS and other platforms.

International Sports Sciences Association

1015 Mark Avenue
Carpentaria, California 93013
(800) 892-4772, (805) 745-8111
www.ISSAonline.edu

The *International Sports Sciences Association* is one of the nation's leading providers of quality health and fitness education. They act as a teaching institution for fitness trainers, athletic trainers, aerobics instructors, and medical professionals. ISSA offers a number of fitness certification options for prisoners. Their programs are widely accepted for continuing education credits (CEUs) by other professional schools and fitness certification organizations.

Be aware: Fitness certification is only good for 2 years from issuance. These courses are advised for prisoners who will be reentering society soon and would like to begin a career in fitness.

Accreditation: Distance Education Accrediting Commission (DEAC); National Board of Fitness Examiners (NBFE)

Available for Prisoners:

Certification courses as a: Fitness Trainer (CFT); Specialist in Exercise Therapy (SFT); Specialist in Fitness Nutrition (SFN); Specialist in Senior Fitness (SSF); Specialist in Sports Nutrition (SSN); Specialist in Strength & Conditioning

Advanced Certifications as an: Elite Trainer; Master Trainer

Tuition Rates:	**$599 per Certification**
	Elite Trainer Study: $1,797
	Master Trainer Study: $3,594
	$249 per Advanced Examination
Payment Plans:	None available
Textbooks:	Included in tuition.
Additional Fees:	**Shipping per course: $25**
Cancellation Options:	Full refund within 15 days of signing the Enrollment Agreement.
Time Limits:	4 months
Proctor Required?	Yes

International Sports Sciences Association
Available Certification Courses

Certified Fitness Trainer (CFT) | PTR211
Comprehensive certification course covering weight training, aerobic conditioning, flexibility, and proper nutrition for the fitness training profession.

Specialist in Sports Nutrition (SSN) | PTR212
Advanced specialty course for fitness trainers that provides important insights into digestion and absorption, metabolism, body composition, eating to enhance athletic performance, and knowing when and what to eat.

Specialist in Exercise Therapy | PTR213
Advanced course for fitness trainers who want to expand their clientele to individuals with medical conditions that require special care when exercising.

Specialist in Strength and Conditioning (SSC) | PTR215
Advanced specialty course for fitness trainers covering the knowledge, expertise and specific training techniques to enable athletes and fitness training clients to expand the capacity of their bodies to perform the most difficult athletic feats – while remaining strong and free from injuries.

Specialist in Senior Fitness (SSF) | PTR216
Advanced certification course for fitness trainers who would like to expand their clientele to work with older adults and the specific health and fitness challenges they face.

Specialist in Fitness Nutrition (SFN) | PTR219
Builds a solid foundation in nutritional science, including how food interacts with cells, how it becomes energy, and how the body balances the food eaten and the work it does as well as the application of this knowledge to help others through nutritional coaching, assessment, and goal attainment.

Youth Fitness Trainer (YFT) | PTR214
Advanced course for fitness trainers who would like to expand their clientele to work with youths. Provides the essential instruction to safely and effectively train kids and teens.

Elite Trainer Study
Combines the Certified Fitness Trainer, Fitness Nutrition, and Exercise Therapy courses. Upon successful completion of the three courses and Advanced Exam I, trainers earn the title of ISSA Elite Trainer and hold CFT, SFN, and SET training credentials.

Master Trainer Study
Combines the Certified Fitness Trainer, Fitness Nutrition, Exercise Therapy, Senior Fitness, Strength and Conditioning, and Youth Fitness courses. Upon successful completion of the three courses and Advanced Exam I and II, trainers earn the title of ISSA Master Trainer and hold CFT, SFN, SET, SSF, SSC, and YFT training credentials.

International Sports Sciences Association
Advanced Examinations

Elite Trainer | Advanced Examination Level I
Examination that assesses competence in personal training, nutrition, and exercise therapy.

Required credentials: Active CFT, SFN or SSN, and SET certifications.

Master Trainer | Advanced Examination Level II
Examination that assesses competence in senior fitness, youth fitness, and strength and conditioning.

Required credentials: Active CFT, SFN or SSN, SET, SSF, YTF, SSC certifications and the ISSA Elite Trainer distinction.

Institute for Writers
(Formerly Long Ridge Writers Group)

32 Wall Street, Suite A
Madison, CT 06443
(203) 792-8600
www.instituteforwriters.com   info@instituteforwriters.com

Institute for Writers provides quality comprehensive courses in the field of writing children's literature. Students are required to first take an Aptitude Test, which is available online (although the school will mail it upon request.) Once accepted, students must be able to submit writing assignments electronically, such as through a family member who will scan completed lessons and email them.

They offer a money-back guarantee if the student is not a better writer by the completion of the program, as well as college credits towards a degree program from *Charter Oak State College*. However, they are not accredited.

Accreditation: None

AVAILABLE TO PRISONERS

Certificates of Completion in Children's Literature
(a comprehensive writing program)

Tuition Rates:	**$737 per course**
Payment Plan:	$59 down payment plus 12 monthly payments of $59.
Textbook Fees:	Included in tuition
Additional Fees:	**Shipping fees of $15 to $25**
Transfer/Exam Options:	7 credits can be transferred, which can be used at Charter Oak State College
Time Limits:	2 years per program
Proctor required?	No

Institute for Writers
Available Courses

Writing for Children & Teenagers (3 credits)
Teaches the essential elements of writing for young readers and help prepare marketable work for publishers and editors. It explores what inspires you to write and provides proper motivation.

Joe Kubert's World School of Cartoon & Graphic Art

37B Myrtle Avenue
Dover, New Jersey 07801
(877) 559-6753, (973) 537-7760
www.kubertschool.edu   info@kebertschool.edu

Joe Kubert's World School of Cartoon & Graphic Art was formed by Joe Kubert in 1976, who has actively been involved in the comic book drawing business for over 70 years. Hundreds of his school's graduates are now professionals in the field as artists, inkers, pencilers, letterers, computer colorists, animators, writers, editors and publishers.

His school now offers correspondence opportunities to learn cartooning from your cell. Courses include spiral-bound study guides and DVDs, but the school is willing to work with prisoners to meet prison guidelines. Students have two options for study. 1) Just the coursework, or 2) the coursework and personal instructor critique.

While the program is non-accredited, the school that provides it is accredited and has been providing cartooning education since 1976.

Accreditation: Accrediting Commission of Career Schools & Colleges

Available for Prisoners:

Certificate course in Cartoon instruction

Tuition:	$225 per course with critique $100 per course without critiques
Payment Plan:	None
Textbooks:	
Additional Fees:	**Shipping and handling fees: $15 per course**
Time Limits:	None
Proctor Required?	No

Joe Kubert's School of Cartoon & Graphic Art
Available Courses

HEROES AND SUPERHEROES

This course helps students to improve drawing skills through step-by-step instructions explaining how the professionals draw heroes.

The Basics: Proportion, Action, Appearance
Character Creation
Costume

Backgrounds & Environment
Story Layout

STORY-GRAPHICS

Learn how to develop characters, create page layouts and panel compositions.

Storytelling
Following a Script
Characterizations

Backgrounds & Environment
Time and Costume

HORROR

This course goes into detail concerning styles, techniques, dramatization, and the use of reference.

Storytelling and Layout
Mood
Lighting and Shadows

Backgrounds & Environment
Characterization

PENCILING

This course shows the use of tools, composition, story sequence, and page design prior to lettering and inking. The penciler's work includes allowing space for balloons, captions, and sound effects.

The Basics: Tools of the Trade
Lighting and Contrast
Perspective and Angles

Backgrounds & Environment
Style

INKING

Inking completes the black and white cartoon illustration. This course teaches how to ink and the proper use of tools.

The Basics: Tools of the Trade
Depth and Dimension
Textures and Tech Effects

Backgrounds & Environment
Styles

SUPER VILLAINS

This course shows how to design and and draw hero's nemesis. It focuses on the development of historical, current and future evildoers in graphic form.

Physical Characteristics and Appearance of Evilness
Light and Shading for Effect
Costumes

Sinister Settings
Characterization

National Tax Training School

PO Box 767
Mahwah, New Jersey 07430-0767
(800) 914-8138, (201) 684-0828
www.nattax.com   *info@nattax.com*

The *National Tax Training School* provides comprehensive and annually updated tax preparation training, which students can use to open their own practice.

Accreditation: Distance Education Accrediting Commission (DEAC)

AVAILABLE TO PRISONERS

Certificates of Completion in Tax Consultation

Certificate of Graduation in Federal Tax Preparation

Tuition Rates:	**$595 for Federal Income Tax Course**
Payment Plan:	$210 per month (3 months) for Federal Income Tax course
Textbook Fees:	Included in tuition
Additional Fees:	**Shipping & Handling: $19.95**
Cancellation Policy:	Full refund within 15 days of receipt of materials; $125 fee if cancelling up to 50% completion of courses.
Transfer/Exam Options:	Not applicable
Time Limits:	12 months per course; $50 per extension of 6 months
Proctor required?	No

National Tax Training School
Available Courses

Federal Income Tax Course

This comprehensive course trains students to professionally prepare tax returns for individuals and small businesses. The lessons are designed to give the student a sound foundation for success in tax work by covering all pertinent phases of the Federal income tax and how it applies to everyday business and personal transactions. Particular emphasis is devoted to tax saving ideas, methods and strategies. Hundreds of examples and illustrations help students understand and retain various tax rules, regulations and procedures. Course comes with an 850-page Federal Tax handbook.

Stratford Career Institute

1 Champlain Commons, Unit 3, PO Box 1560
Saint Albans, Vermont 05478
(800) 556-4559
www.sci-careers.com

Stratford Career Institute offers diploma and personal enrichment certification programs in a number of areas, but they are not an accredited school. If you're looking for the education without a diploma, this is a relatively economical option. Their tuition fee is all-inclusive with convenient payment plans.

These courses will not be good towards credit at most colleges.

Accreditation: NONE

AVAILABLE TO PRISONERS

Numerous career courses with a Certificate of Completion

Tuition Rates:	**$549-1089 per course (depending on course)**
	NOTE: They regularly have discounted specials, such as mid 2017 offering ANY course for $499. Inquire with the school about current specials.
Payment Plans:	$10 down payment, plus 15-21 monthly payments of $35.19-38.60 (depending on course. See below.)
Textbook Fees:	Included in tuition
Additional Fees:	None
Cancellation Policy:	Full refund within 5 days of enrollment; 5 days to first lesson submission, 80% refund; other percentages based on number of courses completed
Transfer/Exam Options:	Not applicable
Time Limits:	Not applicable

Stratford Career Institute
Course Price List

Group 1 **$549 per program** (15 monthly payments @ $35.93)	Computer Training, English as a Second Language, Gardening & Landscaping, Health Care Aide, Home Inspector, Sewing & Dressmaking, Spanish as a Second Language, or Writing Stories for Children
Group 2 **$589 per program** (15 monthly payments @ $38.60)	Art, Bookkeeping, Child Daycare Management, Child Psychology, Creative Writing, Drug & Alcohol Treatment Specialist, Florist/Floral Design, French as a Second Language, Motorcycle/ATV Repair, Photography, Real Estate Appraiser, Security/Police Sciences, Start Your Own Business, Teacher Aide, or Wedding Consultant
Group 3 **$649 per program** (18 monthly payments @ $35.50)	Administrative Assistant/Secretary, Cooking & Catering, Early Childhood Education, Electrician, Medical Office Assistant, or Private Investigator
Group 4 **$689 per program** (18 monthly payments @ $37.72)	Accounting, Beauty Care, Business Management, Conservation/Environmental Sciences, Criminal Justice, Fashion Merchandising & Design, Fitness & Nutrition, Funeral Service Education, Interior Decorating, Natural Health Consultant, PC Repair, Plumbing, Professional Locksmith, Psychology/Social Work, or Video Game Design
Group 5 **$749 per program** (21 monthly payments @ $35.19)	Auto Mechanics, Dental Assistant, Desktop Publishing & Design, Hotel & Restaurant Management, Legal Assistant/Paralegal, Pharmacy Assistant, Physical Therapy Aide, Relaxation Therapist, Small Engine Repair, or Travel & Tourism
Group 6 **$789 per program** (21 monthly payments @ $37.09)	Computer Programming, Contractor/Construction Management, Forensic Science, Medical Billing Specialist, Medical Transcriptionist, or Veterinary Assistant

Stratford Career Institute
Available Courses

BUSINESS

Accounting
Instructs students in a broad range of manual and computerized accounting functions such as maintaining ledgers and journals, creating balance sheets and financial statements, and preparing payroll.

Administrative Assistant/Secretary
Prepares students for the role of administrative assistant in the modern working environment. Learn general duties, management skills, and modern computer applications.

Bookkeeping
Instructs how to create balance sheets and financial statements as the process of controlling cash and preparing payroll.

Business Management
Learn the latest perspectives on all aspects of business management, from business administration to business law, securities, e-commerce and more.

Funeral Service Education
Prepares students for administrative positions in this unique and specialized field. Covers grief psychology, bereavement counseling, business fundamentals, and the theory and practice of embalming.

Hotel & Restaurant Management
Offers a detailed outlook on the management styles and duties of contemporary managers at varied hotel and restaurant establishments.

Insurance Claims Adjuster
Provides instruction on how to investigate accident, health, life, and liability claims for both residential and commercial aid to insurance companies.

Real Estate Appraiser
All aspects of appraising are covered, including gathering and analyzing data, market values, legalities, taxation factors, and providing estimates.

Start Your Own Business
Guides you through the planning, researching, and financing stages of starting a new small business. Provides students with fundamental skills in marketing and management.

Travel & Tourism
Learn what is involved in travel and managing an agency. This includes technical information as well as travel trends and culture as it relates to today's traveler.

COMPUTER TECHNOLOGY

Computer Programming
Covers computer fundamentals, principles of program development, specific commands and formats of C++ program design.

Computer Training
Covers all aspects of computer components and operations, explores fundamental concepts in Windows and trains students on word processing, spreadsheet and presentation software.

PC Repair
Studies PC components and their functions so that students can learn to diagnose and repair a broad range of computer problems.

Video Game Design
Explores the history of video games, game scenarios, character creation, interfacing, audio, and more.

CREATIVE CAREERS

Art
Learn techniques and perform projects in pencil, pastel, water color, acrylic, and oil painting.

Beauty Care
Learn skin care, make-up, hairstyling, nail technology, as well as how to open and operate a salon.

Cooking & Catering
Provides expert instruction on preparing food and other critical catering skills, including booking affairs and financial and legal considerations.

Creative Writing
Develops skills necessary for success as an author and covers all bases in skillful fiction writing.

Fashion Merchandising & Design
Studies the creative and business sides of the fashion industry.

Florist/Floral Design
Incorporates step-by-step instruction in floral arrangements, flower preservation and care, and developing a professional retail environment.

Interior Decorating
Explores the field of professional interior design, design styles, and other components.

Photography
Covers modern cameras, lenses, films, digital photography and accessories. How-to sections cover topics such as exposure, processing, filters, lighting and flash.

Sewing & Dressmaking
Teaches sewing essentials, such as how to lay out patterns, perform hand and machine stitches, hem garments and make pockets.

Wedding Consultant/Event Planning
Comprehensive training program covering everything from theme weddings to networking tips and legal responsibilities.

Writing Stories for Children
Provides a foundation on how to write for children of all ages, developing fundamental writing skills, illustration, and marketing.

EDUCATION/COUNSELING

Child Day Care Management
Learn what is involved in opening and managing a successful day care business. Curriculum includes nutrition, behavior, education concepts and more.

Child Psychology
Covers the biological and cognitive development of children pre-birth through adolescence. Geared for both child care professionals and parents.

Drug & Alcohol Treatment Specialist
Learn the issues related to substance abuse to be able to be a more effective helper for those suffering with addictions.

Early Childhood Education
Provides an overview of the physical, intellectual, social and emotional characteristics of children, as they develop and build guidance skills.

English as a Second Language
Designed for anyone with a desire to communicate effectively in English.

French as a Second Language
Designed for anyone with a desire to communicate effectively in French.

Psychology/Social Work
Studies human behavior, social work as a profession and skills associated with effective helping. Provides students with the training to communicate, comprehend, influence and assist.

Spanish as a Second Language

Designed for anyone with a desire to communicate effectively in Spanish.

Teacher Aide

Gain valuable perspectives on learning experiences for children in a wide variety of educational circumstances and settings.

HEALTH/PHYSICAL FITNESS TRAINING

Exercise Therapy Specialist

Advanced course for fitness trainers who want to expand their clientele to individuals with medical conditions that require special care when exercising.

Fitness & Nutrition

Gain more advanced concepts in both nutrition and fitness as well as means to develop a well-rounded health and wellness plan for others.

Natural Health Consultant

Examines the benefits of holistic health and healing through knowledge of alternative therapies that can help a number of illnesses and ailments.

Physical Therapy Aide

Learn the roles and duties of the Physical Therapy Aide. Medical terminology and the systems of the human body are emphasized.

Relaxation Therapist

Strategies and methodologies for dealing with stress-related health issues. Covers stress management, relaxation techniques, and massage.

LEGAL

Criminal Justice

Focuses on the justice system and American government and provides detailed knowledge about investigations and interrogations, sentencing and corrections.

Forensic Science

Covers everything from processing the crime scene to the fundamentals of DNA analysis, handwriting and document examinations.

Paralegal/Legal Assistant

Explores the role of the paralegal in a modern law office, litigation, criminal procedure, and legal writing.

Private Investigator

General procedures regarding fact gathering, criminal investigation, missing person, and analyzing large amounts of data are all covered.

Security/Police Sciences

Focuses on private security with instruction on corporate security and law enforcement.

MEDICAL

Dental Assistant

Provides instruction in a variety of topics such as dental anatomy, preventative dentistry, dental instruments, radiography and office procedures.

Health Care Aide

Comprehensive course covering medical terminology, body systems, home care, and the health care industry.

Medical Coding & Billing Specialist

Instructs on medical terminology, basics of insurance billing and coding, insurance plans, claim forms and more.

Medical Office Assistant

Covers administrative aspects of running a medical office, from telephone procedures to computerized billing, insurance, prescriptions, banking, bookkeeping and more.

Medical Transcriptionist

Provides skills in transcription as well as an understanding of human physiology.

Pharmacy Assistant

Prepares for work in a pharmacy or other related environment. Topics include medical terminology, human anatomy and physiology, and pharmacology.

Veterinary Assistant

Subject matter includes a blend of technical and administrative topics ranging from anatomy and physiology to medical records, client relations, animal behavior and livestock care.

OTHER VOCATIONAL TRADES

Auto Mechanics

Covers all systems and procedures related to the maintenance and repair of automobiles, including the most modern diagnostic techniques and performance testing.

Canine Specialist

Gain comprehensive knowledge regarding the care and training of a variety of dogs. The course covers of breeds, training, behavior, nutrition, and starting a business of your own

Conservation/Environmental Sciences

Comprehensive study of sustainable living, ecosystems, and maintaining a healthy environment.

Contractor/Construction Management

Teaches all about the construction process from subcontractor coordination to estimating summaries and bids.

Electrician

Covers major aspects of residential and commercial electricians. Topics include electrical connections and circuits, circuit protection devices, signal systems, electrical heating, and more.

Gardening & Landscaping

Topics include gardening under a variety of conditions, controlling pests and diseases, growing plants for food and landscape design.

Home Inspector

Provides a foundation in both the practicalities of inspecting homes as well as the administrative aspects of operating a home inspection business.

Motorcycle/ATV Repair

Comprehensive training program covering everything from engine and transmission disassembly to the business side of motorcycle and ATV repair.

Plumbing

Covers the detailed work and functionality of both commercial and residential plumbing systems.

Small Engine Repair

Covers the fundamentals to intermediate repair techniques and maintenance as well as instruction about all types of small engine vehicles.

Truck Marketing Institute

1090 Eugenia Place, Suite 101
Carpinteria, California 93013-2011
(805) 684-4558
www.tmitraining.com   info@tmitraining.com

The *Truck Marketing Institute* offers specialized training for persons who work, or would like to work, in the truck marketing industry. It trains students how to spec trucks, the meaning of terminology, the intricacies of the product, and how to interpret and compare specifications.

Prisoner students will need to have assistance in accessing truck manufacturer's product information via the internet.

Accreditation: NONE

AVAILABLE TO PRISONERS

Certificate of Completion in several truck-related courses

Tuition Rates:	$375 to $825 per course, depending on course (see below)
Payment Plan:	None
Textbook Fees:	Included in tuition
Additional Fees:	None
Cancellation Policy:	Full refund within 30 days of signing Enrollment Agreement, other refunds are based on the percentage of course completion.
Transfer Options:	Not applicable
Time Limits:	6 to 12 months, depending on course
Proctor Required?	No

Truck Marketing Institute
Available Vocational Courses

Course I — $375
Starter course for Chevy and GMC light truck sales personnel. This five-lesson make-specific course provides product and technical training in every aspect of light trucks.

LT-2: Light Truck Essentials — $395
Provides advanced training, ideal for Class 1-5 commercial and fleet work.

Course II: Medium Truck Basics — $695
Introductory course for medium-duty truck knowledge. Available in make-specific or non-make-specific versions. Also available as make-specific training for International and Ford specializations.

Course III: Heavy Duty Models — $825
For sellers or buyers, this is a complete how-to course on spec'ing out Class 8 straight trucks and tractor-trailer combinations.

Course IV | Mid-Range Diesels — $795
For sellers or buyers, this course focuses on the Class 5-6-7 diesel market.

University of Georgia | Center for Continuing Education

1197 South Lumpkin Street, Suite 193
Athens, Georgia 30602
(800) 811-6640, (706) 542-3537
www.georgiacenter.uga.edu *questions@georgiacenter.uga.edu*

The *University of Georgia* offers a landscape management certificate programs that are industry recognized. These courses provide comprehensive information for anyone looking to advance their qualifications in the landscape industry profession. Typically, these are continued education course for landscape professionals, such as golf course greens managers and sport's field supervisors.

Courses qualify for 12 to 14 CEUs and are reasonably priced. One available in Spanish.

Accreditation: Southern Association of Colleges and Schools. Commission on Colleges

AVAILABLE TO PRISONERS

Principles of Turfgrass Management Certificate

Sports Turfgrass Management Certificate

Tuition Rates:	**$379 per course**
	$319 per course if student is a member of NALP, GSCAA, STMA, or AEdG
Payment Plan:	None
Textbook Fees:	Included in tuition
Additional Fees:	Shipping fee (only if students are outside of the U.S.): $50
Transfer/Exam Options:	Not applicable
Time Limits:	12 months ($50 for one 6-month extension)
Proctor Required?	Yes, for two exams.

University of Georgia
Certificate Program Details

Principles of Turfgrass Management Certificate   **12 CEUs**

Students completing this course qualify to become Landscape Industry Certified by the National Association of Landscape Professionals (NALP). The course features 16 lessons covering up-to-date information on mastering turfgrass management practices and procedures that are standard in the green industry. It addresses the following topics: Turfgrass Growth, Development, & Physiology; Turfgrass Characterization, Identification, & Adaptation; Soils; Establishment; Mowing; Irrigation; Weeds; Insects; Diseases; Pesticides; Turfgrass & the Environment; Troubleshooting, and Customer Relations.

Course is available in Spanish.

Sports Turfgrass Management Certificate   **14 CEUs**

This course provides up-to-date information on the establishment and care of sports fields. The principles covered are applicable to all levels of sports field management, as well as the basics of turf grass management, for all regions of the country.

University of North Carolina

The Friday Center, Campus Box 1020
Chapel Hill, North Carolina 27599-1020
(800) 862-5669, (919) 962-2648
www.fridaycenter.unc.edu

The *University of North Carolina's Friday Center* is a self-paced learning consortium of ten institutions of UNC. They offer college-level print-based for-credit courses in a number of subjects (see listing in *College Studies* section).

Additionally, they offer a Nursing Program, which prisoners can qualify for.

Accredited: SACS

AVAILABLE TO PRISONERS

A variety of for-credit and personal enrichment course options

Tuition Rates:	**$575 for Nursing Review course, plus $250 for clinical practicum placement fee**
Payment Plans:	Not applicable
Textbook Fees:	Not included in tuition
	(used book and book buy-back programs are offered)
Additional Fees:	**Administration Fee: $100**
Transfer/Exam Options:	Not applicable
Time Limits:	12 weeks
Proctor Required?	Yes

University of North Carolina
Available Vocational Courses

NURSING

Medical-Surgical Nursing Review for Registered Nurses | NURS-R

This course is part of the Nursing Refresher Program, which also includes a nursing practicum. The course is designed to address a full range of common nursing problems. Medical-surgical concepts as well as psycho-social aspects of nursing care are presented.

There are two options offered:

Option 1 – Theory Course and clinical practicum. This option is for nurses in North Carolina who have not worked in over five years or who have had a lapsed or inactive license for five years or more and would like to return to nursing either full or part time.

Option 2: Theory course only. This option is intended for licensed nurses who have been practicing during the past five years and desire to update their knowledge of medical-surgical nursing. Nurses who plan to change practice areas may also benefit from this option. Residence in North Carolina is not required for Option 2.

University of Wisconsin-Madison | Disaster Management Center

432 North Lake Street
Madison, Wisconsin 53706
(800) 462-0876, (608) 262-1299
www.dmc.engr.wisc.edu   dmc@engr.wisc.edu

The *University of Wisconsin-Madison* offers a Disaster Management Diploma and several disaster management courses, which can be taken from prison. However, they will not send print materials through the mail. Course materials will have to be downloaded from the internet and printed out for the prisoner-student. Final exam materials are still shipped by postal mail to a proctor. All course requirements can be completed without the use of a computer.

The courses earn CEUs that may be transferred for credit at other schools upon completion. Some courses are available in Spanish.

Accreditation:

North Central Association of Colleges and Schools, The Higher Learning Commission

AVAILABLE TO PRISONERS

Disaster Management Diploma

Disaster Management Courses

Tuition Rates:	**$435 for the first two "required" courses** **$200-$235 per course** **Packages: Take any 10 courses for $1,995**
Payment Plan:	None
Textbook Fees:	Included in tuition
Additional Fees:	**Diploma registration fee: $395**
Transfer/Exam Options:	Up to 25 credits in non-required areas, however the student must first earn at least 25 CEUs from UWDMC.
Time Limits:	Five years for the entire diploma course
Proctor Required?	Yes, for the final exam.

University of Wisconsin-Madison
Disaster Management Center
Available Courses

Aim and Scope of Disaster Management | AA02 (2.0 CEU) $200
A REQUIRED basic UWDMC course that defines the scope and objectives of the field of disaster management.

Principles of Management | AA04 (3.5 CEU) $235
A REQUIRED basic UWDMC course that provides an overview of management for a disaster and emergency standpoint.

Natural Hazards: Causes and Effects | BB02 (3.0 CEU) $230
A basic course that examines in detail the physical characteristics, geographical distribution, impact, response, and mitigation of natural hazards such as earthquakes, tsunamis, volcanoes, tropical cyclones, floods, drought, desertification, and deforestation.

Disaster Preparedness | BB04 (2.5 CEU) $235
A comprehensive look at the prerequisites for preparedness planning, action plans and procedures.

Damage and Needs Assessment | BB06 (3.0 CEU) $230
An examination of common approaches to disaster assessment including assessment teams, survey methods, tools, and techniques.

Disaster Response | BB08 (3.0 CEU) $230
A wide-ranging look at disaster-response planning roles and responsibilities.

Environmental Health Management after Natural Disaster | BC02 (2.0 CEU) $200
A look at the effects on natural disasters on environmental health, from pre-disaster to rehabilitation health measures.

Health Services Organization in the Event of a Disaster | BC04 (2.0 CEU) $200
A look at the organization of first-level care at the disaster site, rural health services for disaster situations, the implementation of a disaster plan in a health care facility, and methods for updating and evaluating hospital disaster management plans.

Emergency Health Management after Natural Disaster | BC06 (2.5 CEU) $225
An overview of the effects of disaster on health and an examination of the issues in disaster preparedness, coordination of national relief activities, management of mass casualties, and epidemiologic surveillance and disease control.

Epidemiologic Surveillance after Natural Disaster | BC08 (2.0 CEU) $200
An overview of risk factors for communicable diseases after disasters, epidemics, and systems for surveillance.

Emergency Vector Control after Natural Disaster | BC 10 (2.5 CEU) $225
A look at three broad areas: disaster preparedness, control measures for specific vectors, and general control actions.

Health Education and Training of Refugee Health Workers | BC16 (3.0 CEU)
$230
A basic refugee track course that looks at the establishment of primary health care programs for displaced populations.

Disasters and Development | DD02 (2.5 CEU) $225
This course introduces the relationships between disasters and development.

Disaster Risk Reduction | DD04 (2.5 CEU) $225
Introduces the basic principles of disaster risk reduction, while utilizing information, tools and instruments to expand knowledge and experience.

Contingency Planning | EP01 (2.0 CEU) $225
A course focusing on the principles of the contingency planning process with its advantages and limitations.

Planning of Emergency Response | EP02 (2.0 CEU) $225
This course provides an overview of planning concepts and definitions of planning terminology as used for refugee emergencies.

Managing of Emergency Response | EP03 (2.0 CEU) $225
This course is devoted to the specific management context of refugee emergencies worldwide.

Managing External Relations in an Emergency | EP04 (2.0 CEU) $225
This course helps the disaster professional to identify a network of contacts and to build and maintain constructive relations.

Designing Participatory Workshops | EP05 (2.5 CEU)   **$225**

A course with many practical tips for designing, organizing and managing workshops that will engage your participant in a more participatory way.

Providing Emergency Support and Advice | EP06 (2.0 CEU)   **$225**

An overview of the need for better emergency training, support and advice, along with some options for meeting those needs.

Coordination | EP07 (2.0 CEU)   **$225**

This course examines the basic need for and constraints to the coordination of international humanitarian assistance.

Security Risk Management | EP08 (3.0 CEU)   **$230**

Designed for humanitarian field workers who want to learn more about managing security for themselves and their co-workers in insecure field environments.

Project Management 100: Just the Basics | PM100 (2.0 CEU)   **$225**

A practical course to start learning about project management or validate what you already know.

U.S. Career Institute | Weston Distance Learning

2001 Lowe Street
Fort Collins, Colorado 80525-3474
(800) 528-7907
www.uscareerinstitute.edu

U.S. Career Institute is one of the oldest correspondence vocational educational institutions in the U.S. They guarantee that students who successfully complete their courses will get a job within six months of completion or they will refund the cost of the course(s) taken (although prisoners will likely not be able to take advantage of this unless their release date is very close.) Their programs are approved for Military education and MyCAA benefits.

They have recently limited their number of available print courses. Most courses are now only available online.

These courses will not be good towards credit at most colleges.

This school is also known as Weston Distance Learning, McKinley College, and At-Home Professions.

Accreditation: Distance Education Accrediting Commission (DEAC); regulated by the Colorado Department of Higher Education, Private Occupational School Board

Available to Prisoners

Numerous career courses with *Certificates of Completion*

Tuition Rates:	**See Table Below**
Payment Plans:	
Textbooks:	Included in tuition
Time Limits:	None
Proctor Required:	No

U.S. Career Center
Course Tuition Rates

Accounting Services	$887	Patient Care Technician	$887
Bookkeeping	$689	Personal Care Assistant	$349
Certified Personal Fitness Trainer	$887	Pharmacy Technician	$887
Home Inspection	$585	Wedding and Event Planner	$887
Paralegal	$887		

U.S. Career Institute
Available Courses

BUSINESS

Accounting
Instructs students in a broad range of manual and computerized accounting functions such as maintaining ledgers and journals, creating balance sheets and financial statements, and preparing payroll.

Bookkeeping
Instructs how to create balance sheets and financial statements as the process of controlling cash and preparing payroll.

CREATIVE CAREERS

Wedding Consultant/Event Planning
Comprehensive training program covering everything from theme weddings to networking tips and legal responsibilities.

HEALTH/PHYSICAL FITNESS TRAINING

Personal Fitness Trainer & Nutrition Specialist
Gain more advanced concepts in both nutrition and fitness as well as means to develop a well-rounded health and wellness plan for others.

LEGAL

Paralegal/Legal Assistant
Explores the role of the paralegal in a modern law office, litigation, criminal procedure, and legal writing.

MEDICAL

Pharmacy Assistant
Prepares for work in a pharmacy or other related environment. Topics include medical terminology, human anatomy and physiology, and pharmacology.

Veterinary Assistant
Subject matter includes a blend of technical and administrative topics ranging from anatomy and physiology to medical records, client relations, animal behavior and livestock care.

OTHER VOCATIONAL TRADES

Home Inspection
Provides a foundation in both the practicalities of inspecting homes as well as the administrative aspects of operating a home inspection business.

Vocational Studies | Religious

Global University | Berean School of the Bible

1211 South Glenstone Avenue
Springfield, Missouri 65804-0315
(800) 443-1083, (417) 862-9533
www.globaluniversity.edu   berean@globaluniversity.edu

Global University Berean School of the Bible offers ministerial and church leadership courses. Transcripts are maintained and diplomas are offered. Course are available in English and Spanish.

NOTE: The General Presbytery of the Assemblies of God has approved the Ministerial Studies Program to fulfill the educational requirements for ministerial credentials. While these credentials are not issued by Global University, they qualify the student to receive credentials from the General Council Credentials Committee of the Assemblies of God church.

Accreditation: North Central Association of Colleges and Schools, The Higher Learning Commission; Distance Education Accrediting Commission

Available for Prisoners:

Diplomas in:

Ministerial Studies; Ministerial Studies with Leadership Honors; Bible & Doctrine; Church Ministries; Royal Rangers Organizational Leaders

Certificates of Completion

Tuition:	**$38.40 per course** **$83.40 per course with study guide (optional)**
Payment Plans:	None available
Textbooks:	Study guide: $35 per course
Additional Fees:	**Shipping: $10 per course**
Time Limits:	None
Proctor Required?	No

Global University | Berean School of the Bible
Diploma & Certificate Programs

Ministerial Studies Diploma Program

Successful completion of this program will prepare the student for credentialing interviews and tests. The student will have mastered basic Bible content, theological principles, and practical ministry skills for service in a church leadership position.

Upon completion of the Ministerial Studies Diploma, the student will have met the minimum academic requirements to apply for the ordination process with the General Council of the Assemblies of God USA.

Level One | Certified Minister

Upon completion of this level the student will possess the basic skills needed to begin serving in a ministerial role in a local church, and will have met the academic requirements to apply for certified minster status in the General Council of the Assemblies of God USA.

Courses	CEUs
Christ in the Synoptic Gospels	BIB114	5
Introduction to Pentecostal Doctrine	THE114	5
Acts: The Holy Spirit at Work in Believers	BIB115	5
Prison Epistles: Colossians, Philemon, Ephesians, and Philippians	BIB121	5
Introduction to Hermetics: How to Interpret the Bible	BIB121	5
The Local Church in Evangelism	MIN123	5
Assemblies of God History, Missions, Governance	THE142	5
Relationships & Ethics in Ministry	MIN181	5
Beginning Ministerial Internship	MIN191	6
Total CEUs	**46**
Total Cost	**$345.60** w/o study guide
	$750.60 w/study guide

Level Two | Licensed Minister

Upon completion of this level students will have a mastery of specified Bible content, systematic theology, and ministry skills, and will have met the academic requirements to apply for licensed minister status in the General Council of the Assemblies of God USA.

Course	CEUs
Introduction to Theology: A Pentecostal Perspective	THE211	5
New Testament Survey	BIB212	5
Old Testament Survey	BIB214	5
Romans: Justification by Faith	BIB215	5
Introduction to Homiletics	MIN223	5
Eschatology: A Study of Things to Come	THE245	5
Effective Leadership	MIN251	5
Introduction to Assemblies of God Mission	MIN261	5
Conflict Management for Church Leaders	MIN281	5
Intermediate Ministerial Internship	MIN291	6
Total CEUs	**51**
Total Cost	**$384** w/o study guides

$834 w/study guides

Level Three | Ordained Minister

Upon completion of this level, students will have a mastery of several of the more difficult books of the Bible, advanced theological concepts, and administrative skills required for ministerial roles, and will have met the academic requirements to apply for ordained minister status in the General Council of the Assemblies of God USA.

Course	CEU
Prayer and Worship | THE311	5
Corinthian Correspondence | BIB313	5
Pentateuch | BIB318	5
Poetic Books | BIB322	5
Preaching in the Contemporary World | MIN325	5
Church Administration, Finance, and Law | MIN327	6
Pastoral Ministry | MIN381	5
Advanced Ministerial Internship | MIN391	6
Total CEUs	42
Total Cost	**$307.20** w/o study guides
	$667.20 w/study guides

Ministerial Studies with Leadership Honors Diploma Program

This diploma program is for students who are seeking a more challenging ministry and leadership training 1experience and who are willing to invest increased time and effort. Students who enroll in this program must accept the responsibility to find a qualified mentor (15 hours per program level), invest time in a mentor relationship, and complete additional requirements related to personal development and ministry.

Course	CEUs
Level One | Certified Minister	
Level One Capstone Project | CAP0110	6
Christ in the Synoptic Gospels | BIB114	5
Introduction to Pentecostal Doctrine | THE114	5
Acts: The Holy Spirit at Work in Believers | BIB115	5
Prison Epistles: Colossians, Philemon, Ephesians, and Philippians | BIB117	5
Introduction to Hermeneutics: How to Interpret the Bible | BIB121	5
The Local Church in Evangelism | MIN123	5
Assemblies of God History, Missions, and Governance | THE142	5
Relationships and Ethics in Ministry | MIN181	5
Beginning Ministerial Internship | MIN191	6
Total CEUs	52
Total Cost	**$380.40** w/o study guides
	$834 w/study guides

Level Two | Licensed Minister	
Level 2 Capstone Project | CAP0120	6
Introduction to Theology: A Pentecostal Perspective | THE211	5
New Testament Survey | BIB212	5
Old Testament Survey | BIB214	5
Romans: Justification by Faith | BIB215	5
Introduction to Homiletics | MIN223	5

Eschatology: A Study of Things to Come | THE245	5
Effective Leadership | MIN251	5
Introduction to Assemblies of God Mission | MIN261	5
Conflict Management for Church Leaders | MIN281	5
Total CEUs	**51**
Total Cost	**$380.40** w/o study guides
	$834 w/study guides

Level Three | Ordained Minister

Level 3 Capstone Project | CAP0130	6
Prayer and Worship | THE311	5
Corinthian Correspondence | BIB313	5
Pentateuch | BIB318	5
Poetic Books | BIB322	5
Preaching in the Contemporary World | MIN325	5
Church Administration, Finance, and Law | MIN327	6
Pastoral Ministry | MIN381	5
Total CEUs	**42**
Total Cost	**$307.20** w/o study guides
	$667.20 w/study guides

Bible & Doctrine Diploma Program

Completion of this course provides a basic knowledge of the Bible and theology that will help in lay ministry roles such as Sunday school instruction, in sharing the gospel with friends and neighbors, and in their personal devotional life. This diploma is designed to prepare students for Christian living, and it cannot be earned in conjunction with other Berean School of the Bible diploma programs. Courses are listed in the recommended order of study.

Course	CEUs
Sequence One	
Old Testament Survey | BIB214	5
New Testament Survey | BIB212	5
Introduction to Hermeneutics: How to Interpret the Bible | BIB121	5
Christ in the Synoptic Gospels | BIB114	5
Acts: The Holy Spirit at Work in Believers | BIB115	5
Introduction to Pentecostal Doctrine | THE114	5
Pentateuch | BIB318	5
Prayer and Worship | THE311	5
Sequence Two	
Introduction to Theology | THE211	5
Geography of the Holy Land | BIB316	4
Prison Epistles: Colossians, Philemon, Ephesians, and Philippians | BIB117	5
Romans: Justification by Faith | BIB215	5
Eschatology: A Study of Things to Come | THE245	5
Poetic Books | BIB322	5
Corinthians Correspondence | BIB313	5
Systemic Theology 1 | THE221	4
Systemic Theology 2 | THE222	4
Total CEUs	**82**
Total Cost	**$652.80** w/o study guides

$1,417.80 w/study guides

Vocational | Paralegal Studies

Adams State University

EXTENDED STUDIES

208 Edgemont Boulevard, Suite 3000
Alamosa, Colorado 81101
(800) 548-6679, (719) 587-7974
www.erxstudies.adams.edu   www.legalstudies.com

Adams State University offers prisoners a variety of college credit course, which can be found under *College Studies*. They also offer paralegal certificate programs through a partnership with the *Center for Legal Studies*.

The *Center for Legal Studies* offers these exact same courses to several schools across the U.S. However, *Adams State University* is the ONLY school to award college credit for these courses. For that reason, taking these courses through Adams State University will cost more than taking the same courses from other schools. Students should determine whether they would like to further their education in the future to determine whether earning credit is necessary for them.

Accreditation:

Available to Prisoners

Paralegal Certificate Course

Advanced Paralegal Certificate Courses

Tuition Rates:	**$644.50 per course for Paralegal I and Paralegal II** (both must be completed to earn a Certificate of Completion) **$525 per Advanced Paralegal course topic**
Payment Plan:	None available
Textbooks:	Prices vary.
Time Limit:	One year per course
Proctor Required:	No

You can find the *Adams State University* Paralegal Certificate Courses under the *Center for Legal Studies* listing in this chapter.

Blackstone Career Institute

PO Box 3717
Allentown, Pennsylvania 18106
(800) 826-9228, (610) 871-0031
www.blackstone.edu   *info@blackstone.edu*

Blackstone Career Institute is the oldest paralegal correspondence program in the U.S. Completion of their paralegal program will qualify the student to be a paralegal in every state except for California and North Carolina (which will require additional exams in these states.) They work well with prison systems.

Accreditation: Middle States Association of Colleges and Schools Commission on Secondary Schools; Distance Education Accrediting Commission (DEAC)

AVAILABLE TO PRISONERS

Certificate in:
Paralegal Studies

Tuition Rates:	**$767 for paralegal certificate program**
	(ask for any current discounts)
Payment Plan:	Monthly payment plans available for paralegal program:
	$59 down, $30 or $59 per month
Textbook Fees:	Included in tuition
Additional Fees:	None
Cancellation Policy:	Full refund within 5 days of enrollment; 85% refund 5 days to first assignment; Other percentages based on percentage of courses completed.
Transfer/Exam Options:	15% of the tuition cost, included in tuition payment
Time Limits:	2 years for paralegal program
Proctor required?	No

Blackstone Career Institute
Available Courses

The Paralegal Studies Program through Blackstone Career Institute is an all-inclusive program. All materials needed to complete the course of study are provided, including ten volumes of Modern American Law, the Blackstone Law Glossary, Writing to Win – The Legal Writer, Legal Research and Writing – Part I and II, How to Find a Job as a Paralegal, Merriam-Webster's Dictionary of Law, Ethics for Paralegals, and all postage. The primary curriculum is based on the following Modern American Law series:

VOLUME I | LAW – ITS ORIGIN, NATURE & DEVELOPMENT & CONTRACTS

Examines the origin of law, including its nature, sources, subject matter, classifications, beginnings, maturity, as well as a comprehensive look at contract law.

VOLUME II | TORTS

Examines all aspects of tort law, including comprehensive studies of trespass, conversion, negligence, defamation, defenses, judgments, interference, liability, and marriage and relationships.

VOLUME III | CRIMINAL LAW

Examines the subject of criminal law in detail, including, criminal capacity, incomplete offenses, homicide, assault, rape, false imprisonment, burglary, arson, larceny, robbery, embezzlement, forgery, counterfeiting, extortion, and offenses against the public, religion, morals and decency, and authority.

VOLUME IV | REAL PROPERTY – PART I

Begins the study of real property with comprehensive examinations of its history, the growth of individual rights, estates, remainders and limitations, rules against perpetuity, rules applied to charities, powers and classes, tenancy and estates arising by marriage.

VOLUME V | REAL PROPERTY – PART II

A continuation of the study of real property, including homestead exemptions, land rights, natural rights, easement, titles, rents, conveyance, recording laws, public lands, forfeiture, adverse possession, and accretion, alluvion, and reliction.

VOLUME VI | PLEADINGS TO CIVIL ACTIONS, PRACTICE IN CIVIL ACTIONS, & CRIMINAL PROCEDURES

Examines all aspects of civil procedure including, pleadings, proceeding, parties, defenses, motions, juries, witnesses, depositions, judgments, appeals, venue, indictment and trials.

VOLUME VII | WILLS & TRUSTS

A comprehensive examination of wills and trusts including descent and distribution, the history of wills, execution, form and revocation of wills, probate, as well as the history of trusts, express versus implied trusts, private versus public trusts, trustee appointment and duties, and beneficiaries.

VOLUME VIII | PARTNERSHIPS & CORPORATIONS

A comprehensive examination of the legalities behind partnerships and corporations, including, transactions, corporate crimes and torts, rights of stockholders, dissolution, foreign corporations, powers of partners, termination and rights of partners.

VOLUME IX | CONSTITUTIONAL LAW – PART I

A comprehensive examination of the constitution and its powers.

VOLUME X | CONSTITUTIONAL LAW – PART II

A comprehensive examination of the constitutional amendments and the Bill of Rights.

VOLUME XI | LEGAL RESEARCH & WRITING – PART I
VOLUME XII | LEGAL RESEARCH & WRITING – PART II

Volume XIII | How to Find a Job as a Paralegal
Volume XIV | Ethics for Paralegals

Center for Legal Studies

523 Park Point Drive, Suite 320
Golden, Colorado 80401
(800) 522-7737
www.legalstudies.com

The *Center for Legal Studies* is an educational training company that provides paralegal education programs to colleges and universities across the nation. They currently partner with nearly 200 schools, which carry their paralegal programs through their continuing education departments. You can take the courses directly from the *Center for Legal Studies* or from one of their partner schools.

One of the partner schools, (see Adams State University), offers credit for these paralegal studies, but other schools offer a Certificate of Completion featuring the school's logo.

Accreditation:

AVAILABLE TO PRISONERS

Paralegal Certificate Course

Advanced Paralegal Certificate Course

Tuition Rate:	**Paralegal Certificate Course: $1,289**
	Advanced Paralegal Certificate Course: $1,800
	Legal Secretary Certificate Course: $645
	Alternative Dispute Resolution Certificate Course: $645
	Legal Investigation Certificate Course: $645
Payment Plan:	Not applicable
Textbook Fees:	Not included in tuition
	Textbook prices vary. Average fees are $315 with shipping
Additional Fees:	None
Transfer/Exam Options:	Not applicable
Time Limits:	Not applicable

Center for Legal Studies
Partner Schools

Adams State University	Offers 3 credits per course and Certificate of Completion
Ohio University	Offers Certificate of Completion
Oklahoma State University	Offers Certificate of Completion

Center for Legal Studies
Available Courses

These courses are noncredit courses, with the exception of courses taken through Adams State University.

The *Paralegal Certificate Course* comes in two parts. Student must complete both parts to receive the Certificate of Completion.

PARALEGAL CERTIFICATE COURSE

Paralegal I   (3 credits from Adams State University)

As the first half of the Paralegal Certificate Course, this portion provides the foundation for the study of paralegalism. During this first session, students gain a detailed understanding of the American legal system, legal terminology and ethics. Students learn how to prepare pleadings, discovery, motions and briefs, and reviews the rules of evidence and civil procedure.

Textbooks: *Federal Civil Rules Booklet: Introduction to Paralegalism; Sample Pages: Illustrations of Organization & Research Techniques in West Group Publications; Paralegal Certificate Course Workbook; & Paralegal Career for Dummies.*

Paralegal II   (3 credits from Adams State University)

As the second half of the Paralegal Certificate Course, this course continues the legal education developed in Paralegal I. Students learn advanced skills including legal research, writing and proper citation format. Students are taught how to prepare important legal documents relating to real property, corporations, partnerships, wills, trusts, bankruptcy, and domestic relationships. Students will study formal and informal advocacy techniques and principles of appellate procedure.

Required textbooks: Same textbooks used in Paralegal I.

ADVANCED PARALEGAL CERTIFICATE COURSES

These course on noncredit courses (with the exception of *Adams State University,* which offers 3 credits per course)
Completion of six courses or more are awarded a certificate of completion by most schools.

Bankruptcy Law

Examines the debtor-creditor relationship and the difference between voluntary and involuntary bankruptcy, both under Chapter 7 (liquidation) and Chapter 11 (reorganization). Examines the Bankruptcy Code in-depth and how to prepare most important bankruptcy forms.

Required textbook: Legal Document Preparation Manual; and Bankruptcy Code, Rules & Forms

Business Law & Practices

Examines the law and practices of business organizations and the paralegal's potential functions in the area of law. Examines basic agency law, fundamental structure and most important legal doctrines relating to general partnerships, limited partnerships, limited liability companies, small closely-held corporations, and large publicly-traded corporations.

Estate Planning

Explores the paralegals role in estate planning. The requirements of creating enforceable wills and trusts are covered, and study of resulting and constructive trusts are provided.

Required textbook: Introduction to Estate Planning in a Nutshell

Intellectual Property

Provides in-depth instruction in one of the most dynamic and challenging areas of law. Paralegals in this specialty work in copyrights, patents, trademarks, unfair competition, protection of trade secrets, and more.

Required textbook: Intellectual Property: The Law of Trademarks, Copyrights, Patents, & Trade Secrets

Alternative Dispute Resolution

Trains and qualifies students to develop or participate in conflict mediation processes. Reviews the growth and application of settlement options in the U.S., and focuses on both traditional and non-traditional dispute resolution options.

Required textbook: Alternative Dispute Resolution in a Nutshell

Legal Investigation

Subjects include investigations related to arson, products liability, personal injury and traffic accident forensics, employment accidents, professional malpractice, and negligence.

Legal Secretary

Students will learn about legal terminology, legal process, jurisdiction and venue, written communications, filing procedures, billing and accounting, time management and more.

Real Property Law

Examines the system of common law property, the recording acts, conveyance, mortgaging, landlord-tenant, financing, land transactions, and the documents which record the purchase, sale, and leasing of real estate. Also covered: dealing with title insurance companies, recorders of deeds, recognizing land finance subjects, foreclosure of mortgages, and the possibility of redeeming a mortgage that has gone in default.

Required textbook: Real Property Law in a Nutshell

Education Law

Focuses on the laws that govern America's public school system and home schooling, including student rights regarding discipline, suspension, personal grooming, testing and grading, and drug testing.

Required textbook: The Law of Schools, Students, and Teachers in a Nutshell.

Constitutional Law

Examines fundamentals of the federal constitution, including the institution of judicial review, the limitations of federal judicial power, the constitutional roles of the legislative and executive branches, due process of law, and individual rights under the Constitution and Bill of Rights. Possible future trends of the U.S. Supreme Court are also explored.

Required textbook: Constitutional Law in a Nutshell

Family Law

Covers the formation and dissolution of domestic relations, including the law of marriage, annulment, separation and dissolution, maintenance, custody and support of children. Studies the differences between community and separate property, the classification of property, and the impact of such classification.

Required textbook: Family Law in a Nutshell

Immigration Law

This course explores all significant aspects of the immigration and naturalization process in the United States, including the Homeland Security Act of 2002 and the Illegal Immigration Reform and Immigrant Responsibility Act of 1996. Topics include student and worker visas, family residence requirements, and the removal process, as well as citizenship and the requirements for an immigrant to become a citizen.

Required textbook: Immigration Law for Paralegals

Criminal Law

This course begins with an overview of the concept of punishment and goes on to study the burden of proof and criminal defenses, and provides a critical look at the most common crimes. Students will learn common terminology in criminal law and how to consider a crime thoroughly in terms of its elements.

Required textbook: Criminal Law in a Nutshell

Criminal Procedure

This intensive study course deals with the constitutional dimensions of criminal law and procedure. Students will leave the course with an appreciation of how the U.S. Constitution focuses on the rights of the accused and the impact on our law enforcement system.

Required textbook: Criminal Procedure: Constitutional Limitations in a Nutshell

Victim Advocacy

This program is designed to train and qualify students to provide assistance to crime victims by providing an overview of criminal procedure and discussing the devastating effects crime can have on its victims.

This course can be taken as a separate certificate course.

Ohio University Southern

CONTINUING EDUCATION

Collins Center 112, 1804 Liberty Avenue
Ironton, Ohio 45638
(800) 444-2420, (740) 533-4548
www.ohio.edu   correctional@ohio.edu

Ohio University is the one largest and most prison-friendly correspondence options for prisoners. They offer many college for-credit opportunities, which you can find in our *College Studies* section, as well as some non-credit options for non-degree seeking students, which you can find in our Vocational/Personal Enrichment section.

The following is a noncredit comprehensive Paralegal Certificate Course offered by OU in partnership with *The Center for Legal Studies*, which awards Certificate of Completion bearing the OU logo.

Upon completion of the Paralegal Certificate Program, *Ohio University* students will also earn 9 CEUs.

Accreditation: North Central Association of Colleges and Schools | The Higher Learning (NCA-HLC)

AVAILABLE TO PRISONERS

Paralegal Certificate Program

Advanced Paralegal Certificate Course

Other Legal Education Course Options

Tuition Rates:	**Paralegal Certificate Course: $1,289**
	$644.50 per part (two parts available)
	(Both parts must be completed to receive a Certificate and CEUs.)
	Advanced Paralegal Certificate (six topics): $1,800
	$300 per topic
	Other Legal Education Courses: $645
Textbook Fees:	Prices vary. Approximately $315 with shipping.
Additional Fees:	Not applicable
Transfer Options:	Not applicable
Time Limits:	Paralegal Certificate: 12 months; Advanced Paralegal Certificate: 6 months per topic; Other courses: 6 months per course.
Proctor Required?	No

You can find the *Ohio University* paralegal courses under the *Center for Legal Studies* listing.

Oklahoma State University | Correspondence Education

309 Wes Watkins Center
Stillwater, Oklahoma 74078-4061
(405) 744-6390
ce.okstate.edu *ics-inf@okstate.edu*

Oklahoma State University offers a number of college-level for-credit courses (see *College Studies* section). Additionally, they offer several non-credit legal studies in partnership with The Center for Legal Studies, which awards certificates of completion bearing the OSU logo.

Accreditation: North Central Association of Colleges and Schools | The Higher Learning (NCA-HLC)

AVAILABLE TO PRISONERS

Paralegal Certificate Course

Advanced Paralegal Certificate Course

Tuition Rates:	**$594.50 per part (two parts available)** **$1289 for complete course** **(Both parts must be completed to receive a Certificate of Completion and CEUs.)**
Payment Plan:	Not applicable
Textbook Fees:	Varies, approximately $315 with shipping
Additional Fees:	None
Transfer/Exam Options:	Not applicable
Time Limits:	Not applicable

You can find the *Oklahoma State University* paralegal courses under the *Center for Legal Studies* listing.

COLLEGE STUDIES

If you are seriously considering a college education, you have reached a crucial point in your journey towards better learning. What you decide now will not only dramatically affect your next years of schooling, but will also influence the rest of your life. Therefore, it is vital that you take the time to carefully plan your education journey from this point on, to understand what you are signing yourself up for, and to have a firm grasp of the destination you want to reach.

ARE YOU READY?

It may sound like an abused cliché to simply state that school is what you make of it. But when it comes to getting an education from the confines of a prison, the statement couldn't be any truer. Getting an education, especially a college-level one, is challenging under the best of circumstances. Therefore, as with any challenging undertaking, it takes thorough preparation. Without this, especially from your cell, your odds of success are greatly diminished.

Before directly addressing what to expect from college, it would be wise to again consider what to expect from yourself. Consider the following:

➢ Can you handle the responsibility?

You are the only one who is responsible for your education. It is not the job of the school you choose, your prison's education coordinator, or your family to make sure that you learn. It is yours and yours alone.

➢ Why are you going to school?

College education is a commendable pursuit, one which may even make those who know and love you proud. But without a proper motivation of doing this *for you*, it will be difficult to experience the full potential of this pursuit.

➢ Are you self-motivated?

Prison is a lonely place when you have an ambition that no one else shares. Even if there are others around you who are going to school, unless they are taking identical classes to yours, you will be alone. Do you work well when there's not a team of people or even one other to motivate you?

➢ Are you in it for the long haul?

Going to college is not like reading a really long enjoyable book. It is an intensive experience that requires focus and hard work for the entire term of study, which is likely to take years.

➢ Are you ready for the cost?

We have emphasized repeatedly how expensive this undertaking can be. However, it comes not only at a financial price, but at a cost to your daily time. You should weigh every cost carefully before determining if you are truly ready.

THE SCHOOLS

All of the following schools have expressed a willingness to work with prisoners and to meet their specific needs, such as print-based courses, catering to prison requirements, and other accommodations.

If a school is not listed in this section, it is for the following reasons. 1) It is likely that they do not offer a convenient means for prisoners to take courses through their school; or 2) it may be one that offers prisoners educational opportunities but do so only in coordination with specific prison systems. These latter schools are not listed because they are already known within your prison system to anyone seeking to gain an education within those prisons.

If you have not already done so, contact your prison education coordinator to find out if there are current educational opportunities being offered to your prison system by schools in your area.

Most Prisoner-Friendly Schools

The following schools have gone out of their way to cater to the needs of prisoners. These schools have generally provided specific courses of study that are especially prison and prisoner friendly. They may not be the most economical for prisoners, but they will present the least amount of challenges for the incarcerated student.

NOTE: See separate listing of *College School Recommendations* ahead.

Adams State University

Coastline Community College

Ohio University

Rio Salado College

Seattle Central Community College

Thompson Rivers University

University of Idaho

University of Mississippi

Degree Programs (for example)

The following degree programs provide a good example of what you can expect to encounter if you are looking to earn a college degree.

These are current examples from the *Adams State University* 2016-2017 course catalog.

These are only examples. There are many more course and degree options at this school and other schools throughout this publication.

ASSOCIATE OF SCIENCE (w/ BUSINESS EMPHASIS)

PROGRAM REQUIREMENTS (60 CREDITS)

General Education = 37 credits

Business Emphasis = 15 credits

Electives = 8 credits

GENERAL EDUCATION (37 CREDITS)

Communication Arts I (3)

Communication Arts II (3)

Art Appreciation (3)

Intro to Philosophy (3)

Ethics (3)

Finite Math (3)

American History to 1865 (3)

American History 1865 to Present (3)

American Government (3)

Intro to Psychology (3)

Intro to Biology (4)

Intro to Astronomy (4)

BUSINESS EMPHASIS (15 CREDITS)

Intro to Business (3)

Principles of Accounting I (3)

Principles of Management (3)

Macroeconomic Principles (3)

Principles of Management (3)

ELECTIVES (8 CREDITS)

Business Law (3)

Sports Marketing (3)

Small Business Management (3)

BACHELOR OF ARTS IN SOCIOLOGY

PROGRAM REQUIREMENTS (120 CREDITS)

General Education = 37 credits

Major -- Sociology = 32 credits

Sociology Electives = 6 credits

Social Welfare Emphasis =12 credits

General Electives = 33 credits

GENERAL REQUIREMENTS (37 CREDITS)

(See General Requirements from the Associate program.)

MAJOR -- SOCIOLOGY (REQUIRED CORE COURSES - 32 CREDITS)

Research Skills for Behavioral Sciences (1)

Sociological Imagination (3)

Criminology (3)

Social Problems (3)

Social Statistics (4)

Race, Class, and Gender (3)

Race, Culture and Ethnicity (3)

Pre-Professional Seminar (2)

Social Psychology (3)

Sociological Theory (3)

Sociological Research Methods (4)

SOCIOLOGY ELECTIVES (6 CREDITS)

Marriages and Families (3)

Deviance and Control (3)

SOCIAL WELFARE EMPHASIS (12 CREDITS)

Human Behavior and Social Environment (3)

Poverty and Social Inequality (3)

Social Welfare Policy (3)

Internship in Social Welfare (3)

ELECTIVES (33 CREDITS)

Eleven courses of your choosing

MISCELLANEOUS GENERAL INFORMATION

The following is general information that you will come across as you explore schools and courses. Not every school is the same in these matters, but you can use these as a general guide.

Course Numbering

By looking at the course numbers you can determine the class level for which those courses were intended.

- Courses numbered below 100 are designed to give students a basic foundation. These courses often offer little to no credit.
- Courses numbered 100 to 199 are designed for first year students (freshman).
- Courses numbered 200 to 299 are designed for second year students (sophomores).
- Courses numbered 300 to 399 are designed for third year students (juniors).
- Courses numbered 400 to 499 are designed for fourth year students (seniors).
- Courses numbered 500 and above are graduate courses.

Class Status

Freshman = A student who has earned fewer than 30 credits.

Sophomore = A student who has earned 30 to 59 credits.

Junior = A student who has earned 60 to 89 credits.

Senior = A student who has earned 90 credits or more.

Registration Status

Full-time Student: One who is registered for 12 or more credits in a semester.

Three-quarter-time Student: One who is registered for 9-11 credits in a semester.

Half-time Student: One who is registered for 6-8 credits in a semester.

Official Student Status

Regular Student: A student who is working towards a degree.

Non-Matriculated Student: A student not admitted as a degree candidate. These students may be able to switch to regular student status if they decide they would like to earn a degree.

Auditor: A student who registers on a non-credit basis for one or more courses, not intending to ever earn a degree. These students will generally not take exams and are usually granted a tuition reduction.

College School Recommendations

Schools, and what you want out of them, vary in so many ways the it is impossible to make an overall recommendation. Therefore, we leave that up to the accrediting agencies. However, one common interest among all prisoners is the quality of the communication between the outside world and your cell.

When researching schools, we send requests to each one as if we are prisoners. We want to know how they respond to your requests, which is a great guide in determining how well the school will work with you should you decide to enroll.

The following schools are recommended as institutions who stood out from the rest in how well they communicated, how accommodating they were to our requests for information, how comprehensive their sent information was, and how willing they were to work with prisoners.

Starred "*" listings are exceptional in meeting the above criteria, proving that they have a good understanding of the unique challenges that prisoners face.

* **Adams State University**
* **Ohio University**
* **Rio Salado College**
* **Thomas Edison State University**
Thompson Rivers University
Upper Iowa University

RELIGIOUS STUDIES

Catholic Distance University
Christian Leadership University
Freedom Bible College & Seminary (non-accredited)
Global University
Hobe Sound Bible College
Vision International (non-accredited)

SCHOOL LISTING LAYOUT

CONTACT INFORMATION

This is the school's address and where you can go for more information on that school. There is always more information than we can provide concerning each school. We encourage you to contact every school you are interested in.

DESCRIPTION

Key details are provided about each school so that you are aware of information of note that may impact you as a prisoner-student.

ACCREDITATION

The following schools are all accredited by a variety of agencies, which are marked under each entry. As you've learned, accreditation is vital in determining the quality of a learning institution. But not all accrediting agencies are created equal. Therefore, you should exercise caution when selecting a school. (For a complete discussion on this topic, see section on *Accreditation* early in this book.)

AVAILABLE TO PRISONERS

This will keep you informed of what you can earn from this school, such as diplomas, degrees, and certificates. School offerings change regularly, which is why we update this book annually.

TUITION

This is the fee the school charges for courses, course credits, grade levels, and other programs.

PAYMENT PLANS

Many schools offer payment plans to make programs more affordable during study. Even if a payment plan is not listed, a school may be willing to work with you to develop an affordable plan that will work with your circumstances.

CREDIT TRANSFER/EXAM OPTIONS

If you have previously earned credits from another school, this section will tell you if this school may allow you to transfer those credits in. It will also let you know if they have credit-by-exam options.

TIME LIMITS

Schools generally place limits on how long you have to take a course. If you cannot complete your course in time, many schools offer extensions, often for a fee.

PROCTOR REQUIRED?

This area will tell you if a school require their examinations to be proctored (supervised by an impartial person.)

CANCELLATION POLICY

If you are unhappy with the school, or you determine that the courses you purchased are just not going to work for you, this section will tell you about the schools course refund policy.

AVAILABLE COURSES

This section provides information on the courses offered by the school, including courses available, descriptions, and prerequisites.

College Studies | General

Colleges | Undergraduate (Accredited) | What They Offer

SCHOOL	DIPLOMA / CERTIFICATE OF COMPLETION	FOR COLLEGE CREDITS	ASSOCIATE'S DEGREE	BACHELOR'S DEGREE
ADAMS STATE UNIVERSITY		✓	✓	✓
CALIFORNIA COAST UNIVERSITY	✓	✓	✓	✓
CENTENNIAL COLLEGE	✓	✓		
COASTLINE COMMUNITY COLLEGE	✓	✓	✓	
COLORADO STATE UNIVERSITY AT PUEBLO		✓		✓
MSU DENVER		✓		
MURRAY STATE UNIVERSITY		✓		
OHIO UNIVERSITY	✓	✓	✓	✓
OKLAHOMA STATE UNIVERSITY	✓	✓		
RIO SALADO COLLEGE	✓	✓	✓	
SAM HOUSTON STATE UNIVERSITY		✓		
SEATTLE CENTRAL COMMUNITY COLLEGE		✓		
SOUTHWEST UNIVERSITY	✓	✓	✓	✓
TEXAS STATE UNIVERSITY		✓		
THOMAS EDISON STATE		✓	✓	✓

School	Diploma / Certificate of Completion	For College Credits	Associate's Degree	Bachelor's Degree
UNIVERSITY				
THOMPSON RIVERS UNIVERSITY	✓	✓		
UNIVERSITY OF IDAHO		✓		
UNIVERSITY OF MISSISSIPPI		✓		
UNIVERSITY OF NORTH CAROLINA		✓		
UNIVERSITY OF NORTH DAKOTA		✓		
UNIVERSITY OF N. IOWA		✓		
UNIVERSITY OF SOUTH DAKOTA		✓		
UNIVERSITY OF WISCONSIN		✓		
UNIVERSITY OF WISCONSIN | PLATTEVILLE		✓		✓
UNIVERSITY OF WYOMING		✓		
UPPER IOWA UNIVERSITY	✓	✓	✓	✓

Colleges | Undergraduate (Accredited) | 2018 Tuition Rates

(cheapest to priciest)

SCHOOL	TUITION RATES (PER CREDIT)	AVERAGE COURSE COST
COASTLINE COMMUNITY COLLEGE (CA RESIDENT ONLY)	$49.00	$138.00
SEATTLE CENTRAL COMMUNITY COLLEGE (WA RESIDENT ONLY)	$71.66	$214.98
RIO SALADO (AZ RESIDENT ONLY)	$81.00	$243.00
GLOBAL UNIVERSITY	$104.80	$314.40
UNIVERSITY OF WYOMING	$124.00	$377.00
CALIFORNIA COAST UNIVERSITY	$150.00	$450.00
UNIVERSITY OF IDAHO	$160.00	$480.00
OKLAHOMA STATE UNIVERSITY	$170.00	$510.00
MSU OF DENVER	$179.00	$537.00
UNIVERSITY OF MISSISSIPPI	$183.33	$550.00
ADAMS STATE UNIVERSITY	$185.00	$555.00
SAM HOUSTON STATE UNIVERSITY	$191.00	$573.00
THOMAS EDISON UNIVERSITY (NJ RESIDENT ONLY) FLAT FEE OPTION (IF TAKING 36 CREDITS)	$200.00	$600.00
SEATTLE CENTRAL COMMUNITY COLLEGE (NON-WA RESIDENT)	$211.50	$634.53
RIO SALADO (NON-AZ RESIDENT)	$215.00	$465.00
UNIVERSITY OF NORTHERN IOWA	$224.00	$448.00
COASTLINE COMMUNITY COLLEGE (NON-CA RESIDENT)	$234.00	$702.00
UNIVERSITY OF NORTH CAROLINA (NC RESIDENT ONLY)	$239.17	$717.51
TEXAS STATE UNIVERSITY	$251.21	$753.64
THOMAS EDISON UNIVERSITY	$272.00	$816.00

School	Tuition Rates (per credit)	Average Course Cost
(Non-NJ resident) Flat Fee Option (if taking 36 credits)		
Southwest University	$275.00	$825.00
University of North Dakota	$278.29	$834.87
Catholic Distance University	$305.00	$915.00
University of Wisconsin | Platteville	$310.00	$930.00
Murray State University	$317.00	$951.00
Upper Iowa University	$325.00	$975.00
University of Wisconsin	$327.00	$981.00
Thompson Rivers University	$329.24	$987.72
University of South Dakota	$333.35	$1,000.05
Ohio University	$343.00	$1,029.00
Colorado State University @ Pueblo	$350.00	$1,050.00
Thomas Edison University (NJ resident only)	$396.00	$1,188.00
University of North Carolina (Non-NC resident)	$489.17	$1,467.51
Thomas Edison University (Non-NJ resident)	$499.00	$1,497.00

Adams State University

OFFICE OF EXTENDED STUDIES

208 Edgemont Boulevard, Suite 3000
Alamosa, Colorado 81101
(800) 548-6679, (719) 587-7671
www.exstudies.adams.edu   exstudies@adams.edu (CorrLinks registered)

Adams State University is one of the most prisoner-friendly colleges, offering several levels of educational opportunities for prisoners, including college degrees. They also offer numerous legal related vocational certificate programs, some of which are eligible for college credits that the student can use towards a degree track, (see *Vocational Studies* section), and one graduate degree option (see *Graduate Studies* section.)

They may award elective credits for prison classes. They ask that your prison education coordinator send a copy of your education data sheet for evaluation.

Accreditation: North Central Association of Colleges and Schools | The Higher Learning Commission (NCA-HLC)

AVAILABLE TO PRISONERS

Associate of Arts in Business

Associate of Science in Business

Bachelor of Arts in Business Administration; English & Liberal Arts; History; Interdisciplinary Studies; Political Science; Sociology (emphasis areas: Criminology and Social Welfare)

Bachelor of Science in Business Administration
(emphasis areas: General Business, Legal Studies, Management, Marketing, Small Business Administration)

Tuition Rates:	**$185 per credit (some courses vary) (Most courses will cost $555 each, plus fees.)**
Payment Plan:	None
Textbook Fees:	Not included in tuition
Additional Fees:	None for prisoners
Cancellation Policy:	90% refund within 30 days of course registration; No refunds after 30 days
Transfer/Exam Options:	45 credit hours per Associate's degree; 90 credit hours per Bachelor's degree. Up to 30 the CLEP or DANTES credits. Credits from non-accredited schools may be transferred after at least 24 credits earned through ASU.
Time Limit:	12 months, although some courses differ
Proctor Required?	Yes

Adams State University
Available Courses
The following courses all earn three (3) credits unless otherwise noted.

ANTHROPOLOGY

Introduction to Anthropology | ANTH 201
Basic theories, methods, and findings of human paleontology, prehistory, and culture.

ART

Art Appreciation | AR 103
Explores the nature of art in various aesthetic, formal, and psychological dimensions, involving analysis of art objects for understanding, enjoyment, and life enhancement.

BUSINESS

Introduction to Business | BUS 103
Characteristics and activities of current local, national, and international business. An overview of economics, marketing, management and finance.

Introduction to Agribusiness | BUS 105
An introductory course designed to provide students with a basic background in agribusiness issues and practices to give them the foundation to be successful in upper level agribusiness courses and meet expectations for basic knowledge in agribusiness relationships. This course will introduce students to potential careers within the fields of agriculture and agricultural business.

Principles of Accounting I | BUS 207
Provides a basic level of knowledge in recording business transactions, summarizing business activities, and preparing, interpreting and utilizing financial statements.

Principles of Accounting II | BUS 208
Accounting procedures for managerial accounting including job/process costing, cost behavior, budgeting, performance evaluation, differential analysis and capital investment.

Business Law | BUS 211
This basic business law course presents those areas most crucial to the legal environment of business. It covers topics encountered in everyday business such as law concerning contracts, property, product liability, sales and commercial paper (Uniform Commercial Code), legal concerns for employers and principal-agents, as well as new issues involving the Internet and e-commerce. This course is the study of legal principles pertaining to contracts, agency, negotiable instruments, corporations, partnerships, and government regulations. Research of actual cases is required. This course is the foundation course for all business students. It provides a legal framework for all business actions and thus relates to all business emphasis.

Business Communication | BUS 265
Business Communication focuses on advanced writing, expression and communication in a professional business atmosphere. Topics covered include team communication, ethical communication, multicultural communication, crisis communication and strategic communication, as well as business networking and etiquette. Course deliverables focus on creating a working resume, cover letter and oral presentation as well as in-depth interview preparation work.

Principles of Marketing | BUS 304
Practical applications-oriented treatment of the activities performed by those involved in marketing. Focuses on analyzing marketing opportunities, product pricing, distribution and promotion decisions, and careers in marketing.

Business Statistics | BUS 318
Business applications of descriptive and inferential statistics, measurement of relationships, and statistical process management. Includes the use of spreadsheet software for business statistical analysis.

Consumer Behavior | BUS 335
Consumer Behavior as it relates to the marketing functions. Emphasis is on models of consumer behavior and their applications to practical marketing problems.

Advertising | BUS 345

Advertising discusses the history, purposes and regulations of the advertising industry. Topics covered include creative principles, industry regulation and structure, advertising planning and promotions, media planning and the importance of integrated brand promotion.

Retailing | BUS 356

Study of marketing and management problems faced in the operation of retail business. Emphasis is given to techniques for solving problems in location, management, and merchandising, especially with the integration of the internet retailing (E-Tailing) as both a competitor and an extension of the storefront business.

Retail Management | BUS 359

Retail Management takes an in-depth look at marketing and management issues involved in retail business. Beginning with an emphasis on relationship building and consumer behavior, this course focuses on the specific elements of retailing strategy; planning the store location; managing a retail business; planning, handling, and pricing merchandise; communicating with the customer; and integrating and analyzing a retailing strategy

Paralegal I | BUS 359

As the first half of the Paralegal Certificate Course, this portion provides the foundation for the study of paralegalism. During this first session, students gain a detailed understanding of the American legal system, legal terminology and ethics. Students learn how to prepare pleadings, discovery, motions and briefs, and reviews the rules of evidence and civil procedure.

Paralegal II: Advanced Paralegal Concepts | BUS 359

As the second half of the Paralegal Certificate Course, this course continues the legal education developed in Paralegal I. Students learn advanced skills including legal research, writing and proper citation format. Students are taught how to prepare important legal documents relating to real property, corporations, partnerships, wills, trusts, bankruptcy, and domestic relationships. Students will study formal and informal advocacy techniques and principles of appellate procedure.

Personal Injury for Paralegals | BUS 359

Governmental and Institutional Accounting | BUS 360

This course is intended to be the student's first exposure to governmental and not-for-profit accounting. Some of the topics covered include; financial analysis and planning, accounting for general capital assets and capital projects, and long term financing. By the end of this course, you should develop a feel for basic concepts of governmental accounting and financial reporting, and be able to perform routine governmental bookkeeping.

Principles of Management | BUS 361

This course is concerned with the principles and methods used in managing and operating organizations, both domestically and abroad. Course coverage includes analysis of the organization's environment and the managerial functions of planning, organizing, leading, motivating, and controlling.

Human Resource Management | BUS 362

This course provides students with an overview of human resource management concepts. It offers the latest findings and thinking in the Human Resource field. Areas of interest include: Recruitment & Selection, Training, Development & Compensation, and Management & Employee Relations.

Managerial Finance | BUS 363

A study is made of financial principles as applied to management of funds, capital budgeting, sources of funds, techniques of financial analysis, cost of capital, financial leverage, capital structure, forecasting financial needs, management of working capital, financial policies, analysis and regulation of security issues, and international finance

Agribusiness Management | BUS 364

Management issues of agricultural business such as the forms of ownership, financial statements, analysis, and planning, investment analysis, strategic marketing, management of organizations, and human resources management.

Small Business Management | BUS 365

Provides an understanding of the tools entrepreneurs require to compete effectively in business. Accounting, marketing, finance and management of human resources are important considerations of this course.

Bankruptcy Law | BUS 379

Examines the debtor-creditor relationship and the difference between voluntary and involuntary bankruptcy, both under Chapter 7 (liquidation) and Chapter 11 (reorganization). Examines the Bankruptcy Code in-depth and how to prepare most important bankruptcy forms.

Estate Planning | BUS 379

Explores the paralegals role in estate planning. The requirements of creating enforceable wills and trusts are covered, and study of resulting and constructive trusts are provided.

Intellectual Property | BUS 379

Provides in-depth instruction in one of the most dynamic and challenging areas of law. Paralegals in this specialty work in copyrights, patents, trademarks, unfair competition, protection of trade secrets, and more.

Labor Relations Management | BUS 379

The basic principles of manpower use, wage structure, use of industrial psychology and collective bargaining, the union movement, human relations in industrial management, and modern labor laws and institutions.

Public Relations | BUS 379

This course provides an inside look at the practice of public relations. Emphasis is on the principles, processes and practices that lead to positive business relationships.

Sports Marketing | BUS 385

Sports Marketing illustrates the dynamic, progressive and influential nature of sports marketing. This course explores the sport marketing concept as a consumer-driven, integrated, goal oriented philosophy for a team, event, organization or athlete. Topics covered include: athletic endorsements, team sports, event sponsorships and alternative sports.

Organizational Behavior | BUS 401

Examination of individual behavior within the organizational setting. Examines the relationship of an individual and their personality, perceptions, motivation with the tasks assigned, groups interacted with management and the dynamics of the organization.

Auditing 1 | BUS 407

This course is intended to be the student's first exposure to auditing. Some of the topics covered include: introduction to financial statement auditing, basic auditing concepts, planning and audit, auditing internal controls, sampling tools for audits, reporting and professional responsibilities. By the end of this course, you should develop a feel for the basic concepts of auditing.

Leadership Strategies | BUS 418

This course presents contemporary theories and approaches to leadership practices in modern organizations. Students learn how effective leadership can assist in the creation of a strong organizational culture and implications external forces have on individual leadership development and continued growth.

Productions/Operations Management | BUS 430

Application of managerial decision making techniques. Covers forecasting, inventory models, linear programming, facility layout and the Transportation Model, process selection and capacity planning, design of work systems, location planning, quality control, scheduling, and project management. Available computer package utilized to solve related problems.

International Marketing | BUS 441

An advanced course in marketing covering the adaptations needed when marketing outside national boundaries. The course includes the discussions of cultures, product and marketing modifications necessary in a variety of situations, and the study of various world regions and their consumption, terrain, demographics, and geographic as they influence marketing practices.

Marketing Research and Information | BUS 454

Marketing research is the study of theory and methods used in marketing research to address marketing problems. Students will be prepared to complete research projects from problem formulation to writing a marketing research report and evaluate research performed by others.

Employment Law | BUS 459

An introduction to the nature and sources of law, and the methods by which laws are made; basic principles of contract law and property law as the foundations for business enterprise; tort law governing business relationships.

Marketing Management | BUS 460

Marketing Management is the capstone course in marketing and is focused on the problems faced by managers as they make decisions and develop policies.

Business Ethics | BUS 466

This course focuses on the concerns and issues of today's challenging business environment. It provides a framework that can be used to identify, analyze, and resolve ethical issues in business decision making.

Agricultural Marketing BUS 478

An overview of current marketing methods used for agricultural products and services, adding value to products, and selling that value to consumers.

Alternative Dispute Resolution | BUS 479

Trains and qualifies students to develop or participate in conflict mediation processes. Reviews the growth and application of settlement options in the U.S., and focuses on both traditional and non-traditional dispute resolution options.

Real Property Law | BUS 479

Examines the system of common law property, the recording acts, conveyance, mortgaging, landlord-tenant, financing, land transactions, and the documents which record the purchase, sale, and leasing of real estate. Also covered: dealing with title insurance companies, recorders of deeds, recognizing land finance subjects, foreclosure of mortgages, and the possibility of redeeming a mortgage that has gone in default.

Global Business Strategies | BUS 480

This course is designed to help you understand planning activities, determination of alternatives, policy formulation, execution of plans, and development of company strategy as currently used by business enterprises. It involves extensive case study to provide a practical, real world learning capability.

Ag. Policy and Farm Bill | BUS 488

The objective of this course is to provide the student with knowledge and comprehension of public policy in agriculture. Students will consider issues in public policy, how those issues relate to agricultural production and management, and related concerns of existing as an industry in a global marketplace.

World Food Distribution and Ag. Economics | BUS 498

This course considers both micro- and macro-economic issues as they are applied to food producing systems, markets, and trade around the world. The goal of this course in this capstone course for the ASU Agribusiness degree is to focus on the global nature of the agricultural industry. This course encompasses a variety of topics and issues related to agriculture, agribusiness, government policy, and international trade agreements.

COUNSELING

Introduction to the Counseling Profession | COUN 279

This course introduces and provides a comprehensive overview to the counseling profession and the basic skills utilized to be an effective professional counselor. The course will provide an overview of the processes of the counseling relationship, approaches and theories used, potential clients, history and future of the field, environments of the counseling profession, and understanding yourself and your impact in the counseling relationship. Through self-reflection assignments, case studies, and readings, students will discover the counseling profession and themselves in relation to a potential future career in counseling.

CRIMINAL JUSTICE

Ethics in Criminal Justice | CRJ 205

An introduction to concepts of ethics and an examination of contemporary ethical issues in the field of criminal justice.

Correctional Institution Organization and Management | CRJ 301

This course is a comprehensive analysis of criminal justice organizational behavior, management, administrative alternatives; and the role of manager as an agent of change will be examined. Also, theoretical and practical aspects of criminal management, including the process of decision-making and human relations, will be explored.

Police, Society and Community Relations | CRJ 307

This course examines the current issues and themes relating to the role of the police in the general community and greater society. It provides an in-depth study of the philosophies, programs, problems, and definitions that have recently been linked in the literature to the concept of community policing. Also covered are related topics including the organizational structure of police departments, problems in policing, new theories of the effects of policing on crime, the effectiveness of community policing, and recent major changes in U.S. policing.

Women, Crime and the Law | CRJ 309

A sociological examination of women who commit crime, who are victims of crime, and who work in the criminal justice system.

Contemporary Issues in Police Organization and Administration | CRJ 401

This course is a study of contemporary police management practices that includes an organizational approach to community policing as well as an in-depth study of departmental philosophy, personnel policies, organizational structure, and other practices. Principles of organization and management in terms of line, staff, and auxiliary functions will be covered as well as the organization of police services, administrative services, operational services, and auxiliary services.

Forensic Evidence | CRJ 407

This course focuses on the context of forensic evidence techniques and how they relate to the law. Modern techniques as well as techniques that have been used in the past will be examined. The crime scene will be looked at, the steps involved in recreating the crime scene, and collecting and testing evidence will be explored. We will also analyze the most recent court decisions that examine the use of forensic science during the investigation and at the trial of criminal cases. Each of the topics will have cases which have set precedence for future court cases.

Current Issues in Criminal Justice Administration | CRJ 409

This course analyzes the criminal justice process and its effects on practitioners, clients, and the public. It examines resources, organizational status, and leadership in regards to law enforcement agencies, courts and correctional settings, with particular emphasis on how leadership influences the effectiveness of the organization. The construct of bureaucracy and the major philosophical foundations of leadership are examined.

Ethics in the Criminal Justice System | CRJ 411

This course focuses on the context of ethics in the criminal justice system. Topics that will be examined include ethical considerations and how these considerations apply to society, the relationship that ethics has with regard to the law, a survey of the law and how these laws have an impact on society, the evolution of ethics, recent court decisions that examine the efficacy of modern law, and the concept of social responsibility. Each of the topics will have cases that have set precedence for future court cases.

Theories of Criminal Behavior | CRJ 415

An advanced, in-depth analysis of the major theories of crime and delinquency. Examines theories in historical context, with emphasis on biological, psychological, sociological, and political frameworks.

ECONOMICS

Macroeconomics Principles | ECON 255

Covers fundamental ideas in economics: scarcity, substitution, opportunity cost, marginal analysis, GDP, real and nominal magnitudes, supply and demand analysis, and microeconomic analysis of pricing in competitive and noncompetitive markets.

Microeconomics Principles | ECON 256

Functioning of the market economy, role of prices in determining the allocation of resources, the functioning of the firm in the economy, and forces governing the production and consumption of economic goods.

Economic Policy | ECON 425

This course in economic policy is the study of the structure and function of the U.S. economic system and the use of monetary, fiscal, and other policies to stabilize the economy. Emphasis is placed on studying macroeconomic issues from a political economy perspective, i.e., how policies are derived from the complex interplay of political, social, and economic forces.

Managerial Economics | ECON 433

This course demonstrates how economics theory is applied to national and international managerial decision-making. The course covers topics such as demand analysis, production and cost functions, market structure, managerial understanding of public policy, and international trade finance topics.

EDUCATION

Education Law | ED 379

Focuses on the laws that govern America's public school system and home schooling, including student rights regarding discipline, suspension, personal grooming, testing and grading, and drug testing.

ENGLISH

College Preparatory Reading and Writing | ENG 096

This course presents the an advanced study of reading and writing English. Students learn, step-by-step, to write unified, coherent papers. While learning to write, students learn to think in an organized, systematic fashion. They also study effective uses of language, as well as methods of connecting ideas and expanding ideas by means of details and examples.

Communications Arts I | ENG 101

Emphasizes the history of mass media and current trends, presenting information and activities to enable students to appreciate and evaluate the quality of print, audio, video, and television.

Communications Arts II | ENG 102

Continues the presentation of information about history of current trends in mass media and activities to enable students to appreciate and evaluate the quality of print, audio, video, and television.

Major Themes in Literature | ENG 203

This course is designed to expose students to a variety of literature and to develop critical and effective thinking, reading, and writing skills. In this course, students will read literature from three major genres; poetry, short stories, and drama. The students will learn basic literary terms and different approaches to literature. Students will come to understand that major human concerns are depicted by literature across time and cultures. There will be units on the following themes; family, men and women, fear and loss, freedom and responsibility, and quest.

Basic English Grammar | ENG 226

A comprehensive study of formal grammar and usage.

Introduction to Creative Writing | ENG 227

Essentials of fiction writing as plot, characterization, point of view, and style. Students will receive feedback on story ideas and drafts, and read and discuss at least ten different stories from two different collections.

Development of Vocabulary | ENG 259

The Prison Memoir | ENG 279

The Prison Memoir is designed to help students explore and understand how well-crafted memoirs written about prisons and the incarcerated life are a significant contribution to literature and the story of humanity. In addition to reading prison memoirs and excerpts written by men and women from diverse cultures, situations, and perspectives, students will study the craft of memoir as a creative writing genre with its own challenges and problems, and will also begin with its own challenges and problems, and will also begin in the process of writing their own memoir. Although this course will have special appeal to prisoners, it is open to any student who wishes to understand the incarcerated life as told by those who have lived it, or are still living it.

Women and Memoir | ENG 279

Women and Memoir is designed to help students explore and understand the recent explosion of women's memoir as a significant contribution not only to literature but also to the story of humanity and its treasure house of collective wisdom.

English Literature I | ENG 309

This course provides an in-depth exploration of English and American literature. Poetry, short stories, drama, novels, and literary essays are analyzed. In addition to discussing works from each of these literary genres, the course concentrates on helping students to form their own interpretations of literary words.

English Literature II, Romantics to Modern Period | ENG 310

The course emphasizes writing and literary analysis, teaching students to express their interpretations in written form using examples from the romantic to modern periods of literature. Poetry, short stories, novels drama and expository prose are covered.

World Literature I | ENG 326

An introductory to reading and understanding world literature. Literary study as a method of thinking critically about historical and contemporary aspects of the human condition. Writing integrated.

Poetry Workshop I | ENG 326

This course will teach students to develop their craft and creativity in the genre of poetry. Students submit original poems weekly, read selected works of contemporary, published poetry, read and respond to professor critiques of their poetry submissions. Students submit revised work in a final portfolio of at least 15 pages and a 4-page analysis and reflection on their revision strategies specific to the portfolio.

Nonfiction Workshop I | ENG 328

Introduction to the writing process. Assignments focus on major strategies of nonfiction prose, with subject matter drawn from firsthand experience and observation

20th & 21st Century British and Anglophone Literature | ENG 350

This course will examine literary contributions from many British authors. Students will read a variety of short fiction and essays. The course addresses common human themes, such as heritage and tradition in the British community.

The Novel | ENG 355

This course will focus on great many works from the eighteenth century to the present, and it is intended to familiarize the student with the various authors who represent (in part) the canon on the novel.

The Bible as Literature | ENG 358

This course analyzes the Bible as literature, examines the use of biblical motifs, imagery, and themes in post-biblical texts, and explores the First Amendment challenges confronting those who plan to teach Bible-as-literature courses in the public school.

Mythology | ENG 359

Deals with the myths and legends of civilizations with the greatest influence upon the development of the literature and culture of the English speaking people, and compares those myths with myths from other cultures.

Advanced Composition | ENG 363

This course reviews grammar and focuses on fundamental writing strategies, and applies those skills to specific types of documents.

Ethnic and Minority Literature | ENG 365

This course is centered on specific literary works (poetry & fiction) by writers from the following Ethnic and Minority backgrounds: Chicano, African-American, Native American and Asian American. The literature is focused on the influences, culture(s), history and heritage that is common to all minority authors. In addition, the works are also selected for their ability to invoke critical thought and discussion.

Topics in Science Fiction | ENG 379

Offered periodically to meet student special interests in the field.

American Literature I | ENG 394

A study of the emergence of a distinctive American literary art, including such writers as Poe, Emerson, Thoreau, Hawthorne, Melville, and Whitman.

American Literature II | ENG 395

Authors, works, and genres of American literature from the end of the Civil War to the end of World War I.

Shakespeare | ENG 403

An advanced study of selected plays of William Shakespeare. The course will include an offering of the comedies, tragedies, and one history. Additionally, the course will focus on Shakespeare's progression as a playwright, regarding the development of language, structure, and themes. Emphasis will be placed on analysis, literary interpretation, Elizabethan/Jacobean world-view, and close reading. We will study the following plays: A Midsummer Night's Dream, Much Ado About Nothing, Henry V, Hamlet, King Lear, Macbeth, The Winter's Tale, and The Tempest.

20th Century American Novel | ENG 443

Selected American Novelists from 1900 to the end of the 20th century.

Reading Poetry | ENG 458

A study from ancient to contemporary with an emphasis on form and technique.

Contemporary Literary Theory | ENG 480

Study of the developments of literary-critical theory and practice from the beginning on the 20th century to the present. Some emphasis on important earlier theories as they relate to contemporary developments.

Studies in Major Authors | ENG 490

Study of [major authors in fiction, dramatic literature, and poetry. Author(s) will be selected by instructor. This section of the course focuses on Herman Melville.

GEOLOGY

Physical Geology | GEOL 111 (4 credits)

Acquaints the student with how earthquakes, active volcanoes and other geologic formations and processes relate to the theory of plate tectonics. The course stresses that Earth continues to evolve and that its future depends on our actions of today.

HISTORY GOVERNMENT AND PHILOSOPHY

Development of Civilization to 1500 | HGP 110

As outlined in Section IV of the General Education Curriculum, this course consists of the first part of a two semester course in global civilization. These two courses attempt to "promote an understanding of the political and social systems developed by diverse cultures throughout history." In the process, it seeks to foster in students "a capacity to develop and maintain a global perspective (cultural, historical, and societal) from which a strong set of ethical and moral values can evolve." It seeks to promote "an ability to initiate inquiry, question conventional wisdom, and analyze problems."

Development of Civilization from 1500 | HGP 111

As outlined in section IV of the General Education Curriculum, this course consists of the second part of a two semester course in global civilization. These two courses attempt to "promote an understanding of the political and social systems developed by diverse cultures throughout history." In the process, it seeks to foster in students "a capacity to develop and maintain a global perspective (cultural, historical, and societal) from which a strong set of ethical and moral values can evolve." It seeks to promote "an ability to initiate inquiry, question conventional wisdom, and analyze problems." Through structured learning activities involved global history, students should develop their ability (a) to "read, write and listen accurately, effectively, and critically" (b) to "distinguish fact from opinion and think independently" and (c) to "think accurately." Formal and informal class activities should help the successful student grow in the understanding of "diverse moral and ethical philosophies" and in assessing "one's place within a larger historical and multicultural framework."

Senior Seminar Government Emphasis | HGP 471

This course is designed to be the academic capstone experience for all students who have majored in History/Government. Each student will write a paper that reflects the student's mastery of library usage, research methodology, breadth of knowledge, and writing ability. All students enrolled in the Senior Seminar will also write their Senior Comprehensive Examines as part of the departmental requirement for all History/Government majors. The Seminar topic will be chosen by the instructor, but sufficient methodological approaches will be explored to accommodate the interests of students from either a History or Government emphasis.

HISTORY

American History to 1865 | HIST 202
From European background through Civil War.

American History 1865 to Present | HIST 203
Development of the United States including the growth of industry and its impact on society and foreign affairs.

Colorado History | HIST 301
This is a survey of events, people, and trends that have shaped Colorado. We will survey the economic, political, social and environmental history of the state, compare the state's history with national trends, and identify the unique features of the state's history.

The American West | HIST 305
This is a survey of the history of the American West, which in this case covers the land from the Great Plains to the Pacific Ocean. It examines the interplay of various peoples, such as Native Americans and European-Americans, and the physical environment of the generally arid, mountainous region. The course will examine the Native American background, the colonizing of the Southwest by the Spanish, then the movement of settlers from the United States over the West. Of particular concern will be the economic and social development of the region.

American Revolution & Federalist Era | HIST 316
An upper division survey of the period from 1763 to 1801, with particular attention to the American Revolution, the Confederation, the Constitutional Convention, and the administrations of President's Washington and Adams.

Foundations of American Diplomacy | HIST 318
An examination of the cultural, institutional and ideological drivers of the American foreign policy experience and how these drivers affect future American foreign policy.

History of American Women | HIST 320
This course is designed to examine the role of women in American History with special emphasis on how the story of women is told by historians over time. It examines not only the lives of many famous white women, but also the experience of women from various ethnicities and economic backgrounds. In addressing how Americans construct their understanding of women's lives in the U.S., the course will also reassess how focusing on women's lives might alter one's understanding of the broader patterns and interpretations of American History.

England | HIST 342

A study of the social, economic, political, and constitutional development of the English state, with emphasis on the evolution of the Empire and contemporary Great Britain.

History of Sports in America | HIST 350

This course covers the development of sports and their significance in American life from colonial times to the present. It is designed both to supplement student's understanding of American History and to examine the role that sports has played in shaping contemporary society. Close attention will be paid to the context of sports development, especially the economic and social environment. Topics will include a study of the role of industrial society in fostering sports, and the changing gender structure of sports.

United States History Since 1950 | HIST 427

Southeast Asia: Culture and Politics | HIST 459

The main objective of this course is to understand the dynamics of local culture and political change in Southeast Asia since the 18th century. The course seeks in particular to examine how politics is shaped by the cultural realities in, and impinging on, the region. The scope of the course covers the transition from the pre-modern world to modernity and our postmodern beyond.

HUMAN PERFORMANCE AND PHYSICAL EDUCATION

Concepts in Wellness | HPPE 120 (2 credits)

Concepts in Wellness is a college-level health promotions course designed to encourage healthy, active lifestyles. Students will learn the vital connection between fitness and health, gain knowledge of the benefits of exercise and be provided a rational basis for choosing a healthy, active lifestyle.

MATHEMATICS

Pre-Algebra Skills | MATH 095

Basic Algebra Skills | MATH 097

Intermediate Algebra | MATH 099

Finite Mathematics | MATH 104

Systems of linear equations and inequalities, matrices, linear programming, and probability.

College Algebra | MATH 106

Trigonometry and Analytical Geometry | MATH 107

A thorough discussion of trigonometric concepts and applications are presented in this course. Students study proofs of trigonometric identities, solutions, of right and oblique triangles, solutions of trigonometric equations and functions, vector applications and polar coordinates.

PHILOSOPHY

Introduction to Philosophy | PHIL 201

An introduction to the scientific study of behavior and mental processes, including major approaches and methodologies. The course samples a broad range of topics, including biological foundations, development, learning, cognition, personality, abnormal psychology and social behavior.

Ethics | PHIL 202

Discussion of classic and/or modern philosophical views of human values, ideals, and morality. Provides introductory survey of some main problems, concepts, and results of ethics including selected philosophers past and present.

Logic | PHIL 205

An introduction to the essential principles of logical thinking, with particular attention to the fundamentals of inductive and deductive reasoning.

Existentialism | PHIL 324

Existentialism concerns itself with the problems of the individual coming to terms with their own existence. The course will concern itself with the structure/nature of subjectivity, relationship between the individual and others, freedom, authenticity, death, despair, and the meaning of life. A special emphasis will be given to religious existentialism: the relationship between the individual and the Divine.

Physics

Introduction to Astronomy | PHYS 201

The ability to take this course is dependent on your facility due to lab requirements. An introductory course in astronomy including historical astronomy, solar system astronomy, the life cycle of stars, the structure of the galaxy, telescope usage, identification of constellations and the apparent motion of celestial objects as seen from Earth. Lab activities are an essential component of the course.

Political Science

Constitutional Law | POLS 379

Examines fundamentals of the federal constitution, including the institution of judicial review, the limitations of federal judicial power, the constitutional roles of the legislative and executive branches, due process of law, and individual rights under the Constitution and Bill of Rights. Possible future trends of the U.S. Supreme Court are also explored.

Family Law | POLS 379

Covers the formation and dissolution of domestic relations, including the law of marriage, annulment, separation and dissolution, maintenance, custody and support of children. Studies the differences between community and separate property, the classification of property, and the impact of such classification.

Immigration Law | POLS 379

This course explores all significant aspects of the immigration and naturalization process in the United States, including the Homeland Security Act of 2002 and the Illegal Immigration Reform and Immigrant Responsibility Act of 1996. Topics include student and worker visas, family residence requirements, and the removal process, as well as citizenship and the requirements for an immigrant to become a citizen.

Psychology

Introduction to Psychology | POLS 101

Explores the brain, biology and behavior; sensation and reality; memory, intelligence and creativity; conditions and learning; motivation and emotion; health, stress and coping; abnormal psychology; gender, sexuality, social behavior and human relations.

Sociology

The Sociological Imagination | SOC 201

This course is designed to encourage students to develop social scientific frameworks for analyzing the social world in a context that transcends conventional wisdom and personal experience. The major question is "What are the social forces operating in society and often beyond the control of individuals that shape individual behaviors and societal changes?" Topics include culture, socialization, social and economic inequities, social structure, organizational behavior, social groups, deviance, and social institutions (e.g., family, religion, education, and political economy.)

Criminology | SOC 245

This course is designed to provide an in-depth study of criminology. A sociological approach to the study of crime and criminals is presented. The course also includes historical material, theory and research, and extensive coverage of conventional topics.

Social Problems and Social Welfare Strategies | SOC 251

The course is designed to provide the student with a survey of selected contemporary social problems. Social problems addressed in the class may include poverty, addiction and substance abuse, mental health, violence with a focus on family violence, crime, teen sexuality and pregnancy, and health care issues. The causes, severity, and consequences of the selected social problems are explored. In addition, strategies for alleviating social problems are explored. This course covers sixteen social problems of our society today. It provides a comprehensive study of these problems by viewing them from three sociological perspectives; the structural functional analysis, the symbolic-interaction analysis, the social conflict analysis for looking at social problems. The problems of social inequity, the problems of deviance, conformity and well-being, problems of social institutions and global social problems are discussed in the text. It also includes political attitudes and values of the left, the right and the radical left when discussing sixteen social problems. This will provide the student issues in these contemporary times and with a focus on global issues.

Social Statistics | SOC 311 (4 credits)

This course presents a general overview of the statistical methods most commonly used in sociology and social sciences. The skills learned in this course will enable the student to: read popular applications of statistics in the media with a critical eye; assess the use of statistics in professional sociological literature; and use statistical tools to answer sociological questions of interest.

Sociology of Education | SOC 315

This course explores the relationship between education and society, with special emphasis on the effects of this relationship on the lives of students in American education system.

Race, Class, and Gender | SOC 318

The focus of this course is on the interrelated, ascribed statuses of race, social class, gender, and sexual orientation in American society, how they are perceived and reinforced, the social tensions that result, and the dynamics of change.

Marriages and Families | SOC 320

Juvenile Delinquency | SOC 347

A study of how delinquents and juveniles in need of supervision are handled within the juvenile system. The nature and extent of delinquent behavior as well as child abuse and neglect are examined.

Human Behavior and the Social Environment | SOC 352

This course is an introduction to the nuts-and-bolts of social work practice. The course is designed with several general objectives in mind: (1) to familiarize the student with specific techniques of social work such as the person-in-environment approach and case management, (2) to provide a fundamental understanding of roles of community and family in social work practice, (3) to explore the needs of selected special populations in the community, (4) to identify the biological, psychological, and social influence on development and behavior across the life cycle, and (5) to introduce the student to fundamental social work practice skills. The course is designed to provide the student with material that will help with the understanding of the underlying reasons why people act as they do. Further, it will help the student to evaluate the strengths and deficits in people's biological, psychological and social development. In order to do this the text presents a variety of theories and research about human growth and development. It uses a life-span approach that shows the student a description of human growth and development from conception through late adulthood.

Poverty and Social Inequality | SOC 370

This course examines the historical and socio-cultural factors which influence the creation and maintenance of poverty and social inequity. Emphasis will be on structural influences on, and theoretical explanations of, poverty and social inequality. This course will also focus on the implications for policy and social programs aimed at poverty and other social class issues. In addition, there will be exploration of systems of power, privilege, and domination that are central to the American social structure. Finally, the issues of empowerment, resistance, and solutions to poverty and social inequality will be assessed.

Criminal Law | SOC 379

This course begins with an overview of the concept of punishment and goes on to study the burden of proof and criminal defenses, and provides a critical look at the most common crimes. Students will learn common terminology in criminal law and how to consider a crime thoroughly in terms of its elements.

Criminal Procedure | SOC 379

This intensive study course deals with the constitutional dimensions of criminal law and procedure. Students will leave the course with an appreciation of how the U.S. Constitution focuses on the rights of the accused and the impact on our law enforcement system.

Victim Advocacy | SOC 379

This program is designed to train and qualify students to provide assistance to crime victims by providing an overview of criminal procedure and discussing the devastating effects crime can have on its victims.

Family Violence | SOC 380

An exploration of the incidence, scope, and contributing factors in family violence. Various perspectives are examined. Topical issues include patriarchy, marital rape, domestic assault, and child sex abuse. Coverage includes theories of violence, alternatives to violent interactions, and criminal justice system's response.

Drug Abuse and Society | SOC 381

Fundamentals of mood-altering chemicals other than ethyl alcohol and the symptomatology and treatment of the abuse of them. Provides facts and insight concerning the abuse of wide variety of "legal" and "illegal" mood-altering chemical substances and approaches to treatment and prevention of drug abuse.

Pre-Professional Seminar | SOC 395

This class is a hybrid correspondence course. It is designed for two types of students; those who choose the Correspondence format and DO NOT have access to the internet, and those who choose the Correspondence format and DO have access to the Internet. For students who DO NOT have access to the Internet, this class provides the opportunity to critically examine one's professional goals and objectives, identify one's job strengths and skills, develop one's resume, and construct cover letters. For students who DO have access to the Internet, this course provides and introduction to the profession of sociology and the various career options available to graduates. Occupational and graduate school options are explored in detail. In formal job interviewing, resume development, and professional correspondence are explored. The course is also designed to prepare students for their Internship class by becoming informed about the requirements for placement in sociological, social service and criminal justice settings.

Social Psychology | SOC 401

Theory and research on the ways that people think about, influence, and relate to one another. Specific topics include attitude and behavior, social perception and cognition, conformity, persuasion, group influence, aggression, attraction, and helping behavior.

Gender and Society | SOC 419

A study of the way culture shapes and defines the positions and roles of both men and women in society. Major emphasis on social conditions which may lead to a broadening of gender roles and a reduction of gender role stereotypes and implications of these changes. Open to both men and women.

Correctional Systems | SOC 447

A study examining the entire correctional system from law enforcement through the administration of justice, probation, parole and correctional institutions.

Social Welfare Policy | SOC 470

This course provides information about the analysis of Social Welfare policy in the United States from the pluralist perspective. It is an upper division course and goes beyond introductory type of analysis of Welfare eligibility, financing and administration. It provides the student with information about the basic framework for Social Welfare policy analysis, an overview of discrimination that is based on racism, sexism, alternative sexual lifestyles, ageism, and people with disabilities. The course also provides a review of some theoretical formulations about poverty and strategies to combat poverty. The text covers the basic concepts, policies, and programs that have typified the U.S. welfare state. In addition, it details information about our voluntary nonprofit welfare sector and corporate for-profit sector. It further delves into discussing the social welfare policy strategy of tax expenditures. Beyond that it directs attention to the often neglected role of religion and social welfare policy. The text does a comprehensive job of covering the influence of global capitalism and international social policy.

Terrorism | SOC 480

This course seeks to understand the origin of terrorism. This course has been designed to analyze the ever changing society with the influence of terrorism. A survey of different terrorist attacks will be examined. This course will take a multicultural perspective as different groups of people are studied and the threat of terrorism is applied. This course will also offer practical approaches to dealing with the threat of terrorism.

WOMEN'S STUDIES

Women and the American Experience | WS 294

An interdisciplinary analysis of women's position in society as presented through the disciplines of history, sociology, anthropology, theology, psychology, literature, and the fine arts. The course will examine theoretical approaches to the differential access to power between men and women and the existence of patriarchy in Western culture while specifically examining these issues relating to women in American society.

COLLEGE STUDIES | 233

California Coast University

925 North Spurgeon Street
Santa Ana, California 92701
(888) 228-8648, (714) 547-9625
www.calcoast.edu   admissions@calcoast.edu

California Coast University provides quality distance education that is widely respected by employers, including the U.S. government, the military, and civilian corporations. They have extensive paper-based course offerings at a reasonable tuition rate.

Accreditation: Distance Education Accrediting Commission (DEAC)

AVAILABLE TO PRISONERS

Associate of Science *in:*

Business Administration, Business Marketing, Criminal Justice, General Studies, Health Care Administration, Psychology

Bachelor of Science *in:*

Business Administration, Business Marketing, Criminal Justice, General Studies, Health Care Administration, Management, Psychology

A Variety of Professional Certificate Programs

Tuition Rates:	**$150 per credit**
	(Most courses will cost $450 each, plus fees.)
Payment Plan:	$500 down, $100 per month, or
	$300 down payment, $125 per month
Textbook Fees:	Not included in tuition.
	Textbook rental program available ($25 per book for 120 days)
Additional Fees:	**Application fee: $75**
Transfer/Exam Options:	30 credit hours per Associate degree; 93 credit hours per Bachelor degree
Time Limit:	5 years per degree
Proctor Required?	Yes

California Coast University
Professional Certificate Programs

The following certificate programs are ideal for students who wish to specialize in a particular field without having to take all of the courses that do not apply to that field. Each certificate earns twelve credits that can be applied to further education, such as a degree.

Business Administration

Courses:	Credits
° Introduction to Business	3
° Business Communications	3
° Business & Society	3
° Organizational Theory & Behavior	3
Total credits:	12
Total Tuition:	**$1,800.00**

Fundamentals of Marketing

Courses:	Credits
° Introduction to Marketing	3
° Consumer Behavior	3
° Advertising & Promotions	3
° Marketing Management	3
Total credits:	12
Total tuition:	**$1,800.00**

Fundamentals of Criminal

Courses:	Credits
° Introduction to Criminal Justice	3
° Criminal Investigation	3
° Procedures in the Justice System	3
° Forensic Science	3
Total credits:	12
Total tuition:	**$1,800.00**

Fundamentals of

Courses:	Credits
° Introduction to Psychology	3
° Developmental Psychology	3
° Personality Theories	3
° Abnormal Psychology	3
Total credits:	12
Total tuition:	**$1,800.00**

Fundamentals of Finance

Courses:	Credits
° Introduction to Accounting	3
° Principles of Economics	3
° Intro to Financial Mgmt.	3
° International Business	3
Total credits:	12
Total tuition:	**$1,800.00**

Health Care Administration

Courses:	Credits
° The U.S. Health Care Sys	3
° Essentials of Managed Care	3
° Cultural Diversity in Health & Illness	3
° Medical Law & Ethics	3
Total credits:	12
Total tuition:	**$1,800.00**

Fundamentals of Management

Courses:	Credits
° Principles of Management	3
° Human Resource Management	3
° Small Business Management	3
° Operations Management	3
Total credits:	12
Total tuition:	**$1,800.00**

California Coast University
Available Courses
The following courses earn three (3) credits each.

BUSINESS ADMIN & MANAGEMENT COURSES

Introduction to Business
Introduction to Accounting
Computing Concepts
Principles of Economics
Information Management
Principles of Marketing
Introduction to Financial Management
Business Law
International Business
Public Relations
Business and Society
Organizational Theory and Behavior
Human Resource Management
Small Business Management
Operations Management

HEALTH CARE ADMINISTRATION COURSES

The United States Health Care System
Introduction to Community Health Care
Information Technology for Health Professionals
Essentials of Managed Health Care
Cultural Diversity in Health and Illness
Medical Law and Ethics

MARKETING COURSES

Introduction to Marketing
Customer Service
Consumer Behavior
Advertising and Promotions
Social Media Marketing
Marketing Management

BEHAVIORAL SCIENCE COURSES

Introduction to Psychology
Psychology of Gender
Health Psychology
Introduction to Organizational Psychology
Developmental Psychology

Social Psychology
Learning Theories
Marriage and Family
Tests and Measurements in Psychology
History and Systems in Psychology
Personality Theories
Abnormal Psychology
Counseling Psychology
Educational Psychology

CRIMINAL JUSTICE COURSES

Introduction to Criminal Justice
Juvenile Justice
Computer Forensics & Cyber Crime
Homeland Security
Criminal Investigation
Procedures in the Justice System
Terrorism
Criminal Behavior
Forensic Science
Criminal Law
Theory and Practices of Law Enforcement
Theory and Practices of Corrections
Domestic Violence
Research Methods in Criminal Justice and Criminology

GENERAL EDUCATION COURSES

The Human Body
Environmental Science
Introduction to Humanities
Introduction to Civilization
United States Government
Mathematics
English
Introduction to Cultural Anthropology
Introduction to Sociology
Early United States History
Art History
World Religions
Criminology

Centennial College

DISTANCE LEARNING

PO Box 631 Station A
Toronto, Ontario, M1K 5E9 Canada
(416) 289-5000, (416) 289-2646
www.centennialcollege.ca/programs-courses/distance-learning   *success@centennialcollege.ca*

Centennial College is a Toronto, Canada based school. They offer business-related print-based courses that prisoners can take, as well as certificate programs in various business specialties.

Rates cited are in Canadian dollars. U.S. dollar conversion estimate is in parenthesis below.

Accreditation: Association of Universities and Colleges of Canada

Available for Prisoners:

Certificate Programs in the following:

Business Management – Entrepreneurial; Business Management – International; Business Management -- Marketing

Tuition Rates:	**$12,400 per program (Canadian dollars. U.S. currency exchange estimate: $9,500)**
Payment Plans:	None
Textbooks:	Not included in tuition
Additional Fees:	**Administrative and other incidental fees: $24.50 to $31.80 per credit (Canadian dollars), which include health insurance, service fee, technology fee, student activity fee and other program fees.**
Cancellation Policy:	Full refund within one month of enrollment, less a $40 administrative fee.
Transfers:	
Time Limit:	6 months per course
Proctor required?	Yes

Centennial College
Certificate Programs

These certificate programs are designed to meet the needs of students who are interested in a specific professional specialization.

These are groups of courses that provide a concentration in a particular study area, without the need to take the general education courses of degree programs. They are more economical options than a full degree track.

Once completed, each of the following certificate earns college credit as marked, which can be used towards future learning.

This certificate program is designed to meet the needs of students seeking a broad knowledge of business administration and specializing in the area of entrepreneurial studies.

The following are the required courses for this program (see course descriptions on the following pages):

Course	Credit
Financial Accounting I	ACCT-112	3
Organizational Behaviour	BUSN-221	3
Human Resource Management	HRMT-301	3
Business Law	BUSN-331	3
Business Culture	BUSN-333	3
Entrepreneurship	CEIL-896	3
Fundamentals of Operational Management – CEMG-103	3
Total Credits	21 Credits

This certificate program is designed to meet the needs of students seeking a broad knowledge of business administration and specializing in the area of international studies.

The following are the required courses for this program (see course descriptions on the following pages):

Course	Credit
Business Fundamentals	BUSN-119	3
Principles of Marketing	MKTG-116	3
Choose any six of the following:	
Organizational Behaviour	BUSN-221	3
Fundamentals of Operational Management	CEMG-103	
International Economics	ECON-201	3

Course	Credit
Human Resource Management | HRMT-301	3
International Business Concepts | INTL-220	3
Mathematics of Finance | MATH-106	3
Market Research | MKTG-224	3
Total Credits	**24**

This certificate program is designed to meet the needs of students seeking a broad knowledge of business administration and specializing in the area of marketing. Topics covered are: Product management, pricing, distribution and promotion strategies, advertising, sales promotions, publicity, media and creative execution.

The following are the required courses for this program (see course descriptions on the following pages):

Course	Credit
Financial Accounting I | ACT-112	3
Business Fundamentals | BUSN-119	3
Organizational Behaviour | BUSN-221	3
Principles of Marketing | MKTG-116	3
Choose any three of the following:	
Management Accounting I | ACT-222	3
Fundamentals of Operations Management | CEMG-103	3
Management Principles | MGMT-222	3
Market Research | MKTG-224	3
Marketing Communications | MKTG-331	3
Total credits	**21**

COLLEGE STUDIES | 239

Coastline Community College

Incarcerated Students Education Services
Fountain Valley, CA 92708-2597
(714) 241-6315
www.coastlinecc.com

Coastline Community College offers programs specifically designed for prisoners, serving more incarcerated students in the state of California than any other in-state college. If you are a California resident, their tuition rates are exceptionally low. Otherwise, their rates are on the high side for the out-of-state students.

Unfortunately, unlike most correspondence schools, they require students to follow stringent registration dates in order to be enrolled – generally between late-June and late-August. If you are not enrolled before the deadline, you will have to wait until the next year to enroll.

As a California community college, they offer some unique opportunities, including scholarships and tuition fee waivers. Concerning fee waivers: if you are a California resident, you may qualify for the 2017-2018 Board of Governors Fee Waiver (discussed on page 71.)

Accreditation: Western Association of Schools and Colleges

AVAILABLE TO PRISONERS

Associate of Arts
Areas Of Emphasis include: *American Studies, Arts & Humanities, Science & Math, Social & Behavioral Sciences*

Associate of Science
Areas Of Emphasis include: *Business: General or Sociology*

Tuition Rates:	**California residents: $46 per credit** **Non-residents: $234 + $37 capital outlay + $46 per credit**
Payment Plan:	None
Textbook Fees:	Not included in tuition. They offer a book buy-back program.
Additional Fees:	**Distance Learning "Scantron" fees: $0.60-$4.50 (per course, depending on course chosen.)**
Cancellation Policy:	Full refund prior to class start date. Limited refund up to 10% of class completion. None thereafter.
Transfer/Exam Options:	Some
Time Limits:	Generally 16 weeks per course
Proctor required?	Yes

Coastline Community College
Course Options

ANTHROPOLOGY

Cultural Anthropology | Anthropology | C100

This course offers an introductory study of the structure and process of culture. It focuses on the major features of the culture and the methods of anthropological research and theoretical orientations with examples of culture variations in both traditional and modern societies.

Physical Anthropology | Anthropology | C185

Formerly ANTH C110. The course provides students with an understanding of human evolution and diversity from a biological perspective. Students will explore the central patterns of anatomical, behavioral, and genetic similarities and differences among living primates and humans, in addition to reconstructing the evidence for human evolution found in the fossil record.

ASTRONOMY

Introduction To Astronomy | Astronomy | C100

Origin; characteristics; and evolution of the solar system, the stars, the galaxies, and the universe. Historical milestones in the science of astronomy from ancient astronomers to the space probes of today. Consideration of the future of astronomical research and current theories in astronomy.

BIOLOGY

Introduction to Biology | Biology | C100

An introduction to the fundamental principles of biology, including cell structure, chemistry and function, genetics, evolution, adaptation, and ecology.

BUSINESS

Introduction To Business | C100

Characteristics and activities of current local, national, and international business. An overview of economics, marketing, management and finance.

Business Law/Legal Environment Of Business | C110

Fundamental legal principles pertaining to business transactions. Introduction to legal process and law as an instrument of social political control in society. Topics include sources of law and ethics, contracts, torts, agency, criminal law, business organizations, judicial and administrative processes, employment law, forms of business organizations, and domestic and international governmental regulations.

Personal finance | C120

A study of the problems of personal financial management. Topics include savings, risks, investment considerations, insurance, taxation, governmental programs in financial planning, etc. Also recommended for non-business majors.

Introduction To Marketing | C150

Provides an introduction to marketing as it relates to contemporary living and society's changing needs. Topics include consumer markets, planning and forecasting, and wholesaling and retailing.

Entrepreneur & SM Bus OPS/MGT | C222

Provides a study of the practical problems encountered in finding, organizing and operating small business enterprises. Included are topics related to initiating the business, developing strategies, marketing, financial and administrative control, and related topics.

COUNSELING

Strategies For College Success | C105

Course designed to increase success in achieving educational, career, and life goals. It includes information on learning styles and strategies, time management, decision making, goal setting, college resources and services, memory techniques, note-taking, test-taking, and other successful techniques. Students will develop educational and career plans.

ENGLISH

Basic Grammar | C020 | 1.5 Units
Students learn the technology and structure of the English language in an easy-to-understand, step-by-step fashion. Parts of speech, sentence structure, choice and use of words, capitalization and punctuation are covered.

College Spelling I | C021 | 1.5 Units
A beginning, self-paced, programmed course designed to help students master the basic rules of spelling. Among other topics, it addresses phonics, silent letters, plurals, suffixes, commonly misspelled words, and apostrophes.

College Vocabulary I | C204 | 1.5 Units
A beginning course designed to help students develop a college-level vocabulary. Students learn word usage and ways to build words using context clues, word derivatives, and prefixes and suffixes.

College Vocabulary II | C025 | 1.5 Units
This is the second of a series designed to help students develop a college-level vocabulary. Students learn word usage and ways to build words using context clues, word derivatives, and prefixes and suffixes.

Business English | C103
Focuses of real world English skills that contribute to good workplace communication. Students study grammar, English usage, punctuation, spelling, vocabulary, and dictionary use from a businessperson's viewpoint.

Business Writing | C135
A pre-professional course concentrating on the planning and writing an extensive, business-focused research paper. Also covers effective letters, memos, position papers, and resumes.

HEALTH

Nutrition | Foods & Nutrition | C170
Scientific concepts of nutrition relating to the functioning of nutrients in basic processes of life. Individual needs, food sources of nutrients, current nutrition issuers, scientific principles to analyze and evaluate nutritional; information, and diet analysis are emphasized.

General Geology | Geology | C105
Acquaints the student with how earthquakes, active volcanoes and other geologic formations and processes relate to the theory of plate tectonics. The course stresses that Earth continues to evolve and that its future depends on our actions of today.

Personal Health | Health | C100
Designed to educate students about wellness through the acquisition of knowledge, attitudes, and behaviors. The major health-related problems in society are addressed, as well as an understanding of individual developmental patterns and health needs. Broad ranges of factors affecting wellness, including identification of risks and health promotion behaviors, are covered. Topics include, but are not limited to, substance use and abuse, nutrition, sexually transmitted diseases, health risk factors, mental and emotional health, and exercise.

HISTORY

U.S. History To 1876 | C170
Political, diplomatic, economic, social, and cultural history; earliest times to 1876.

U.S. History Since 1876 | C175
Political, diplomatic, economic, social, and cultural history; 1876 to present.

Western Civilization I | C180
Surveys the history of Western societies, institutions and ideas, and the impact they have had on global culture over time. This course traces the major developments in the formation of Western civilization to the final defeat of Napoleon in 1815, with a focus on political as well as social events.

HUMANITIES

Humanities Through The Arts | C110

Surveys Western civilization's cultural achievements in music, literature, drama, film, painting, sculpture and architecture.

MANAGEMENT & SUPERVISION

Business Organization & Management | C100

Comprehensive review of the role of management in the current business environment. Students will be introduced to the terminology, theories, and principles that make up the core of business management.

MARINE SCIENCE

Introduction To Marine Science | Marine Science | C100

A general study of the marine environment. Examines the chemical, biological, and geological properties of the sea, the sea as a natural resource and its geo-political and economic impact.

MASS COMMUNICATIONS

Introduction To Mass Communications | C100

Emphasizes the history of mass media and current trends, presenting information and activities to enable students to appreciate and evaluate the quality of print, audio, video, and television.

MATHEMATICS

Basic Mathematics | Mathematics | C005

Review of basic mathematics for business; bank records; merchandising; payroll; finance; real estate; accounting; annuities and investments.

Pre-Algebra | Mathematics | C008

Students acquire knowledge of addition, subtraction, multiplication, and division of whole numbers, fractions, and decimals; averages; exponents; percent's; rations and proportions; weights and measures, including metric system; signed numbers; and introductory geometry and algebra.

Elementary Algebra | Mathematics | C010 | 4.0 Units

Develops skills in problem solving, graphing, working with functions, and critical thinking. Topics include solving and graphing linear inequalities, graphing linear functions, solving linear systems of equations in two variables, exponents, and factoring polynomials.

Intermediate Algebra | Mathematics | C030 | 4.0 Units

Review of algebra including factoring, rational expressions, exponents, radicals, quadratic equations, and equations of lines.

Liberal Arts Mathematics | Mathematics | C100

Examines the mathematics involved in personal finance, environmental issues, the social sciences, politics of voting, business and economics, graph theory, fractals, art, and music. The course will also include a writing and research component.

College Algebra | Mathematics | C115 | 4.0 Units

Develops skills in problem solving, graphing, working with functions, and critical thinking. Topics include solving and graphing linear inequalities, graphing linear functions, solving linear systems of equations in two variables, exponents, and factoring polynomials.

Trigonometry | Mathematics | C120

A thorough discussion of trigonometric concepts and applications are presented in this course. Students study proofs of trigonometric identities, solutions, of right and oblique triangles, solutions of trigonometric equations and functions, vector applications and polar coordinates.

Introduction To Statistics | Mathematics | C160 | 4.0 Units

Covers mathematical foundations of elementary statistical methods, application and theory, probability in discrete and continuous distribution, correlation and regression, sampling distribution and significance tests.

Precalculus | Mathematics | C170 | 5.0 Units

A Precalculus course combining topics from college algebra and trigonometry. Preparation for analytic geometry and calculus.

Calculus 1 | Mathematics | C180 | 5.0 Units

Emphasizes physical science applications. Includes plane analytic geometry, differentiation, and application of the derivative, differential equations, integration and applications.

Calculus 2 | Mathematics | C185 | 5.0 Units

Includes elementary functions, derivatives, integrals, analytical geometry, infinite series and applications.

Introduction to Philosophy | Philosophy | C100

General consideration of human nature and the nature of the universe. Knowledge, perception, freedom and determinism, and the existence of God.

Logic And Critical Thinking | Philosophy | C115

This course introduces logic and critical thinking. It covers persuasion, argument, semantic and logical consistency, and the accurate use of language, both meaning and structure. It evaluates the effects of advertising, politics, religion, and the news media. The course also explores the gulf between reasoning in theory and in practice. Students critically evaluate world philosophies, religions, cultural influences, and history, and analyze deductive proofs through categorical and essential logic.

Ethics | Philosophy | C120

Discussion of classic and/or modern philosophical views of human values, ideals, and morality. Provides introductory survey of some main problems, concepts, and results of ethics including selected philosophers past and present.

American Government | Political Science | C180

Organization, processes, and functions of the national government of the United States.

Introduction To Psychology | Psychology | C100

To acquaint the student with basic principles, methods and fields of psychology such as learning, memory, emotion, perception, physiological, developmental, intelligence, social and abnormal.

Child Growth And Development | Psychology | C116

Course includes foundation of child development; conception, prenatal, and birth; heredity; infant social and emotional development; growth and maturation; the developing child learning, language, social processes; sexuality. Morality and self-control; and the 'special needs' child.

Life Span Development Psychology | Psychology | C118

Psychological study of human development across the lifespan from prenatal development through childhood, adolescence, adulthood, and dying, paying particular attention to the biological, cognitive, and psychosocial process.

Abnormal Psychology | Psychology | C255

Formerly PSYC C120. An introduction to emotional and mental disorders from a biological, socio-cultural and psychological approach. The course covers the field's historical approaches and range of psychological disorders as well as their symptoms, treatment, and the prevention of mental problems.

Introduction To Sociology | Sociology | C100

Nature of human society and factors affecting its development. Fundamental concepts of sociology, culture, personality, socialization, social organization, groups, and institutions.

Introduction To Marriage And Family | Sociology | C110

A study of family as a social institution. Examines the process of family development including: dating, courtship, engagement, mater selection, marriage, parenthood, and divorce. Crisis and challenges facing families today will be examined from a sociological perspective.

Introduction To Gerontology | Sociology | C120

A multidisciplinary overview of the biological, psychological aspects of the aging process.

Elementary Spanish 1 | Spanish | C180 | 5.0 Units

Emphasizes acquiring conversational and comprehension skills by focusing on vocabulary recognition and pronunciation. Not recommended for students who have already taken a Spanish course.

Elementary Spanish 2 | Spanish | C185

Studies more of the fundamentals of Spanish grammar, composition, conversation and reading.

Colorado State University at Pueblo

2200 Bonforte Boulevard
Pueblo, Colorado 81001
(800) 388-6154, (719) 549-2316
www.coned.colostate-pueblo.edu   coned@colostate-pueblo.edu

Colorado State University at Pueblo provides quality education for a reasonable tuition rate. Depending on the degree, students may need to transfer 15 credit hours to be accepted.

Accreditation: North Central Association of Colleges and Schools, The Higher Learning Commission

AVAILABLE TO PRISONERS

Bachelor of Arts in Social Science
Bachelor of Arts in Sociology
Bachelor of Science in Social Science
Bachelor of Science Sociology

Tuition Rates:	**$350 per credit**
	(Most courses will cost $1,050 each, plus fees.)
Payment Plan:	None
Textbook Fees:	Not included in tuition
Additional Fees:	**$25 Application fee**
Transfer/Exam Options:	Up to 90 credit hours
Time Limit:	6 months
Proctor Required?	Yes

Colorado State University | Pueblo
Available Courses
The following courses earn three (3) credits each.

ACCOUNTING

Principles of Financial Accounting
Principles of Managerial Accounting
Anthropology
Cultural Anthropology
Crime and the Mind

ART

Visual Dynamics

History of Art I, II
Music Appreciation: History of R and R

BUSINESS ADMINISTRATION

Inferential Statistics and Problem Solving
Ethics in Business
Economics
Principles of Macroeconomics
Principles of Microeconomics

ENGLISH

Composition I, II
Introduction to Literature
Women in Literature
Women Writers in Science Fiction
Rediscovering the Fairy Tale
Finance
Principles of Finance

GEOGRAPHY

Physical Geography
Cultural Geography
World Regional Geography

HISTORY

U.S. History I, II
History of U.S. Foreign Policy
The American Civil War
Military History

MANAGEMENT

Principles of Management
Organizational Behavior
Operations and Quality Management
Human Resource Management
Purchasing and Materials Management
Management Information Systems
Labor Management Relations
Entrepreneurship
Operations Strategy
Quality Management

MARKETING

Principles of Marketing
Sales Force Management
Marketing Strategies
International Marketing

MATHEMATICS

Mathematical Explorations
College Algebra

NURSING

Ethical Issues in Health Care
Gerontological Nursing

POLITICAL SCIENCE

American National Politics
International Relations
Comparative Politics
Introduction to Homeland Security
Terrorism
Critical Incident Management

PSYCHOLOGY

General Psychology
Introductory Psychology for Majors
Understanding Human Diversity
Human Development
Sport Psychology
Childhood & Adolescence
Theories of Personality
Memory and Cognition
Educational Psychology
Psychology of the Exceptional Individual
Abnormal Psychology
History and Systems of Psychology

SCIENCES

Chemistry and Society
Introduction to Organic Chemistry
Geology
Earth Science
Nutrition
Environmental Conservation

SOCIOLOGY

Introduction to Sociology
The Criminal Justice System
Marriage and Family Relationships
Sociological Methods
Crime and Deviance
Crime and Women
Delinquency and Juvenile Justice
Social and Cultural Theory
Penology
Social Stratification
Poverty
Family Violence
Victimology
Structural and Elite Crime
Police and Society
Serial Murder

Forensic Criminology
Crime in the Mind
Explaining Crime
Terrorism and Mass Murder

Gangs in Contemporary America
Correctional Administration
Research
Society and Technology

Huntington College of Health Sciences

117 Legacy View Way
Knoxville, Tennessee 37918
(800) 290-4226, (865) 524-8079
www.hchs.edu   studentservices@hchs.edu

Huntington College of Health Sciences specializing in providing correspondence education in diet, nutrition, and health management. They offer several diplomas where students can comprehensively learn a specialty, while gaining college credit, without having to take full degree programs. They also offer graduate diploma and degree options (see *Graduate Studies* section)

Accreditation: Distance Education Accrediting Commission (DEAC)

AVAILABLE TO PRISONERS

Associate of Science in Applied Nutrition

Bachelor of Health Science in Nutrition

Diplomas in the following subjects:

Comprehensive Nutrition; Dietary Supplement Science; Integrated Personal Training; Small Business Management; Sports Nutrition; Women's Nutrition

Tuition Rates:	**$245 per credit** **$4,410 to $31,605 per program**
Payment Plan:	Limited payment options (2 payments over 2 months)
Textbook Fees:	$600 to $6000 estimated cost per program; individual courses vary
Additional Fees:	**Application fee: $75** **Enrollment fee: $50 per individual course; $100 per diploma program: $200 per degree program**
Cancellation Policy:	Full refund within 5 days of enrollment; full refund, less $75, for cancellation 5 days to prior to beginning of course assignments, other percentages based on percentage of course completion.
Transfer/Exam Options:	6 credit hours per diploma program 45 credit hours per associate program 95 credit hours per bachelor program
Time Limit:	4 months per course; $50 for a 3-month extension
Proctor Required?	Yes

Louisiana State University

CONTINUING EDUCATION

1225 Pleasant Hall
Baton Rouge, Louisiana 70803-1500
(800) 234-5046, (225) 578-2500
www.outreach.lsu.edu/idl   iservices@outreach.lsu.edu

Louisiana State University does not currently offer any degrees by correspondence, but they do offer a variety of paper-based courses. Even classes that require some web-based study will be printed by the school.

Their courses may be useful to prisoner-students looking to gain credits or to fulfill other course requirements.

Accreditation: Southern Association of Colleges and Schools, Commission on College

AVAILABLE TO PRISONERS

Variety of for-credit courses

Tuition Rates:	$184 per single credit hour $245 for noncredit courses
Payment Plan:	None
Textbook Fees:	Not included in tuition
Additional Fees:	None
Cancellation Policy:	80% of the course fees are refundable within 30 days of enrollment and prior to any assignment submissions
Transfer/Exam Options:	CLEPS (English/Math); AP Exam; Math/English ACT scores; Quantitative Reasoning/Critical Reading SAT scores. Note: No ACE credits accepted.
Time Limit:	9 months per course; $25 for a 3-month extension (2 allowed)
Proctor Required?	Yes

Metropolitan State University of Denver
CONTINUING EDUCATION

Student Success Building, 890 Auraria Pkwy #410, Denver, CO 80204
(303) 556-5740, (303) 450-5111, (303) 721-1313
www.msudenver.edu/extendedcampus/self-paced/distancelearning *askmetro@msudenver.edu*

Metropolitan State University of Denver offers a few unique print-based courses that can be used to earn college credit.

Accreditation: American Association of State Colleges and Universities (AASCU) and the North Central Association of Colleges and Schools (NCA).

AVAILABLE TO PRISONERS

Variety of for-credit courses

Tuition Rates:	**$179 per credit** **(Most courses will cost $522 each, plus fees.)**
Payment Plan:	None
Textbook Fees:	Not included in tuition
Additional Fees:	Metro Bond Fee: $20.50 per credit; Immunization Fee: $2.10
Cancellation Policy:	Full refund within 30 days of course registration.
Transfer/Exam Options:	Not applicable
Time Limit:	One year
Proctor Required?	Yes

Metropolitan State University of Denver
Available Courses

Each of the following courses earns three (3) credits.

World History Since 1500 | HIS 1040
Provides an introduction to important theories, concepts, methods, and content for understanding history since 1500, exploring social, cultural, religious, economic, and political themes.

Western Heroes | HIS 340B
Examines the lives, personalities and historical importance of the West's most colorful characters. From the Spanish explorations through the early 20th century, each significant era is examined through eyes of about 30 of the region's most important figures.

American Revolution Early Nation | HIS 3430
Examines politics, society and economics during the Revolutionary period, with emphasis on American Society on the eve of the Revolution; the causes of the war; diplomatic and military aspects of the eras; the development of political parties; reform movements; and the changing status of native and African Americans and women.

Civil War & Reconstruction | HIS 3520
Traces the background of the Civil War, the war itself, and its aftermath, while familiarizing students with Civil War and Reconstruction historiography.

The Cold War | HIS 367C
Examines the Cold War from 1917 to 1881, with emphasis on the events preceding the confrontation from the Russian Revolution of 1917 through World War II; the impact of the atomic bomb; Soviet occupation of Eastern Europe; the Cuban Missile Crisis; Detente and contributions of Gorbachev to the ending of the Cold War and the USSR.

Murray State University

REGIONAL ACADEMIC OUTREACH

303 Sparks Hall
Murray, Kentucky 42071-3312
(800) 669-7654, (207) 809-4150
www.murraystate.edu/rao   msu.selfpaced@murraystate.edu

Murray State University offers a limited number of paper-based courses.

Accreditation: Southern Association of Colleges and Schools, Commission on College

AVAILABLE TO PRISONERS

Variety of College-Credit Courses

Tuition Rates:	**$317 per credit**
	(Most courses will cost $951 each, plus fees.)
Payment Plan:	None
Textbook Fees:	Not included in tuition
Additional Fees:	None
Cancellation Policy:	Students may withdraw up to six months after enrollment
Transfer/Exam Options:	Not applicable
Time Limit:	12 months per course; 3 and 6-month extensions are allowed on a case-by-case basis
Proctor Required?	Yes

Murray State University
Available Courses

AGRICULTURE

Animal Science | AGR 100 (3 credit hours)
This is a basic course in animal science including the importance and place of livestock in agriculture; types, market classes, and grades of beef, sheep, and swine; origins and characteristics of breeds; and judging of beef, sheep, and swine.
Textbook: Scientific Animal Production, 10th Edition (Robert E. Taylor/Thomas G. Field)

Poultry Science | AGR 321 (3 credit hours)
An introductory study of the various phases of poultry production, diagnosis and treatment of diseases, nutrition, processing and management practices for commercial poultry operations.   Textbook: Poultry Science, 4th Edition (Colin G. Scanes/George Brant)

HEALTH

Personal Health Issues | HEA 190 (2 credit hours)
Designed to educate students about wellness through the acquisition of knowledge, attitudes, and behaviors. The major health-related problems in society are addressed, as well as an understanding of individual developmental patterns and health needs. Broad ranges of factors affecting wellness, including identification of risks and health promotion behaviors, are covered. Topics include, but are not limited to, substance use and abuse, nutrition, sexually transmitted diseases, health risk factors, mental and emotional health, and exercise.   Textbook: Fit & Well, 10th Edition (Thomas D. Fahey/Paul Insel/Walton Roth)

POLITICS

American National Government | POL 140 (3 credit hours)
The American political system, its constitution, institutions and processes. An approved social science University Studies elective. Textbook: We the People: A Concise Introduction to American Politics, 9th Edition (Thomas E. Patterson)

State and Local Politics | POL 240 (3 credit hours)
Study of the three branches of state government coupled with an examination of the politics, organizations and functions of counties, townships, and special districts.   Textbook: Politics in American States & Communities, 7th Edition (Dennis Dresang/James Gosling)

Foundations of Public Administration | POL 470 (3 credit hours)
The theory and practice of the administration and management of governmental operations; politics, policy and the bureaucracy.
Textbook: Public Administration: Understanding Management, Politics, and Law in the Public Sector, 7th Edition (Davis Rosenblum/Robert Kravluk)

Ohio University

Haning Hall 102
Athens, Ohio 45701
(800) 444-2420
www.ohio.edu   *correctional@ohio.edu*

Ohio University is the one largest and most prison-friendly correspondence options for prisoners. They offer many college degree and for-credit opportunities, which you can find here, as well as several noncredit options for non-degree seeking students. They also offer several Paralegal/Legal Certificate Programs, which can be found in the *Paralegal* portion of our *Vocational Studies* section.

Accreditation: NCA-NLC

AVAILABLE TO PRISONERS

Associate in Arts
(with emphasis options of Arts and Humanities or Social Sciences)

Associate in Applied Business
(Business Management Technology Major)

Associate in Individualized Studies.

Associate in Science

Bachelor of Technical & Applied Studies

Bachelor of Specialized Studies.

Tuition Rates:	**$343/credit hour** (applies to courses and Credit-by-Examination options) **(Most courses will cost $1,029 each, plus fees.)**
Textbook Fees:	Included in tuition, as are any other materials a course requires, such as a calculator.
Additional Fees:	**Application fee: $25 (non-refundable); Student Info System fee: $3 per course**
Transfer/Exam Options:	Provides credits through CLEP credits earned prior to enrollment and Experiential Learning Program options. They also offer Course Credit by Examinations (CCE) (see separate listing below).
Time Limits:	8 months. Course Credit by Examination (CCE) requires 6-month completion from date of enrollment.
Proctor Required?	Yes

Ohio University
Available Courses

Each of the following courses are print-based and earn 3 credit hours each, unless otherwise marked. Students can also earn college credit by "testing out" through Course Credit-by-Examination (CCE) courses, also listed below.

ASTRONOMY

Survey of Astronomy | ASTR 1000

General introduction to astronomy, with emphasis on the structure of the universe beyond our solar system. Topics include historical astronomy, the sun, stars, galaxies, interstellar matter, black holes, the "Big Bang" theory, and the evolution of the universe.

ACCOUNTING

Financial Accounting Procedures | ATCH 1030

Provides a basic level of knowledge in recording business transactions, summarizing business activities, and preparing, interpreting and utilizing financial statements.

Managerial Accounting Procedures | ATCH 1040

Accounting procedures for managerial accounting including job/process costing, cost behavior, budgeting, performance evaluation, differential analysis and capital investment.

BIOLOGY

Human Biology I: Basic Principles | BIOS 1030

Humans as biological organisms: our origins, ecology, and functioning of our body systems.

Bioethics: Bioethical Problems in Biology and Medicine | BIOS 3840

Discusses the ethics behind a variety of medical topics, procedures and medicines that are frequently used or avoided in the medical profession.

BUSINESS LAW

Law & Society | BUSL 2000

Conceptual approach to origin, nature, structure, functions and procedures of law, with study of corporate responsibility, ethics, and introduction to constitutional, administrative, criminal, tort, product liability, contractual, international, property, agency, partnership, corporation and employment law.

BUSINESS MANAGEMENT

Business and Its Environment | BMT 1010

Nature of business, and of economic social, and political environments of business firms. Emphasis on ways in which such surroundings affect business policies and operations.

Introduction to Management | BMT 1100

Provides introduction to effective management strategies, philosophies, and concepts, including fundamental management skills, internal and external factors that managers must confront in today's work ecosystem, functions of management, historical and current management theories, and social responsibility and managerial ethics.

Foundations of Quality & Continuous Improvement | BMT 1150

Introduction to quality management as it relates to the workplace environment. Explores several quality theories, the process of continuous improvement, and the use of specific tools to improve organizational systems and resources. Prerequisite: BMT 1100

Concepts of Marketing | BMT 1400

Introduction to problems of manufacturers, wholesalers, and retailers as they relate to modern marketing, market and product.

Elements of Supervision | BMT 1500

Concepts of modern-day supervision from a behavioral science approach, emphasizing the supervisor's major functions and development of sensitivity to human facets of management.

Small Business Operations | BMT 1700

Balanced program of all major aspects confronting small business operators, including finance, personnel, sales, success and failure factors, and business planning activities.

Intro to Business Computing | BMT 2000

Focuses on PC-based applications used in business and industry, such as word processing, spreadsheets, databases, and presentation packages, including web applications.

Practical Personnel Procedures | BMT 2500

Provides a general overview of the human resource management field.

Business Report Writing | BMT 2600

Practice in planning and writing effective business letters, memoranda and reports.

Government & Business | BMT 2850

Business and government relations, with emphasis on analysis of selected areas involving public policy and business.

Computer and Applications for Management | BMT 2880

Spreadsheet, database management, word processing, and graphics applications are used to create comprehensive business reports or application processes for business analysis.   Requires use of Microsoft Office 2007 or newer. Prerequisite: BMT 2750 (Managerial Training)

ECONOMICS

Principles of Microeconomics | ECON 1030

Functioning of the market economy, role of prices in determining the allocation of resources, the functioning of the firm in the economy, and forces governing the production and consumption of economic goods.

Principles of Macroeconomics | ECON 1040

Covers fundamental ideas in economics: scarcity, substitution, opportunity cost, marginal analysis, GDP, real and nominal magnitudes, supply and demand analysis, and microeconomic analysis of pricing in competitive and noncompetitive markets.

Labor Economics | ECON 3200

Demand for labor, supply of labor, household production, compensating wage differentials, education and training, discrimination, unions, and unemployment.   Prerequisite: ECON 1030 (Microeconomics)

Money & Banking | ECON 3600

Influence of money and banking on economic activity; influence of monetary policies to achieve society's economic goals.

ENGLISH

Developmental Writing Skills | ENG D150

Study of the practice of basic writing techniques. Students will write numerous short paper, as well as on complete story, and keep a journal. Students read and analyze literary stories by well-known writers.

Writing & Rhetoric I | ENG 1510

Practice in composing and revising expository essays that are well organized, logically coherent, and effective for their purpose and audience. Topics from personal experience, non-fiction reading, and research material.   Prerequisite: ENG 150 or ENG D150, or 1510 placement

Critical Analysis of Fiction and Non-Fiction Prose | ENG 2010

Introduces students to the different forms of fiction and non-fiction prose (novels, short stories, essays, life-writing) as they have developed and changed over time. Students will acquire and deploy a critical vocabulary in learning to read and analyze these texts. Every student should have access to a quality, hardbound dictionary, and they should be able to demonstrate an aptitude for written English. Prerequisite: Eng 1510 (formerly ENG 151)

Critical Analysis of Poetry & Drama | ENG 2020

Introduces students to different forms of poetry and drama as they have changed over time. Students will acquire and deploy a critical vocabulary in learning to read and analyze these texts.

American Literature to 1865 | ENG 3210

The historical development of American literature from the colonial period to 1900 is the central theme of this course. Students gain an understanding of the ideas that fostered the growth of the United States and the ways in which its literature became distinctively American. Students develop composition skills by analyzing the literary selections and applying the basic organizational pattern of a good essay. The course also covers modernist prose and poetry, and American nonfiction and drama. Writing is central to the course.

Women & Literature | ENG 3250

Surveys poetry, prose and theoretical text by women writers.

Creative Writing: Fiction | ENG 3610

Study and practice in the techniques of writing fiction.

Creative Writing: Poetry | ENG 3620

Study and practice in the techniques of writing poetry and/or drama, with emphasis on invention, craft, and criticism of student writing and published poetry.

Writing and Rhetoric II | ENG 3080J

Focuses on skills in writing s variety of genres (i.e. rhetorical analysis, research-based argument, report, etc.) Coursework includes learning to read rhetorically and using effective strategies for searching academic databases and evaluating sources. Also focuses on using correct documentation and mechanics.   Prerequisite: ENG 1510 or 1610

American Literature 1865-1918 | ENG 3220

Authors, works, and genres of American literature from the end of the Civil War to the end of World War I. Prerequisite: ENG 2010 or 2020, or two courses above ENG 200.

ENVIRONMENTAL TECHNOLOGIES

Intro to Environmental Engineering Technology | EVT 1000

Topics include toxicology, air pollution, groundwater contamination, transportation of hazardous materials, waste characterization, waste management, and waste treatment and disposal, with discussions of how regulations affect each. It is recommended that students have previously taken courses in chemistry, algebra, and calculus.   Materials needed: Scientific calculator (Casio FX260SLR or equivalent).

Environmental Engineering Instrumentation & Computation | EVT 1100

Intro to Environmental Chemistry | EVT 1200

Topics covered include measurements in the metric system and temperature conversions; the nature of atoms, molecules, and ions; chemical calculations using chemical formulas and equations; thermochemistry; electronic structure of atoms; properties of elements; chemical bonding and shapes of molecules; and an introduction to organic molecules.

HAZWOPER | EVT 1250

Provides certification required to work on a majority of environmental cleanup sites. Covers regulatory obligations, handling hazardous materials, personal protective equipment, monitoring instrumentation, emergency response, site control, medical assessment, confined space entry, and respiratory protection. It is recommended that students have taken course in general chemistry, algebra, and calculus.   Materials needed: Scientific calculator (Casio FX260SLR or equivalent)

Site Investigation: Sampling & Monitoring Samples | EVT 2000

Field oriented course involving hazardous materials, site investigation, and cleanup. Topics include planning and organization, training and medical programs, site assessment, sampling and monitoring, site control, hazardous materials handling, and emergency response.

Intro to Health Physics | EVT 2100

Addresses fundamental principles of health physics and radiation protection. Topics include atomic structure, types of radiation, radioactive decay, methods of radiation detection, dosimetry, biological effects, and radiation protection.

Fluid Mechanics | EVT 2200

Fundamentals of fluid mechanics as applied to surface and groundwater, wastewater, and air emissions management. Topics include, basic hydraulics, friction loss, pressure, flow measurement, pump types and characteristics, and schematic interpretation.

Analysis of Environmental Pollutants | EVT 2500

Covers important techniques necessary for analyzing environmental samples. Methods established by the EPA are used to analyze samples for heavy metals, volatiles, and semi-volatiles.

Alternative Energy Systems & Applications | EXT 2900

Provides an opportunity to complete individual projects that involve special topics concerning environmental engineering technology problems.

GEOGRAPHY

Human Geography | GEOG 1200

Examination of spatial dimensions of culture, emphasizing patterns of selected cultural elements – language, religion, population, settlement, political and economic landscapes, and human/environment interactions.

Environmental Geography | GEOG 2400

HISTORY

The Rise of Modern Asia | HIST 2460

Introductory survey of the history of Asia from India to Japan, beginning in the mid-19th century. Emphasis is on the rise of modern nationalism, economic development, and social and cultural achievements.

Ancient Greece | HIST 3291

Begins with the emergence of the ancient Greeks of the Mycenaean Age and Homer's epics, moving on to the emergence of city-states with focus ion Athens and Sparta. Covers political and military history from the Persian wars to the conquest of Alexander the Great.

World War I | HIST 3750

Covers the course of the "Great War" including its origins, conduct and aftermath. Considers the military, diplomatic, and cultural factors that led to its outbreak as well as how and why European governments and peoples were willing and able to sustain and expand their war. Special topics will include (among others) the American Genocide, the deployment of WMDs, wartime tech and military developments, the war at sea, the break-up of multi-national empires and the changing understanding and representation of the war.

MATH

Intermediate Algebra | MATH D005

Review of algebra including factoring, rational expressions, exponents, radicals, quadratic equations, and equations of lines.

College Algebra | MATH 1200 (4 credits)

Develops skills in problem solving, graphing, working with functions, and critical thinking. Topics include solving and graphing linear inequalities, graphing linear functions, solving linear systems of equations in two variables, exponents, and factoring polynomials.

Pre-Calculus | MATH 1300 (4 credits)

Survey of Calculus | MATH 1350

Calculus I | MATH 2301 (4 credits)

Emphasizes physical science applications. Includes plane analytic geometry, differentiation, and application of the derivative, differential equations, integration and applications.

Calculus II | MATH 2302 (4 credits)

Includes elementary functions, derivatives, integrals, analytical geometry, infinite series and applications.

MARKETING

Marketing Principles | MKT 2020
Provides a broad understanding of marketing activities, decisions, and terms with an emphasis on the practices and problems of marketing managers and the analysis of the marketing environment. No credit if taken after MKT 2400

MUSIC

Exploring Musical Styles | MUS 1200 (2 credits)
Development of listening skills for understanding elements of musical style in historical perspective and significance of music as fine art.

NUTRITION

Introduction to Nutrition | NUTR 1000
Nutrients, their food sources and functions in the body; application to planning adequate diet through life cycle.

PHILOSOPHY

Fundamentals of Philosophy | PHIL 1010
An introduction to the scientific study of behavior and mental processes, including major approaches and methodologies. The course samples a broad range of topics, including biological foundations, development, learning, cognition, personality, abnormal psychology and social behavior.

Principles of Reasoning | PHIL 1200
Basic concepts of logic and techniques for judging validity of arguments introduced. System for symbolizing arguments and deriving conclusions from premises employed. Some of the following topics are covered: informal fallacies in reasoning, syllogistic of Aristotelian logic; Venn diagrams, truth tables. Most sections are traditional lecture/test format, some taught in computer-assisted format, others use self-paced approach.

Introduction to Ethics | PHIL 1300
Discussion of classic and/or modern philosophical views of human values, ideals, and morality. Provides introductory survey of some main problems, concepts, and results of ethics including selected philosophers past and present.

PHYSICS

Physical World | PSC 1010
Designed for non-science majors. Fundamental ideas of measurement, motion, energy, electricity and magnetism, heat, atomic and nuclear physics. Introduction to relativity and quantum phenomena.

Introduction to Physics | PHYS 2001 (4 credit hours)
First course in physics, open to students from all areas. Students should have a background in algebra, trigonometry and geometry, but no calculus required. Recommended for students in liberal arts, architecture, industrial technology, geological sciences, plant biology, and pre-medicine. Mechanics of solids and liquids, oscillations, heat, thermodynamics. Prerequisite: MATH 1200 or math placement 2 or higher.

POLITICAL SCIENCE

American National Government | POLS 1010
Explores four topics related to American national government. 1) the philosophical and constitutional foundations of our government system; 2) various factors that link citizens to their government (i.e. media, public opinion, campaigns and elections, political parties, and interest groups); 3) governmental institutions – each branch studied with respect to its functions, memberships, and the relationships it engages in with the other branches of government; and 4) public policy (domestic/social welfare policy, and foreign policy/national security).

PSC

Color, Light, and Sound | PSC 1050

Designed for non-science majors. Physical nature of light and sound including transmission, absorption, reflection, interference, and resonance. Applications include analysis of musical instruments, acoustics, optical systems, perception of color and sound.

PSYCHOLOGY

General Psychology | PSY 1010

Explores the brain, biology and behavior; sensation and reality; memory, intelligence and creativity; conditions and learning; motivation and emotion; health, stress and coping; abnormal psychology; gender, sexuality, social behavior and human relations.

Statistics for Behavioral Sciences | PSY 2110 (4 credit hours)

Introduction to descriptive and inferential statistics, with emphasis on inferential statistics. MATH 1200 or 1300 or 2301, or math placement 2 or higher

Educational Psychology | PSY 2420

Social Psychology | PSY 2510

Theory and research on the ways that people think about, influence, and relate to one another. Specific topics include attitude and behavior, social perception and cognition, conformity, persuasion, group influence, aggression, attraction, and helping behavior. Prerequisite: PSY 1010 or PSY101D

Psychology of Personality | PSY 2720

Development, organization and assessment of personality, with evaluation of major theoretical perspectives and research on personality.

Behavior Genetics & Individual Differences | PSY 3410

Extensive survey of individual differences and their relationship to genetic factors. Topics include chromosomal abnormalities, inborn errors of metabolism, genetic and prenatal screening, behaviors in infants, genetics and intellectual differences.

Psychology of Adulthood & Aging | PSY 3420

Behavioral change and continuity over adult years through old age. Emphasis is on interaction of psychological, sociocultural, and biological variables as they contribute to behaviors, of aging individual from perspective of developmental framework.

Motivation | PSY 3510

Survey of theories of motivation, with emphasis on human motivation.   Prerequisite: 9 hours in PSY including 101D or 1010

Social Psychology of Justice | PSY 3520

Theory and research on the interface of psychology and the legal system (with emphasis on social psychology). Specific topics include dilemmas faced by psychologists in the legal system; legality vs. morality; the socialization, training and ethics of lawyers and police officers; perception memory and error in eyewitness testimony; hypnosis; lie detection and confessions; rights of victims and accused; rape and rapists; arrests and trial; jury selection; jury dynamics and deliberations; insanity and the prediction of dangerousness; sentencing; death penalty; rights of special groups; theories of crimes.   Prerequisite: 6 hours in PSY, including 1010 or 101D

SOCIOLOGY

Introduction to Sociology | SOC 1000

Nature of human society and factors affecting its development. Fundamental concepts of sociology, culture, personality, socialization, social organization, groups, and institutions.

Criminal Justice | SOC 2600

Examination of structures and decision processes of agencies that deal with crime and criminal offenders. An emphasis is based on how practice is based on politically derived policies, and how sociology can be used to analyze the practice of these agencies. Topics include criminal law, policing, court systems, sentencing, and corrections. None   Prerequisite: SOC 1000

Deviant Behavior | SOC 2610

Theory and research concerning the social processes through which behaviors and statuses come to be defined as deviant, individuals become identified as deviants, and social control practices are directed toward perceived deviants. Case studies of specific categories of deviant behavior, including criminality, suicide, drug addictions, and mental disorders. Prerequisite: SOC 1000

Development of Sociological History | SOC 3000

An introduction to sociological theory. Students will examine the historical roots of sociological theory. Students will examine the historical roots of sociological theory and understand major theoretical paradigms with an emphasis on social and intellectual contexts, conceptual frameworks and methods, and contributions to contemporary social analysis. Prerequisite: 6 hours in SOC, including SOC 1000

Race and Ethnic Relations | SOC 3290

Racial and ethnic problems in society; causes and consequences of prejudice and discrimination. Focuses on differences and patterns in inequality in the U.S., as well as other societies. This course is designed so that even if the student has not yet had many sociology courses, they can do well by focusing on the readings and carefully thinking through the course materials and questions. Prerequisite: 6 hours in SOC, including SOC 1000

Elementary Research Techniques | SOC 3500

An introduction to the techniques employed by social scientists to identify research problems, gather and analyze data, and reach conclusions about their research ideas. Topics include how to identify a research problem, ways to develop data gathering procedures, techniques of data gathering, ways to summarize and analyze data. The overall goal is to provide the tools to be able to design and carry out a research project. Prerequisite: SOC 1000 and either SOC 404 or SOC 3000, and either COMS 3520. ECON 3810, MATH 2500, PSY 2110, or QBA 2010

Criminology | SOC 3600

This course is designed to provide an in-depth study of criminology. A sociological approach to the study of crime and criminals is presented. The course also includes historical material, theory and research, and extensive coverage of conventional topics.

Juvenile Delinquency | SOC 3630

A study of how delinquents and juveniles in need of supervision are handled within the juvenile system. The nature and extent of delinquent behavior as well as child abuse and neglect are examined.

Punishment and Society | SOC 3660

Examination of history, operation, and problems of punishment. Patterns of prison organization, inmate group structure, personnel organization, and racism are examined. Purpose and effectiveness of penal institutions described. Prisons, juvenile institutions, parole, halfway houses, and alternatives to punishment studied. This course has been designed so that even if you haven't had many courses in sociology, you can do well by focusing closely on the readings and carefully thinking through course material and questions. Prerequisite: SOC 2600 (Criminal Justice)

STYLE

Sport Aesthetics | T3 4710

Examines the relationships between sports, aesthetics, and art. Two general themes permeate: Viewing sports as a medium for creating aesthetic appeal via dynamic human motion involving a pleasing form and style, and appreciation of the artist's work.

Clothing & Culture | T3 4720

Study of apparel, appearance and cross-cultural influences in variation of dress and its function. Emphasis on research methods. Resources and activities relating to cultural and sub-cultural patterns.

TECHNICAL AND APPLIED STUDIES

Intro to Technical & Applied Studies | TAS 3010

Historical overview of the development of various technologies and their influence on civilization will lead to the consideration of the nature of technology and its impact on society.

Research for Technical and Applied Studies | TAS 3210

Emphasizes both an understanding of research methods and development of the critical skills necessary to interpret and to convey research results. Prerequisite: TAS 3010 and either ATCH 2090, MATH 2500, MATH 250, PSY 1110, 2110, or QBA 2010

Creating a Work & Life Plan | TAS 4900 CWLP

Students identify their needs and desires in regards to the future and their future careers. Emphasis is on matching the student's potential with several potential areas of work.

Effective Teamwork | TAS 4900 ET
Explores the advantages of teamwork, as well is the disadvantages, on several jobs. Examines the elements that comprise effective teams and the ability to recognize the strengths and weaknesses in a given situation.

Human Interaction & Cultural Development | TAS 4900 HICD
Covers components of developing healthy relationships, particularly in the workplace.

Managing Stress in the Workplace | TAS 4900 SIW
Introduces techniques for calming the body and mind in an overstimulated environment. Assists students in identifying stressors and managing them.

Leadership and Organizational Development | TAS 4900 LOD
Covers contemporary organization development that guides individual, team, and organizational change, exploring all aspects of organizational development. Provides insight into what is driving leadership theory and practice today, assisting students in developing their leadership expertise.   Textbook required: Robert's Rules of Order, Newly Revised: In Brief, 2nd Edition

THEATER STUDIES

The Theatrical Experience | THAR 1710
Examines the nature and function of theater by exploring the creative development and cultural significance of dramatic art. Students will also read and analyze selected plays.

PORTFOLIO DEVELOPMENT

Credit For Work Experience: Portfolio Development | UC 2030 (2 credit hours)

Learning Strategies | UC 1100 (2 credit hours)
Helps students assess current study behaviors and attitudes and then adopt techniques that increase effectiveness in managing time, taking notes, reading and comprehending test material, and preparing for exams. Emphasizes regular practice and application of strategies discussed. Especially recommended for new students who didn't study very much in high school and/or have no well-developed system in effective studying.   Freshmen only

Ohio University
Course-by-Credit Examination

The following courses offer a "testing out" option. If a prisoner is already educated on these subjects, they can opt to take an exam to earn the college credits. The tuition rate is the same as the regular course fees.

ASTRONOMY

Survey of Astronomy | ASTR 1000
General introduction to astronomy, with emphasis on the structure of the universe beyond our solar system. Topics include historical astronomy, the sun, stars, galaxies, interstellar matter, black holes, the "Big Bang" theory, and the evolution of the universe.

BIOETHICS

Bioethics: Bioethical Problems in Biology & Medicine

ENGLISH

Clinical Analysis of Fiction and Non-Fiction Prose | ENG 2010
Introduces students to the different forms of fiction and non-fiction prose as they have developed and changes over time. Students will acquire and deploy a critical vocabulary in learning to read and analyze these texts.

American Literature: 1865-1918 | ENG 3220
Authors, works, and genres of American literature from the beginnings through the Civil War.

American Literature: 1918 to Present | ENG 3230
Authors, works, and genres of American literature from the end of the Civil War to the end of World War I.

HISTORY

Ancient Egypt and Mesopotamia | HIST 3290
Survey of the history of ancient Egypt and Mesopotamia, with emphasis on economic development, and social and cultural achievements.

LANGUAGES

Elementary French I | FR 1110

Elementary French II | FR 1120

Intermediate French I | FR 2110

Intermediate French II | FR 2120

Elementary Italian I | ITAL 1110

Elementary Italian II | ITAL 1120

Elementary Italian I | ITAL 2110

Elementary Italian II | ITAL 2120

Elementary Spanish I | SPAN 1110

Elementary Spanish II | SPAN 1120

Intermediate Spanish I | SPAN 2110

Intermediate Spanish II | SPAN 2120

MATH

College Algebra | MATH 1200

Equations, functions and graphs, including linear equations and systems, polynomials, rational and radical expressions, quadratic equations, exponential and logarithmic functions, and inequalities.

Pre-Calculus | MATH 1300

Graphs, inverses, and operations of functions. Study of polynomial, rational, exponential, logarithmic, and trigonometric functions. Additional topics from trigonometry and analytical geometry.

Survey of Calculus | MATH 1350

Further study of graphs, inverses, and operations of functions. Further study of polynomial, rational, exponential, logarithmic, and trigonometric functions. Additional topics from trigonometry and analytical geometry.

Calculus II | MATH 2302

Second level course in calculus and analytic geometry with applications in the sciences and engineering. Includes techniques of integration, conic sections, polar coordinates, infinite series, vectors, and vector operations.

PHILOSOPHY

Principles of Reasoning | PHIL 1200

Basic concepts of logic and techniques for judging validity of arguments introduced. System for symbolizing arguments and deriving conclusions from premises employed. Some of the following topics are covered: informal fallacies in reasoning, syllogistic of Aristotelian logic; Venn diagrams, truth tables. Most sections are traditional lecture/test format, some taught in computer-assisted format, others use self-paced approach.

Introduction to Sociology | SOC 1000

Nature of human society and factors affecting its development. Fundamental concepts of sociology, culture, personality, socialization, social organization, groups, and institutions.

PHYSICS

Intro to Physics | PHYS 2002

Mechanic of solids and liquids, oscillations, heat and thermodynamics.

PSYCHOLOGY

Educational Psychology | PSY 2420

Applications of psychological theories to educational settings. Emphasis is on the role that teachers and parents play as facilitators of learning and development.

Oklahoma State University

CORRESPONDENCE EDUCATION

317 PIO
Stillwater, Oklahoma 74078
(405) 744-6390
www.ce.okstate.edu   ics-inf@okstate.edu

Oklahoma State University offers a number of college-level for-credit and CEU course options. Additionally, they offer several non-credit legal studies in partnership with *The Center for Legal Studies* (see *Paralegal Studies* portion of our *Vocational Studies* section).

Accreditation: North Central Association of Colleges and Schools, The Higher Learning Commission

AVAILABLE TO PRISONERS

Certificate of Completion showing CEU credits earned in a variety of courses

Several for-credit courses

Tuition Rates:	**$170 per credit** **(Most courses will cost $510 each, plus fees.)** **Continuing Education courses: $510 each**
Payment Plan:	None
Textbook Fees:	**$50 to $125 per course**
Additional Fees:	**Administration fee: $30; Tech fee: $12;** **Records Maintenance fee: $4.35; Course shipping: $20 per course**
Cancellation Policy:	Total refund within 30 days, 50-% refund 31-45 days, no refund after 46 days.
Transfer/Exam Options:	DANTES options available.
Time Limits:	12 months per course. 30 to 90-day extensions available: $105 for 3 credit hours, $140 for 4 credit hours, $175 for 5 credit hours
Proctor required?	Yes

Oklahoma State University
Available Courses

ANIMAL SCIENCE

Basic Nutrition for Pets | ANSI 3753
Nutrients, nutrient requirements, feeding practices, food sources and diet management for pets and companion animals as well as exotic animals and birds.

Agricultural Animals of the World | ANSI 3903
The production and utilization of agricultural animals by human societies.

Introduction to the Animal Sciences | ANSI 1124
Species adaptability, product standards and requirements, areas and types of production, processing, and distribution of products, includes meat animals, dairy and poultry.

Principles of Animal Nutrition | ANSI 3543
Basic principles of animal nutrition including digestion, absorption, and metabolism of the various food nutrients; characteristics of the nutrients; measure of body needs; ration formulation.

Basic Nutrition for Pets | ANSI 3753
Nutrients, nutrient requirements, feeding practices, food sources, and diet management for pets and companion animals, as well as exotic animals and birds.

Agricultural Animals of the World | ANSI 3903
The production and utilization of agricultural animals by human societies.

ELECTRICAL ENGINEERING TECHNOLOGY

Advanced Electronic Problems: Fiber Optics | GENT 2650
Provides practical foundation for technicians needing to understand the basics of fiber optics, including necessary techniques needed to service typical systems.

ENGLISH

Composition I | ENGL 1113
The fundamentals of expository writing with emphasis on structure, development and style.

Composition II | ENGL 1213
Expository composition with emphasis on technique and style through intensive and extensive readings.

Introduction to Literature | ENGL 2413
Fiction, drama/film, and poetry. Written critical exercises.

Survey of American Literature I | ENGL 2773
The Puritans through the Romantic period.

Survey of American Literature II | ENGL 2883
The Romantic period to the present.

Fiction Writing | ENGL 3030
Directed readings and practice in writing fiction with special attention to techniques.

Poetry Writing | ENGL 3040
Directed readings and practice in writing poetry with special attention to techniques.

Technical Writing | ENGL 3323
Applied writing in areas of specialization. Intensive practice in professional writing modes, styles, research techniques, and editing for specialized audiences and/or publications.

Short Story | ENGL 3333

Origins, development, theory, and craft of the short story.

Shakespeare | ENGL 4723

Major plays and selected criticism of Shakespearean works.

FIRE PROTECTION & SAFETY TECHNOLOGIES

Studies in Loss Control: Basic Principles of Auto. Fire Sprinkler Protection | FPST 2050

Problems in applied fire protection technology, occupational safety, industrial hygiene or hazard materials management of particular interest to the loss control specialist.

Fire Protection Management | FPST 2153

Applied human relations, technical knowledge, and skills for achieving optimum effectiveness from a protection organization.

Fire Protection Hydraulics and Water Supply Analysis | FPST 2483

Fluid flow through hoses, pipes, pumps, and fire protection appliances. Water supply and distribution analysis using hydraulic calculations. Testing techniques to detect anomalies in design or performance capabilities.

Industrial Safety Organization | FPST 3013

Recognition, evaluation, and control of occupational health and safety hazards. Accident prevention, accident analysis, training techniques, workman compensation insurance, guarding and personal protective equipment.

Hydraulic Design of Automatic Sprinkler Systems | FPST 3713

Hydraulic calculation technique for the design and analysis of automatic sprinkler fire extinguishing systems.

Industrial Fire Pump Installations | FPST 3723

Applications, design, and analysis of industrial fire pump installations. Graphical analysis of fire pump contributions to existing fire protection water supply systems emphasized.

Sprinkler System Design for High-Piled and Rack Storage | FPST 3733

Specific design techniques for sprinkler systems protection of commodities stored in solid piles and racks over 12 feet in height.

Structural Designs for Fire and Life Safety | FPST 4050.1

Building construction standards and codes to assign maximum life and property safety from fires, explosions, and natural disaster. Egress design specifications, occupancy and construction classification.

FOREIGN LANGUAGES

Independent Study in a Modern Foreign Language | FLL 3500

Instruction and/or tutorial work in a modern foreign language other than those offered in a major program.

Elementary French I | FREN 1115

Main elements of grammar and pronunciation, with emphasis on the four basic skills of listening: comprehension, speaking, reading, and writing. NOTE: CD-ROM access required.

Elementary French II | FREN 1225

Continuation of Elementary French I. NOTE: CD-ROM access required.

Elementary German I | GRMN 1115

Main elements of grammar and pronunciation, with emphasis on the four basic skills of listening: comprehension, speaking, reading, and writing. NOTE: CD-ROM access required.

Elementary German II | GRMN 1225

Continuation of Elementary German I. NOTE: CD-ROM access required.

German for Reading Requirements I | GRMN 3013

Reading in the humanities and the sciences. Translation from German to English. NOTE: CD-ROM access required.

German for Reading Requirements II | GRMN 3023

Intermediate and advanced reading in the humanities and sciences. Translation from German to English. NOTE: CD-ROM access required.

GEOGRAPHY

World Regional Geography | GEOG 2253

The world's major culture regions, with emphasis on geographic aspects of contemporary economic, social, and political relationships with the physical environment.

Meteorology | GEOG 3033

A non-quantitative introduction to weather. Physical elements that cause and influence weather. Interpretation of weather maps and satellite imagery.

Geography of Oklahoma | GEOG 3703

Geographic interpretation of physical, economic, historical, and scenic features.

Historical Geography of the United States | GEOG 4103

Examination of the spatial dynamics of frontier encounter and settlement, regional development, and cultural landscape evolution of the United States from pre-European to modern times.

Geography of Music | GEOG 4223

Geographical and historical analysis of music as a culture trait. The cultural significance of music and how it varies from place to place as well as how music helps shape the character of a place.

HEALTH & HUMAN PERFORMANCE

Introduction to Gerontology and Health | HHP 2222

Concentrated study of selected areas of health and human performance, including problems in instruction and administration not usually addressed in the undergraduate curriculum.

HISTORY

Survey of American History | HIST 1103

Meaning, vitality, and uniqueness of United States history since 1492 through a thematic examination of the nation

American History to 1865 | HIST 1483

From European background through Civil War.

American History Since 1865 | HIST 1493

Development of the United States including the growth of industry and its impact on society and foreign affairs.

Western Civilization to 1500 | HIST 1613

History of Western Civilization from ancient Rome to Reformation.

Western Civilization After 1500 | HIST 1623

History of Western Civilization from Reformation to present

Oklahoma History | HIST 2323

Early exploration and establishment of Indian Territory; the rise and demise of the Five Indian Nations; and the organization and development of 46th state to the present.

Ancient Near East | HIST 3013

The ancient world from the beginnings of recorded history through the Egyptian, Mesopotamian, Hebrew, and Persian civilizations, in addition to the many civilizations of the area.

Ancient Greece | HIST 3023D

The Greek world from the Bronze Age through Alexander the Great with special emphasis on politics, cultures, and institutions of classical Greece.

Ancient Rome | HIST 3033

Political, social, economic, and cultural history of the Roman Republic and Empire.

HORTICULTURE

Home Horticulture | HORT 1003

An introduction to horticulture practices for the home gardener. Planning and care of home grounds, orchards, and vegetable gardens, and the selection and use of indoor plants.

MATHEMATICS

Mathematical Functions and Their Uses: Functions and Change | MATH 1483
Analysis of functions and their graphs from the viewpoint of rates of change; linear, exponential, logarithmic and other functions.

Elementary Calculus | MATH 2103
An introduction to differential and integral calculus.

Calculus for Technology Programs I | MATH 2123
First semester of a terminal sequence in calculus for students in the School of Technology. Functions and graphs, differentiation and integration with applications.

Linear Algebra | MATH 3013
Algebra and geometry of finite-dimensional linear spaces, linear transformations, algebra of matrices, eigenvalues, and eigenvectors.

POLITICAL SCIENCE

American Government | POLS 1113
Organization, processes, and functions of the national government of the United States.

PSYCHOLOGY

Introductory Psychology | PSYC 1113
Principles, theories, vocabulary, and applications of the science of psychology.

STATISTICS

Elementary Statistics for Business and Economics | STAT 2023
Descriptive statistics, basic probability, discrete and continuous distributions, point and interval estimation, hypothesis testing, correlation, and simple linear regression.

Intermediate Statistical Analysis | STAT 3013
Applications of elementary statistics, introduction to experimental design, introduction to the analysis variance, simple and multiple linear regression, nonparametric statistics, survey sampling, time series, and Bayesian analysis.

Engineering Statistics | STAT 4033
Introduction to probability, random variables, probability distributions, estimation, confidence intervals, hypothesis testing, and linear regression.

Oklahoma State University
Continuing Education Credit Courses
Students will earn 5 CEUs and a certificate of completion with each of the following courses.

Review & Evaluation of Automatic Sprinkler System Plans & Designs | ICS 0790
Helps develop the basic skills in sprinkler plan review for fire marshals, insurance industry employees and those with fire protection responsibilities in business and industry. Should already understand the composition of a sprinkler system and its purpose.

Basic Principles of Automatic Fire Sprinkler Protection | ICS 2050

Problems in applied fire protection technology, occupational safety, industrial hygiene and hazardous materials management of particular interest to loss control specialist.

Fire Protection management | ICS 2153

Applied human relations, technical knowledge and skills for achieving optimum effectiveness from a protection organization.

Fire protection Hydraulics and Water Supply Analysis | ICS 2483

Fluid flow through hoses, pipes, pumps and fire protection appliances. Water supply and distribution analysis using hydraulic calculations. Testing techniques to anomalies in design or performance capabilities.

Industrial Safety Organization (Computer-Assisted) | ICS 3013

Recognition, elevation and control of occupational health and safety hazards. Accident prevention, accident analysis, training techniques, workman's compensation insurance, guarding and personal protective equipment. Requires use of CD-ROM.

Hydraulic Design of Automatic Sprinkler Systems | ICS 3713

Hydraulic calculation techniques for the design and analysis of automatic fire extinguishing systems.

Industrial Fire Pump Installations | ICS 3723

Applications, designs and analysis of industrial pump installations. Graphical analysis of fire pump contributions to existing fire protection water supply systems emphasized. Familiarity with basics of automatic sprinkler protection as well as standpipe and hose systems helpful in order to complete this course.

Sprinkler System Design for High-Piled and Rack Storage | ICS 3733

Specific design techniques for sprinkler system protection of commodities stored in solid piles or racks over 12 feet in height. A working knowledge of the hydraulic design and calculation process is necessary in order to complete this course.

Structural Designs for Fire and Life Safety | ICS 4050.1

Building construction standards and codes to assure maximum life and property safety from fires, explosions and natural disaster. Egress design specifications, occupancy and construction classifications and fire protection requirements for building construction and materials.

Rio Salado College

2323 West 14th Street
Tempe, Arizona 85281-6950
(877) 517-8345, (480) 517-8345
www.riosalado.edu   incarcerated.reentr@riosalado.edu

Rio Salado College offers programs specifically designed for prisoners, at reasonable tuition rates. They also offer a reentry program and some scholarship opportunities.

Accreditation: North Central Association of Colleges and Schools, The Higher Learning Commission

AVAILABLE TO PRISONERS

Degrees:

Associate in Applied Science in Addiction & Substance Use Disorder

Associate in Applied Science in Workforce Development & Community Reentry

Associate of Arts

Associate of Applied Sciences

Associate of General Studies

Certificates of Completions in:

Addictions & Substance Use Disorder (Level I/II)
Workforce Development & Community Reentry
Small Business Start-Up
Quality Customer Service

Tuition Rates:	**$216 per credit for nonresidents (Most courses will cost $645 each, plus fees.)**
	$81 per credit for Arizona residents
Payment Plan:	None
Textbook Fees:	Not included in tuition. They offer a book buy-back program.
Additional Fees:	**Registration fee: $15**
	Materials fee: $15 per course
Cancellation Policy:	Full refund within 9 days of enrollment; Other percentages based on percentage of course completion.
Transfer/Exam Options:	Not applicable
Time Limits:	12 to 16 weeks
Proctor required?	Some

Rio Salado
Certificate Programs

These certificate programs are designed to meet the needs of students who are interested in a specific professional specialization, and which may be helpful toward parole board consideration and reentry planning.

These are groups of courses that provide a concentration in a particular study area, without the need to take the general education courses of degree programs. They are more economical options than a full degree track.

Once completed, each of the following certificate earns college credit as marked, which can be used towards future learning.

(see course descriptions on the following pages)

ADDICTIONS & SUBSTANCE USE DISORDERS | LEVEL I

Course	Credit
Foundations of Addictions & Substance Use Disorders	ASD100	3
Communication Skills in Treating Addictions	ASD102	3
Pharmacology of Substances of Abuse & Dependency	ASD110	3
Professional Ethics in Addictions & Substance Use Disorders	ASD120	1
AIDS & Addictions	ASD145	1
Principles of Self-Help Groups	ASD150	2
Beginning Clinical Documentation Skills	ASD161	3
Theories & Techniques in the Treatment of Addictions	ADS165	2
Therapeutic Intervention Models	BHS205	3
Total Credits	21
Total Cost	$4,536 plus fees

ADDICTIONS & SUBSTANCE USE DISORDERS | LEVEL II

Course	Credit
Family Dynamics & Addictions	ASD220	3
Counseling Multicultural & Diverse Populations	ASD226	3
Relapse, Recovery, & Addiction	ASD236	2
Co-Occurring Disorders	ASD245	2
Group Interventions	ASD250	2
Advanced Theory & Techniques in Addiction Disorders	ASD275	3
Restricted Elective	PSY2xx, SOC2xx, or ASD285xx	2

Total Credits	18
Total Cost	$3,888 plus fees

WORKFORCE DEVELOPMENT

Personal Skill Development | WFR110	3
Family Reunification | WFR112	3
Social Skill Development | WFR114	1
Substance Abuse Education | WFR116	1
Job Readiness | WFR118	3
Job Retention | WFR120	3
Total Credits	13
Total Cost	$2,808 plus fees

SMALL BUSINESS START-UP

Owning & Operating a Small Business | MGT253	3
Principles of Marketing | MKT271	3
Hiring & Managing Employees | SBS213	1
Small Business Customer Relations | SBS214	1
Internet Marketing for Small Business | SBS220	2
Financial & Tax Management for Small Business | SBS230	2
Total Credits	12
Total Cost	$2,592 plus fees

QUALITY CUSTOMER SERVICE

Interpersonal Communication | COM110	3
Professional Development | GBS175	3
Quality Customer Service | TQM101	3
Business Communication | GBS233	3
Elements of Intercultural Communication | COM263	3
or Gender & Society | SOC212	
Teamwork Dynamics | TQM230	2
Total Credits	20
Total Cost	$4,320 plus fees

Rio Salado
Available Courses

ACCOUNTING

Accounting Principles | ACC111 (3 credits)
Fundamental theory of accounting principles and procedures.

Uses of Accounting Information | ACC230 (3 credits)
Introduction to the uses of accounting information for internal and external purposes with emphasis on financial statement analysis. Prerequisites: ACC111 or ACC211 and ENG101 and MAT151 and CRE101, or equivalent, or satisfactory score on District placement exam.

Uses of Accounting Information II | ACC240 (3 credits)

AGRICULTURAL SCIENCE

Plant Growth and Development | AGS164 (4 credits)
Principles of growth in relation to seed germination, emergence, growth and reproduction processes of plants and the environmental influences on plant growth processes.

ADDICTIONS AND SUBSTANCE USE DISORDERS

Therapeutic Intervention Models | BHS205 (3 credits)
Familiarization with at least five models of therapeutic intervention. Defines the key concepts, therapeutic process, techniques and procedures of each model.   Prerequisites: BHS105 or ASD102 or permission of Department or Division. NOTE: Course requires viewing DVDs provided on loan by the college.

Foundations of Addictions and Substance Use Disorders | (3 credits)
Introduction to the foundations of the alcohol and drug abuse rehabilitation field. Emphasis on the roles and responsibilities of the addiction paraprofessional counselor, ethical issues, pharmacology, family dynamics, dual diagnosis, intervention techniques, self-help groups, level of care, symptom identification, and conducting alcohol/drug histories. Interactive work stress. NOTE: Course requires viewing DVDs and utilizing CD-ROMs provided on loan by the college.

Communication Skills in Treating Addiction | ASD102 (3 credits)
Further examination and refinement of communication and beginning paraprofessional counseling skills as they relate to the chemically dependent client and family members. Emphasis on practicing the application of these skills to various situations associated with treatment planning. Recordkeeping/documentation skills emphasis.

Pharmacology of Substances of Abuse and Dependency | ASD 110 (3 credits)
Exploration of the pharmacology of substance of abuse and dependency. Examines the effect of psychopharmacological chemicals on human physiology. Emphasis on identification and management of substances of abuse and dependency.

Professional Ethics in Addictions and Substance Use Disorders | ASD120 (1 credit)
Exploration of topics relative to the professional and ethical development of the chemical dependency counselor, including manpower utilization, professionalism, and the meeting of individual counselor needs within the field.

Aids and Addictions | ASD145 PB: At-Home (1 credit)
Exploration of AIDS and its relationship to Chemical Dependency. Emphasis on myths and realities of AIDS, personal values, feelings, and limitations and treatment goals.

Principles of Self-Help Groups | ASD150 (2 credits)
Overview of the fundamental principles, concepts and historical antecedents of the various self-help groups. Emphasis on the self-help groups of Alcoholics Anonymous, Al-non, Alteen, Narcotics Anonymous, Co-Dependents Anonymous, and Adult Children of Alcoholics. NOTE: Course requires viewing DVDs provided on loan by the college.

Beginning Clinical Documentation Skills | ASD161 (3 credits)
Overview of interviewing/paraprofessional counseling and documentation skills. Record keeping/documentation skills. Alcohol and drug abuse paraprofessional counselor core functions emphasized.

Theories and Techniques in The Treatment of Addiction | ASD165 (2 credits)

Overview of counseling theories including the application to chemical dependency groups. Record-keeping skills and beginning paraprofessional counseling skills emphasized.

Family Dynamics and Addiction | ASD220 (3 credits)
Analysis of the impact of addictions on all the members of a family. Interviewing, assessment and therapeutic approaches particularly useful for these family members presented.

Counseling Multicultural and Diverse Populations | ASD226 (3 credits)
Exploration of influences of culture and diversity on substance abuse and dependency. Emphasis on recovery and therapeutic relationships.

Relapse, Recovery and Addiction | ASD236 No Exams (2 credits)
Review of the Bio-psycho-social model. Includes causes, consequences, assessment, and treatment of the dually diagnosed person. Emphasizes the psycho-educational model of treatment.

Co-Occurring Disorders | ASD245 (2 credits)
Examines dual diagnosis (mental illness and chemical dependency) from the bio-psycho-social model. Includes causes, consequences, assessment, and treatment of dually diagnosed person. Emphasizes the psycho-educational model of treatment.

Group Interventions | ASD250 (3 credits)
Focus on group dynamics and group process as they relate to chemical dependency. Exploration of group developmental stages, family intervention models, various counseling approaches/techniques and their application to therapeutic, education and family groups.

Advanced Theory and Techniques in The Treatment of Addiction Disorders | ASD275 (3 credits)
Capstone course for level two certificate in chemical dependency program. Focus on chemical dependency counseling theories and techniques used by chemical dependency counselors as they relate to the client and family members.   Prerequisites: ASD220, ASD226, ASD245 and ASD250 with a grade of C or better, or permission of instructor.

COMMUNICATION

Interpersonal Communication | COM110 (3 credits)
Theory and practice of communication skills which affect day-to-day interactions with other persons. Topics may include using verbal and nonverbal symbols, interactive listening, resolving interpersonal conflict, developing and maintaining personal and professional relationships.

Elements of Intercultural Communication | COM263 (3 credits)
Basic concepts, principles, and skills for improving oral communication between persons from different minority, racial, ethnic, and cultural backgrounds.

ECONOMICS

Macroeconomic Principles | ECN211 (3 credits)
A descriptive analysis of the structure and functioning of the American economy. Emphasis on basic economic institutions and factors that determine national income and employment levels. Consideration given to the macroeconomic topic of national income, unemployment, inflation and monetary and fiscal policies.

ENGLISH

Basic Writing Skills | ENG 081 (3 credits)
Emphasis on preparation for college-level composition with a focus on foundational skills. Establishing effective writing strategies through six or more writing projects comprising 1500 words in total.   Prerequisites: Appropriate English placement test score, or ENG071 with a grade of C or better, or permission of Department Chair.

Fundamentals of Writing | ENG091 (3 credits)
Emphasis on preparation for college-level composition with a focus on organizational skills. Developing effective writing strategies through five or more writing projects comprising at least 2000 words in total.   Prerequisites: Appropriate writing placement test score, or a grade of C or better in ENG081 or ESL087, or permission of Department or Division.

First-Year Composition | ENG101 No Exams (3 credits)
Emphasis on rhetoric and composition with a focus on expository writing and understanding writing as a process. Establishing effective college-level writing strategies through four or more writing projects comprising at least 3,000 words in total. Prerequisites: Appropriate writing placement test score, or grade of "C" or better in ENG091 or ESL097.

First-Year Composition | ENG102 No Exams (3 credits)
Emphasis on rhetoric and composition with a focus on persuasive, research-based writing and understanding writing as a process. Developing advanced college-level writing strategies through three or more writing projects comprising at least 4,000 words in total.   Prerequisites: Grade of C or better in ENG101.

ENGLISH HUMANITIES

Mythology | ENH251 (3 credits)
Deals with the myths and legends of civilizations with the greatest influence upon the development of the literature and culture of the English speaking people, and compares those myths with myths from other cultures.

Children's Literature | (Cross-references EDU291) ENH291 (3 credits)
Review of folk and modern literature from a variety of world cultures, including application of literary criteria to folk and modern literature for children.

GENERAL BUSINESS

Introduction to Business | GBS151 (3 credits)
Characteristics and activities of current local, national, and international business. An overview of economics, marketing, management and finance.

Professional Development | GBS175 (3 credits)
Examines personal qualities and prof. skills needed to find a good job. Explores techniques required to build a successful career.

Legal, Ethical, and Regulatory Issues in Business | GBS205 (3 credits)
Legal theories, ethical issues and regulatory climate affecting business policies and decisions.

Business Statistics | GBS221 (3 credits)
Business applications of descriptive and inferential statistics, measurement of relationships, and statistical process management. Includes the use of spreadsheet software for business statistical analysis. In order to register for this course, Rio will need to verify that you have completed the prerequisites. How do I do this? See Syllabus for full course description.   Grade of "C" or better in GBS220 or MAT217. Course designation: CS

Business Communication | GBS233 (3 credits)
Internal and external business communications, including verbal and nonverbal techniques.   Prerequisites: ENG101 or ENG107 with grade of "C" or better, or permission of Department or Division.

Management and Leadership 1 | MGT229 (3 credits)
Covers management concepts and applications for business, industry, and government organizations.

Human Relations in Business | MGT251 No Exams (3 credits)
Analysis of motivation, leadership, communications, and other human factors. Cultural differences that may create conflict and affect morale individually and within organizations.   MGT101 or MGT175 or MGT229 suggested, but not required.

Owning and Operating a Small Business | MGT253 Proctored (3 credits)
Starting, organizing, and operating a small business, including location, finance management processes, advertisement and promotion, credit, inventory control and ethics.

Principles of Marketing | MKT271 No Exams (3 credits)
An analysis of the marketing process and environment with regard to the product, pricing, distribution, and communication in order to satisfy buyer needs.

GEOGRAPHY

World Geography 1: Eastern Hemisphere | GCU121 (3 credits)

Description and analysis of areal variations in social, economic, and political phenomena in major world regions. Emphasis on Europe, Russia, North Africa, and the Asian world. This course satisfies Global Awareness and Social and Behavioral Sciences in the MCCD AGEC-A, AGEC-B, and/or AGEC-S.

Introduction to Physical Geography | GPH111 (4credits)
Spatial and functional relationships among climates, landforms, soils, water, and plants.

HEALTH SCIENCE

Healthful Living | HES100 At-Home (3 credits)
Health and wellness and their application to an optimal life style. Explores current topics of interest such as stress management, nutrition, fitness, and environmental health. Evaluates common risk factors associated with modern lifestyles.

MATHEMATICS

Precalculus | MAT187 PB: Proctored (5credits)
A Precalculus course combining topics from college algebra and trigonometry. Preparation for analytic geometry and calculus. May receive credit for only one of the following: MAT150, MAT151, MAT152, or MAT187. Prerequisites: Grade of B or better in MAT120, or MAT121, or MAT122, or equivalent, or satisfactory score on a placement test. Strongly recommended that students have some knowledge of trigonometry.

PHILOSOPHY

Introduction to Philosophy | PHI101 No Exams (3 credits)
General consideration of human nature and the nature of the universe. Knowledge, perception, freedom and determinism, and the existence of God.

PSYCHOLOGY

Introduction to Psychology | PSY101 (3 credits)
To acquaint the student with basic principles, methods and fields of psychology such as learning, memory, emotion, perception, physiological, developmental, intelligence, social and abnormal.

Introduction to Statistics | PSY230 (3 credits)
An introduction to basic concepts in descriptive and inferential statistics, with emphasis upon application to psychology, Consideration given to the methods of data collection, sampling techniques, graphing of data, and the statistical evaluation of data collected through experimentation. Required of psychology majors. Prerequisites: PSY101 with a grade of C or better and MAT092 or equivalent, or permission of Instructor.

Developmental Psychology | PSY240 (3 credits)
Human development from conception through adulthood. Includes: physical, cognitive, emotional and social capacities that develop at various ages. Recommended for students majoring in nursing, education, pre-med, and psychology. Prerequisites: PSY101 with a grade of C or better, or permission of Instructor.

Psychology of Personality | PSY260 (3 credits)
Introduction to theories of personality with emphasis upon application of specific theories towards the understanding of individuals. Prerequisites: PSY101 with a grade of C or better, or permission of Instructor.

Abnormal Psychology | PSY266 (3 credits)
Distinguishes between normal behavior and psychological disorders. Subjects may include stress disorders, problems with anxiety and depression, unusual and abnormal sexual behavior, schizophrenia and addictive behaviors. Causes and treatment of psychological problems and disorders are discussed. Prerequisites: PSY101 with a grade of C or better, or permission.

RELIGIOUS STUDIES

World Religions | REL100 (3credits)
The development of various religions from the prehistoric to modern times. Political, economic, social and geographic relationships among world religions. Consideration of both Eastern and Western religions.

Introduction to Religion | REL101 (3 credits)
Various religious expressions of humankind. Focuses on basic religious themes common to religions, such as encounter with the Holy, search for self and community, mystical illumination, spiritual discipline.

SMALL BUSINESS SKILLS

Hiring and Managing Employees | SBS213

Small Business Customer Relations | SBS214

Internet Marketing for Small Business | SBS220

Financial and Tax Management for Small Business | SBS230

SOCIOLOGY

Introduction to Sociology | SOC101 (3 credits)
Fundamental concepts of social organization, culture, socialization, social institutions and social change.

Gender and Society | SOC212 (3 credits)
A study of the way culture shapes and defines the positions and roles of both men and women in society. Major emphasis on social conditions which may lead to a broadening of gender roles and a reduction of gender role stereotypes and implications of these changes. Open to both men and women.

TEAM QUALITY MANAGEMENT

Teamwork Dynamics | TQM230
Theory and practice of how team members and team leaders use listening, negotiating and interpersonal skills for the enhancement of team process. Included are concepts of team development and team problem solving techniques.

WORKFORCE RE-ENTRY

Re-entry Skills: Personal Skill Development | WFR110 (3 credits)
Personal skill development necessary for transition from incarceration to community. Includes development of a personal value system and decision-making strategies as well as a conflict management. Also covers time and money management. Also covers time and money management, goal setting, and the basics for everyday life.

Re-entry Skills: Family Reunification | WFR112 (3 credits)
Reunification procedures for the incarcerated person's effective transition. Includes building and maintaining self-esteem and effective communication for healthy families or support systems. Also covers family and networking culture, discipline, and expectations, for release.   Prerequisites: Permission of Department or Division.

Re-entry Skills: Social Skills Development | WFR114 No Exams (1 credit)
Re-entry Skills: Substance Abuse Education | WFR116 At-Home MD/FN 1credit.

Re-entry Skills: Job Readiness | WFR118 No Exams (3 credits)
Preparing the incarcerated person for release into the working world. Includes education, skills assessment, and work experience. Also covers job search skills such as resume writing, applications, and interviewing.

Re-entry Skills: Job Retention | WFR120 No Exams (2 credits)
Job retention procedures and techniques for incarcerated persons in transition. Includes workplace protocol, job performance, and employer-employee interaction. Also covers stress management and communication skills as well as interpersonal relationships in the work place.

Sam Houston State University | University Heights

2405 Avenue I
Huntsville, Texas 77340
(936) 294-1003
www.shsu.edu

Sam Houston State University is a member of the Texas State University system and offers a limited number of paper-based for-credit courses in a variety of subjects.

Accreditation: Southern Association of Colleges and Schools, Commission on Colleges (SACS – COC)

AVAILABLE TO PRISONERS

A variety of for-credit courses

Tuition Rates:	**$73 per 3 credit-hour course**
Payment Plan:	None
Textbook Fees:	Not included in tuition
Additional Fees:	**Application fee: $30**
Transfer/Exam Options:	Not applicable
Time Limits:	12 months per course
Proctor required:	Yes

Temporarily suspended enrollment in print-based courses for incarcerated students. Check back with the school if your are interested in their courses for current availability.

Sam Houston State University
Available Courses

ECONOMICS

INTRODUCTION TO ECONOMICS | ECON 2300 (ECO 230)

12 lessons, 1 final exam. Combines micro-economic and macro-economic principles in one semester. It is designed for those who are neither majors nor minors in economics, but who would benefit from a one semester introduction to economic principles. No credit given for ECO 230 if ECO 233 or ECO 234 previously completed.

PRINCIPLES OF MICROECONOMICS | ECON 2302 (ECO 233)

12 lessons, 1 final exam. Basic economic principles including price theory, analysis of the firm, competition and monopoly, and the distribution of income.

PRINCIPLES OF MACROECONOMICS | ECON 2301 (ECO 234)

The economic role of government, public finance and taxation, national income analysis, national income theory, money and banking, economic fluctuations and growth, and international trade and finance.

ENGLISH

SURVEY OF AMERICAN LITERATURE, BEGINNING TO 1865 | ENGL 3360 (ENG 360W)

Prerequisite: ENGL 1301/164, 1302/165 and 2331/265 or 2342/266.

A survey of themes, genres, and authors in American literary history from the period of exploration and settlement through the American Renaissance and the Civil War. Required of all English majors; also required of all English minors not seeking certification.

SURVEY OF AMERICAN LITERATURE: 1865 TO THE PRESENT | ENGL 3361 (ENG 361W)

Prerequisite: ENGL 1301/164, 1302/165 and 2331/265 or 2342/266.

A survey of authors, genres, and movements in American literature from 1865 to the present, involving representatives works of Realism, Naturalism, Modernism, and Post-Modernism. Required of all English majors; also required of all English minors not seeking certification.

EARLY ENGLISH MASTERWORKS | ENGL 3384 (ENG 384W)

Prerequisite: ENGL 1301/164, 1302/165 and 2331/265 or 2342/266.

A study of the major figures of English literature from the beginning until 1798. Required for all English majors.

LATER ENGLISH MASTERWORKS | ENGL 3385 (ENG 385W)

Prerequisite: ENGL 1301/164, 1302/165 and 2331/265 or 2342/266.

A study of the major figures in English literature from 1798 to the present. Required for all English majors.

AMERICAN LITERATURE: 1820 TO 1860 | ENGL 4372 (ENG 472W)

Prerequisite: ENGL 1301/164, 1302/165, 2331/265, 2342/266 and 3 hours of ENGL 300-level.

A study of the emergence of a distinctive American literary art, including such writers as Poe, Emerson, Thoreau, Hawthorne, Melville, and Whitman.

FINANCE

PERSONAL FINANCE | FINC 1307 (FIN 171)

A study of the problems of personal financial management. Topics include savings, risks, investment considerations, insurance, taxation, governmental programs in financial planning, etc. Also recommended for non-business majors. Not open to students who have credit for FIN 367

FINANCIAL INSTITUTIONS AND MARKETS | FINC 3310 (FIN 334)

This course will explore the structure of the financial system with emphasis on the role, operations, and regulations of financial institutions and markets, including international. The nature, participants, instruments, and relationships of the money and capital markets will be examined. Only students who have successfully completed sixty or more semester credit hours are permitted to take 300-400 level business courses by correspondence.

BUSINESS FINANCE | FINC 3320 (FIN 367)
Prerequisites: ACCT 2302/232 and MATH 1324/199 or MATH 1420/142 OR 1314/170
A study is made of financial principles as applied to management of funds, capital budgeting, sources of funds, techniques of financial analysis, cost of capital, financial leverage, capital structure, forecasting financial needs, management of working capital, financial policies, analysis and regulation of security issues, and international finance. Only students who have successfully completed sixty or more semester credit hours are permitted to take 300-400 level business courses by correspondence.

GENERAL BUSINESS ADMINISTRATION

BUSINESS PRINCIPLES IN AN INTERNATIONAL ENVIRONMENT | BUAD 1301 (GBA 181)
A survey course of all the major business disciplines with an emphasis on helping define career objectives and supporting academic interest areas. An overview of what is involved in accounting, marketing, management, legal aspects of business, economics and finance. An ideal choice for non-business majors wanting to learn of opportunities in business and how to pursue them. Not open to business majors with junior or senior standing.

BUSINESS LEGAL ENVIRONMENT | BUAD 2301 (GBA 281)
This course covers legal environment from a "preventive law," practical perspective. Specific subjects include: Litigation, Alternative Dispute Resolution, Torts, Business Organizations, Real and Personal Property-(including Asset Protection-Estate Planning, and Administrative Law. The course provides an introduction to Environmental Law, Consumer Law, Securities Law, Human Resources Management Law (Labor Law), and Marketing Law (Anti-Trust).

BUSINESS LAW | BUAD 3355 (GBA 362)
The focus of this course is on areas of modern commercial law as needed by business professionals in conducting business transactions in buying and selling goods and services. Common Law Contracts and negotiation strategies are presented. An examination of the Uniform Commercial Code includes Sales Law, Leasing, Commercial Paper-Negotiable Instruments, Commercial Storage and Distribution of Goods, and Transfer of Securities. Creditor's rights and U.S. Federal Bankruptcy Code are also covered. Only students who have successfully completed fifty or more semester credit hours are permitted to take 300-400 level business classes by correspondence.

REAL ESTATE LAW | BUAD 3365 (GBA 385)
This course covers the legal aspects of real estate including the legal principles and the legal instruments used in real estate transactions. Only students who have successfully completed fifty or more semester credit hours are permitted to take 300-400 level business courses by correspondence.

GEOGRAPHY

PEOPLE, PLACE AND THE ENVIRONMENT | GEOG 1321 (GEO 161)
An introductory course designed to acquaint students with the breadth of Geography. This includes an examination of the physical environment, environmental issues, and the cultural, economic, and political factors that influence human activities and societies. Attention will be focused upon the spatial interrelationships that exist between man and his environment. In addition, selected geographic skills will be covered, including latitude and longitude determination, earth-sun relationships, time, map projections and map scale.

WORLD REGIONAL GEOGRAPHY: EUROPE, ASIA, AUSTRALIA | GEOG 2355 (GEO 265)
This is an introductory level course giving a general overview of the land and people. Topics discussed will include the physical environment, cultural characteristics, and the various ways people live and make their living. Attention will be focused upon the relationships which exist between location, the physical environment, and human activity. Examples of countries covered are the former Soviet Union, Germany, France, China, Japan, and United Kingdom. No prerequisites are needed to take this course.

WORLD REGIONAL GEOGRAPHY: LATIN AMERICA, AFRICA and SOUTH ASIA | GEOG 2356 (GEO 266)

World Regional Geography is a course whose relevance is on the upswing. In this era of increased globalization, it is imperative to have a population that is globally conscientious. This course is designed to provide students with a survey of global and regional interactions among people, their geographic location and the utilization of space, and the physical environment. This course is not just about the memorization of countries and their capital cities, it is about understanding why places are where they are, and the sorts of issue that are important there today. This is a writing enhanced course that will focus on the geographic realms of Latin America; Africa (including the Middle East); and South Asia.

Weather and Climate Lecture and Laboratory | GEOG 1401 (GEO 141) 4 credit course

The basic concepts of meteorology and climatology are introduced. Atmospheric temperature, pressure, winds, moisture, and air masses and storms are systematically covered, followed by an overview of the major climates and ecosystems of the earth. Environmental problems related to weather, climate, and ecosystems are considered throughout. The lab portion of weather and climate is an activity-related treatment of the basic components of meteorology and climatology. Specific topics covered are similar to the lecture.

Regional Geography: United States and Canada | GEOG 3359 (GEO 369)

This course provides a general overview of the land and people of the United States and Canada. Topics covered include the physical environment (weather patterns, landforms and water resources), cultural differences, and the various ways people live and make their living. Attention is focused upon the relationships which exist between location, the physical environment and human activity.

Geography of Texas | GEOG 4358 (GEO 471)

A survey of the regional geography of Texas. Consideration is given to the significance of primary and secondary activity within the state, urbanization, and potential for development.

HEALTH

Due to the added number of courses offered online and face-to-face, the Department of Health will only approve enrollment in a health course via Correspondence for extenuating circumstances. If you feel you have an extenuating circumstance, please contact Isabel Kirwin (isabel@shsu.edu) for approval. Proof of approval should be submitted to the school's office by email at SHSUCorrespondence@shsu.edu.

LIFESTYLE AND WELLNESS | HLTH 3366 (HED 166)

This course explores a variety of health issues which influence the well-being of an individual throughout the life cycle. The student is given an opportunity to develop a personal philosophy of wellness and self-responsibility for health through self-assessment, investigation of factors affecting one's health, and the examination of behavior modification strategies.

DRUG USE AND ABUSE | HLTH 3380 (HED 280)

This course explores the use and misuse of drugs and their effects on the health of man.

CHILD & ADOLESCENT HEALTH | HLTH 3382 (HED 382)

This course focuses on the causes of and approaches to physical, social, mental, and emotional health problems among young people. Emphasis is placed on creating an environment in which children and adolescents can learn to make prudent decisions regarding health related behaviors.

KINESIOLOGY

Due to the added number of courses offered online and face-to-face, the Department of Kinesiology will only approve enrollment in a Kinesiology course via Correspondence for extenuating circumstances.

If you feel you have an extenuating circumstance, please contact Dr. Liette Ocker (Liette.Ocker@shsu.edu) for approval. Proof of approval should be submitted to the school's office by email at SHSUCorrespondence@shsu.edu.

FOUNDATIONS OF KINESIOLOGY | KINE 1331 (KIN 131)

This course serves as a base for all kinesiology courses. Units will include historical development, philosophical implications, physical fitness, scientific bases of movement, and educational values of kinesiology.

Kinesiology and Sports | KINE 3378 (KIN 378)

The first half of this course is concerned with the organization and administration of physical education and recreation in the public schools; the second half, with the organization, administration, and business management of a high school athletic program.

ADVANCED TOPICS IN PHYSIOLOGY OF EXERCISE | KINE 4373 (KIN 473)

This course bridges the gap between basic undergraduate and graduate physiology. Selected topics will include: bioenergetics, hormonal regulation, hemodynamics, effects of high altitude, ergogenic aids, gender differences and exercise performance, and exercise with older adults.

MANAGEMENT

PRINCIPLES OF MANAGEMENT | MGMT 3310 (MGT 380)

This course is concerned with the principles and methods used in managing and operating organizations, both domestically and abroad. Course coverage includes analysis of the organization's environment and the managerial functions of planning, organizing, leading, motivating, and controlling. Only students who have successfully completed fifty or more semester credit hours are permitted to take 300-400 level business courses by correspondence.

ORGANIZATION BEHAVIOR | MGMT 3320 (MGT 381)

Prerequisite: MGMT 3310/380.

Advanced study of individual and group behavior in organizations and how it affects the achievement of organizational objectives. Only students who have successfully completed fifty or more semester credit hours are permitted to take 300-400 level business courses by correspondence.

MARKETING

PRINCIPLES OF MARKETING | MKTG 3310 (MKT 371)

Prerequisite: ECON 2302/273 or ECON 2300/230, or AGRI 2317/164

This course includes marketing functions, transportation, assembling, storage, trade channels, cost, co-operative marketing, trade association, market analysis, marketing structures and agencies, types of middlemen, international marketing, and current marketing practices. Only students who have successfully completed fifty or more semester credit hours are permitted to take 300-400 level business courses by correspondence.

RETAILING | MKTG 3385 (MKT 383)

Prerequisite: MKTG 3310/371

This course includes the evolution of retailing, the scope of retailing, store location, store layout, organization, the customer, buying markets, receiving and marketing merchandise, mark-up, stock control, merchandise plan, fashions, retail credit, accounting, insurance and sales promotion. Only students who have successfully completed fifty or more semester credit hours are permitted to take 300-400 level business courses by correspondence.

MATHEMATICS

PLANE TRIGONOMETRY | MATH 1316 (MTH 163)

Prerequisites: Two years of high school algebra and one year of high school geometry.

Topics include coordinate systems, circular functions, solutions of triangles, identities, trigonometric equations, and inverse functions.

ELEMENTARY STATISTICS | MATH 1369 (MTH/STA 169)

Prerequisites: Two years of high school algebra.

This is a survey course in elementary statistics designed to acquaint students with the role of statistics in society. Coverage includes graphical descriptive methods, measures of central tendency and variation, the basic concepts of statistical inference, the notion of estimators, confidence intervals, hypothesis testing, linear regression, and correlation. A knowledge of probability and statistics will allow a quantitative assessment with the risk involved with each inference and allows for more intelligent actions. This course is designed as both a terminal course for those not likely to be intimately in research in their academic fields and as an introductory course for those who are. Also offered as STA 169.

PRE CALCULUS ALGEBRA | MTH 170 [MATH 1314]

Prerequisites: Two years of high school algebra and one year of high school geometry.

Topics include a brief review of introductory algebra, variation, elementary theory of equations, functions (including exponential and logarithmic), inequalities, systems of equations, and other related topics.

STATISTICAL METHODS IN PRACTICE | MATH 3379 (MTH/STA 379)

Prerequisites: Three semester hours of mathematics and consent of instructor.

This course includes the fundamentals of statistical concepts and will guide the student through basic statistical procedures to permit crictical insight into the science of collecting, classifying, presenting, and interpreting information from the data. The three primary topics covered are: 1) descriptive statistics (geographic presentation of data, histograms, plots, charts, measures of central tendency, dispersion, position, bivariate data analysis, linear correlation, and regression analysis; 2) probability concepts and rules for calculating probabilities of compound events. The probability coverage also includes the more commonly occurring probability distributions such as the binomial and normal distributions; and 3) inferential statistics including inferences involving one and two populations. A knowledge of probability and statistics will allow quantitive assessment of the risk involved with each inference and allows for more intelligent actions. This course is designed as both a terminal course for those not likely to be intimately in research in their academic fields and as an introductory course for those who are. Also offered as STA 379.

PHILOSOPHY

INTRODUCTION TO PHILOSOPHY | PHIL 2361 (PHL 261)

A general examination of the fields and issues of philosophy as discussed by both classical and modern philosophers. Philosophical problems discussed include the existence of God, the nature of knowledge and truth, the issue of human free will, and the ultimate nature of reality.

SOCIOLOGY

PRINCIPLES OF SOCIOLOGY | SOCI 1301 (SOC 131)

Introduction to the discipline with a focus on concepts and principles used in the study of group life, social institutions and social processes. This course is a prerequisite to many other courses taught in the department or is required of all sociology majors and minors.

SOCIAL PROBLEMS | SOCI 1306 (SOC 261)

Application of sociological principles to the major problems of contemporary society. Special attention given to mental disorders; use and abuse of drugs and alcohol; sexual deviance and crime and delinquency; problems of youth and the family in contemporary society; institutionalized aspects of inequality, prejudice and discrimination; and population and environmental concerns.

CULTURAL ANTHROPOLOGY | SOCI 3381 (SOC 381)

Prerequisite: SOCI 1301/131 or consent of instructor.

Cultural and social organization among primitive or preliterate societies, marriage, property, religion, magic, and tribal control. Significance of the study of primitive cultures for understanding of urban industrial civilizations.

STATISTICS

ELEMENTARY STATISTICS | STAT 3379 (STA/MTH 379)

Prerequisites: Two years of high school algebra.

This is a survey course in elementary statistics designed to acquaint students with the role of statistics in society. Coverage includes graphical descriptive methods, measures of central tendency and variation, the basic concepts of statistical inference, the notion of estimators, confidence intervals, hypothesis testing, linear regression, and correlation. A knowledge of probability and statistics will allow a quantitative assessment of the risk involved with each inference and allows for more intelligent actions. This course is designed as both a terminal course for those not likely to be intimately involved in research in their academic fields and as an introductory course for those who are.

STATISTICAL METHODS IN PRACTICE | STAT 3379 (STA/MTH 379)

Prerequisites: Three semester hours of mathematics. This course introduces the fundamentals of statistical concepts and will guide the student through the basic statistical procedures to permit critical insight into the science of collecting, classifying, presenting, and interpreting information from the data. The three primary topics covered are: 1) descriptive statistics (geographic presentation of data, histograms, plots, charts, measures of central tendency, dispersion, position, bivariate data analysis, linear correlation, and regression analysis); 2) probability concepts and rules for calculating probabilities of compound events. The probability coverage also includes the more commonly occurring probability distributions such as the binomial and normal distributions; and 3) inferential statistics including inferences involving one and two populations. A knowledge of probability and statistics will allow a quantitive assessment of the risk involved with each inference and allows for more intelligent actions. This course is designed as both a terminal course for those not likely to be intimately involved in research in their academic fields and as an introductory course for those who are. Also offered as MTH 379

Seattle Central Community College

1701 Broadway BE1140
Seattle, Washington 98122
(206) 587-4060
www.seattlecentral.edu   *cometocentral@seattlecolleges.edu*

Seattle Central Community College offers several for-credit courses. Students have the option of registering as degree-earning students or non-matriculated students (those students who are taking courses solely for learning and not for credit or certificates.) The non-matriculated option allows students to study at their own pace.

Accreditation: Northwest Commission on Colleges and Universities

AVAILABLE TO PRISONERS

A variety of for-credit courses, which can be taken without the for-credit option

Tuition Rates:	**$71.67 per credit for Washington residents (most courses will cost $215 each.)**
	$211.51 per credit for nonresidents (most courses will cost $634.55 each.)
Payment Plan:	Monthly payment plans are available
Textbook Fees:	Not included in tuition
Additional Fees:	None
Transfer/Exam Options:	Not applicable
Time Limits:	12 months per for-credit course; $50 for 90-day extension.
	No time limits for non-matriculated students
Proctor required?	No
Cancellation Policy:	Full refund up to week two of study, 50% refund up to week four of study. No refunds after 30 days.

Seattle Central Community College
Available Courses
All courses earn 3 credits unless otherwise marked.

APPLIED HEALTH

Medical Terminology | AHE 168

Introduction to the concept of "word building" with Greek and Latin root words, prefixes and suffixes. Strengthen the understanding of definitions through interpreting medical terms in the context of a variety of medical reports.   Prerequisite: Placement into ENGL& 101 or equivalent

ASTRONOMY

Astronomy | ASTR 100

Emphasis on astronomic concepts fundamental to an understanding of the solar system, stars, galaxies, origin and history of the universe. Prerequisite: Eligibility for MAT 084and ENG 101, or equivalent

BUSINESS

Intro to Business | Bus&101

Overview of U.S. business structure: economy, forms of business ownership, management styles, marketing, and financing. Covers small business, franchising and international business. (May require access to library or news media resources.)

COMMUNICATIONS

Intro to Mass Media | CMST 102

History, characteristics and influence of today's media on the individual and society. Covers newspapers, magazines, advertising, radio, television and film. (May require access to library or news media resources.)

ENGLISH LITERATURE

Composition I | ENGL&101

Introduction to the writing process. Assignments focus on major strategies of nonfiction prose, with subject matter drawn from firsthand experience and observation.

Intro to Fiction | ENGL&112

Study and analysis of the art, elements, and techniques of short stories, novellas and novels of American and international authors. Prerequisite: ENGL&101

American Literature III | ENGL&246

Writers of the 20th century with emphasis on major modern fiction, drama, poetry, and trends in current literature. Prerequisite: ENGL&101

ENVIRONMENTAL SCIENCES

Environmental Issues & Problems | ENV 150

A survey of topics in environmental science (ecosystems, populations, air and water pollution, etc.) with an emphasis on understanding environmental issues and problems.

Prerequisite: Eligibility for MATH 084, 087, 091 and ENGL&101

HISTORY

World Civilizations III | HIST 128

Study of world civilization during the 19th and 20th centuries. Intro to dramatic events and often-conflicting forces and ideologies affecting contemporary life. Account of modern peoples' solutions to challenges and problems that confront civilization.

OCEANOGRAPHY

Survey of Oceanography | OCE 100

Examines the ocean in terms of physical, chemical, geological and biological process; and human influence upon the oceans natural equilibrium. Prerequisite: Eligibility for MAT 084 and ENG 101, or equivalent

LANGUAGE

Intro to Linguistics | LAN 101

Introduces the study of natural language. The similarities in the basics of language as an instrument of thought and communication will be presented as well as the sources for cultural differentiation between all linguistic materials.

METEOROLOGY

Meteorology | MEY 100

Introduction to the principles of meteorology as well as weather and climate controls and their effect. Surveys weather forecasting, use of weather maps, and satellite data.

Prerequisite: Eligibility for MAT 084 and ENG 101, or equivalent

PHILOSOPHY

Intro to Philosophy | PHIL& 120

Introduction to philosophical thought and issues, intellectual systems and writings of the great philosophers; the nature of philosophy, the meaning of knowledge, values, reality, and related subjects.

Symbolic Logic | PHIL& 120

Examination of principles of Aristotelian and symbolic logic, deductive argument and proof; meaning of language and its place in the reasoning process.

Prerequisite: MAT 098 or equivalent

PSYCHOLOGY

General Psychology | PSYC&100

Introduction to the scientific study of human behavior, including learning and thinking, development, perception, motivation, emotion, personality and individual differences, social and abnormal behavior and research methods.

SOCIOLOGY

Intro to Sociology | SOC& 101

Basic problems and concepts in human social interaction with emphasis on group aspects of human behavior. Covers culture, socialization, family, education, religion, urbanization, sex roles, social class, deviance, race, age, sexuality, demography and social change.

Southwest University

2200 Veterans Boulevard
Kenner, Louisiana 70062
(504) 468-2900
www.southwest.edu   southwest@southwest.edu

Southwest University offers a wide selection of paper-based business-related degrees and certificates. They are only accredited by the DEAC, which may hinder credit transfer options if the student chooses further education beyond SU.

Accreditation: Distance Education Accrediting Commission

AVAILABLE TO PRISONERS

Certificates in:
General Management; Criminal Justice Human Resource Management; International Business; Leadership & Management; Management; Marketing; Organizational Management

Associate of Science in:
Business Administration; Criminal Justice; General Studies

Bachelor of Science in *Criminal Justice*

Bachelor of Science, Business Administration *in*:
General Management; Criminal Justice Human Resource Management; International Business; Leadership & Management; Management; Marketing; Organizational Management

Tuition Rates:	**$275 per credit (Most courses will cost $825 each.)**
	Individual courses: $460 per credit (Most courses will cost $1,380 each.)
	Certificate Program: $5,520
	$250 per credit for DANTES qualified students
Payment Plans:	Certificate programs: $3,725 down payment, $2,070 within 10 weeks
	Degree programs: $1,025 down payment, 24 equal monthly payments for the remainder due.
Textbooks:	Not included in tuition
Additional Fees:	Application fee: $75; Registration fee: $200; Graduation/Certificate of Completion fee: $125; Shipping fee: $70; Handling fee: $16.50; Study guide: $90; Library fee: $25
Transfer/Exam Options:	30 credits per associate degree; 90 credits per bachelor degree **Experiential credit:** up to 15 credits/associate; 30/bachelor degree. **Credit-by-Exam:** up to 25% of credit required for degree.
Time Limits:	10 weeks per course; 24 weeks per degree program. $100 per month extension.
Proctor required?	No

Southwest University
Certificate Programs

These certificate programs are designed to meet the needs of individuals who are interested in a specific professional specialization. These are groups of courses that provide a concentration in a particular study area, without the need to take the general education courses of degree programs. They are more economical options than a full degree track. (See 'Tuition' above.)

Once completed, each of the following certificate earns 12 college credits, which can be used towards future learning, as well as a Southwest University Certificate of Completion.

HUMAN RESOURCE MANAGEMENT CERTIFICATE

SELECT ANY FOUR COURSES: (SEE COURSE DESCRIPTIONS ON THE FOLLOWING PAGES)

- HR: Issues, Decision making and Challenges | HRM 370
- Training, Strategies and Practices | HRM 440
- Global Human Resource Management | INT 448
- Labor Relations & Collective Bargaining | HRM 462
- Strategic Compensation | HRM 472
- Staffing Processes & Strategies | HRM 475

LEADERSHIP & MANAGEMENT CERTIFICATE

SELECT ANY FOUR COURSES: (SEE COURSE DESCRIPTIONS ON THE FOLLOWING PAGES)

- Management | MGT 340
- Human Relations at Work | HR 348
- Organizational Behavior Structure & Processes | ORG 435
- Leadership in Organization | BUS 445
- Supervisory Management | MGT 450
- Strategic Management & Policy | BUT 478

INTERNATIONAL BUSINESS CERTIFICATE

SELECT ANY FOUR COURSES: (SEE COURSE DESCRIPTIONS ON THE FOLLOWING PAGES)

- International Business | Int 360
- Global Marketing | Int 430
- Leadership in Organizations | Bus 445
- Global Human Resource Marketing | Int 448
- International Organizational Behavior | Int 454
- International Management | Int 465

MANAGEMENT CERTIFICATE

SELECT ANY FOUR COURSES: (SEE COURSE DESCRIPTIONS ON THE FOLLOWING PAGES)

- Management | MGT 340
- Human Relations at Work | HR 348

- Supervisory Management | MGT 450
- Entrepreneurial Management | BUS 460
- International Management | INT 465
- Strategic Management & Policy | BUS 478

MARKETING CERTIFICATE

SELECT ANY FOUR COURSES: (SEE COURSE DESCRIPTIONS ON THE FOLLOWING PAGES)

- Principles of Selling | MKT 335
- Public Relations | BUS 350
- Promotional Marketing | MKT 358
- Global Marketing | INT 430
- Sales Management | MGT 452
- Consumer Purchasing & Behavior | MKT 470

ORGANIZATIONAL MANAGEMENT

SELECT ANY FOUR COURSES: (SEE COURSE DESCRIPTIONS ON THE FOLLOWING PAGES)

- Human Relations at Work | HR 348
- HR: Issues, Decision Making & Challenges | ORG 435
- Organizational Behavior Structures & Processes | ORG 435
- Leadership in Organizations | BUS 445
- Supervisory Management | MGT 450
- Strategic Management & Policy | BUS 478

CRIMINAL JUSTICE INTRODUCTORY CERTIFICATE

SELECT ANY FOUR COURSES: (SEE COURSE DESCRIPTIONS ON THE FOLLOWING PAGES)

- Introduction to Criminal Justice | CJ 110
- Introduction to Police Operations | CJ 176
- Survey of Corrections | CJ 180
- Introduction to Juvenile Justice | CJ 185
- Introduction to Criminal Procedures | CJ 201
- Survey of the American Legal System | CJ 209
- Introduction to Criminal Law | CJ 250

CRIMINAL JUSTICE ADVANCED CERTIFICATE

Select any four courses: (see course descriptions on the following pages)

- Introduction: Law Enforcement & Criminal Justice | CJ 302
- Constitutional Law | CJ 329
- Criminology | CJ 335
- Introduction to Police Administration | CJ 360
- Criminal Investigation | CJ 370
- Criminal Procedures | CJ 440
- Criminal Law | CJ 450

Southwest University
Available Courses

ACCOUNTING

Accounting I | ACC 203
This course presents information in a broad business context emphasizing what accounting information is, why it is important, and how it is used to make economic decisions.

Accounting II | ACC 204
This course provides valuable information covering the introduction to management accounting and explains its significant role in making sound business decisions.

BUSINESS

Introduction to Business | BUS 210
This course emphasizes the important issues and challenges facing businesses today. Students will gain practical knowledge about business and focus on issues of concern. This course will help students build and enlarge on decision-making skills.

Public Speaking | BUS 214
This course is designed to cover all aspects of speech preparation and presentation. Real-world scenarios are used to demonstrate how public speaking is used in everyday life. This course provides a friendly learning approach to becoming a better public speaker.

Practical Business Law | BUS 239
This course provides an overview of the law of commercial transactions and a variety of other business legal issues. It presents a practical approach to law that emphasizes current and relevant topics students need to understand business transactions and issues such as contracts, property, insurance and employer/employee relations.

Special Topics in Business Administration | BUS 280
Subject to faculty approval. A project or an independent paper the will demonstrate knowledge and understanding of a specific subject.

Building Customer Service | BUS 310
This course covers the concepts and skills needed for success in business careers. It provides students the opportunity to develop or enhance customer service skills. It discusses how to handle service problems, conflict and stress. Tips are provided for customer service supervisory personnel.

Information and Records Management | BUS 320
This course provides in-depth coverage of current issues in records and information management. Its focus considers past, current, and future records and information trends which substantiate the need for assurance that information will be found or be available when needed. Topics include storage, retrieval, disaster recovery and ethical and legal practices.

Business Ethics | BUS 345
This course focuses on the concerns and issues of today's challenging business environment. It provides a framework that can be used to identify, analyze, and resolve ethical issues in business decision making.

Public Relations | BUS 350
This course provides an inside look at the practice of public relations. Emphasis is on the principles, processes and practices that lead to positive business relationships.

Leadership in Organizations | BUS 445
This course is designed to provide insight into leadership research, findings and practice. It places emphasis on application and skill building, and includes an array of opinions of practitioners, consultants and authors who base their conclusions on observations. Various leadership roles and personal qualities of leaders are introduced.

E-Commerce | BUS 456

This course describes the essentials of electronic commerce. It assesses major opportunities, limitation, issues and risks. This course provides all the basic definitions as well as logical support. Students are presented examples from large corporations, small businesses, governments and not-for-profit agencies.

Strategic Management & Policy | BUS 478

This course focuses on the organization as a whole and its interactions with its environments. It presents concepts and theories useful in understanding the strategic management process and discusses social responsibilities and ethics. Strategic issues such as technology/innovation and entrepreneurship are also emphasized.

COMMUNICATIONS

Principles of Communication | COM 105

This course is designed to survey the field of communication. It covers classic approaches and theory. Significant attention is directed toward communication skills. Emphasis is also on public speaking. Interpersonal and small group communication and interviewing.

COMPUTER INFORMATION SYSTEMS

Computer Concepts | CIS 122

This course introduces students to the basic concepts to the fields of information systems and computer science. This course provides a theoretical foundation and introduces applications that put theory into practice.

Basic Communications Technologies | CIS 205

This course provides an overview of electronics communications systems and telecommunications. Students will gain a solid foundation in telecommunication technology applications, network and telephone fundamentals, and internet Web tools and resources.

CRIMINAL JUSTICE

Introduction to Criminal Justice | CJ 110

This course examines Criminal Justice as an interdisciplinary endeavor, sharing elements from criminology, law, history, psychology, and political science. It offers a solid foundation of information about the subject. Students are provided the essential content and the critical tools involved in understanding criminal justice.

Introduction to Police Operations | CJ 176

This course covers the major areas of police operations. It describes what police officers do and why. It provides a large body of information on practical application as it presents what policing is all about. The course is student-friendly and is geared toward individuals pursuing a career in law enforcement.

Survey of Corrections | CJ 180

This course provides a practical approach to the practices of modern corrections. It presents an overview of the day-to-day operations of correctional agencies, prisons and jails. Professionalism in corrections is the main focus.

Introduction to Juvenile Justice | CJ 185

This course focuses on the issues, trends, and challenges facing juvenile justice today. It provides students with a complete and realistic view of the system's efforts at controlling youths and providing help to those in need. The course is student friendly and enables students to move easily through the material.

Introduction to Criminal Procedures | CJ 201

This is a basic course that details the elements of criminal procedures. It provides an in-depth presentation of criminal procedures in sequential steps. A significant offering of procedural concepts and terms are presented throughout the course.

Introduction to Criminal Law | CJ 250

This course provides a comprehensive survey of all the major components of substantive criminal law. Students are exposed to the language of criminal law in a friendly, understandable style. The course also provides coverage of current issues.

The Criminal Court System | CJ 311

Course explores the roles of all the courtroom participants such as the judge, prosecutor, defense attorney and the jury panel. The curriculum provides insight into what happens in the courtroom when a defendant is tried and some basic evidence rules that will be followed for the admission of evidence. Course also explains the various bail options available to arrested persons and what role the bail bondsmen play in assisting the first time offender through the court system.

Constitutional Law | CJ329

This course focuses primarily on the Fourth Amendment (reasonable search and seizure) and Fifth Amendment (double jeopardy, testifying against oneself). It also covers the Second Amendment (the people's right to bear arms). Cases are also summarized.

Survey of The American Legal System | CJ 209

This course offers an examination of the system of justice used in the United States. It enables students to easily trace the evolution of law and justice and the historical events related to them. It prepares students to examine a modern society's need for rational law.

Victimology | CJ 212

This course examines sources of violence and its effects on society and situations. It also discusses the social and environmental factors that influence victimization.

Basic Criminal Investigation | CJ 220

This course is designed to provide an understanding of the investigative process and its challenges. The course integrates theory and practical aspects of crime detection and solution. Historical and future possibilities are discussed. This course allows students to easily comprehend the criminalistic potential of evidence.

Introduction to Forensic Science | CJ 230

This course introduces the non-scientific student to the field of forensic science through an exploration of its application to criminal investigation. The course provides definition and scope of forensic science as well as history and development of forensic science.

Introduction to Criminology | CJ 234

This course is designed to provide an in-depth study of criminology. A sociological approach to the study of crime and criminals is presented. The course also includes historical material, theory and research, and extensive coverage of conventional topics.

Leadership and Motivation | CJ 237

This course addresses leadership development for police officers with a focus on the ethical leadership competencies required of all police personnel.

Domestic Violence | CJ 258

This course explores the causes, consequences, and prevalence of domestic violence and the positive law enforcement response. The course focuses on the full range on contemporary domestic violence, including the myths about both victims and offenders and legal resources for victims. It also includes information of the effects of family violence and witnessing family violence in children.

Introduction to Drugs and Crime | CJ 259

This course provides comprehensive coverage of the history, policy, and theory of drug use. It includes reports on the latest concerns, the impact of drugs on society, and the criminal justice system response. The course is highly informative and current.

Security Management | CJ 264

This course provides a comprehensive overview of the global and interdisciplinary field of security. It addresses the nature, scope, and history of security services. The course presents management strategies for loss prevention.

Community Policing Strategies | CJ 270

This course focuses on police involvement and interaction with the communities they serve. It explores the practical strategies of community policing. This course introduces the skills criminal justice professionals need to implement an effective community policing program.

Special Topics in Criminal Justice | CJ 280

Subject to faculty approval. A project or independent paper that will demonstrate knowledge and understanding of a specific subject.

Introduction: Law Enforcement and Criminal Justice | CJ 302

A study of the history and heritage of law enforcement and the Criminal Justice system in the United States. Addresses contemporary police systems in the United States and also police issues and constitutional law and legal precedents. Discusses specific problems and people, including crime, criminals, gangs and victims. An excellent learning experience.

Juvenile Delinquency | CJ 304

A study of how delinquents and juveniles in need of supervision are handled within the juvenile system. The nature and extent of delinquent behavior as well as child abuse and neglect are examined.

Administration of Justice | CJ 310

A study of the judicial procedure as it applies to national, state and local law enforcement agencies. Also, studies; arrest, arraignment, preliminary hearing, bail and jurisdiction of the courts on all levels.

Criminology | CJ 335

This course is intended to provide an overview of the sociological perspectives of crime and the related aspects of human behavior. Topics covered include theories, social-structural theories, methods of criminology, punishment, AIDS and policing.

Introduction to Corrections | CJ 340

A study examining the entire correctional system from law enforcement through the administration of justice, probation, parole and correctional institutions.

Community Policing and Program Solving | CJ 355

This course discusses up-to-date information on community policing and problem-oriented policing. It explores operational perspectives and provides examples of existing strategies and future considerations.

Introduction to Police Administration | CJ 360

This course begins with the evolution of American policing and ends with changes and the future. Topics include politics, organizational theory, leadership, communication, human resource management and many others.

Criminal Investigation | CJ 370

Course addresses major topics including investigation techniques, crimes against persons, crimes against property, organized crime, gangs and the investigator's role in the judicial process. Includes proven investigative techniques in all forms of investigations.

Corrections in America | CJ 425

Discusses the dynamics of corrections that encourages attention in the field. Includes correctional context, practice and issues and perspectives. "Real-life" examples are presented.

Policing in America | CJ 435

This course provides an overview of contemporary police works. It introduces students to a better understanding of the relationship between police and society. It also focuses on critical concerns facing American police.

Criminal Procedure | CJ 440

Course provides practical guidelines for criminal justice professionals with respect to the legal aspects of their daily duties. Major issues addressed are individual rights, criminal court system, arrest warrants, consent search, to mention a few.

Criminal Evidence | CJ 445

A study of important rules concerning evidence. Focus is on the use of rules in criminal proceedings. Includes: published sources of law, the rule against hearsay, confessions, opinions, expertise and experts. Discussion on scientific evidence is included.

Criminal Law | CJ 450

Presents the study of criminal law including topics on misdemeanors, organized crime, drugs, hate crimes and other offenses. Also includes discussions of common law, federal law and the Model Penal Code.

Drugs Crime Society | CJ 459

Focuses on the critical areas of America's drug problem. Some topics covered include the business of drugs and the role of organized crime in the drug trade and drug legalization and discrimination.

Critical Issues in Criminal Justice | CJ 460

This course presents current information on major topics of interest in Criminal Justice. Stress is a continuing issue. Other important issues include deviant behavior, crime and the political process and murder and injury of police officers.

Supervision of Police Personnel | CJ 469

This course is designed to provide a range of information about the role of the supervisor in the law enforcement system. It takes a straight-forward look at the responsibilities of supervisors and the effective methods in which they have for fulfilling these responsibilities.

Proactive Management | CJ 472

Emphasis includes the duties and responsibilities of the police supervisor, personnel problems and handling complaints, grievances and disciplinary problems. Principles of leadership, communication and techniques of teaching are presented.

The Police Manager | CJ 475

This course provides step-by-step procedures to help administrators fulfill responsibilities and perform their duties effectively. The course also discusses the behavioral aspect of police management and modern management. It introduces a wide range of topics with which police managers should be familiar.

Special Topics in Criminal Justice | CJ 380/480

Subject to faculty approval. A project or an independent paper that will demonstrate knowledge and understanding of a specific subject.

ECONOMICS

Economic Principles | ECO 230

This course teaches students how to think and act like an economist. It introduces economic concepts and applies them to the real-world examples. It is organized around five key principles of economics, and covers micro- and macro-economics.

ENGLISH

English Composition I | ENG 100

This course provides and introduction to the basic concepts and requirements of college-level English. An excellent study of grammatical structures of standard, formal and written English. Topics include parts of speech, punctuation, choice and usage of words, effective use of sentences and paragraphs.

English Composition II | ENG 101

This course is designed to meet the English requirements for students desiring the General Education for the first two years of college, or for students transferring to a four-year college. The course is directed toward assisting students with techniques necessary for writing, Emphasis is placed on sentence structure, word choice, organization, editing and usage skills to successful written communication.

FINANCE

Personal Finance | FIN 218

This course is designed to help students plan for a successful financial future. It provides information on tax laws and gives students an accurate reflection of the trends affecting their financial present and future. It also discusses the importance of achieving long-term goals through investing. This course lets students know what is available on the web and how the sites can help them.

Business Finance | FIN 355

This course covers the three major financial areas: Institutions and Markets, Investments, and Financial Management. It provides a valuable overview and a solid foundation of the major concepts of the discipline.

Investment Management | FIN 425

This course provides a survey of the important areas of investments. It established an appropriate theoretical base of investments while simultaneously applying this theory to real world examples.

HISTORY

American History (1500-1877) | HIS 110

This course weaves together the social and historical forces that have shaped the U.S. It surveys history from European discovery concluding with the Civil War.

American History (1863-present) | HIS 111

This course surveys the history following the Civil War concluding with a discussion of the United States in a global age, 1863 to present.

HUMAN RESOURCE MANAGEMENT

Introduction to Human Resource Management | HRM 215

This course provides students with an overview of human resource management concepts. It offers the latest findings and thinking in the Human Resource field. Areas of interest include: Recruitment & Selection, Training, Development & Compensation, and Management & Employee Relations.

Principles of Human Relations | HR 225

This course provides students a basic framework for understanding how interactions at work will affect them and what they should do to be effective in their interactions with others in any organizational setting. This course offers students the opportunity to profile and develop skills and competencies.

INTERNATIONAL AFFAIRS

International Business | Int 360

This course applies a cross-functional approach to the study of international business. The course introduces a practical side of international business. It focuses on the global manager, world business consumers and also entrepreneurial and small business topics. The cultural aspect is addressed early and often throughout the course.

Global Marketing | Int 430

This course covers the essential concepts of global marketing. It includes real-life examples and cases. The course discusses how global marketers must be able to navigate among varied cultures. The effects that government policy can have on international markets and global marketing are also discussed. The course provides excellent regional balance.

Global Human Resource Management | Int 448

This course covers key topics in International Human Resource Management. It discusses issues and theories which managers must handle as they sustain a competitive advantage. The course states that international business is high on management's list of priorities and that finding the human resources to implement a global strategy is of critical importance.

International Organizational Behavior | Int 454

This course provides a comprehensive introduction to international organizational behavior and management. It presents a unique cultural perspective on the roots of organizational behavior around the world. Comparative perspectives of work motivation and leadership are discussed. An explanation of the changes which are reshaping organizations is also included.

International Management | Int 465

This course applies management concepts and techniques to firms working in multinational, multi-cultural environments. The course is research based. It presents a balance between culture, strategy and behavior.

MANAGEMENT

Administrative Office Management | MGT 243

This course provides an introduction to office management. It includes information on word processing, software, and desktop publishing, and introduces organizational principles, supervision and training techniques. The management of office and record systems are also presented.

MATH

College Math I | MATH 150

This course presents the basic fundamentals of college-level mathematics.

College Math II | MATH 151

This course presents the basic fundamentals of college-level mathematics. It introduces key terms, helpful graphics, and new symbols. Students are introduced to real-world applications of mathematics.

NATURAL SCIENCES

Earth Science | NSC 136

This course provides an overview of our physical environment with well-balanced, up-to-date coverage of geology, oceanography, astronomy, and meteorology. The course introduces three themes: Earth as a System, People and the Environment, and the Nature of Scientific Inquiry.

PHILOSOPHY

Ethics | PHIL 161

This course provides students with a solid foundation in understanding classical and contemporary moral problems.

POLITICAL SCIENCE

International Relations | POLS 112

This course combines basic concepts and vocabulary with a substantial amount of historical background and examples from current events. Students will examine major historical events arranged by geographic area which illustrate concepts of international relations. This course also provides up-to-date information on the world economy.

World Politics | POLS 125

This course combines contemporary and historical coverage of the central issues in world politics. This course encourages independent thinking and active evaluation of real-world problems. Students will be able to recognize the connections between international and domestic politics.

PSYCHOLOGY

Introduction to Psychology | PSY 130

This course is designed to provide scientific, accurate, and thorough understanding of the essential concepts of psychology. It provides comprehensive coverage of concepts in the science of behavior. The approach is practical and easy to understand.

SOCIOLOGY

Introduction to Sociology | SOC 134

This course comprehensively introduces theoretical approaches and explores diversity of human living and social interaction in everyday life. Three main themes are presented: Global Perspective, Social Diversity, and Critical Thinking.

Race & Ethnic Relations | SOC 241

This course presents the theories and operational definitions of the study of race relations. It defines the relationship between subordinate groups and the study of stratification. This course covers areas of prejudice and discrimination, religious groups, and major racial and ethnic groups in the United States.

STATISTICS

Business Statistics | STAT 156

This course presents concepts and applications of statistics used in the functional areas of business – accounting, marketing, management, economics, and finance.

Texas State University

OFFICE OF EXTENDED & DISTANCE LEARNING

601 University Drive
San Marcos, Texas 78666-4616
(800) 511-8656, (512) 245-2322
www.studyanywhere.txstate.edu   corrstudy@txstate.edu

Texas State University does not currently offer any degrees by correspondence, and only offers a limited number of paper-based courses. Additionally, they no longer offer paper-based registration. Prisoner-students will need outside assistance registering for courses.

Accreditation: Southern Association of Colleges and Schools, Commission on Colleges

AVAILABLE TO PRISONERS

A very small variety of for-credit courses

Tuition Rates:	$251.21 per credit
	(Most courses will cost $753.63 each.)
Payment Plan:	None
Textbook Fees:	Not included in tuition
Additional Fees:	None
Transfer/Exam Options:	Not applicable
Time Limits:	9 months
Proctor required?	Yes

Texas State University
Available Courses

ENGLISH

ENG 1310 and 1320 are prerequisites the following English courses, which are only available in online format.

American Literature from 1865 to 1930 | ENG 3335 (WI)

A survey of American literature from the Civil War to 1930.

PSYCHOLOGY

Introduction to Psychology | PSY 1300

A survey of the major principles derived from research on human and animal behavior. Topics studied include learning, thinking, motivation, emotion, personality, the senses, perception, and the form and functions of the nervous system.

SOCIOLOGY

SOCI 3328 Complex Organizations

The study and analysis of complex organizations, bureaucracies, and professions; and their influence on individuals and society and its institutions.

Thomas Edison State University

167 West Hanover Street
Trenton, New Jersey 08618
(609) 984-1141
www.tesu.edu *info@tesu.edu*

Thomas Edison State University is unique in their approach to evaluating student's prior experience and awards credit accordingly. They offer several degree options for prisoners and the unique option of paying an annual flat fee, which students can use to select up to 36 credits worth of courses at a steep discount from their usual per credit tuition rate – worth it for students taking at least 21 credits in a year.

NOTE: Degrees can be earned directly from *Thomas Edison* through a combination of "e-Pack" courses, "Guided Study" courses and credit-by examination (TECEPS).

They also offer the option of registering as degree-earning students or non-matriculated students (those students who are taking courses solely for learning and not for credit or certificates.) The non-matriculated option allows students to study at their own pace without time limits.

Accreditation: Middle States Commission on Higher Learning

AVAILABLE TO PRISONERS

Associate of Applied Science in *Administrative Studies*
Associate of Arts
Associate of Science in *Business Administration*

Bachelor of Arts in *Liberal Studies* (Humanities or Social Sciences concentration)
Bachelor of Science in *Business Administration/General Management*

Tuition Rates:	**$499 per credit (non-NJ resident) (Most courses will cost $1,497 each.)**
	$396 per credit (NJ resident) (Most courses will cost $1,188 each.)
	Flat-fee tuition plan (non-NJ residents): $9,820 for up to 36 credits per year (This works out to approximately and $272 per credit if taking the max allowed number of courses.)
	Flat-fee tuition plan (NJ residents ONLY): $7,300 for up to 36 credits per year (approximately $202 per credit if taking the max allowed number of courses.)
	Non-matriculated student tuition plan: $525 per credit
Payment Plan:	Three equal payments plus $35 payment plan fee.
Textbook Fees:	Not included in tuition
Additional Fees:	**Application fee: $75; Graduation fee: $332**
	TECEP fee: $39 per credit for credit students, $53 per credit for non-matriculated students
Transfer Options:	80 credits toward associates; 120 credits toward bachelor degree.
	Credit by examination option (TECEP) available.
	Portfolio assessment available: $389 for up to 12 credits, $221 each additional 6 credits.
Time Limits:	None for non-matriculated students
Proctor required?	Yes
Cancellation Policy:	Full refund up to first course assignment submission, less $10 fee; 50% refund within 30 days of first submission.

Thomas Edison State University
Available Courses

Thomas Edison University courses are available to prisoners in courses are available in two formats:

e-Pack (EP) Courses – Designed for students who want the structure of a 12-week course without the interaction. Courses are completed in a 12-week semester and based around a textbook, short paper-based quizzes with answer keys that can be taken at the students own pace, which help the student prepare for the comprehensive proctored final examination.

Guided Study (GS) Courses – 12-week independent study courses with weekly assignments, proctored midterms and final examinations.

Look for **EP** or **GS** to determine what courses are available in which format.

ACCOUNTING

Principles of Financial Accounting | ACC-101 (3 credit hours)   **EP/GS**

Provides a basic level of knowledge in recording business transactions, summarizing business activities, and preparing, interpreting and utilizing financial statements.

Principles of Managerial Accounting | ACC-102 (3 credit hours)   **EP/GS**

Emphasizes the information managers need to make decisions and the types of analyses appropriate to each decision. Includes such topics as budgeting, cost accounting systems and cost profit relationships.   Prerequisites: Knowledge in course equivalent to ACC-101

Federal Income Taxation | ACC-121 (3 credits)   **GS**

Covers federal income tax structure as it pertains to individuals, partnerships, and corporations.   Prerequisite: It is advisable that students have completed ACC-101 and ACC-102.

ASTRONOMY

Introductory Astronomy | AST-101 (3 credits)   **GS**

Explores the broad range of concepts and principles in astronomy, placing emphasis on the scientific evidence that astronomers use to support their conclusions. The origin, characteristics and evolution of the solar system, the stars, the galaxies and the universe will be covered in this course.

BIOLOGY

The Science of Nutrition | BIO-208 (3 credit hours)   **EP/GS**

This introductory course is intended to provide accurate and scientifically sound information on human nutrition. Topics covered include food choices; the digestive system; metabolism; the effects of carbohydrates, fats and proteins on health; nutrition in various stages of life cycle; vitamins and minerals; and the effect of diet in the presence of diabetes and cardiovascular disease.

BUSINESS

Introduction to Business | BUS-101 (3 credits)   **GS**

This course outlines a concise overview of the world of business. The primary objective is to introduce students to the world of business and formulate an opportunity to define and apply the language of business to various endeavors in which businesses operate.

Business Mathematics | BUS-161 (3 credits)   **GS**

Presents a practical approach to the use of mathematics in business. Topics include mathematical applications in finance, retailing and business accounting.

Strategic Management | BUS 421 (3 credits)   GS

Senior-level Capstone course that focuses on the development and implementation of strategy as a means of success in business. Integrates concepts and applications from various functional areas of business. Prerequisite: Advisable to have knowledge in FIN-301, MAN-301, MAR-301, ACC-101, ACC-102, ECO-111, and ECO-112.

CHEMISTRY

Survey of Chemistry | CHE-101 (3 credits)   GS

Developed for non-science majors. Presents chemical facts, principles and theories through practical applications, illustrations and experiments.

COMPUTER INFORMATION SYSTEMS

Computer Concepts and Applications | CIS-107 (3 credits)   GS

Provides an overview of computers, focusing on historical development; hardware, application software; communications; internet use; how to purchase, install, and maintain a computer; information systems; system analysis and design programming; careers in the computer field; security, ethics, and privacy issues; and multimedia.

COMMUNICATIONS

Introduction to Mass Communications I | COM-120 (3 credits)   GS

Emphasizes the history of mass media and current trends, presenting information and activities to enable students to appreciate and evaluate the quality of print, audio, video, and television.

Introduction to Mass Communications II | COM-121 (3 credits)   GS

Continues the presentation of information about history of current trends in mass media and activities to enable students to appreciate and evaluate the quality of print, audio, video, and television.   Prerequisite: COM-120

Elements of Intercultural Communication | COM-335 (3 credits)   GS

Examines the process of interpersonal communication from various perspectives, including dyadic interactions, how we perceive others, listening skills, emotions, language and nonverbal communications.   Prerequisite: Knowledge equivalent to an introductory communications course.

COMPUTER SCIENCE

Computer Architecture | COS-330 (3 credits)   GS

Covers the nature and limitations of computers. The CPU is covered in detail, including processor, control and memory design. Data path design and the ALU are covered. Also includes pipeline and super scalar processing, and the I/O system. Prerequisite: Two computer science courses.

Operating Systems | COS-352 (3 credits)   GS

Concentrated on the design and function of the operating systems of multi-user computers. Topics include time sharing methods of memory allocation and protection, files, CPU scheduling, I/O management, interrupt handling, process sync, deadlocking and recovery, and design principles.   Prerequisite: COS-241 (Data Structures) or equivalent, and COS-330 (Computer Architecture) or equivalent, or experience with UNIX.

ECONOMICS

Macroeconomics | ECO-111 (3 credits)   GS

Deals with the economy as a whole. Includes the meaning and measurement of the gross domestic product, the effects of government expenditure and taxation, causes of inflation and unemployment, government deficit and debt, and international trade and the balance of trade.   Prerequisite: Three credits of college-level mathematics.

Microeconomics | ECO-112 (3 credits)   GS

Deals with the economic behavior of individuals and companies. Includes supply and demand, elasticities, consumer behavior, competition and the labor market.   Prerequisite: Three credits of college-level mathematics.

International Economics | ECO-490 (3 credits)   GS

Examines in depth the basic principles of international economics, providing perspective on the growing global economic interdependence among nations. Includes strategic trade policy, exchange rate forecasting and environmental regulatory policies, among other topics. Prerequisite: Advisable for students to have earned six credits in economics.

ENGLISH COMPOSITION

English Composition I | ENC-101 (3 credits)   GS

Emphasizes basic expository writing skills that enhance the skills needed for academic and business writing. Includes essay writing.

English Composition II | ENC-102 (3 credits)   GS

Presentation of expository writing skills that expand upon skills learned in English Composition I. Emphasizes research-paper writing.   Prerequisite: ENC-101 or equivalent.

Technical Writing | ENG-201 (3 credits)   GS

Focuses on developing the skills needed to communicate effectively in the workplace. Provides strategies for writing clear and concise reports, proposals and correspondence, and explores the principles of good design and how to use visuals in documents.   Prerequisite: ENC-101 and ENC-102 equivalent.

ENVIRONMENTAL SCIENCE

Global Environmental Change | ENS-314 (6 credits)   GS

Covers the fundamentals of global environmental science and the ecological principles necessary to understand the factors required to maintain ecological stability and preserve worldwide resources.   Prerequisite: One three-credit science course.

FILM

American Cinema | FIL-110 (3 credits)   GS

Introduction to the history and language of the most influential art form. Students study the significance of the invention of the motion picture camera, the rise of the studio system, The Hollywood style, the production of popular genres such as the Western, the comedy, the combat film and horror films/science fiction.

FINANCE

Principles of Finance | FIN-301 (3 credits)   GS

Provides an introduction to financial management and the business environment in which financial decision makers function. Emphasizes analytical tools and their use in solving financial problems.   Prerequisite: ACC-101 or equivalent.

GEOLOGY

Physical Geology | GEO-151 (3 credits)   GS

Acquaints the student with how earthquakes, active volcanoes and other geologic formations and processes relate to the theory of plate tectonics. The course stresses that Earth continues to evolve and that its future depends on our actions of today.

HISTORY

Western Civilization I | HIS-101 (3 credits)   GS

Surveys the history of Western societies, institutions and ideas, and the impact they have had on global culture over time. This course traces the major developments in the formation of Western civilization to the final defeat of Napoleon in 1815, with a focus on political as well as social events.

Western Civilization II | HIS-102 (3 credits)   GS

This course continues the survey of Western societies, institutions and ideas, and the impact they have on global culture over time. Starting with the Industrial Revolution, it traces the major developments in Western civilization from emergence of an industrial society to modern times.

American History I | HIS-113 (3 credits) GS

Focuses on the origin and growth of the United States from 1492 to 1865. Examines the social, economic and political development of the country, highlighting major events that took place from the settlement of Jamestown to the Civil War.

American History II | HIS-114 (3 credits) GS

Focuses on the transformation of the United States from 1877 to the present, from its reconstruction after the civil war to its emergence as a world leader.

American Civil Rights Movement | HIS-210 (3 credits) GS

Examines the impact of the civil rights movement on the 20th century on American society. Offers a comprehensive history of the people, stories, events and issues in the struggle for social justice in the U.S.

American Civil War | HIS-235 (3 credits) GS

Examines the Civil War – its causes, the reasons the North won and the assassination of Abraham Lincoln – featuring both the generals and enlisted men on the battlefields, and the politicians and families on the home front.

Introduction to Chinese History & Culture | HIS-261 (3 credits) GS

Provides insight into the Chinese people, their history and the challenges they face – political, social, economies and cultural – in their search for the Chinese pattern of modernity.

African History & Culture | HIS-301 (3 credits) GS

Examines the history and evolution of Africa's geography, people and societies, including the impact of external influences, identities and explores geographic and climactic processes and the ecological context in which they occurred. Prerequisite: Knowledge equivalent to an introductory history course.

War & American Society | HIS-356 (3 credits) GS

Focuses on the various ways in which America has dealt with war and the changes that have taken place in American society as a result of war. Considers all major American wars from the Revolutionary War to the Global War on Terror.   Prerequisite: Knowledge equivalent to an introductory history course.

JOURNALISM

News Writing | JOU-352 (3 credits) GS

A comprehensive journalism course designed to teach students how to start, develop and polish hard news and feature stories. Explores both traditional and emerging styles in broadcast journalism and public relations as well as print journalism. Prerequisite: Familiarity with reporting terminology and procedures covered in introductory journalism.

LAW

Business Law | LAW-201 (3 credits) GS

Introduces the concepts and applications of laws that affect the business enterprise. Identification of the sources of law, including the courts, administrative agency rules and regulations, executive orders and judicial decisions will be addresses. The law of contract, sales and agency are covered in detail as well as remedies for breach of these agreements.

LIBERAL ARTS

Liberal Arts Capstone | LIB-495

Provides engagement in a student-centered, content-related learning experience that serves as a summary and synthesis of courses in a student's academic career. Student selects an area of interest related to their academic studies and engage in an activity leading to a research project reflective of comprehensive knowledge gained in undergraduate studies and demonstrate their knowledge of the outcomes of the Bachelor of Arts degree.   Prerequisite: Completion or near completion of area of study.

LITERATURE

Introduction to Children's Literature | LIT-221 (3 credits) GS

Examines the history and diversity of children's fiction and nonfiction through examination of a variety of recommended works. Also suggests criteria for selecting and evaluating alternative books. Prerequisite: Successful completion of English Composition I and II.

Analysis & Interpretation of Literature | LIT-291 (3 credits)   GS
Examines the literary elements of character, plot and symbolism through both traditional and contemporary works of short fiction, poetry and drama. Includes the perspective of critics and noted authors.   Prerequisite: Successful completion of English Composition I and II.

MANAGEMENT

Principles of Management | MAN-301 (3 credits)   EP
Provides an introduction to the study of essential principles and practices in business management. Focuses on skills involved in planning, staffing, directing, organizing and decision making in a business environment.

Organizational Behavior | MAN-311 (3 credits)   EP
Examination of individual behavior within the organizational setting. Examines the relationship of an individual and their personality, perceptions, motivation with the tasks assigned, groups interacted with management and the dynamics of the organization.

Human Resources Management | MAN-331 (3 credits)   EP/GS
An upper-level undergraduate course that focuses on human resources as the dynamic foundation for organizational competitiveness.

International Management | MAN-372 (3 credits)   GS
Emphasizes business behavior and organization in various cultures, and companies and contrasts their operating principles and strategies with those practiced firms by the United States. Prerequisite: MAN-301 or equivalent.

Managerial Communications | MAN-373 (3 credits)   GS
Explores key theories and strategies of contemporary organizational communications. It recognizes that challenges exist for creating and implementing communication both inside organizations, with markets, partners and influential third parties.

Small Business Management | MAN-432 (3 credits)   GS
Provides an understanding of the tools entrepreneurs require to compete effectively in business. Accounting, marketing, finance and management of human resources are important considerations of this course.

MARKETING

Introduction to Marketing | MAR-301 (3 credits)   EP/GS
Provides an introduction to marketing as it relates to contemporary living and society's changing needs. Topics include consumer markets, planning and forecasting, and wholesaling and retailing.

MATHEMATICS

College Algebra | MAT-121 (3 credits)   GS
Provides an understanding of algebraic concepts, processes and practical applications. Topics include linear equations and inequalities, quadratic equations, systems of equations and inequalities, complex numbers, exponential and logarithmic expressions, and functions and basic probability. Prerequisite: MAT-115 (Intermediate Algebra) or equivalent. Scientific calculator permitted.

Precalculus | MAT-129 (3 credits)   GS
Prepares students for courses in calculus and higher mathematics and for courses in science and technology where knowledge of Precalculus is required. Topics include exponential and logarithmic functions and equations; trigonometric functions, identities and equations; applications of trigonometry; systems of equalities and inequalities; series and sequences; and analytic geometry. Prerequisite: MAT-121 or equivalent. Scientific calculators are permitted.

Calculus I | MAT-231 (4 credits)   GS
A higher-level course that helps students become efficient and creative problem solvers. Topics include Cartesian plane, limits and continuity, problems of tangents, velocities and instantaneous rates of change, rules for differentiation, implicit differentiation,

maxima and minima theory, anti-derivatives and the indefinite integral, exponential and logarithmic functions, and the area between curves.   Prerequisite: MAT-129 or equivalent. Scientific calculator is needed. Graphing calculator is optional.

Calculus II | MAT-232 (4 credits) GS

Builds on Calculus I. Topics include inverse functions, techniques of integration, parametric equations and polar coordinates, infinite sequences and series, three-dimensional analytic geometry and vectors, and partial derivatives.   Prerequisites: MAT-231 or equivalent. Scientific calculator is needed. Graphing calculator is optional.

Discrete Mathematics | MAT-270 (3 credits) GS

Provides tools for formal reasoning with a particular focus on applications in computer science, although no knowledge of programming is required. Topics include counting rules, propositional and first-order logic, set theory, functions, partial order and equivalence relations, Boolean algebra, switching circuits, and graphs and trees.   Prerequisite: MAT-121 or equivalent.

PHILOSOPHY

Ethics & the Business Professional | PHI-384 (3 credits) GS

Prepares students to meet the ethical demands facing employees in modern organizations. Places emphasis on equipping participants with the concepts, strategies and skills needed to improve ethical performance. Students will assess and develop their ability as ethical decision makers. Prerequisite: Knowledge of introductory philosophy or equivalent.

POLITICAL SCIENCE

American Government | POS-110 (3 credits) GS

Explores the developmental nature of American political culture, constitutional and structural arrangements, policy-making processes and sources of conflict and consensus.

Constitutional Issues | POS-310 (3 credits) GS

Examines critical constitutional issues, including capital punishment, abortion and affirmative action. Covers, among other issues, landmark U.S. Supreme Court cases that have helped define the Bill of Rights.   Prerequisite: Knowledge of introductory political science.

PSYCHOLOGY

Introduction to Psychology | PSY-101 (3 credits) EP/GS

This course provides a broad general introduction to psychology and examines its basic subject matter, its approaches to gathering and evaluating evidence about the causes and correlates of behavior, and the ways psychological knowledge can be applied to improve the quality of individual and community life.

Developmental Psychology | PSY-211 (3 credit hours) EP/GS

Introduces the theories, methods and research findings associated with the study of the human life span. The course examines the developmental process from birth through old age.

Thanatology: An Understanding of Death & Dying | PSY-300 (3 credits) EP/GS

Provides an introduction to the concept of death in society. It is designed to help students understand the many dimensions of death and to become empathetic to and effective caregivers.

Prerequisite: Knowledge equivalent to an introductory psychology course.

World's of Childhood | PSY-317 GS

Research in Experimental Psychology | PSY-322 (3 credits) EP/GS

Introduction to the research methods used by experimental psychologists, this course provides examples of research studies from a variety of areas of experimental psychology and offers an understanding of the knowledge these studies have produced. Prerequisite: Knowledge in a course equivalent to PSY-101.

Introduction to Counseling | PSY-331 (3 credits) EP/GS

This course offers a discussion of the theories and techniques of counseling, with an emphasis on developing listening, attending and observational skills.   Prerequisite: Knowledge level equivalent to an introductory psychology course.

Abnormal Psychology | PSY-350 (3 credits) EP/GS
This course explores the complex causes, manifestations and treatments of common behavioral disorders. Prerequisite: Knowledge level equivalent to an introductory psychology course.

Psychology of Personality | PSY 352 EP

Organizational Theory | PSY-360 (3 credits) GS
Explores organizational structures, processes and outcomes, and also examines the history of organizational theory through the words and idea of major theorists. Prerequisite: Knowledge level equivalent to an introductory psychology course.

Industrial Psychology | PSY-363 (3 credits) EP
This course surveys major theoretical approaches to the study of personality. Students explore concepts regarding the basic components of personality, processes underlying behavior and methods of research. Both scientific discoveries and personal insights are explored. Prerequisites: Knowledge equivalent to an introductory psychology course.

Introduction to Social Psychology | PSY-370 (3 credits) ES
Introduces the field of social psychology, its theories and its research methods and findings. Knowledge equivalent to an introductory psychology course.

Social Psychology | PSY-379 (6 credits) GS
Explores how humans think and behave in social situations. Examines concepts such as perception, thinking, evaluating the social world and application of social psychology to legal and health environments. Prerequisite: Knowledge level equivalent to an introductory psychology course.

RELIGION

World Religions | REL-405 (3 credits) GS
Examines the complexity of religion as a multidimensional phenomenon characterized by heightened experience, ritual practice, powerful myths, ethical teaching, social organization and theological doctrine. Explores religious traditions that are alive today and that involve the lives of the majority of people worldwide. Prerequisite: Knowledge level equivalent to an introductory religious studies course.

Eastern Religions | REL-406 (3 credits) GS
A detailed examination of the major expressions of Asiatic religions, with special attention to Hindu, Buddhist, Jain, Confusion, Taoist and Shinto traditions. Prerequisite: Knowledge level equivalent to an introductory religious studies course.

Western Religions | REL-407 (3 credits) GS
Judaism, Christianity and Islam receive detailed attention in this course, together with new religious movements. Samples of key texts drawn from the sacred writings of each tradition will be examined. Prerequisite: Knowledge level equivalent to an introductory religious studies course.

SOCIOLOGY

Introduction to Sociology | SOC-101 (3 credits) EP/GS
This course examines the broad range of human social relationships and structures and the many forces – historical, cultural and environmental – that shape them.

Marriage & Family | SOC-210 (3 credits) EP/GS
Explores the various approaches to studying the family. Also covers the varieties of family forms, the family life cycle and some problems facing U.S. families.

Social Gerontology | SOC-315 (3 credits) EP/GS
This course provides an understanding of the processes of aging, examines old age as a stage of life and discusses the impact of aging on society and society on aging.

Cultural Diversity in the United States | SOC-322 (3 credits) GS
Investigates and explains the cultural, racial and ethnic diversities in the United States through the lens of sociological investigation. Using fundamental tools of sociological inquiry and cultural learning, students engage in socio-historical discovery of various waves of immigration, amalgamation and assimilation to the United States. Prerequisite: Knowledge level equivalent to an introductory sociology course.

Complex Organizations | SOC-361 (3 credits)   GS

Introduces students to the foundations of complex organizational life in modern society. Examines the history and function of complex organizations, institutional power and culture, and issues of communication and diversity. Helps students to apply organizational concepts to the workplace and in their everyday lives. Prerequisite: Knowledge level equivalent to an introductory sociology course.

Sociology of Work | SOC-362 (3 credits)   GS

Analyzes the many forces that shape today's workplace and lives of workers. Examines the historical and conceptual foundations of the sociological study of work, the changes in the workplace in the last century, and analyzes workplace issues such as global, social, economic and cultural trends; gender and racial inequality; varied types of work; and the interplay between work and personal life.   Prerequisite: Knowledge level equivalent to an introductory sociology course.

SOCIAL SCIENCES

Drugs & Society | SOS-304 (3 credits)   GS

Examines the physiological, psychological and sociological impact of substance use and abuse on individuals and on society. Includes current and historical approaches to treatment and prevention of substance abuse as well as pertinent legal and ethical issues.   Prerequisite: Knowledge level equivalent to an introductory social sciences course.

SPANISH

Elementary Spanish I | SPA-101 (3 credits)   GS

Emphasizes acquiring conversational and comprehension skills by focusing on vocabulary recognition and pronunciation. Not recommended for students who have already taken a Spanish course.

STATISTICS

Principles of Statistics | STA-201 (3 credits)   EP/GS

An introductory course in statistics that develops skills for performing statistical computations and analyzing data. Topics include measures of central tendency and variation; probability concepts, rules and distribution; normal and sampling distributions; hypothesis tests; and descriptive and inferential methods in regression correlations.   Prerequisite: Knowledge in a course equivalent to MAT-121 (College Algebra).

Thomas Edison State University
TECEP Testing Options

The Thomas Edison State University Examination Program (TECEP) offers students the opportunity to earn college credit by taking exams rather than courses. It is a credit-by-examination program specifically designed to allow students to demonstrate the college-level knowledge they have gained through job experience, personal interests and activities, or independent study.

Each successfully passed TECEP is worth three (3) college credits.

The following are the TECEP test options available.

NOTE: In order to succeed on a TECEP you need specific knowledge of the subject. Even previous background in the subject is no guarantee that you can simply take and pass the exam. Refer to the credit-by-examination portion of this book for tips on taking TECEPS and other credit-by-examination options.

TECEP OPTIONS

ENGLISH COMPOSITION

English Composition I | ENC-101-TE
English Composition II | ENC-102-TE
Technical Writing | ENG-201-TE
Technical Communication | ENG-202-TE

HUMANITIES

Public Relations, Thought & Practice | COM-210-TE
Environmental Ethics | ETH-210-TE
Introduction to News Reporting | JOU-110-TE
Introduction to Critical Reasoning | PHI-130-TE

MUSIC

Music History | MUS-221-TE

SOCIAL SCIENCES

Microeconomics | ECO-112-TE
World History from 1600 to Present | HIS-126-TE
Introduction to Political Science | POS-101-TE
Introduction to Comparative Politics | POS-282-TE
Psychology of Women | PSY-270-TE
Abnormal Psychology | PSY-350-TE
Introduction to Sociology | SOC-101-TE
Marriage & the Family | SOC-101-TE

NATURAL SCIENCES | MATHEMATICS

The Science of Nutrition | BIO-208-TE
Applied Liberal Arts Mathematics | MAT-105-TE
College Algebra | MAT-121-TE
Principles of Statistics | STA-201-TE

BUSINESS & MANAGEMENT

Principles of Financial Accounting | ACC-101-TE
Principles of Management Accounting | ACC-102-TE
Federal Income Taxation | ACC-421-TE
Introduction to Business | BUS-101-TE
Business in Society | BUS-311-TE
Strategic Management | BUS-421-TE
Computer Concepts & Applications | CIS-107-TE
Security Analysis & Portfolio Management | FIN-321-TE
Financial Institutions & Markets | FIN-331-TE
Introduction to Entrepreneurship | MAN-230-TE
Managerial Communications | MAN-373-TE
Introduction to Marketing | MAR-301-TE
Marketing Communications | MAR-321-TE
Sales Management | MAR-322-TE
Advertising | MAR-323-TE
Negotiations & Conflict Management | NEG-401-TE
Operations Management | OPM-301-TE

COMPUTER SCIENCE TECHNOLOGY

Network Technology | CMP-354-TE

APPLIED SCIENCE & TECHNOLOGY

Medical Terminology | APS-100-TE
Radiation Safety Officer | APS-289-TE

Thompson Rivers University

BC CENTER FOR OPEN LEARNING

3rd Floor, 805 TRU Way
Kamloops, BC V2C 0C8 Canada
(800) 663-9711, (250) 852-7000
www.truopen.ca   student@tru.ca

Thompson Rivers University is Canada's leading correspondence education provider. They have a variety of paper-based course options as well as courses specifically designed for prisoners, which are "self-paced," giving students more time to complete coursework. Print courses include the cost of all required materials, the cost of tuition, administration, and shipping and handling fees.

They also offer an extensive selection (over 500) web-based courses, some of which can be converted to print-based studies (for a fee.) If interested in seeing other courses this school has to offer in addition to the following print courses, write the school for a current course guide.

NOTE: They are not accredited in the U.S. and may be difficult to transfer credits from for students who continue their education beyond TRU.

Accreditation: Association of Universities and Colleges of Canada

AVAILABLE TO PRISONERS

A variety of for-credit courses

Tuition Rates:	**$414.29 per credit** (Canadian dollars) (**$329.24** in U.S. dollars*) **(Most courses will cost $987.72 each** (in U.S. dollars*)**)**
Payment Plan:	None
Textbook Fees:	Included in most courses
Additional Fees:	**Application fee: $24** (in U.S. dollars*) **Non-residence fee: $24.06 per credit** (in U.S. dollars*) **Transcript Assessment fee: $72.04** (in U.S. dollars*) **Web-based to print conversion: $96 (approx.)** (for courses not listed in the following print-based course catalog.)
Cancellation Policy:	Full refund if canceled within five weeks of registration, void if an assignment has been submitted.
Transfer/Exam Options:	Various credit transfer options
Time Limits:	30 weeks; 18-week extension available for $95.48
Proctor required?	Yes

*Tuition Fee based on recent Canadian-to-U.S. Currency exchange rate of $0.79 (as of July 20, 2017)

Thompson Rivers University
Available Print Courses

The following are TRU's current print course offerings and some of the courses the school has verified that they can convert to print courses (as marked). They also offer an extensive selection (over 500) web-based courses, some of which can be converted to print-based studies (for a fee.) If interested in seeing other courses this school has to offer in addition to the following print courses, write the school for a current course guide.

ANESTHESIA

Anesthesia Assistant Placement Exam | ANES 0011

Registration in this course allows students to write the placement exam for the Anesthesia Assistant program. Once registered, students have 30 weeks to write the exam.

BUSINESS

Introduction to Production and Operations Management | BBUS 3331

This course examines the functional area of production and operations management as practiced in the manufacturing industries. The course includes decision making, capacity planning, aggregate planning, forecasting, inventory management, distribution planning, materials requirements planning (MRP), project management, and quality control. Advanced standing may be approved by CMA, PMAC.

Motivation and Productivity | BBUS 4135

This course integrates theory and practice to examine the effect supervisory practices have on employee motivation. Up-to-date supervisory techniques are introduced. Skills learned in this course can be applied to organizations in either the public or private sector. Topics discussed include leadership, job design, goal-setting, management by objectives, rewards, and communications. (CPA, CUIC)

BIOLOGY

General Biology | BIOL 0501

This course presents the basic concepts of biology: it is intended for non-science majors. Recommended to satisfy the general education requirement for science.

NOTE: This is a web-based course that can be converted to a print-based course (for a fee).

Provincial Biology | BIOL 0601

NOTE: This is a web-based course that can be converted to a print-based course (for a fee).

Principles of Biology | BIOL 113

An introduction to the fundamental principles of biology, including cell structure, chemistry and function, genetics, evolution, adaptation, and ecology.

NOTE: This is a web-based course that can be converted to a print-based course (for a fee).

Principles of Biology II | BIOL 1213

NOTE: This is a web-based course that can be converted to a print-based course (for a fee).

Introduction to Genetics | BIOL 2341

In this introduction to a fascinating and controversial area of contemporary science, students are presented with basic terms, principles, and research methods used in the study of genetics. Students learn about the transmission, distribution, arrangement, and alteration of genetic information and how it functions and is maintained in populations.

NOTE: This is a web-based course that can be converted to a print-based course (for a fee).

Community and Ecosystem Ecology | BIOL 3021

This course is a survey of the theoretical development of community and ecosystem ecology as a science. Students examine the major influences on the organization and development of ecological communities, including physical constraints and processes, biological interactions within and among species, and the complex interaction of all these factors at varied spatial and temporal scales. Students also examine the classification, diversity and conservation of ecological communities. The course provides extensive experience in the practice ecology through a field research project.

NOTE: This is a web-based course that can be converted to a print-based course (for a fee).

Animal Behaviour | BIOL 3101

This course provides a basic introduction to the study of behavior. Students concentrate on the evolution of behavior by natural selection, and briefly consider behavioral genetics, development, and mechanistic aspects. The major topics considered include feeding, habitat choice, anti-predator behavior, parental care and reproductive tactics, mating systems, social behavior, and human behavior. Students develop a basic understanding of the evolution and adaptation of behavior.

NOTE: This is a web-based course that can be converted to a print-based course (for a fee).

BUSINESS LAW

Commercial Law | BLAW 2911

Students examine the legal environment in which business operate and how common law, provincial and federal government status influence decision making. Topics include the legal system and the law relating to torts, contracts, forms of business organization, agency, sale of goods, consumer protection, real estate, intellectual property, and employment.

NOTE: This is a web-based course that can be converted to a print-based course (for a fee).

CHEMISTRY

Principles of Chemistry | CHEM 0501

This course is equivalent to Grade 11 chemistry. Students start with the basics of chemistry as a science, SI metric system, and safety rules. Then students study properties and classification of matter, the periodic table, chemical names and formulae, molecular shapes and polarity, chemical reactions, the mole concept, solutions, the gas laws, and organic compounds.

NOTE: This is a web-based course that can be converted to a print-based course (for a fee).

Principles of Chemistry | CHEM 1523

Topics covered include rates of reactions, chemical equilibria, precipitation reactions, acids and bases, spontaneity criteria for reactions, electrochemical cells, redo reactions, and coordination compounds.

NOTE: This is a web-based course that can be converted to a print-based course (for a fee).

Organic Chemistry 1 | CHEM 2123

Topics covered include measurements in the metric system and temperature conversions; the nature of atoms, molecules, and ions; chemical calculations using chemical formulas and equations; thermochemistry; electronic structure of atoms; properties of elements; chemical bonding and shapes of molecules; and an introduction to organic molecules.

Organic Chemistry II | CHEM 2223

Topics covered include rates of reactions, chemical equilibria, precipitation reactions, acids and bases, spontaneity criteria for reactions, electrochemical cells, redox reactions, and coordination compounds.

COMMUNICATIONS

Intro to Professional Writing | CMNS 1291

CMNS 1291 will introduce students to the theories and practice of professional business and technical writing. Students will learn writing techniques and practice editorial skills as these relate to business and technical writing. Elements of style, awareness of audience, and clarity of purpose will be stressed as integral aspects of effective writing and speaking. CMNS 1291 is designed to be non-program specific and to complement the foundations of academic composition.

Business, Professional and Academic Composition | CMNS 1811

Students in this course learn the theory and the practice of successful academic, business, and professional writing. They examine the similarities and differences involved in writing for business and academic purposes. Students also study and apply conventional methods of academic research and documentation involved in completing essays and reports.

ECONOMICS

Managerial Economics | ECON 3041

NOTE: This is a web-based course that can be converted to a print-based course (for a fee).

ENGLISH LITERATURE

Reading and Writing English | ENGL 0401 (non-credit course)

This course is designed to develop skills as a writer by practicing the stages of writing from rough draft, grammar and sentence structure, revising the draft, editing, and final draft. The course covers both narrative and expository writing, with an emphasis on the expository form for both academic and business purposes.

Survey of British Literature (Grade 12 equivalency) | ENGL 0641

Survey of the English literature. It considers the main historical, philosophical, and aesthetic currents at work during the period, and studies the effects of those currents on a number of great literary works. It helps students develop critical-thinking skills so they might increase their understanding and appreciation of all literature.

NOTE: This is a web-based course that can be converted to a print-based course (for a fee).

Written Communication | ENGL 0661 (non-credit course)

This course provides an introduction to writing , clear positive messages and to understanding basic writing strategies. It is designed to help you to be more proficient at the kind of writing you need to do-at home, at school, and in the workplace. This course will show you some typical techniques for effective writing and will give you practice in writing various sorts of E-mail messages, memos, letters, college essays, and workplace reports.

Literature and Composition I | ENGL 1001

Readings in fiction, drama, and poetry to acquaint students with literature and aesthetic form, as well as an introduction to composition.

Literature and Composition II | ENGL 1011

Skills of effective business communication, intended for students who have completed two college-level composition courses. This course reviews grammar and focuses on fundamental business writing strategies, and applies those skills to specific types of business documents and creating a substantial business report.

Composition and Indigenous Literature in Canada 1 | ENGL 1021

This course introduces students to an exciting range of Indigenous Canadian literature and orature, including autobiographies, speeches, essays, short stories and storytelling. Students will also have the opportunity to listen to audio CDs of interviews and readings by many of the authors studied in the course, and view a video of a storytelling performance, and an interview with a contemporary Indigenous multimedia artist.

Composition and Indigenous Literature in Canada II | ENGL 1301

This course is comparable to the second half of other first-year university English courses. It satisfies the second half of the introductory English literature and composition requirement for degrees offered through TRU. Course requirements include reading novels, a novel excerpt, one-act and full-length plays and a wide range of poems. The course offers a broad and exciting range and depth of literature written in English by Canadian Indigenous writers, beginning in the 20th century. Students develop an appreciation for the significance of oral storytelling to contemporary Aboriginal writers as well as the diverse contributions of these writers to contemporary literature. Students also identify, analyze and discuss many literary conventions related to fiction, drama, and poetry. In addition, students gain further experience in composition and in writing critical essays, including a formal research paper.

Composition | ENGL 1101

Practice in the skills, research, and documentation needed for effective academic writing. Analysis of a variety of academic and non-academic texts, rhetorical structures, critical thinking, and audience are included.

English Literature from Chaucer to Milton | ENGL 2111

Survey of the English language from about 1385 to 1745. It considers the main historical, philosophical, and aesthetic currents at work during the period, and studies the effects of those currents on a number of great literary works. It helps students develop critical-thinking skills so they might increase their understanding and appreciation of all literature.

NOTE: This is a web-based course that can be converted to a print-based course (for a fee).

English Literature of the Eighteenth and Nineteenth Centuries | ENGL 2211

A chronological survey of British literature from the 18th and 19th centuries.

Modern British Fiction | ENGL 4241

This course provides a survey of modern British fiction from its development early in the 20th century to its current achievements and trends. The course focuses on the work of six representative novelists and examines the way these writers perceive the world around them and how they construct their fiction. An in-depth critical reading of six novels allows students to understand each work on its own terms, to place it in the context of each writer's full body of work, and to see in it reflections of the major themes of modern British fiction.

NOTE: This is a web-based course that can be converted to a print-based course (for a fee).

Modern Canadian Fiction | ENGL 4321

Like all literature courses, this course aims to make students feel at home among good writers and their writing; in particular it is meant to encourage a lifetime of enjoying Canadian fiction and criticism. Students learn to recognize the stylistic fashions that distinguish the periods of Canadian writing since the 1920s. By exploring novels and short stories published between 1920 and the present, the course acquaints students with major Canadian authors, the record of Canadian life that their works have laid down, their penetrations of a wider human experience and the questions of literary judgment that they raise, notably the question of realism. The chosen texts address questions not only about writing, but also about Canadian concerns of regionalism, mythology and identity and multiculturalism.

Modern Canadian Theatre | ENGL 4341

This is a survey course in Canadian drama from 1967 to 1992, a very rich 25-year period that saw Canadian playwriting, performance, and production grow from obscurity to lively, thriving component of Canadian literature and culture, as well as an international export. This course is designed to introduce students to contemporary drama and theatre in Canada through the study of 12 plays.

Modern American Fiction | ENGL 4351

Literature is one way of making sense of the world. This course looks at some of the ways modern American writers have made sense, or tried to make sense, of the rapidly changing 20th century. Although there's a world of difference between, say, the disturbing introspection of Sylvia Plath's heroine and Vladimir Nabokov's rapturous villain, students learn to evaluate each work in its social and artistic context. Students examine how the positions we occupy, for example, our gender, class, or race- determine in part the kind of sense we make of the world, as both writers and readers.

Directed Studies | ENGL 4991

This course is a requirement for the completion of the Bachelor of Arts, English major and may be taken for completion of the Post-Baccalaureate Certificate in Liberal Arts. Students review the original and interpretive literature in their particular area of study, offer critical assessment of that literature and submit a major research paper based on the reading list prepared for the course.

FINANCIAL MANAGEMENT

Financial Management | FNCE 2121

This course is designed to provide students with a basic understanding of the financial reporting process, including the accounting cycle and the concepts and principles that underlie financial statements. In addition to learning and supplying many bookkeeping techniques used in the accounting process, students will learn how to analyze and communicate the financial information generated by the accounting processes.

NOTE: This is a web-based course that can be converted to a print-based course (for a fee).

FRENCH

Introduction to French I | FREN 1001

Elementary communication skills through a systematic introduction to the basic grammatical patterns and vocabulary of the French language.

NOTE: This is a web-based course that can be converted to a print-based course (for a fee).

Introduction to French II | FREN 1011

Elementary communication skills through a systematic introduction to the basic grammatical patterns and vocabulary of the French language begun in FREN 1001.

NOTE: This is a web-based course that can be converted to a print-based course (for a fee).

GEOGRAPHY

Introduction to Human Geography 1: People and the Environment | GEOG 1191

This course traces the development of present-day attitudes concerning the complex interrelationship between people and the environment. Students look at both "determinist" and "possibilist" views and focus on topics such as resource exploitation growth and the impact of human activities on the environment.

NOTE: This is a web-based course that can be converted to a print-based course (for a fee).

Introduction to Physical Geography | GEOG 1221

A survey of the Earth from a broad global framework through the differentiation of the world in terms of both natural and human environmental features and characteristics on a regional basis.

NOTE: This is a web-based course that can be converted to a print-based course (for a fee).

Regional Geography of Canada | GEOG 2221

This course examines the physical geography of Canada, from a regional context. Students focus on the many interconnections and relationships between the different regions, between different areas in the regions, and between cities and the rural areas of the region.

HISTORY

Modern European History: 1450-1800 | HIST 1161

MATH

Practical Mathematics | MATH 0101 (non-credit course)

Intermediate Mathematics | MATH 0401 (non-credit course)

Students develop an understanding of fractions, decimals and percentages, and develop skills using these operations. They learn to handle data through graphs, scientific notation and means of comparison; and they apply their understanding of concepts, operations and data to practical problems in interest, insurance, taxes, banking and budgeting.

Advanced Mathematics | MATH 0523 (non-credit course)

Advanced Mathematics begins with a review of the number system and the basic operations of addition, subtraction, multiplication, and division. Next students will learn about lines, angles, triangles, and finding volume, surface area, and area of shapes. Lastly, the course will focus on formulas and equations. Students will learn how to solve linear algebraic equations and graphing inequalities.

Pre-Calculus | MATH 0633 (non-credit course)

Finite Mathematics | MATH 1101

Systems of linear equations and inequalities, matrices, linear programming, and probability.

Calculus III-Multivariable Calculus | MATH 2111

This course takes calculus from the two dimensional world of single variable functions into the three dimensional world, and beyond, of multivariable functions.

MANAGEMENT

Motivation and Productivity | MNGT 2131

Students explore the supervisory aspects of management, with a specific focus on effectively motivating employees as a means of increasing productivity. Topics include motivational obstacles and their causes; job design: leadership; goal setting and management by objectives; rewards; and supervisory communications.

ORGANIZATIONAL BEHAVIOR

Organizational Behavior | ORGB 2811

Examination of individual behavior within the organizational setting. Examines the relationship of an individual and their personality, perceptions, motivation with the tasks assigned, groups interacted with management and the dynamics of the organization.

PHYSICS

General Physics I | PHYS 1103
A traditional, non-calculus-based, first semester physics course in three modules. Students study the motion in one dimension, vectors and two-dimensional motion, and the laws of motion; work and energy, momentum and collisions, circular motion and the law of gravity, rotational equilibrium and rotational dynamics, and solids and fluids; and the thermal physics, heat, the laws of thermodynamics, vibrations and waves, and sound.

General Physics II | PHYS 1203
A traditional, non-calculus-based second semester course in three modules. Students will study electric forces and electric fields, electrical energy and capacitance, current and resistance, direct-current circuits, magnetism, induced voltage and inductance, and alternating current circuits and electromagnetic waves; reflection and refraction of light, mirrors and lenses, wave optics, and optical instruments; and relativity, quantum physics, atomic physics, nuclear physics, and nuclear energy and elementary particles.

PSYCHOLOGY

Introduction Psychology I | PSYC 1111
An introduction to the scientific study of behavior and mental processes, including major approaches and methodologies. The course samples a broad range of topics, including biological foundations, development, learning, cognition, personality, abnormal psychology and social behavior.

Abnormal Psychology | PSYC 2161
A survey of the major classifications of psychopathology, including conceptual approaches to the understanding of psychopathology, etiology and treatment.

Developmental Psychology of Children | PSYC 3151
Introduces the theories, methods and research findings associated with the study of the human life span. The course examines the developmental process from birth through teenage years.

Adolescent Development | PSYC 3451

Psychology of Adulthood and Aging | PSYC 3461

Social Psychology I | PSYC 3611
A basic introduction to sociology as a scientific analysis of the social relations and practices of human beings. Specific attention is given to social psychology, various forms of social stratification and inequality, social institutions and social change.

Social Psychology II | PSYC 3621
Explores how humans think and behave in social situations. Examines concepts such as perception, thinking, evaluating the social world and application of social psychology to legal and health environments.

SOCIOLOGY

The Social Construction of Crime and Deviance | SOCI 4221
An advanced examination of the processes involved in the social construction of crime and deviance from the perspectives of structural conflict theory, symbolic interactionism, and ethnomethodology.

Family Life in Contemporary Canada | SOCI 4301
Students examine the many facets of contemporary family life in Canada, beginning historically and looking cross-culturally within the nation.

Sociology of Families: Families in a Multicultural World | SOCI 4311

An exploration of cultural diversity among the world's family systems; students are provided a comparison of families from Asia, Africa and North America to illustrate how households, family, relationships and community bonds vary from society to society.

SOCIAL WORK

Introduction to Social Work Practice | SOCW 2061

Introduces students to social work practice through an exploration of the history, philosophical foundation and theoretical perspectives of the profession of social work.

Social Welfare in Canada | SOCW 2121

Provides an overview of the income security system in Canada – its development, programs, and major policy debates. It is intended for those seeking an understanding ODF the many income security policies and programs, how they reflect ideologies, and how they work.

Human Development | SOCW 3551

Provides an understanding of human development and its crucial effect on social work practice. It integrates a life-span development approach with a multi-disciplinary perspective on the topic.

STATISTICS

Introduction to Probability & Statistics | STAT 1201

Introduction to the concepts and methods of statistics, including variability, randomness and probability. Many jobs or professions require that objective decisions be made based on statistical date. Students are taught hoe to collect, analyze, ad interpret data correctly.

VISUAL ARTS

Colour: An Introduction | VISA 1101

Studio course on the understanding and use of color, designed for anyone wanting to use color effectively in their art. It covers the basic color theory, mixing pigments, color energy and temperature, and color schemes.

Mark & Image | VISA 1201

Studio course exploring a new approach to drawing and communication. Students begin with the fundamentals of physical mark-making, visual literacy, and points, lines and shapes, then proceeding to human form.

Material & Form | VISA 1301

Studio course helping students to gain an understanding and appreciation of the materials that make up our physical world, and how these materials can be used in art and design. Each unit focuses on one material, such as wood, metal, plastics, paper, fibre, particles, earth, stone, liquids and space.

University of Idaho

INDEPENDENT STUDY

875 Perimeter Drive, MS 3081
Moscow, Idaho 83844-3081
(877) 464-3246, (208) 885-6641
www.uidaho.edu/isi *indepst@uidaho.edu*

The *University of Idaho* provides a variety of for-credit undergraduate to prisoners at a reasonable tuition. They are accustomed to working with prisoner-students.

NOTE: The courses listed on the following pages are specifically available to prisoners. However, will allow third-parties to make arrangements for courses that require internet access.

Accreditation: Northwest Commission on Colleges and Universities

AVAILABLE TO PRISONERS

A variety of for-credit courses

Tuition Rates:	**$160 per credit** **(Most courses cost $480 each.)**
Payment Plan:	None
Textbook Fees:	Not included in tuition
Additional Fees:	**Administration fee: $30 per course**
Cancellation Policy:	Full refund within 21 days of registration; 50% between 22 and 45 days of registration
Transfer/Exam Options:	Not applicable
Time Limits:	12 months; $80 for a 4-month extension plus $30 administrative fee per course
Proctor required?	Yes, unless marked otherwise

University Of Idaho
Available Courses

ANTHROPOLOGY

Introduction to Anthropology | ANTH 100 (3 credit hours)

Basic theories, methods, and findings of human paleontology, prehistory, and culture.

Belief Systems | ANTH 327 (3 credit hours)

Method and theory of comparative anthropological study of religion.

ART

Survey of Art | ART 100 (3 credit hours)

An interdisciplinary consideration of the historical sequence of art styles; slides, lectures and discussions of architecture, painting, sculpture and other arts are seen from the viewpoints of the philosopher, the artist and the layperson.

BUSINESS

Principles of Marketing | BUS 321 (3 credit hours)

Examining the basic elements of marketing theory, terminology and concepts with emphasis placed on analyzing consumer motivation.

Prerequisite: Must have junior standing or higher, or permission of the instructor.

BUSINESS LAW

Legal Environment of Business | BLAW 265 (3 credit hours)

Law and its relationship to society; legal framework of business enterprises; court organization and operation; private property and contracts as basic concepts in a free enterprise system.

ECONOMICS

Principles of Macroeconomics | ECON 201 (3 credit hours)

Organization and operation of American economy; supply and demand, money and banking, macroeconomic analysis of employment, aggregate output and inflation, public finance, and economic growth.

ECON 201 and 202 can be taken in any order. Recommended: Computer with CD drive.

Principles of Macroeconomics | ECON 202 (3 credit hours)

Macroeconomic principles governing production, price relationships, and income distribution.

ECON 201 and 202 can be taken in either order. Recommended: Computer with CD drive.

Money and Banking | ECON 343 (3 credit hours)

Influence of money and banking on economic activity; influence of monetary policies to achieve society's economic goals.

Prerequisite: ECON 201 and 202

ENGLISH

Introduction to College Writing | ENGL 101 (3 credit hours)

Workshop on strategies for generating ideas for writing, for planning and organizing material, and for revising and editing; intended to prepare students for the demands of college writing, focusing on reading critically and incorporating source material.

Corequisite: ACT score of 1-17, SAT verbal scores of 200-440, COMPASS scores 1-67, or no standardized test scores must concurrently enroll in ENGL 090 [Developmental Writing].

NOTE: Does NOT require a proctored exam.

Research Writing | ENGL 102 (3 credit hours)

A continuation of ENGL 101 with an emphasis on general research techniques with applications to various academic disciplines. Successful students will be able to: 1) Continue to demonstrate competency in the course outcomes of ENGL 101; 2) Locate, identify, and participate in academic discourse; 3) Read critically, synthesize and evaluate information; 4) Use a variety of research tools to locate appropriate information sources; 5) Develop a focused research topic or project; 6) Conduct a review of the literature for a specific topic; 7) Understand what constitutes evidence in a particular discipline; 8) Use valid evidence to support claims; 9) Understand and use APA and MLA formats for organizing and documenting multiple source papers; 10) Understand and demonstrate the ethical responsibility of the research writer to explore multiple perspectives on a topic and to cite sources and report findings accurately. Writing integrated and computer intensive.

NOTE: Does NOT require a proctored exam.

Introduction to Literature | ENGL 150 (3 credit hours)

An introductory to reading and understanding world literature. Literary study as a method of thinking critically about historical and contemporary aspects of the human condition. Writing integrated.

Prerequisite: ENGL 101 or ENGL 109 [College Writing and Research]

Survey of World Literature (Beginnings through 16th Century) | ENGL 2257 (3 credit hours)

Examination of major works and authors in historical perspective, with emphasis upon literary and cultural backgrounds.

Survey of World Literature II (17th Century to Present) | ENGL 2258 (3 credit hours)

Examination of major works and authors in historical perspective, with emphasis upon literary and cultural backgrounds.

American Literature I | ENGL 277 (3 credit hours)

Literary history of America, from the Colonial period to the Civil War. Writing integrated.

Prerequisite: ENLG 102 or ENGL 109.

American Literature II | ENGL 278 (3 credit hours)

Topics and issues in American literature, from the 1870s to present. Writing integrated.

Prerequisite: ENGL 102 or ENGL 109.

HEALTH CARE ADMINISTRATION

Medical Terminology and Communication | HCA 2210 (2 credit hours)

Terminology and vocabulary basic to all areas of medical science, hospital services, and allied health specialties. Develops skills in correct written and oral usage of medical terms.

No graded lesson is submitted for this course.

HISTORY

History of Civilization (Before 1650) | HIST 101 (3 credit hours)

Contributions to the modern world to 1650.

History of Civilization (1650 to Present) | HIST 102 (3 credit hours)

Contributions to the modern world 1650 to present.

Introduction to U.S. History (Before 1877) | HIST 111 (3 credit hours)

Political, diplomatic, economic, social, and cultural history; earliest times to 1877.

Recommended preparation: an English composition course.

Introduction to U.S. History (1877 to present) | HIST 112 (3 credit hours)

Political, diplomatic, economic, social, and cultural history; 1877 to present.

Introduction to East Asian History | HIST 180 (3 credit hours)

Survey of traditional and modern Chinese and Japanese history.

Idaho and the Pacific Northwest | HIST 329 (3 credit hours)

Political, economic, social development; earliest times to present.

KINESIOLOGY

Motor Learning/Motor Development | KIN 370 (3 credit hours)

Provides the teacher, coach, or self-instructing athlete with a comprehensive understanding of the developmental (physical, psychological, and social) processes involved in the learning of sport's skills. Explores useful training ideas for all types of performers in all types of sports and wellness professionals.

MATHEMATICS

Intermediate Algebra | MATH 108 (3 credit hours)

Review of algebra including factoring, rational expressions, exponents, radicals, quadratic equations, and equations of lines.

Carries no credit after MATH 137 (Algebra with Applications) or MATH 143 (Pre-Calculus Algebra and Analytic Geometry)

Mathematics Applied to the Modern World | MATH 123 (3 credit hours)

Discussion of some aspects of mathematical thought through the study of problems taken from areas such as logic, political science, management science, geometry, probability, and combinatorics; discussion of historical development and topics discovered in the last 100 years.

Finite Mathematics | MATH 130 (3 credit hours)

Systems of linear equations and inequalities, matrices, linear programming, and probability.

Prerequisite: Sufficient score on SAT, ACT, or COMPASS Math Test; or MATH 108.

Pre-Calculus Algebra and Analytic Geometry | MATH 143 (3 credit hours)

Algebraic, exponential, logarithmic function; graphs of conics; zeros of polynomials; systems of equations, induction.

Prerequisite: sufficient score on SAT, ACT, or COMPASS Math Test; or MATH 108. It is recommended that MATH 143 be taken within two years of passing MATH 108 or equivalent.

Survey of Calculus | MATH 160 (4 credit hours)

Functions, graphing, derivative, integral, exponential, and logarithmic functions, functions of several variables. Primarily for students in business, life sciences, or architecture who need only one semester of calculus.

Prerequisite: Sufficient score on SAT, ACT, or COMPASS Math Test, or MATH 137 (Algebra with Applications), or MATH 143

Analytic Geometry and Calculus | MATH 170 (4 credit hours)

Functions, limits, continuity, differentiation, integration, applications, differentiation and integration of transcendental functions. Primarily for students in engineering, mathematics, science or computer science.

Prerequisite: MATH 143 and MATH 144 (Analytic Trigonometry), or demonstrated proficiency through a sufficiently high score on the SAT, ACT, or COMPASS tests.

POLITICAL SCIENCE

Introduction to Political Science and American Government | POLS 101 (3 credit hours)

Introduction to the study of politics focusing on basic concepts, processes, and institutions; emphasis on government and politics of the U.S. examined in comparative perspective; probable topics include nature of constitutional democracy, ideologies, parties and elections, and formation of public policy.

American State and Local Governments | POLS 275 (3 credit hours)

American state and local politics from a comparative perspective; focus on parties, interest groups, voting behavior, legislative and executive government, judiciary, intergovernmental relations, and public policy.

Public Administration | POLS 451 (3 credit hours)

Environment of public administration, politics of organizations, public decision-making, public relations, leadership, personnel administration, financial administration, administration ethics; related topics.

Recommended prerequisite: POLS 275

PSYCHOLOGY

Introduction to Psychology | PSYC 101 (3 credit hours)

Intro to psychology topics, including perception and sensation, learning and thinking, motivation, personality and adjustment, social processes, psychological testing; emphasis on fundamental principles.

Developmental Psychology | PSYC 305 (3 credit hours)

Conception through late adolescence, genetics, anatomy, physiology, biological changes during development, learning, socializations, cognition and personality.

Prerequisite: PSYC 101 or EDCI 301 (Learning, Development, and Assessment)

Physiological Psychology | PSYC 372 (3 credit hours)

Physiological bases of animal and normal behavior.

Prerequisite: PSYC 101 and Biology 102/102L (Biology and Society) or higher. Requires: Computer with CD drive.

Sports Psychology | PSYC 410 (3 credit hours)

Application of the principles and methodologies of psychology to athletics. Topics include individual philosophies of sport, motivation, personality of coaches and athletes, recreational sports for children, psychological testing, training and learning principles, mind/body relationships, and the effects of anxiety, arousal, and relaxation on performance and current research in the field.

Prerequisite: PSYC 101 or PSYC 205 (Developmental Psychology), or permission from instructor.

History and Systems of Psychology | PSYC 415 (3 credit hours)

History of psychology as a field of scientific inquiry; overview of development of schools of thought, prominent figures, and key theories.

Prerequisite: PSYC 101. Recommend preparation: Two upper-division psychology courses.

Adult Development and Aging | PSYC 419 (3 credit hours)

Analysis of change from early adulthood through death in the areas of social, cognitive, and physical development; examination of theories, concepts and research in the area of lifespan development; study of problems of aging, plasticity of functioning, and ingredients of successful aging.

Prerequisite: PSYC 101

Disorders of Childhood and Adolescence | PSYC 422 (3 credit hours)

Overview of psychological disorders that affect children and adolescents; emphasis on how childhood mental illness is defined, diagnosed and treated within multiple theoretical perspectives. Examines how multiple, interaction events shape both adaptive and maladaptive developmental outcomes.

Prerequisite: PSYC 101 and 305, or permission from instruction.

SOCIOLOGY

Introduction to Sociology | SOC 101 (3 credit hours)

Basic theories, concepts, and processes involved in scientific study of society; includes socialization process, social inequality, the family, religion, deviance, population, the environment, and social change.

Social Problems | SOC 230 (3 credit hours)

Contemporary social issues and personal deviations; crime and delinquency, poverty and wealth, drugs, sexual variations, racism, sexism, and the environment.

Marriage and the Family | SOC 315 (3 credit hours)

A study of the institutions of marriage and the family in a cross-cultural perspective, and an analysis of the various factors and forces at work in our time which are affecting relationships within the family.

Race and Ethnicity | SOC 360 (3 credit hours)

An introduction to the theoretical and substantives issues in the study of race and ethnicity. Students learn about the historical development of race and ethnicity as social categories and examine contemporary race and ethnic relation in the U.S. and other societies.

University of Mississippi | iStudy

OUTREACH AND CONTINUING EDUCATION

PO Box 1848
University, Mississippi 38677-0729
(662) 915-7313
www.olemiss.edu/istudy   *istudy@olemiss.edu*

The *University of Mississippi* is dedicated to working with prisoners, and for reasonable rates. They do not currently offer degrees by correspondence, but their online courses can all be converted to paper courses upon request, allowing them to offer a wide variety of courses for prisoners.

Accreditation: Southern Association of Colleges and Schools, Commission on Colleges

AVAILABLE TO PRISONERS

A variety of for-credit courses

Tuition Rates:	**$183.33 per course** **(Most courses will cost $550 each.)**
Payment Plan:	None
Textbook Fees:	Not included in tuition
Additional Fees:	None
Cancellation Policy:	80% refund if canceled within 30 days of enrollment
Transfer/Exam Options:	Not applicable
Time Limits:	12 months; $150 for one 3-month extension
Proctor required?	Yes

University of Mississippi | iStudy
Available Courses

ACCOUNTANCY

Introduction to Accounting Principles | ACCY 101

A study of accounting theory, record keeping, and the accounting cycle, with emphasis on accounting for the assets and related revenues and expenses reported on financial statements of a business organization.

Introduction to Accounting Principles | ACCY 102

A continuation of ACCY 101, with emphasis on accounting for the liabilities, owners' equity and related revenues and expenses reported in financial statements of a business organization; and preparation and analysis of financial statements and an introduction to managerial accounting including product costing using job orders and process costing systems and cost-value-profit relationships.

APPLIED SCIENCES

Introduction to Criminal Justice | CJ 100

History of the development of the criminal justice system in America. The everyday practices in this subsystem and the articulation among policing, judicial and correctional institutions.

Introduction to Homeland Security | CJ 115

An examination of the modern U.S. security structure, its rights and the effect on citizen rights.

Introduction to Corrections | CJ 120

Study of the history and the theory of justice and the treatment of the adult and juvenile offender, considering the processes from trial through execution of sentence.

Principles of Investigation | CJ 230

Fundamentals of criminal investigation: crime scene search and recording: collection and preservation of physical evidence; scientific aids; modus operandi; sources of information; interview and interrogation; Follow-up and case preparation. Special emphasis on leadership and management actions taken to enhance investigative efforts.

Law Enforcement Process and Policy | CJ 310

This course studies the management and control of the criminal justice system. The learner will be able to discuss the reasons for and effectiveness of management techniques applied to the justice system.

Correctional Treatment Strategies | CJ 320

The history of corrections in American society, corrections and punishment in contemporary America, alternatives to institutional treatment. 14-lessons addressing the micro-level details of the counseling and treatment process, explaining how correctional counseling is done in the field and in institutions.

Law of Corrections | CJ 444

An introduction to concepts of ethics and an examination of contemporary ethical issues in the field of criminal justice.

Safety Education | EDDE 507

A survey of safety instruction.

Allied Health Terminology | ES 396

Comprehensive study of medical terminology.

Personal and Community Health | HP 191

A macro-level examination of the origin, structure and operation of the American health system and its subsystems and components. Topics include the hospital system, public health system, long-term care systems, financing system, health service delivery system, health care providers and contemporary issues confronting the American Health System.

First Aid | HP 203

Comprehensive study of first aid instruction including how to perform first aid in a variety of situations and how to train others.

Behavioral Aspects of Weight Management | HP 312

A study of the physiology and psychology behind weight loss.

Parks & Recreation Program Leadership | SRA 200

Foundations of Leisure and Recreation | SRA 194

Parks & Recreation Program Leadership | SRA 200

Outdoor Recreation | SRA 332

BUSINESS ADMINISTRATION

Money and Banking | FIN/ECON 303

Influence of money and banking on economic activity; influence of monetary policies to achieve society's economic goals.

Finance Fundamentals for MBA Applicants | FIN 411

A presentation of the organization and operation of small enterprises in services, retailing, wholesaling and manufacturing for those aspiring to own, operate, and/or manage a small business or to work for importance, status, problems and requirements of small businesses.

EDUCATION

Educational Psychology | COUN 307

Intro to educational psychology topics, including perception and sensation, learning and thinking, motivation, personality and adjustment, social processes, psychological testing; emphasis on fundamental principles.

Psychology of Adolescence | COUN 309

Conception through late adolescence, genetics, anatomy, physiology, biological changes during development, learning, socializations, cognition and personality.

Psychology of Human Growth and Development | COUN 333

Analysis of change from early adulthood through death in the areas of social, cognitive, and physical development; examination of theories, concepts and research in the area of lifespan development; study of problems of aging, plasticity of functioning, and ingredients of successful aging.

Safety Education | EDDE 507

Teaches foundational methods for safety instruction.

Children's Literature K-8 | EDLS 301

Fundamentals of children's literature and the skills to teach it.

Foundations of Reading Instruction | EDRD 300

Teaches foundational methods for reading instruction.

Diagnosis in Remediation of Reading Disabilities | EDRD 317

Overview of reading disorders that affect children and adolescents; emphasis on how childhood it is defined, diagnosed and treated within multiple theoretical perspectives.

Methods & Materials for Teaching Reading in Elementary School | EDRD 415

Teaches foundational methods for reading instruction in elementary school.

Reading in Secondary School | EDRD 429

Teaches foundational methods for reading instruction in secondary school

Introduction to Special Education | EDSP 308

Overview of psychological disorders that affect children and adolescents; emphasis on how childhood mental illness is defined, diagnosed and treated within multiple theoretical perspectives. Examines how multiple, interaction events shape both adaptive and maladaptive developmental outcomes.

First-Year Writing I | WRIT 101

Study of the practice of basic writing techniques, assisting students in recognizing and understanding different audiences and rhetorical purposes for reaching those audiences. Students will write numerous short paper, as well as on complete story, and keep a journal. Students read and analyze literary stories by well-known writers.

First Year Writing II | WRIT 102

ECONOMICS

Principles of Microeconomics | ECON 202
Functioning of the market economy, role of prices in determining the allocation of resources, the functioning of the firm in the economy, and forces governing the production and consumption of economic goods.

Principles of Macroeconomics | ECON 203
Covers fundamental ideas in economics: scarcity, substitution, opportunity cost, marginal analysis, GDP, real and nominal magnitudes, supply and demand analysis, and microeconomic analysis of pricing in competitive and noncompetitive markets.

Money & Banking | ECON/FIN 303
Influence of money and banking on economic activity; influence of monetary policies to achieve society's economic goals.

ENGINEERING

Survey of Computing | CSCI 103
Covers the nature and limitations of computers. The CPU is covered in detail, including processor, control and memory design. Data path design and the ALU are covered. Also includes pipeline and super scalar processing, and the I/O system.

Office Applications | CSCI 191
Concentrated on the design and function of the computer software applications and design principles.

Environmental Geology | GEOL 105

HISTORY

The United States to 1877 | HIS 130
U.S. history during a turbulent era punctuated by the Civil War, the nation's deadliest conflict. In addition to covering key causes of war – slavery, territorial expansion, and the breakdown of national politics – students examine military aspects of war, paying particular attention to Abraham Lincoln as the Union's wartime leader.

The United States Since 1877 | HS 131
Focuses on the transformation of the United States from 1877 to the present, from its reconstruction after the civil war to its emergence as a world leader.

The United States Since 1945 | HS 407
Provides an introduction to the social, economic, and political history of the world since 1945, focusing international problems and the case histories of individual countries.

History of Europe to 1648 | HIS 120

JOURNALISM

Introduction to Integrated Marketing Communication | IMC 204

LANGUAGE ARTS

Elementary French I | FR 101
Studies fundamentals of French grammar, composition, conversation and reading.

Elementary French II | FR 102
Studies more of the fundamentals of French grammar, composition, conversation and reading.

Intermediate French I | FR 201
Develops the skills in the four areas of grammar, reading, writing, and pronunciation, as well as grammatical structures.

Intermediate French II | FR 202
Further develops the skills in the four areas of grammar, reading, writing, and pronunciation, as well as grammatical structures.

Elementary Italian I | ITAL 101
Studies fundamentals of Italian grammar, composition, conversation and reading.

Elementary Portuguese I | PORT 101
Studies fundamentals of Portuguese grammar, composition, conversation and reading.

Elementary Portuguese II | PORT 102
Studies more of the fundamentals of Portuguese grammar, composition, conversation and reading.

Elementary Spanish I | SPAN 101
Studies fundamentals of Spanish grammar, composition, conversation and reading.

Elementary Spanish II | SPAN 102
Studies more of the fundamentals of Spanish grammar, composition, conversation and reading.

Accelerated Elementary Spanish | SPAN 121

Intermediate Spanish I | SPAN 201
Develops the skills in the four areas of grammar, reading, writing, and pronunciation, as well as grammatical structures.

Intermediate Spanish II | SPAN 202
Further develops the skills in the four areas of grammar, reading, writing, and pronunciation, as well as grammatical structures.

LIBERAL ARTS

Introduction to Western Art | AH 101
Surveys western art ranging from traditional to contemporary.

History of Art | AH 201
Art and architecture in the historical and contextual development of the role of visual arts including crafts, drawing, painting, sculptures and architecture, in the historical and cultural development of world civilizations from prehistory through the 14th century.

Intro into Life – Human Biology | BISC 102

Inquiry into Life – The Environment | BISC 104

Cinema Survey I: 1880s – 1945 | CINE 201
Introduction to the history and language of the most influential art form. Students study the significance of the invention of the motion picture camera, the rise of the studio system, The Hollywood style, the production of popular genres such as the Western, the comedy, the combat film and horror films/science fiction from inception to World War II.

Cinema Survey II: WWII through 21st Century | CINE 202
Introduction to the history and language of the most influential art form. Students study the significance of the invention of the motion picture camera, the rise of the studio system, The Hollywood style, the production of popular genres such as the Western, the comedy, the combat film and horror films/science fiction from World War II to present.

PSYCHOLOGY

General Psychology | PSY 101
An introduction to the scientific study of behavior and mental processes, including major approaches and methodologies. The course samples a broad range of topics, including biological foundations, development, learning, cognition, personality, abnormal psychology and social behavior.

Abnormal Psychology | PSY 311
A survey of the major classifications of psychopathology, including conceptual approaches to the understanding of psychopathology, etiology and treatment.

Cognitive Psychology | PSY 320

Lab in Psychology: Cognition & Perception | PSY 394

An analysis of cognitive processes, including attention, perception, concept formation, language, memory, problem solving and decision making.

Introduction to Religion | REL 101

An investigation of the phenomenon of religion with special emphasis on systems of belief, codes of conduct, use of ritual and notions of the sacred. Several religious traditions (e.g., Hinduism, Buddhism, Taoism, Judaism, Christianity, Islam) will be examined and compared with reference to these issues. Meets the humanities requirement.

SCIENCES

Chemical Concepts | CHEM 101

Survey of Chemistry I | CHEM 103

Topics covered include measurements in the metric system and temperature conversions; the nature of atoms, molecules, and ions; chemical calculations using chemical formulas and equations; thermo-chemistry; electronic structure of atoms; properties of elements; chemical bonding and shapes of molecules; and an introduction to organic molecules.

Environmental Chemistry I | CHEM 201

Topics covered include measurements in the metric system and temperature conversions; the nature of atoms, molecules, and ions; chemical calculations using chemical formulas and equations; thermochemistry; electronic structure of atoms; properties of elements; chemical bonding and shapes of molecules; and an introduction to organic molecules.

Environmental Chemistry II | CHEM 202

Topics covered include rates of reactions, chemical equilibria, precipitation reactions, acids and bases, spontaneity criteria for reactions, electrochemical cells, redox reactions, and coordination compounds.

Biochemical Concepts | CHEM 271

University of North Carolina

THE FRIDAY CENTER

Campus Box 1020
Chapel Hill, North Carolina 27599-1020
(800) 862-5669, (919) 962-2648
www.fridaycenter.unc.edu

The *University of North Carolina's Friday Center* is a self-paced learning consortium of ten institutions of UNC. They offer college-level print-based for-credit courses in a number of subjects (below).

Students in North Carolina may be eligible for their *Outreach to Inmates* program, which provides FREE courses to a limited number of North Carolina prisoners.

Accredited: Southern Association of Colleges and School, Commission on Colleges

AVAILABLE TO PRISONERS

For-credit courses in a number of subjects

Tuition Rates:	**$239.17 per credit for North Carolina residents**
	(Most courses will cost $717.51 each.)
	$489.17 per credit for nonresidents
	(Most courses will cost $1,467.51 each.)
Payment Plans:	None
Textbook Fees:	Not included in tuition (used book and book buy-back programs are offered)
Additional Fees:	None
Transfer/Exam Options:	Transfers only accepted from some NC schools within the consortium
Time Limits:	9 months; $30 for a 4-month extension; $75 for 2nd extension
Proctor Required?	Yes

OUTREACH TO INMATES PROGRAM

Outreach to inmates enables qualified North Carolina prisoners to enroll in correspondence courses at no charge. Funded through a contract between the North Carolina department of public safety and the Friday Center, outreach to inmates pays the course costs enabling a limited number of qualified North Carolina prisoners to enroll in correspondence courses each year. Students in the program are limited to one course enrollment at a time, and must provide their own funds for second renewals.

University of North Carolina
Available Courses

BIOLOGY

Principles of Biology | BIOL 101

An introduction to the fundamental principles of biology, including cell structure, chemistry and function, genetics, evolution, adaptation, and ecology.

Required textbooks: Campbell Biology: Concepts & Connections, with study guide, 7th Edition (2012, Reese, et al.)

Introduction to Human Anatomy | BIOL 251

Covers the various ways by which different body structures maintain normal, healthy functioning.

Required textbooks: Seeley's Essentials of Anatomy and Physiology, 8th Edition (2013, Russo, et al.)

CHEMISTRY

General Chemistry | CHE 111

Topics covered include measurements in the metric system and temperature conversions; the nature of atoms, molecules, and ions; chemical calculations using chemical formulas and equations; thermo-chemistry; electronic structure of atoms; properties of elements; chemical bonding and shapes of molecules; and an introduction to organic molecules.

Required textbooks: Chemistry, the Central Science, 13th Edition and Student Guide, plus Solutions to Red Exercises (2015, Brown, et al.). Requires: Scientific calculator that can perform logs, sines, and cosines.

General Chemistry | CHE 114

Topics covered include rates of reactions, chemical equilibria, precipitation reactions, acids and bases, spontaneity criteria for reactions, electrochemical cells, redo reactions, and coordination compounds.

Required textbooks: Same as CHE 111. Prerequisite: CHE 111

General Descriptive Chemistry I | CHEM 101

Topics covered include measurements in the metric system and temperature conversions; the nature of atoms, molecules, and ions; chemical calculations using chemical formulas and equations; thermochemistry; electronic structure of atoms; properties of elements; chemical bonding and shapes of molecules; and an introduction to organic molecules.

Required textbooks: Same as CHE 111. Prerequisite: MATH 101

General Descriptive Chemistry II | CHEM 102

Topics covered include rates of reactions, chemical equilibria, precipitation reactions, acids and bases, spontaneity criteria for reactions, electrochemical cells, redox reactions, and coordination compounds.

Required textbooks: Same as CHE 111. Prerequisite: CHEM 101

CLASSICS

Word Formation & Etymology | CLAS 125

Introduction to the Latin and Greek elements that make up over half the vocabulary in the English language. It is designed to improve vocabulary skills, promote precision of expression in writing and speaking, and increase the student's appreciation of the historical developments of their language.

Required textbooks: Etyma: An Introduction to Vocabulary Building from Latin & Greek (1982, Luschnig)

Medical Word Formation & Etymology | CLAS 126

Acquaints the student with the elements from which most medical terms are formed – roots taken from Greek and Latin, which were the languages of doctors and philosophers form the time of Hippocrates.

Required textbooks: Dunmore and Fleischers Medical Terminology: Exercises in Etymology, Edition III (2004, Walker-Esbaugh, et al.), & a medical dictionary.

COMMUNICATIONS

Introduction to Interpersonal & Organizational Communication | COMM 120

Explores key theories and strategies of contemporary interpersonal organizational communications. It recognizes that challenges exist for creating and implementing communication both inside organizations, with markets, partners and influential third parties.

ENGLISH

British Literature: Medieval to 18th Century | ENGL 120

Survey of the English language from about 1385 to 1745. It considers the main historical, philosophical, and aesthetic currents at work during the period, and studies the effects of those currents on a number of great literary works. It helps students develop critical-thinking skills so they might increase their understanding and appreciation of all literature.   Required textbook: Norton Anthology of English Literature, Volumes A, B, and C, 9th Edition (2012, Greenblatt, ed.)

Prerequisite: ENGL 105, or second-semester college-level composition course, or with permission.

Contemporary Literature | ENGL 124

Literature of the present generation. Freshman and sophomore elective, open to juniors and seniors. Literature studies include:

The House of Special Purpose (2013, Boyne), The Best American Short Stories 2001 (2001, Kingsolver), Unaccustomed Earth (2009, Lahiri), The Best American Essays 2000 (2000, Lightman), The Real Thing (2000, Stoppard)

Prerequisite: ENGL 105, or second-semester college-level composition course, or with permission from the instructor.

Introduction to Fiction Writing | ENGL 130

Study of the practice of basic fiction writing techniques. Students will write numerous short paper, as well as on complete story, and keep a journal. Students read and analyze literary stories by well-known writers.

Required textbooks: Norton Anthology of Short Fiction, 7th Edition (2005, Cassill and Bausch), Writing Fiction, A Guide to Narrative Craft, 8th Edition (2010, Burroway) Prerequisite: ENGL 105, or second-semester college-level composition course, or with permission from the instructor.

Shakespeare | ENGL 225

A survey of representative comedies, tragedies, histories, and romances by William Shakespeare. Required textbook: The Necessary Shakespeare, 3rd Edition (2009, Bevington)

Prerequisite: ENGL 105, or second-semester college-level composition course, or with permission from the instructor.

Advanced Composition: Business Writing | ENGL 304

Skills of effective business communication, intended for students who have completed two college-level composition courses. This course reviews grammar and focuses on fundamental business writing strategies, and applies those skills to specific types of business documents and creating a substantial business report.

Required textbooks: Business and Administrative Communication, 8th Edition (2008, Locker), and an American Heritage Dictionary, or equivalent.Prerequisite: ENGL 105, or second-semester college-level composition course, or with permission from the instructor.

Grammar of Current English | ENGL 313

Advanced Fiction Writing| ENGL 406

This course seeks to discover and develop students' creative writing abilities in the planning and preparing of five short stories. No text required.

Prerequisite: ENGL 206 and the permission of the instructor.

Writing for Business & Industry | ENGL 3880

The course is designed to help students learn the basic skills and strategies for responding to a variety of communication situations; write responsibly, professionally, and ethically; realize the importance of creative problem-solving; and recognize the needs of multiple and diverse audiences.

Required textbooks: Writing in the Workplace (1998, Allen)

GEOGRAPHY

North America's Landscape | GEOG 260

Introduces a geographic framework for understanding the regional landscapes of the U.S. and Canada. Emphasis is on variation across space, change over time, and the role of the physical environment in the development of today's human geographies in North America.

Required textbooks: Regional Landscapes of the United States and Canada, 7th Edition (2008, Birdsall, et al), Mapping Census 2000: The Geography of U.S. Diversity (2001, Brewer, et al), and a world atlas. This course is not available through the 'Outreach to Inmates' program.

HISTORY

American History to 1865 | HIST 127

American history from the earliest days of European contact to the conclusion of the Civil War. Studies and discusses the evolution of the American colonies and the subsequent nation building that occurred throughout the late 18th and 19th centuries. Emphasis is on the most vital political, economic, and social events of the period.

Required textbooks: America Past and Present, Volume 1, 7th Edition (2005, Divine), After the Fact: The Art of Historical Detection, Vol. 1, 5th Edition (2005), Undaunted Courage: Meriwether Lewis, Thomas Jefferson, and the Opening of the American West (1996, Ambrose), Victims: A True Story of the Civil War (1981, Paludan), Remembering Slavery: African Americans Talk About Their Personal Experiences of Slavery and Emancipation (1998, Berlin and Favreau)

American History Since 1865 | HIST 128

Political, diplomatic, economic, social, and cultural history; 1865 to present.

The World Since 1945 | HIST 140

Provides an introduction to the social, economic, and political history of the world since 1945, focusing international problems and the case histories of individual countries.

Required textbooks: How We Survived Communism and Even Laughed (1993, Drakulic), When Heaven and Earth Changed Places (1990, Hayslip), Son of the Revolution (1983, Heng and Shapiro), Matigara (1998, Thiong'o), I, Rigoberta Menchu (1999, Menchu and Burgos-Debray), Our World, Ready or Not (1999, Greider)

North Carolina History Since 1865 | HIST 367

Examines the social, economic and political forces that shaped North Carolina from the end of the Civil War to the beginning of the 21st century. Subjects covered include the shift of an agricultural economy to manufacturing, followed by service and high tech; the rise of racial segregation and disenfranchisement at the turn of the 20th century, and its dismantling in the 1960s by the Civil Rights movement; the effects of the Great Depression and the New Deal; the changing role of women; and the development of public education.

Required textbooks: The North Carolina Century: Tar Heels Who Made the Difference, 1900-2000 (2002, Covington and Ellis); Like a Family: The Making of a Southern Cotton Mill World (2000, Hall, Leloudis, Korstad, Murphy, Jones, and Daly); Sorting Out the New South City: Race Class and Urban Development in Charlotte, 1875-1975 (1998, Hnachett); Schooling the New South: Pedagogy, Self, and Society in North Carolina, 1880-1920 (1996, 1999, Leloudis); North Carolina: Change and Tradition in a Southern State (2009, Link)

HOSPITALITY MANAGEMENT

Meeting and Convention Management | HOS 4050

Studies the many issues impacting the management of large convention and exposition centers, taught from an organizational marketing base. Topics include meeting site selection, program planning and budgeting, legal issues and insurance problems, housing, food and beverage arrangements, transportation, exposition management, and audiovisual services.

Required textbooks: Meetings, Expositions, Events, and Conventions, 3rd Edition (2011, Fenich)

LANGUAGES

Elementary Italian I | ITAL 101

Elementary communication skills through a systematic introduction to the basic grammatical patterns and vocabulary of the Italian language.

Required textbooks: Prego! An Invitation to Italian, 7th Edition and workbook (2008, Lazzarino) This course is not available through the 'Outreach to Inmates' program.

Elementary Italian II | ITAL 102

Elementary communication skills through a systematic introduction to the basic grammatical patterns and vocabulary of the Italian language begun in ITAL 101.

This course is not available through the 'Outreach to Inmates' program. ITAL 101 or equivalent

Intermediate Italian I | ITAL 203

Develops the skills in the four areas of grammar, reading, writing, and pronunciation, as well as grammatical structures.

Same materials as ITAL 101. This course is not available through the 'Outreach to Inmates' program. Prerequisite: ITAL 102 or equivalent.

Intermediate Italian II | ITAL 204

Further develops the skills in the four areas of grammar, reading, writing, and pronunciation, as well as grammatical structures, as learned in ITAL 203.

Required textbooks: A vincenda Cultura (2009, Capek-Habekovic and Mazzola); a good Italian/English dictionary. This course is not available through the 'Outreach to Inmates' program. Prerequisite: ITAL 203 or equivalent.

Elementary Latin I | LATN 101

Introduces the important vocabulary, grammatical structure, and reading skills that are necessary to understand and appreciate the Latin language, culture, and literature.

Required textbook: Oxford Latin Course, Part I and Part II (1996, Balme and Morwood) This course is not available through the 'Outreach to Inmates' program.

Elementary Latin II | LATN 102

Introduces the important vocabulary, grammatical structure, and reading skills that are necessary to understand and appreciate the Latin language, culture, and literature.   Required textbook: Oxford Latin Course, Part III, 2nd Edition (1997, Balme and Morwood) This course is not available through the 'Outreach to Inmates' program.

Prerequisite: LATN 101

Intermediate Spanish I | SPAN 203

An introduction to representative literary works and a study of the fine points of Spanish structure.

Required textbook: Graded Spanish Reader, Segunda Etapa, 5th Edition (1996, Ulloa and Ulloa). This course is not available through the 'Outreach to Inmates' program. Prerequisite: SPAN 102, or equivalent.

Intermediate Spanish II | SPAN 204

Provides a thorough examination of the Spanish language and Hispanic culture through a study of representative cultural readings, songs, and literary texts of fourteen Latin American countries. Grammar and vocabulary exercises are interwoven with interesting material with the ultimate goal of improving students' communication skills in Spanish.

Required textbook: Metas: Spanish in Review, Moving Toward Fluency, and Workbook (2008, Foerster and Lambright). This course is not available through the 'Outreach to Inmates' program. Prerequisite: SPAN 203 or equivalent.

MATH

Review of Basic Algebra | MATH 0

Algebra | MATH 101

Reviews basic algebra, including algebraic expressions, functions, exponents, and logarithms.   Required Textbook: College Algebra, 8th Edition (2009, Sullivan) Requires a scientific calculator.

Special Topics in Math | MATH 118

Precalculus Mathematics | MATH 130

Covers the basic concepts of trigonometry and analytic geometry, including trigonometric functions and their graphs, relationships and applications.

Required Textbook: Precalculus: Functions and Graphs, custom edition (2010, Swakowski and Cole); requires scientific or graphing calculator. Prerequisite: MATH 110

Calculus for Business and Social Sciences | MATH 152

Introductory survey of differential and integral calculus, with emphasis on techniques and applications of interest for business and the social sciences.   Required Textbooks: Applied Calculus for the Managerial, Life, and Social Sciences: A Brief Approach, 8th Edition (2009, Tan); a scientific or graphing calculator is necessary.

Prerequisite: MATH 110, or a score of at least 520 on the Math SATs, or a score of 2 on the Calculus AP exam.

Calculus of Functions of One Variable I | MATH 231

First semester course in differential and integral calculus, including limits, derivatives, and integrals of functions of one variable. Required Textbook: Calculus: Early Transcendentals, 7th Edition (2010, Stewart); a scientific calculator with graphing capabilities.

Prerequisite: MATH 130 or permission of the instructor

PHILOSOPHY

Bioethics | PHIL 165

Discusses the ethics behind a variety of medical topics, procedures and medicines that are frequently used or avoided in the medical profession.

POLITICAL SCIENCE

Introduction to Government in the United States | POLI 100

Broad introduction to the study and workings of the American national government. Students learn how scholars study our government, enhance their ability to comprehend and analyze the world of politics, be better qualified for more advance poli-sci courses.

Required Textbooks: We the People: An Introduction to American Politics, shorter 8th Edition (2011, Ginsburg, Lowi, and Weir); The Enduring Debate: Classic and Contemporary Readings in American Politics, 5th Edition (2008, Canon, Coleman, and Meyer)

State and Local Government in the United States | POLI 101

Introductory course on the politics and policies of sub-national governments in the U.S, concentrating on state government and emphasizing the role of states and localities on the federal system and the importance of recent political changes affecting them.

Required Textbook: State and Local Government, 7th Edition (2008, Bowman and Kearney); Annual Editions: State and Local Government, 14th Edition (2009, Steinbrickner)

PSYCHOLOGY

General Psychology | PSYC 101

An introduction to the scientific study of behavior and mental processes, including major approaches and methodologies. The course samples a broad range of topics, including biological foundations, development, learning, cognition, personality, abnormal psychology and social behavior. Meets the social science requirement.

RELIGION

Introduction to New Testament Literature | RELI 104

Introduces students to the literature of the New Testament and to the faith of the early Christian communities, focusing on Jewish and Greco-Roman background, the proclamation of the early church, the development of the gospel traditions, the life and ministry of Jesus, the ministry and theology of Paul, developments during the post-Pauline era, and the literature of the Johannine circle.

Required Textbooks: The New Testament: A Historical Introduction to the Early Christian Writings, 5th Edition (2011, Ehrman); The New Testament and the Other Early Christian Writings: A Reader, 2nd Edition (2003, Ehrman)

SOCIOLOGY

Marriage and the Family | SOC 335

Introduction to the sociological perspective of the American family. Primary focus is on critical thinking skills in studying and reading about the family. Through contemporary articles and novels, students are assisted in learning to interweave the emotional experience of their own family with the scientific analysis of family as a social institution.

Required Textbooks: The Measure of Our Success (1991, Edelman); Raney (1985, Edgerton); Love You Forever (1980, Muncsh); The Paper Bag Princess (1980, Muncsh); Worlds of Pain (1992, Rubin); Clover (1990, Sanders); You Just Don't Understand (1990, Tannen); Dinner at the Homesick Restaurant (1982, Tyler)

Sociological Perspectives | SOCI 101

Introduces the essentials of contemporary sociology. It asks two basic questions: 1) What holds society together? 2) How are individuals related to society? These questions are answered through the study of specific fields of substantive fields of sociology.

Required Textbooks: The Sociologically Examined Life, 4th Edition (2008, Schwalbe); Ain't No Makin' It, 3rd Edition (2009, McLeod)

Social Interaction | SOCI 112

Broad introduction to the study of human interaction. Introduces students to the social psychological theories and research to demonstrate new ways of looking at behavior.

Crime and Delinquency | SOCI 123

Introduction to the sociological study of crime. Concentrates on the social facts of crime, such as the criminal justice system and the structure of economic inequality, as well as social processes, such as development of criminal identities through interaction with criminals. Also discusses are the environments in which people are embedded, with particular attention to the disruptive settings of the American urban underclass, and several important sociological theories concerning crime and their implications on public policy.

Required Textbooks: Criminology: A Sociological Understanding, 5th Edition (2012, Barkan); Code of the Street (2000, Anderson)

Family and Society | SOCI 130

Introduction to the sociological perspective of the American family. Primary focus is on critical thinking skills in studying and reading about the family. Through contemporary articles and novels, students are assisted in learning to interweave the emotional experience of their own family with the scientific analysis of family as a social institution.

Required Textbooks: The Measure of Our Success (1991, Edelman); Raney (1985, Edgerton); Love You Forever (1980, Muncsh); The Paper Bag Princess (1980, Muncsh); Worlds of Pain (1992, Rubin); Clover (1990, Sanders); You Just Don't Understand (1990, Tannen); Dinner at the Homesick Restaurant (1982, Tyler)

STATISTICS

Basic Statistics I | STAT 251

This introductory statistics course includes collecting, presenting, and displaying data; statistical description, including measures of central tendency and variation; statistical interference, including estimating population values, and testing hypothesis; regression, correlation, and analysis; design of experiments; and probability distributions.

University of North Dakota
OFFICE OF EXTENDED LEARNING

3264 Campus Road, Stop 9021
Grand Forks, North Dakota 58202-9021
(800) 225-5863, (701) 777-3000
www.distance.und.edu   und.info@email.und.edu

The *University of North Dakota* offers very limited for-credit course options. They do not currently offer degrees by correspondence and are currently only offering one course by correspondence. If you are interested in attending this school, inquire of any other courses they may be offering as of the print date of this publication (August 2017.)

Accreditation: North Central Association of Colleges and Schools, The Higher Learning Commission

AVAILABLE TO PRISONERS

A variety of for-credit courses

Tuition Rates:	**$278.29 per credit**
	(Most courses will cost $834.87 each.)
Payment Plan:	None
Textbook Fees:	Not included in tuition
Additional Fees:	**Application fee: $35**
Transfer/Exam Options:	60 credit hours
Time Limits:	9 months; $35 for a 3-month extension
Proctor required?	Yes

University of North Dakota
Available Courses

GEOLOGY

Intro to Geology Lab | GEOL 101L
Acquaints the student with how earthquakes, active volcanoes and other geologic formations and processes relate to the theory of plate tectonics. The course stresses that Earth continues to evolve and that its future depends on our actions of today.

(1 credit)

University of Northern Iowa

GUIDED INDEPENDENT STUDY

2637 Hudson Road
Cedar Falls, Iowa 50614-0223
(800) 772-1746, (319) 273-2123
www.uni.edu/continuinged/gis   gis-program@uni.edu

The *University of Northern Iowa* currently offers only a few print-based courses for prisoners. These are unusual courses that may be useful for credit if these topics are of interest to you. These courses earn two credits each and may be completed in as little as two weeks.

Accreditation: North Central Association of Colleges and Schools, The Higher Learning Commission

AVAILABLE TO PRISONERS

A limited variety of for-credit courses

Tuition Rates:	**$224 per credit** **(Most courses will cost $448 each.)**
Payment Plan:	None
Textbook Fees:	Not included in tuition
Additional Fees:	**Application fee: $10**
Transfer/Exam Options:	Not applicable
Time Limits:	9 months; $10 for a 90-day extension
Proctor required?	Yes

University of Northern Iowa
Available Courses

The following courses earn two (2) credits each.

Psychology of Adolescence | EDPSYCH 4116

Psychological concepts applied to adolescent intellectual, physical and psycho-social behaviors; designed to improve understanding of, and relationships with, adolescents and their search for identity. Prerequisites: EDPSYCH 2030 or equivalent or consent from instructor.

Introduction to Music Theory | MUS THEO 1100

Designed for non-music majors with a limited background in music fundamentals or as preparation for music major theory courses. Emphasis on notation, key/time signatures. rhythm and rural training.

Organization and Administration of Competitive Sports | PEMES 4217

Organization, administration and management of interscholastic, intercollegiate and intramural sports programs.

University of South Dakota

DIVISION OF CONTINUING EDUCATION

414 East Clark Street
Vermillion, South Dakota 57069-2390
(800) 233-7937, (605) 658-6140
www.usd.edu/cde

University of South Dakota does not currently offer degrees by correspondence, but they do offer a comprehensive selection of for-credit courses that provide prisoner-students with all of the general courses they would need to complete the first two years of school. Many of their courses are specifically designed for prisoners through their *Pathways to Overcome* program. Their program goal is integrated development and learning so that prisoners can reenter society as successful and productive members of their community.

Accredited: North Central Association of Colleges and Schools, The Higher Learning Commission

AVAILABLE TO PRISONERS

A variety of for-credit college courses

Tuition Fees:	**$333.35 per credit**
	(Most courses will cost $1,000.05 each.)
Payment Plans:	Not applicable
Textbook Fees:	Varies by course
Additional Fees:	NONE
Transfer/Exam Options:	Yes
Time Limits:	8-week or 16-week, your choice (on select courses)
Proctor Required?	Yes

University of South Dakota
Course Descriptions

ALCOHOL & DRUG SERIES

Study of Alcohol Use & Abuse | ADS 116
Provides an introduction to the use, abuse and addictive nature of ethyl alcohol. Students will explore the history of alcohol use, basic knowledge of the medical effects of alcohol use and abuse, the basic premise behind the bio-psychosocial model, the continuum of care and personal risk for alcohol problems.

Study of Drug Use & Abuse | ADS 117
Fundamentals of mood-altering chemicals other than ethyl alcohol and the symptomatology and treatment of the abuse of them. Provides facts and insight concerning the abuse of wide variety of "legal" and "illegal" mood-altering chemical substances and approaches to treatment and prevention of drug abuse.

Adolescents & Substance Abuse | ADS 320
Understand the key adolescent developmental tasks, gain knowledge on how alcohol and other drugs impact adolescent developmental tasks and understand the complex nature of determining adolescent substance abuse or addiction.
Prerequisites: ADS 116 & 117

Alcohol & Drug Use in Diverse Populations | ADS 412
Fundamentals of mood-altering chemicals other than ethyl alcohol and the symptomatology and treatment of the abuse of them. Provides facts and insight concerning the abuse of wide variety of "legal" and "illegal" mood-altering chemical substances and approaches to treatment and prevention of drug abuse.

Native Americans & Substance Use & Abuse | ADS 415
Designed to acquaint the substance abuse student/professional with the cultural and spiritual basics of effective substance abuse prevention and treatment with the Native American populations and individuals. This will aid the student in applying culturally and spiritually appropriate prevention and treatment with Native American clients.

ANTHROPOLOGY

Cultural Anthropology | ANTH 210
Introduces the nature of human culture as an adaptive ecological and evolutionary system, emphasizing basic anthropological concepts, principles, and problems. Draws data from both traditional and industrial cultures to cover such concepts as values and beliefs, social organization, economic and political order, science, technology, and aesthetic expression.

Socio Cultural Theory | ANTH 280
An introduction to the nature of theories of human, social, and cultural behavior and their construction. Major approaches from anthropology and sociology are examined in order to better comprehend elements essential to generating knowledge of social behavior.
Prerequisites: SOC 100, ANTH 210

ART HISTORY

Art Appreciation | ARTH 100
Explores the nature of art in various aesthetic, formal, and psychological dimensions, involving analysis of art objects for understanding, enjoyment, and life enhancement.

History of World Art I | ARTH 211
Art and architecture in the historical and contextual development of the role of visual arts including crafts, drawing, painting, sculptures and architecture, in the historical and cultural development of world civilizations from prehistory through the 14th century.

History of World Art II | ARTH 212
Art and architecture in the historical and contextual development of the role of visual arts including crafts, drawing, painting, sculptures and architecture, in the historical and cultural development of world civilization from the renaissance through the 20th century.

American Indian Art History | ARTH 251

Surveys American Indian art ranging from traditional to contemporary.

American Art History | ARTH 303

Surveys American visual arts form the period of Colonial settlements of the 16th century to 1945, a demarcation symbolic of the shift from international European influence to international American influence in the visual arts.

History of Women's Art | ARTH 401

Focuses on women as both subjects and creators of art, while exploring the role of femininity through a variety of crucial topics and issues. A primary focus is on the critical analysis of the creation, modification and persistence of these images throughout history due to varied social, economical, technological, psychological and intellectual conditions.

20th Century Art History | ARTH 412

Surveys the visual arts from the 20th century to the present. This period will be examined as an overview for its technical, stylistic, and aesthetic changes.

Introduction to Fine Arts | GFA 101

Explores why and how the arts exist. Drama, dance, literature, music, visual arts, etc., are examined as inventions for sharing experiences.

CRIMINAL JUSTICE

Introduction to Criminal Justice | CJUS 201

Overviews the criminal justice institutions involved in the operations of criminal law, including the police, the attorney, the bail system, the trial, the guilty plea, sentencing, corrections and an analysis of criminal law in terms of why certain kinds of conduct are criminal in our society.

Policing in Free Society | CJUS 203

Presents the role of law enforcement within the criminal justice system, including law enforcement organizations and functions of separate operational units. Also examines the role of the police in a democratic society, covering concepts such as police services, crime deterrence, discretion and enforcement policies.

Criminology | CJUS 351

Sociology of criminal behavior and juvenile delinquency, with an emphasis on etiological theory. Extent and forms of crime are considered together with the characteristics of offenders.

Family Violence | CJUS 419

An exploration of the incidence, scope, and contributing factors in family violence. Various perspectives are examined. Topical issues include patriarchy, marital rape, domestic assault, and child sex abuse. Coverage includes theories of violence, alternatives to violent interactions, and criminal justice system's response.

Advanced Policing Issues | CJUS 426

An in-depth study and analysis of the problems and issues facing law enforcement agencies in the 21st century. Particular emphasis is placed on specialized topics such as federalization, technology, corruption, and police-community relations.

Prisons & Penology | CJUS 452

Study of the history and theory of justice and the treatment of the adult and juvenile offender, considering the processes from trial through execution of sentence.

Juvenile Delinquency | CJUS 455

The study of the youthful offender, the causes of delinquent behavior pattern and what can be done to help.

Community Corrections | CJUS 456

An examination of the history of adult and juvenile treatment and punishment. Emphasis is on community based treatment as well as traditional prison-based incarceration. The process of sentencing, particularly the role of pre-sentence investigation (PSI) is covered. Special attention is devoted to internship and career possibilities in the corrections arena.

Advanced Criminology | CJUS 460

An extensive examination of major criminological issues including sociological definitions of crime, and developing theories of crime causation.

ENGLISH

Composition I | ENGL 101

Practice in the skills, research, and documentation needed for effective academic writing. Analysis of a variety of academic and non-academic texts, rhetorical structures, critical thinking, and audience are included.

Composition II | ENGL 201

Study and practice in writing persuasive prose, with the aim to improve writing skills in all disciplines.

English Grammar | ENGL 203

A comprehensive study of formal grammar and usage.

Business Writing | ENGL 205

A pre-professional course concentrating on the planning and writing an extensive, business-focused research paper. Also covers effective letters, memos, position papers, and resumes.

Introduction to Literature | ENGL 210

Readings in fiction, drama, and poetry to acquaint students with literature and aesthetic form.

Prerequisite: ENGL 101

British Literature II | ENGL 222

A chronological survey of British literature from the 19th century to the present.

Prerequisite: ENGL 101 & 210

Creative Writing I | ENGL 283

Study and practice in the techniques of writing fiction, poetry and/or drama.

Prerequisites: ENGL 101 & 210

Contemporary Poetry | ENGL 469

British and/or American poetry of recent decades.

GEOGRAPHY

World Regional Geography |

A survey of the Earth from a broad global framework through the differentiation of the world in terms of both natural and human environmental features and characteristics on a regional basis.

World Regional Geography | GEOG 210

Surveys the earth from a broad global framework through the differentiation of the world in terms of both natural and human environmental features and characteristics on a regional basis.

GRAPHIC/FINE ARTS

Introduction to Fine Arts | GFA 101

This course explores how and why the arts exist. Drama, dance, literature, music, visual arts, and more are examined as inventions for sharing experiences.

HEALTH

Personal Health | HLTH 103

The dynamics of health in modern life in a rapidly changing world; modern concepts of health, disease, and longevity; current medical findings relative to emotional health, human sexuality, family planning, disease control, environmental health, and quackery are included.

HISTORY

Western Civilization I | HIST 121

Surveys the evolution of western Civilization from its beginnings into the Reformation and religious wars.

Western Civilization II | HIST 122

Surveys the development of western civilization from the Reformation era to the present.

United States History I | HIST 151

Surveys the background and development of the United States from its colonial origins to the Civil Way and reconstruction.

United States History II | HIST 152

Surveys development of the United States since the Civil War and reconstruction.

History of World Art I | HIST 211

Art and architecture in the historical and contextual development of the role of visual arts including crafts, drawing, painting, sculptures and architecture, in the historical and cultural development of world civilizations from prehistory through the 14th century.

History of World Art II | HIST 212

Art and architecture in the historical and contextual development of the role of visual arts including crafts, drawing, painting, sculpture, and architecture, in the historical and cultural development of world civilization from the renaissance through the 20th century.

INDIAN STUDIES

South Dakota Indian Studies | INED 411

A basic knowledge of Indian history with emphasis on the Lakota, Dakota, and Nakota speaking people. Current cultural issues are presented including values, family structures, traditional religion, fine arts, legends, economics, governmental policies, treaties, acts and related areas.

MASS COMMUNICATION

Introduction to Mass Communication | MCOM 151

A comprehensive look at mass media in the U.S. and the world. Includes discussions of newspapers, magazines, radio, television, books, movies, recordings, advertising, and public relations. Also studies mass media rights and responsibilities, ethics and censorship.

Public Relations Principles | MCOM 243

An introduction to the theory and practice of public relations, emphasizing its publics, management functions, writing skills, communication processes, tools and professional ethics.

Advertising Principles | MCOM 370

Study of advertising as an institution. Discussion of historical foundations, economics, social consequences, structure, planning, execution, and evaluation phases of the advertising process.

MATH

Pre-College Algebra | MATH 095

College Algebra | MATH 102

Reviews basic algebra, including algebraic expressions, functions, exponents, and logarithms.

POLITICAL SCIENCE

American Government | POLS 100

Broad introduction to the study and workings of the American national government. Students learn how scholars study our government, enhance their ability to comprehend and analyze the world of politics, be better qualified for more advance poli-sci courses.

Introduction to Criminal Justice | POLS 201

Public Administration | POLS 320

This course uses simulations and public management cases, as well as contemporary public administration literature to introduce students to the theory and practice of public administration.

RELIGION

World Religions | REL 250

Introduces the major religions of humankind, examining the function and diversity of religious expression in human experience, and the role of these religions in international relations.

World Religions | REL 371

Topics selected from the teachings of the great religious leaders of the world or individual world religions or comparative issues in world religions. Course may be repeated with change of topic.

SOCIOLOGY

Introduction to Sociology | SOC 100

Comprehensive study of society, with analysis of group life, and other forces shaping human behavior.

Social Problems | SOC 150

A study of present day problems in contemporary societies, such as sexism, racism, ageism, alcoholism, drug addiction, physical and mental health, war and environmental issues – their significance and current policies and action.

Courtship & Marriage | SOC 250

Courtship and marriage period given special emphasis, as are problems of mate selection, marital adjustments, reproduction, child-parent relations, divorce, and later years of marriage.

Socio Cultural Theory | SOC 281

An introduction to the nature of theories of human, social and cultural behavior and their constructions. Major approaches from anthropology and sociology are examined in order to better comprehend elements essential to generating knowledge of social behavior.

Prerequisites: SOC 100; ANTH 210

Criminology | SOC 351

Focuses on theories of crime, juvenile delinquency and justice, laws, systems of criminal behavior, victimization, and corrections.

Prerequisite: SOC 100

Urban Sociology | SOC 440

Study of urban community, focusing on its development, social structures and institutional patterns.

Prerequisite: SOC 100

Prison & Penology | SOC 452

Study of the history and the theory of justice and the treatment of the adult and juvenile offender, considering the processes from trial through execution of sentence.

Methods of Social Research | SOC 451

An examination of the research process, including research design, questionnaire construction, interviewing techniques and the analysis and interpretation of data.

Prerequisites: SOC 100 or 150; SOC 309

Race & Ethnic Minorities | SOC 450

An examination of ethnic and cultural minorities in American society. Particular attention is directed to the etiology and consequences of prejudice and discrimination.

Prerequisite: SOC 100

Juvenile Delinquency | SOC 455

Study of the youthful offender and the courses of consequences of delinquent behavior; preventative and rehabilitation programs are also discussed.

Prerequisite: SOC 100

Community Corrections | SOC 456

An examination of the history of adult and juvenile treatment and punishment. Emphasis is on community based treatment as well as traditional prison-based incarceration. The process of sentencing, particularly the role of pre-sentence investigation (PSI) is covered. Special attention is devoted to internship and career possibilities in the corrections arena.

Sociology of Aging | SOC 458

Comprehensive study of the aged population in American society. Included are discussions of socio-demographic changes, life course issues, relevant social policy, and cross-cultural comparisons.

Prerequisite: SOC 100

Advanced Criminology | SOC 460

An extensive examination of major criminological issues and theories including sociological definitions of crime.

Prerequisite: SOC 351

Sociology of Education | SOC 480

An examination of educational systems from a sociological point of view. The social organization of the American public school, and the relations between the school and the community are emphasized.

Seminar in Sociology: Medical Sociology | SOC 490

This course discusses how the medical system in the U.S. is tied to many other parts of our culture and how all of these factors interact.

Seminar in Sociology: The Woman Criminal | SOC 490

Studies the female criminal, exploring important factors that help us understand male criminals and capacity within minority groups within our society.

STATISTICS

Introduction to Statistics | STAT 281

This introductory statistics course includes collecting, presenting, and displaying data; statistical description, including measures of central tendency and variation; statistical interference, including estimating population values, and testing hypothesis; regression, correlation, and analysis; design of experiments; and probability distributions.

THEATRICAL STUDIES

Introduction to Theater | THEA 100

Introductory course designed to enhance the student's enjoyment and understanding of the theatrical experience. Play readings, films, and demonstrations acquaint students with the history and techniques of the theatrical art.

Film Appreciation | THEA 201

This course explores the art of film and its impact on society. Students explore American and International cultures through the study of their films, filmmaking and critical analysis.

University of Wisconsin | Extension

CONTINUING EDUCATION, OUTREACH & LEARNING

5602 Research Park Boulevard, Suite 300
Madison, Wisconsin 53719-1245
(877) 895-3276, (608) 262-2011
ll.wisconsin.edu   *il@uwex.edu*

The *University of Wisconsin* offers a variety of for-credit courses that students will not typically find anywhere else, specifically in the subject of English & Humanities and Language studies.

Online registration is required, so prisoner-students may need some assistance with signing up for courses. But the remainder of the correspondence can be done through the mail.

Accreditation: North Central Association of Colleges and Schools, The Higher Learning Commission

AVAILABLE TO PRISONERS

A variety of for-credit courses

Tuition Rates:	**$327 per credit**
	(Most courses will cost $981 each.)
Payment Plan:	None
Textbook Fees:	Not included in tuition
Additional Fees:	**Administrative fee: $75 per course**
Transfer/Exam Options:	Not applicable
Time Limits:	12 months; $100 for a 3-month extension, $200 for a second 3-month extension
Proctor required?	Yes

University of Wisconsin | Extension
Available Courses

ENGLISH & HUMANITIES

The Bible as Literature | U350-151 (3 credits)

Careful analysis of the prose and verse of the Old and New Testaments. No systematic knowledge of the Bible is required. Students will do close readings of scriptural passages to identify their use of narrative, imagery, suspense, dialogue, and other literary elements.

American Indian Literature | U 350-269 (3 credits)

Fiction, prose, and poetry of America's original inhabitants. You will read works that explore our relationship to nature, the struggle between old traditions and new ways. American history, the family, spiritual values, and the roles of women.

Willa Cather | U350-312 (1 credit)

Portrait of the immigrant experience, the fear of aging, and the hunger for love and acceptance. You will study three novels – My Antonia, Death Comes from the Archbishop, and The Professor's House – that demonstrate Cather's remarkable versatility.

Ernest Hemingway | U350-431 (1 credit)

Two of Hemingway's greatest novels, The Sun Also Rises and The Old Man and the Sea, and a selection of short stories. Students will consider the controversial Hemingway code of masculine behavior and the dramatic action, objective tone, and psychological portraits associated with this famous author.

The Contemporary Short Story | U350-611 (3 credits)

Provocative short fiction of our time. Students will examine high-interest contemporary issues such as relationships, self-discovery, poverty, career and workplace, and escape from reality, in works by Raymond Carver, John Updike, Joyce Carol Oates, Louise Erdrich, Richard Ford, Stephen King, Ray Bradbury, and Iris Murdock.

The Civil War Era, 1848-1877 | U448-393 (3 credits)

U.S. history during a turbulent era punctuated by the Civil War, the nation's deadliest conflict. In addition to covering key causes of war – slavery, territorial expansion, and the breakdown of national politics – students examine military aspects of war, paying particular attention to Abraham Lincoln as the Union's wartime leader. To explore the consequences of the war, course materials include a novel about Reconstruction penned by "carpetbagger" Albion Tourgee.

Introduction to Latin Literature | U524-204 (4 credits)

Fourth semester of university Latin. Using the Oxford Latin Course reader, students do readings in Cicero, Caesar, Catullus, Virgil, Livy, and Ovid. While exploring historical, cultural, and critical backgrounds, students read and interpret passages, perform drills and translations, and do simple reports on syntax and style.

Elementary Survey of Spanish Literature: 12th to the 18th Centuries | U912-322 (3 credits)

An introduction to the principle works, authors, and current Spanish literature from the Middle Ages through the eighteenth century, with a special look at Siglo de Oro, The Golden Age. Students read selections from masterpieces of poetry, narrative Prose, and theater, and consider the historical contexts in which works were created. Lessons may be written in English or Spanish.

Prerequisite: Spanish 324 or equivalent is strongly recommended. Not open to high school students.

Miguel de Unamuno | U912-407 (1 credit)

Prose works of extraordinary philosophical and aesthetic interest. Students study Miguel de Unamuno (1864-1936), one of Spain's most celebrated essayists and novelists, particularly his personal philosophy and literary theories as developed in three of his novels. Lessons may be written in English or Spanish.

ETHNIC STUDIES

American Indian Literature | U350-269 (3 credits)

Fiction, prose and poetry of American's original inhabitants. Students read works that explore our relationship with nature, the struggle between old tradition and new ways, American history, the family, spiritual values, and the roles of women.

FOREIGN LANGUAGES

Modern African Prose & Poetry in French | U400-454 (3 credits)

Modern fiction, drama, and poetry by Africans from tropical Africa and the West Indies. Explore great works by Mariama Ba, Aime Cesaire, Birago Diop, Cheikh Hamidou Kane, Ousmane Sembene, Leopold Senhor, and others. While much of the course is in French, the unit assignments are to be written English.

First Semester Greek | U428-103 (4 credits)

First semester course in classical Greek. In this reading-intensive introduction to Greek grammar, syntax, and culture, the basic elements of Greek grammar are covered, including all declensions of the noun and principal tenses of the verb. For teachers, the course is intended as a review; for advanced students, as a rapid survey; and for beginners, as a foundation for reading Greek.

Second Semester Greek | U428-104 (4 credits)

Continuation of Greek 103. Students explore more advanced topics of grammar, such as the subjunctive and objective moods, the passive voice, complex sentences, conditionals, the genitive absolute, and all remaining tenses not discussed in Greek 103 (future, perfect, and pluperfect). Reading passages, continuing the narrative began in Greek 103, including adaptive passages from Herodotus, Thucydides, and Aristophanes.

Elementary Latin I | U524-103 (4 credits)

An introductory look at Latin. You will acquire a sufficient foundation for reading Caesar. The course emphasizes reading ability.

Elementary Latin II | (4 credits)

A continuation of Latin 103. Students will do readings and translation, using a passage adapted from Petronius's Satyricon. Special attention is paid to historical background and to exercises in grammar and composition.

Intermediate Latin | U524-203 (4 credits)

Third semester of university Latin. Using the Oxford Latin Course reader, students will continue the work in basic Latin syntax and style begun in Latin 103 and 104. While exploring historical and cultural backgrounds, there will be readings of Latin passages, questions answered, and translation performance and interpretation drills.

Third Year Language Practice | U912-225 (3 credits)

A third-year (fifth semester) language course, to be taken after Spanish 204 and before Spanish 226 (or equivalent). Students begin by reviewing Spanish grammar they may have studied previously and by learning more advanced new material.

Advanced Language Practice | U912-311 (3 credits)

A fourth-year composition and grammar course, emphasizing grammatical subtleties, translation, and original composition. Students will consider lexical items and their subtleties, as drawn in short literary texts.

SCIENCE

Weather & Climate | U640-100 (3 credits)

A study of earth's atmospheric environment. Students explore the powerful, extensive physical forces the affect economic and political affairs worldwide. Topics include chemical and physical structure of the atmosphere, the nature and variability of winds, the causes for the observed seasonal and spatial temperature patterns, cloud and precipitation formation, atmospheric optics, atmospheric circulation regimes, severe weather systems, weather forecasting, and climate change.

General Physics I | U754-103 (3 credits)

A traditional, non-calculus-based, first semester physics course in three modules. Students study the motion in one dimension, vectors and two-dimensional motion, and the laws of motion; work and energy, momentum and collisions, circular motion and the law of gravity, rotational equilibrium and rotational dynamics, and solids and fluids; and the thermal physics, heat, the laws of thermodynamics, vibrations and waves, and sound.

General Physics II | U754-104 (3 credits)

A traditional, non-calculus-based second semester course in three modules. Students will study electric forces and electric fields, electrical energy and capacitance, current and resistance, direct-current circuits, magnetism, induced voltage and inductance, and alternating current circuits and electromagnetic waves; reflection and refraction of light, mirrors and lenses, wave optics, and optical instruments; and relativity, quantum physics, atomic physics, nuclear physics, and nuclear energy and elementary particles.

University of Wisconsin – Platteville

DISTANCE LEARNING CENTER

1 University Plaza
Platteville, Wisconsin 53818-3099
(800) 362-5460, (608) 342-1468
www.uwplatt.edu/disted   disted@uwplatt.edu

The *University of Wisconsin – Platteville* offers one bachelor degree option for prisoners, however, most of the required courses are not paper-based. Therefore, prisoners seeking a degree through UW-Platteville will have to transfer in several credits.

Accreditation: North Central Association of Colleges and Schools, The Higher Learning Commission

AVAILABLE TO PRISONERS

Bachelor of Science in Business Administration

Several for-credit courses

Tuition Rates:	**$310 per credit**
	(Most courses will cost $930 each.)
Payment Plan:	None
Textbook Fees:	Not included in tuition
Additional Fees:	**Application fee: $50**
Transfer/Exam Options:	72 credit hours
Time Limits:	7 years for bachelor degree program.
	Portfolio Assessment Fee: $75
Proctor required?	Yes

University of Wisconsin - Platteville
Available Courses
The following courses earn three (3) credits each.

ACCOUNTING

Financial Accounting
A study of accounting theory, record keeping, and the accounting cycle, with emphasis on accounting for the assets and related revenues and expenses reported on financial statements of a business organization.

Management Accounting
This course provides a review of financial reporting standards and statements and analysis of those financial statements. Managerial accounting principles will be explored as well as budgeting, cost allocation, accumulation, cost behavior, and relevant costs; revenues are approached from a manager's perspective.

Accounting Issues for Managers
Interpretation and analysis of accounting information for internal and external decisions. Includes topics of control systems, individual income tax preparation, and key popular cost management techniques.

Intermediate Accounting I
An extension of the theory and principles of financial accounting, with emphasis on FASB pronouncements applicable to accounting for assets.

Intermediate Accounting II

Advanced Accounting
An extension of the theory and principles of financial accounting, with emphasis on FASB pronouncements applicable to liabilities and owner's equity, and Cash Flow Statements; as well as analysis and interpretation of financial position and results of operations of a business organization.

Cost Accounting
A study of cost concepts and application related to the use of cost information by internal managers for purposes of planning, control, evaluation and decision making.

Budgets and Budgetary Control
Theory and procedure of financial and operating budgets for managerial planning and controls.

BUSINESS ADMINISTRATION

Global Business
This course deals with management of organizations that operate, directly and indirectly, in more than one country. While the major focus will be the multi- national corporation, management of smaller firms, which only export, will also be considered. The primary emphasis will be on the special management problems, which are unique to multi-national operations.

Leadership and Management
This course presents comprehensive information on major theories and research on leadership and managerial effectiveness in formal organizations. It also provides advice and practical suggestions for business leaders to improve leadership skills.

Introduction to Marketing
Provides an introduction to marketing as it relates to contemporary living and society's changing needs. Topics include consumer markets, planning and forecasting, and wholesaling and retailing.

Human Resources Management
An overview of the policies and procedures in personnel administration in American business, including uses, sources, motivation and maintenance of employees, with major emphasis on the dynamics of social organization.

Compensation Management

The processes of job analysis and job evaluation are discussed as methods to determine internal pay equity. Wager scale development and various employee benefit options are discussed. Other topics include wage and benefit related laws, performance appraisal, and motivation theories.

Retailing

Study of marketing and management problems faced in the operation of retail business. Emphasis is given to techniques for solving problems in location, management, and merchandising, especially with the integration of the internet retailing (E-Tailing) as both a competitor and an extension of the storefront business.

Legal Environment of Business

Describes areas of law that seem to be of greatest importance to business managers, legal environment topics that mangers frequently deal with, as well as the basic core of business law topics.

Management, Gender and Race

Reviews the changing nature of management and explains why gender and race have become important concerns of business.

Employee Training and Development

Upper division course that examines the principles and practices of these two critical processes in a variety of organizational settings. At the end of the course, students are prepared to conduction efficient and effective training and development programs within the Human Resources division of an organization.

Organizational Behavior

This course deals with human behavior in a variety of organizations. Conceptual frameworks, case discussions, and skill-oriented activities are applied to each topic. Topics include communications, motivation, group dynamics, leadership, power, the influence of technology, and organizational design and development. Class sessions and assignments are intended to help participants acquire the skills that managers need to improve organizational relationships and performance.

Corporate Finance

An introduction to the finance function of and financial management of the firm, including techniques of financial analysis, working capital management, capital budgeting, the acquisition and management of corporate capital and dividend policy.

Advertising

Advertising discusses the history, purposes and regulations of the advertising industry. Topics covered include creative principles, industry regulation and structure, advertising planning and promotions, media planning and the importance of integrated brand promotion.

Marketing Research

This course is an examination of the information link between organizations and the consumers they seek to serve. Emphasis is placed on developing an understanding of the nature of marketing problems, types of research available, sampling techniques, applied statistics and questionnaire formulation. The steps of the research process are explored in depth.

International Marketing

An advanced course in marketing covering the adaptations needed when marketing outside national boundaries. The course includes the discussions of cultures, product and marketing modifications necessary in a variety of situations, and the study of various world regions and their consumption, terrain, demographics, and geographic as they influence marketing practices.

Investments

An exploration of investing in stocks, bonds and other financial instruments; securities exchanges; financial planning; technical and fundamental analysis and market indicators.

Financial Decision Making

International Management

Presents a cross-culture perspective on managing global organizations. Focuses on understanding the influence of culture on international management, and how managers in multinational organizations address such issues as strategic analysis, organizational structure, global coordination and control, communications, inter-organizational cooperation, and human resource management.

Employee Recruitment and Selection

Prepares students to conduct efficient and effective recruiting and selection programs within the Human Resource division of an organization.

Marketing Management

This course focuses on strategy, concepts, and techniques involving the marketing function in organizations, with emphasis on marketing planning and decision making.

Business Policy and Strategy

A comprehensive review and evaluation of strategic decision-making, critical thinking, reflection, and integration of the functional organizational areas of business processes through the analysis of case studies and related readings.

Portfolio Development

Assists in building a proper portfolio for skills assessment.

COMPUTER SCIENCE

Microcomputer Applications

Recommended for non-computer science majors that need to know how to use a microcomputer.

ECONOMICS

Principles of Microeconomics

This course explores consumer choice and producer behavior, price theory, monopoly/oligopoly and competitive market structures, production costs, labor and wages.

Principles of Macroeconomics

A look at unemployment and inflation, fiscal and monetary policies, GDP, poverty and income distribution, exchange rates and international trade.

Interpretation of Business and Economic Data

The nature of statistical data in business and economics; the use of tabular, graphical and numerical analysis; probability, estimation and hypothesis testing; correlation and regression; index numbers, time series; and forecasting.

MEDIA

Business Communication

This course will discuss workplace communications, including speeches, presentations, office etiquette, business letters, emails, resumes, job applications, etc. Students will learn how to present themselves effectively in formal situations and learn real-life skills that will help them succeed in the business world.

MATHEMATICS

Mathematics of Finance

Simple and compound interest, annuities, amortization, depreciation valuations of securities, and bonds.

MUSIC

Music Appreciation

Music is often described as a universal language because it exists in all cultures. This course approaches music from a global perspective. Students will learn to notice cultural influences on music while exploring the common human ideas that music addresses. They will analyze the musical traditions of Western Europe, Asia, India, Africa, Latin America, South America and the United States. They will learn about the significance of music from multiple perspectives: as art, a science, and a business.

SPEECH

Public Speaking

This course increases the ability of students to make effective speeches and includes speech organization, presentation and extemporaneous talks.

University of Wyoming | Outreach Credit Programs

CORRESPONDENCE STUDY

1000 East University Avenue, Department 3294
Laramie, Wyoming 82071-3294
(800) 448-7801, (307) 766-5632
www.uwyo.edu   uwcorr@uwyo.edu

The *University of Wyoming Outreach Credit Program* offers prisoners reasonable priced paper-based correspondence for-credit and noncredit courses. However, their course options are limited.

Accreditation: North Central Association of Colleges and Schools, The Higher Learning Commission

AVAILABLE TO PRISONERS

A variety of for-credit courses

Tuition Rates:	**$124 per credit (Most courses will cost $372 each.)**
	Non-credit courses: $372
Payment Plan:	None
Textbook Fees:	Not included in tuition
Additional Fees:	**Administrative/Delivery fee: $25 per credit**
	Non-credit course delivery fee: $75
Cancellation Policy:	90% refund is given within the first six weeks after enrollment, 50% refund is given within six to 12 weeks of enrollment
Transfer/Exam Options:	Not applicable
Time Limits:	9 months; 3-month extensions available for $30
Proctor required?	Yes

University of Wyoming | Outreach Credit Programs
Available Courses
All courses earn 3 credits unless otherwise noted.

ACCOUNTING

Principles of Accounting I | ACCT 1010
Provides a basic level of knowledge in recording business transactions, summarizing business activities, and preparing, interpreting and utilizing financial statements.

Principles of Accounting II | ACCT 1020
Accounting procedures for managerial accounting including job/process costing, cost behavior, budgeting, performance evaluation, differential analysis and capital investment.

ENGLISH

Teaching Reading and Study Strategies in the Content Areas | EDSE 3540 (2 credits)
Provides students majoring in secondary education programs with a knowledge of reading factors as they relate to various disciplines. Content includes estimating students' reading ability, techniques for vocabulary development, questioning strategies, and developing reading related study skills. Prerequisites: Junior standing and minimum of 12 hours in discipline area.

English Composition | ENGL 1010
A composition course emphasizing expository writing and close analytical reading.

Introduction to Literature | ENGL 2020
An introduction to literary study including poetry, fiction and drama. Prerequisite: sophomore standing

Technical Writing in the Professions | ENGL 4010
Deals with professional writing for various audiences. Includes research methods, audience analysis, organization and developmental techniques, abstracting, types of reports and popularization. Part of the last half of the course devoted to solution of student-initiated problem, culminating in the writing of a long-form report. Prerequisites: WA and WB; junior standing.

FINANCE

Personal Finance | FCSC 3010
This course is designed to help students plan for a successful financial future. It provides information on tax laws and gives students an accurate reflection of the trends affecting their financial present and future. It also discusses the importance of achieving long-term goals through investing.

GEOGRAPHY

Conservation of Natural Resources | GEOG 4040
Geographically analyzes conservation of natural and human's resources, as well as political, social and ethical ramification of our environmental policy. Prerequisites: 6 hours of GEOG courses or ENR.

HEALTH

Resources in Adapted Physical Education | KIN 4065
Offers flexible credit for students interested in pursuing intensive study of resources for adapted physical education. Required for state endorsement in Adapted Physical Education. Prerequisites: KIN 4055, junior status, and minimum 2.5 GPA.

MATH

Pre-Algebra | MATH 0900 (Noncredit course)

Students acquire knowledge of addition, subtraction, multiplication, and division of whole numbers, fractions, and decimals; averages; exponents; percent's; rations and proportions; weights and measures, including metric system; signed numbers; and introductory geometry and algebra.

Algebra I | MATH 0921 (Noncredit course)

This course involves study of algebraic expressions and equations. Successful students acquire knowledge and develop skills that enable them to simplify algebraic expressions, solve linear equations and inequalities, graph linear equations, use of rules of exponents, perform operations on polynomials, and factor polynomials.

Prerequisite: Required MPE score of a 1 or ACT score of 21, or MATH 0900.

Algebra II | MATH 0925 (Noncredit course)

This course involves a study of algebraic equations and functions. Successful students acquire knowledge and develop skills that enable them to solve linear systems of equations and inequalities, solve quadratic equations, perform operations on rational and radical expressions, and identify functions and use function notation.

Prerequisite: Required MPE score of a 2 or ACT score of 21, or a grade of C or better in MATH 0921.

Problem Solving | MATH 1000

Examines modern topics chosen for their applicability and accessibility. Provides students with mathematical and logical skills needed to formulate, analyze and interpret quantitative arguments in a variety of settings. Introduces statistics and stresses the use of a calculator.

Prerequisite: MATH 0921 or level 2 on Math Placement Exam or MATH ACT of 21, or MATH SAT of 600.

College Algebra | MATH 1400

Emphasizes aspects of algebra important in the study of calculus. Includes notation of algebra, exponents, factoring, theory of equations, inequalities, functions, graphing and logarithms.

Prerequisite: MATH 0925 or Level 3 on the Math Placement Exam, or MATH ACT of 23 or MATH SAT of 600.

Calculus I | MATH 2200 (4 credits)

Emphasizes physical science applications. Includes plane analytic geometry, differentiation, and application of the derivative, differential equations, integration and applications.

Prerequisites: MATH 1405 or 1450, or Level 5 on the Math Placement Exam, or MATH ACT of 27, or MATH SAT of 600.

Calculus II | MATH 2205 (4 credits)

Follow-up to MATH 2200. Includes elementary functions, derivatives, integrals, analytical geometry, infinite series and applications.

Prerequisites: Grade of C or better in MATH 2200 or Advanced Placement credit in MATH 2200.

SPANISH

First Year Spanish I | SPAN 1010 (4 credits)

Studies fundamentals of grammar, composition, conversation and reading.

First Year Spanish II | SPAN 1020 (4 credits)

Studies more of the fundamentals of grammar, composition, conversation and reading.

Prerequisites: SPAN 1010 or two years of high school Spanish.

STATISTICS

Fundamentals of Statistics | STAT 2050 (4 credits)

Presents central ideas and fundamental techniques of statistical inference on applications in the biological sciences. Includes probability models and inferences for means, variances and parameters of discrete distributions.

Prerequisites: Grade C or better in MATH 1000, 1400, or equivalent.

WOMEN'S STUDIES

Introduction to Women's Studies | WMST 1080 (3 credits)

An introduction to key issues in women's studies. A topical examination of women's participation in, and relationship to, institutions of society, such as family and school, as well as processes and activities as work, art, literature and politics in historical and cross-cultural analysis.

Upper Iowa University

CENTER FOR DISTANCE EDUCATION

PO Box 1861
Fayette, Iowa 52142-1861
(800) 553-4150, (563) 425-5200
www.uiu.edu/cde selfpaced@uiu.edu

Upper Iowa University offers a variety of degree options and for-credit paper-based courses. Students also have the option of "auditing" self-paced courses for a reduced tuition fee, although no credit is awarded for these courses.

Accreditation: North Central Association of Colleges and Schools, The Higher Learning Commission

AVAILABLE TO PRISONERS

Associate of Arts degrees in:
General Business; Liberal Arts; Psychology; Criminal Justice

Bachelor of Science degrees in:
Accounting; Business Administration; Criminal Justice; Emergency & Disaster Management; Management; Financial Management; Psychology; Public Administration (with emphasis in Fire Science and Law Enforcement); Social Science; Health Services Administration; Human Resources Administration; Marketing

Certificates of Completion in:
Management; Organizational Leadership; Emergency & Disaster Management; Human Resources Management; Marketing; Psychology

A variety of for-credit courses

Tuition Rates:	**$325 per credit (Most courses will cost $975 each.)** **Auditing option: $95 per credit**
Payment Plan:	Not available for correspondence education
Textbook Fees:	Not included in tuition
Additional Fees:	**Application fee: $50**
Cancellation Policy:	Full refund before first assignment is submitted, less $99 administrative fee; 90% refund through the first 10% of course; 50% refund between 10 and 25% of course completion.
Transfer/Exam Options:	30 credits per associate program; 90 credits per bachelor program; CLEP/DSST/Excelsior College and/or ACT-PEP examinations; Experiential Learning Portfolio Credit ($60 fee per credit earned, all fees due within 90 days of assessment.)
Time Limits:	6 months; one free 6-month extension available. If no course work has been submitted within the first 60 days, student may be dropped.
Proctor required?	Yes

Upper Iowa University
Certificate Programs

These certificate programs are designed to meet the needs of students who are interested in a specific professional specialization, and which may be helpful toward parole board consideration and reentry planning.

These are groups of courses that provide a concentration in a particular study area, without the need to take the general education courses of degree programs. They are more economical options than a full degree track.

Once completed, each of the following certificate earns college credit as marked, which can be used towards future learning.

Emergency & Disaster Management Certificate

Course	Credit
Principles of Emergency Management | PA 306	3
Political & Policy Basis or Emergency Management | PA 320	3
Emergency Preparedness & Planning | PA 332	3
Disaster Response & Recovery | PA 346	3
Select one of the following:	3
Integrated Emergency Management | PA 404	
Psychology of Disaster | PSY 409	
Business & Industrial Crisis Management | BA 449	
Total Credits	**15**
Total Cost	**$4,875 plus fees**

Human Resource Management Certificate

Course	Credit
Management Principles | BA 210	3
Human Resources Management | BA 361	3
Select three of the following:	3
Training & Development | BA 371	
Compensation & Benefits Management | BA383	
Personnel Selection & Evaluation | BA 393	
Labor Relations & Negotiations | BA 411	
Total Credits	**15**
Total Cost	**$4,875 plus fees**

MANAGEMENT CERTIFICATE

Course	Credit
Management Principles	BA 210	3
Business Ethics	BA 225	3
International Management	BA 317	3
Human Resources Management	BA 361	3
Select one of the following:	3
Supervision	BA 362	
Leadership Theory	BA 365	
Total Credits	15
Total Cost	$4,875 plus fees

ORGANIZATIONAL LEADERSHIP CERTIFICATE

Course	Credit
Management Principles	BA 210	3
Supervision	BA 362	3
Leadership Theory	BA 365	3
Complex Organizations	BA 390	3
Select one of the following:	3
Business Ethics	BA 225	
Entrepreneurship & Small Business Management	BA 370	
Total Credits	15
Total Cost	$4,875 plus fees

PRE-PROFESSIONAL ARTS ADMINISTRATION CERTIFICATE

Course	Credit
Choose five of the following:	3
Grant Writing	PA 305	
Writing for Media	COMM 332	
Consumer Behavior	BA 358	
Public Administration	PA 364	
Communication & Media Ethics	COMM 415	
Public Budgeting Process	PA 440	
Organizational Behavior	BA/PSY 474	
Total Credits	15
Total Cost	$4,875 plus fees

Upper Iowa University
Available Courses
All courses award three (3) credits unless otherwise noted.

BIOLOGY

General Biology | BIO 100
This course presents the basic concepts of biology: it is intended for non-science majors. Recommended to satisfy the general education requirement for science.

BUSINESS

Microeconomic Principles | BA 160
This course explores consumer choice and producer behavior, price theory, monopoly/oligopoly and competitive market structures, production costs, labor and wages.

Prerequisite: MATH 105 or above.

Macroeconomic Principles | BA 161
A look at unemployment and inflation, fiscal and monetary policies, GDP, poverty and income distribution, exchange rates and international trade.

Prerequisite: BA 160.

Accounting Principles 1 | BA 201
A study of accounting theory, record keeping, and the accounting cycle, with emphasis on accounting for the assets and related revenues and expenses reported on financial statements of a business organization.

Accounting Principles 2 | BA 202
A continuation of BA 201, with emphasis on accounting for the liabilities, owners' equity and related revenues and expenses reported in financial statements of a business organization; and preparation and analysis of financial statements and an introduction to managerial accounting including product costing using job orders and process costing systems and cost-value-profit relationships.

Prerequisite: BA 201.

Marketing Principles | BA 208
This course surveys the role of marketing and its place in society, in profit and not-for-profit organizations. Emphasis is placed on consumer orientation, the marketing concept, product, price, distribution and promotion. The course provides a basis of understanding for advanced marketing courses.

Management Principles | BA 210
A look at modern management theory, including both functional and behavioral approaches to the administration of business enterprises.

Management Information Systems | BA 222
A study of the procedures involved in the accumulation, processing and dissemination of various types of information within an organization.

Prerequisites: BA 210 and MIS 101 or CS 102

Business Ethics | BA 225
A course that seeks to recognize the distinctive set of problems encountered in the work environment, to study contrasting theories currently being used to make ethical decisions, and to apply those theories through examples and case studies.

Business Law 1 | BA 302
An introduction to the nature and sources of law, and the methods by which laws are made; basic principles of contract law and property law as the foundations for business enterprise; tort law governing business relationships.

Business Law 2 | BA 303
A survey of particular fields of law relevant to business operations; agency, partnerships, corporations; sales, commercial transactions, and bankruptcy; antitrust law; employment law; consumer protection.   Prerequisite: BA 302 recommended.

COLLEGE STUDIES | 361

Money and Capital Markets | BA 310

A study of the commercial banking system; thrift institutions; the Federal Reserve System; money, interest rates, savings and credit; government regulatory institutions and policies.

Prerequisite: BA 161.

International Management | BA 317

Presents a cross-culture perspective on managing global organizations. Focuses on understanding the influence of culture on international management, and how managers in multinational organizations address such issues as strategic analysis, organizational structure, global coordination and control, communications, inter-organizational cooperation, and human resource management.

Prerequisites: BA 210 and the general education cultures requirement.

Intermediate Financial Accounting 1 | BA 321

An extension of the theory and principles of financial accounting, with emphasis on FASB pronouncements applicable to accounting for assets.

Prerequisite: BA 202.

Intermediate Financial Accounting II | BA 322

An extension of the theory and principles of financial accounting, with emphasis on FASB pronouncements applicable to liabilities and owner's equity, and Cash Flow Statements; as well as analysis and interpretation of financial position and results of operations of a business organization.

Prerequisite: BA 321.

Federal Taxation 1 | BA 323

A study of the theory and application of federal tax law, with emphasis on income tax law applicable to individuals.

Prerequisite: BA 202.

Corporate Financial Management | BA 341

An introduction to corporate financial management. Topics include financial statement analysis, time value of money, risk and return, bond valuation, stock valuation, capital budgeting and the capital asset pricing model.

Prerequisites: BA 161 and BA 202 or permission of instructor.

Investments | BA 343

An exploration of investing in stocks, bonds and other financial instruments; securities exchanges; financial planning; technical and fundamental analysis and market indicators.

Prerequisite: BA 341.

Quantitative Decisions in Business | BA 356

This course is designed for business students who have a good foundation in pre-calculus mathematics, algebra, and elementary statistics. Topics will include an introduction to business quantitative methodology, decision making and planning under conditions of uncertainty, resource allocation, distribution and scheduling, inventory management, and business simulation. This course will be case driven as part of the learning process.

Prerequisites: MIS 101 or CS 102 and MATH 220.

Consumer Behavior | BA 358

This course provides a survey of research findings on consumer behavior drawn from marketing, economics, sociology, psychology, and anthropology. Emphasis is placed on application of research to consumer satisfaction and on developing an understanding of the consumer decision-making process.

Prerequisites for Marketing majors: BA 208. Recommended for all majors: BA 208 and PSY 190 or SOC 110.

Human Resources Management | BA 361

An overview of the policies and procedures in personnel administration in American business, including uses, sources, motivation and maintenance of employees, with major emphasis on the dynamics of social organization.

Prerequisite: BA 210

Supervision | BA 362

A detailed examination of the fundamental concepts, principles and dynamics of the supervisory process.

Prerequisites: BA 210 and BA 361.

Leadership Theory | BA 365

This course examines and contrasts process theories, relationship theories, and management theories of leadership. Various definitions of leadership and their underlying implications for application and research will be investigated. The role the leader will be examined in relation to the various leadership theories and definitions.

Prerequisite: BA 210 and BA 361.

Entrepreneurship and Small Business Management | BA 370

A presentation of the organization and operation of small enterprises in services, retailing, wholesaling and manufacturing for those aspiring to own, operate, and/or manage a small business or to work for importance, status, problems and requirements of small businesses.

Prerequisite: BA 210.

Training and Development | BA 371

This course involves the application and study of trends in human resource training, education and development activities within organizational settings.

Prerequisite: BA 361.

Marketing Management | BA 380

This course focuses on strategy, concepts, and techniques involving the marketing function in organizations, with emphasis on marketing planning and decision making.

Prerequisite: BA 358.

Personnel Selection and Evaluation | BA 393

Policies, procedures and problems in the selection of personnel, focusing on job analysis, validation, legal constraints, criteria and application of specific techniques.

Prerequisite: BA 361.

Labor Relations and Negotiation | BA 411

The basic principles of manpower use, wage structure, use of industrial psychology and collective bargaining, the union movement, human relations in industrial management, and modern labor laws and institutions.

Prerequisites: BA 210 and BA 361.

Managerial Cost Accounting | BA 421

A study of cost concepts and application related to the use of cost information by internal managers for purposes of planning, control, evaluation and decision making.

Prerequisite: BA 202.

Production and Operations Management | BA 423

Productions and operations management is designed to provide students with an in-depth look at the components of organizational operations and how they are managed. Successful management incorporates theories and practices that apply to a variety of operational areas involving factory and service operations, inventory management, quality management, capacity planning, supply chain management. Elements of shop floor control, status reporting, facilities design, cost estimating, inventory control, procurement, quality assurance, forecasting, labor loading, scheduling, and productivity measurement will be explored. Important tools of production and operations management that will be covered include Theory of Constraints, MRP, MRPII, CAD/CAM, CIM, JIT, SPC, and TQM.

Prerequisites: BA 210 and MATH 220.

Auditing | BA 425

An exploration of the concepts and procedures applicable to an audit of financial statements, with emphasis on procedures to substantiate amounts reported; along with the impact of internal control, quality of available evidence, and statistical sampling on the determination of appropriate procedures.

Prerequisites: Senior status and BA 322.

Advanced Financial Accounting | BA 431

An extension of the theory and principles of financial accounting, with emphasis on FASB pronouncements applicable to accounting for business combinations, international operations and partnerships.

Prerequisite: BA 322.

Accounting for Not-For-Profit Organizations | BA 432

An overview of the theory and application of FASB and other authoritative pronouncements related to accounting for governmental, fiduciary and other not-for-profit organizations.

Prerequisite: BA 202 or substantial experience in accounting is recommended.

Intermediate Financial Management | BA 442

A study of long-term financial decisions made by managers (e.g., capital structure, divided policy, lease-or-buy, mergers, issuances of new securities).

Prerequisite: BA 341.

Business and Industrial Crisis Management | BA 449

Through case studies and discussion learners explore governmental emergency management and private sector crisis management in the context of fundamental concepts such as crisis management, disaster recovery, organizational continuity, and vulnerability and risk analysis. Learners will gain practice with tools including business area impact analysis, and explore risk management and loss control strategies. Learners will explore the characteristics of realistic and effective contingency, response, business recovery, and crisis management plans and discuss the purpose, value, and types of exercise and training needed to support an effective crisis management, disaster recovery, and organizational continuity program.

Prerequisites: BA 210 and PA 306.

Marketing Research | BA 451

This course is an examination of the information link between organizations and the consumers they seek to serve. Emphasis is placed on developing an understanding of the nature of marketing problems, types of research available, sampling techniques, applied statistics and questionnaire formulation. The steps of the research process are explored in depth.

Prerequisites: Completion of all other marketing/business core requirements.

Management Cases | BA 454

A study of the current strategies and techniques of administration and management, including; business objectives: policies, functions, executive leadership and organizational structure; control standards; case studies in organization, financing and operations.

Prerequisites; BA 361 and BA 423.

Marketing Cases | BA 456

This course provides an in-depth exposure to strategic planning for marketing, using cases as illustrative examples. Emphasis is placed on extensive situation

analysis, objective and criterion formulation, and alternative selection and implementation.　　Prerequisite: Completion of all marketing/business core requirements.

Strategic Management | BA 460

This course is a culminating experience for students completing majors in business. Upon the successful completion of the course, students will have a practical knowledge of strategic application in the activities, procedures, and techniques unique to business operations.

Prerequisites; senior standing and within 9 credits of program completion.

CRIMINAL JUSTICE

Introduction to Criminal Justice | CJ 224

History of the development of the criminal justice system in America. The everyday practices in this subsystem and the articulation among policing, judicial and correctional institutions. Same as SOC 224.　　Prerequisite: SOC 110.

Criminal Law | CJ 237

Surveys the historical development of criminal law in America. Analysis of the effects of English common law, a federal structure, court decisions, legislated codes, historical events and social changes. Same as SOC 237.

Prerequisite: SOC 110.

Criminology | CJ 333

An analysis of various forms of crime, as well as various elements of the criminal justice system. The emphasis is on theories of crime and juvenile delinquency. Topics will include; street crime, organized crime, white-collar crime and the role of substance abuse in criminality and delinquency. Same as SOC 333.

Prerequisite: SOC 110.

Victimology | CJ 337

Development and operation of policies and programs for the victims of crime, victim compensation schemes from colonial to modern times, victim/offender confrontation programs. Same as SOC 337.

Prerequisite: SOC 110.

NOTE: Now web-based ONLY.

Criminal Investigations | CJ 362

Fundamentals of criminal investigation: crime scene search and recording: collection and preservation of physical evidence; scientific aids; modus operandi; sources of information; interview and interrogation; Follow-up and case preparation. Special emphasis on leadership and management actions taken to enhance investigative efforts. Same as SOC 362.

Prerequisite: SOC 110.

Ethics in Criminal Justice | CJ 367

An introduction to concepts of ethics and an examination of contemporary ethical issues in the field of criminal justice. Same as SOC 367.

Prerequisite: SOC 110.

Corrections and Punishment | CJ 380

The history of corrections in American society, corrections and punishment in contemporary America, alternatives to institutional treatment. Same as SOC 380.

Prerequisite: SOC 110.

Justice Administration | CJ 398

This course studies the management and control of the criminal justice system. The learner will be able to discuss the reasons for and effectiveness of management techniques applied to the justice system. Same as SOC 398.

Prerequisite: SOC 110

NOTE: Now web-based ONLY.

COMMUNICATION

Public Speaking | COMM 105

This course increases the ability of students to make effective speeches and includes speech organization, presentation and extemporaneous talks.

COMPUTER SCIENCE

Introduction to Computer Application and Techniques | CS 102

This course is an introduction into the computer applications and technology and their social implications. The course covers popular applications for personal and business use, including; Office Suite, image, audio, web, backup and security applications. The course also covers the foundational technologies enabling these applications, including; hardware, software, and communications devices. This course meets the general education requirement in computer skills.

ENGLISH

Basic Composition | ENG 101

A study and practice of expository writing, with narrative and descriptive compositions assigned regularly. Emphasis is on the development of sound understanding of rhetorical principles.

English Composition II | ENG 102

A further study and practice of expository writing, with emphasis on research technique, persuasion and explanation. A formal research paper is required.

Prerequisite: ENG 101. Meets the written communication requirement.

Best Sellers | ENG 352

This class introduces students to bestselling books from the New York Times best seller list in order to learn more about American psyche, what energizes a writer in creating a book, how long it takes a writer to create a book and what factors cause a book to become a best seller. Meets the humanities requirement.

HEALTH SERVICE ADMINISTRATION

Introduction to the American Health System | HAS 205

A macro-level examination of the origin, structure and operation of the American health system and its subsystems and components. Topics include the hospital system, public health system, long-term care systems, financing system, health service delivery system, health care providers and contemporary issues confronting the American Health System.

Health Care Ethics | HAS 340

An examination of the major ethical theories and their relationship to health services delivery and profession ethics codes. Topics include public health ethics and private practice ethics, the Nuremberg Trials, the Helsinki Accord and the Belmont Report, Case histories such as the Tuskegee Study will be addressed.

Prerequisite: ID 301.

Financial Management of Health Service Organizations | HAS 362

An analysis of the financial management of health services organizations and issues related to the financial management of health services organizations, particularly acute care facilities such as hospitals. Topics include the economic analysis of public and private financing, health insurance, and other forms of health services payment.

Prerequisites: BA 201 and BA 210.

Health Service Administration | HAS 440

An analysis of the structure and operation of various types of health services organizations, including their internal departments, and management of the facilities with particular emphasis on acute care facilities.

Prerequisite: BA 210

INTERDISCIPLINARY

Critical Thinking | ID 301

This course helps the student develop and strengthen the ability to reason soundly and critically. It addresses the purpose and process of critical thinking, language and critical thinking, patterns of argument, and modes of reasoning.

Prerequisites: ENG 102 or 202 and Junior Standing. May not be used to satisfy a humanities general education requirement.

Senior Project | ID 498

A capstone project intended to integrate the general education learning outcomes with the learning outcomes in the major demonstrating baccalaureate level achievement.

(Psychology, Human Services, Social Science, Public Administration, Public Administration-Law, Criminal Justice, Public Administration-Fire Science, Emergency and Disaster Management.) Prerequisites: ENG 102, ID 301, senior status, with 15 or fewer credits remaining to be completed through Upper Iowa University.

MATHEMATICS

College Mathematics with Applications | MATH 105

This course is a survey of mathematical applications of functions. Topics that will be covered include: fundamental concepts of algebra, algebraic equations and inequalities; functions and graphs; zeros of polynomial functions; exponential and logarithmic functions; systems of equations and inequalities. The mathematics of finance will also be studied.

Prerequisite for Fayette campus only: Pass MATH095 or ACT math score >19

Elementary Statistics | MATH 220

An introduction to the similar problems of statistical inference; descriptive statistics, probability distributions, estimation of parameters and level of significance, regression and correlation. This course may not be completed for additional credit by students who have completed MATH 226.

Prerequisite: MATH 105 or above, MATH 095, or ACT math score >19 and pass MATH 100, or ACT math score >24

PUBLIC ADMINISTRATION

Grant Writing | PA 305

This course is designed to introduce students to grantsmanship principles and practices. Students will develop grant-seeking and grant-writing skills through practical learning opportunities. Students will learn to develop strong problem statements and designs for grants, seek out resources for funding, write a proposal, and develop budget and management strategies for the proposed project.

Prerequisite: ENG 102

Emergency Preparedness and Planning | PA 332

Explores the needs of public safety officials who have responsibility for emergency preparedness planning and response. Includes contexts for emergency planning-legal and jurisdictional; responsibility for planning and responding to emergencies; different types of emergencies, and an approach to planning that can be applied to emergency situations. Address specific issues associated with the planning for multi-agency involvement, various analytical techniques employed in planning, and different elements of the plan. Utilizes case analysis and discussion.

Prerequisites: PA 306 and PA 320.

Public Administration | PA 364

A study of politics, administration and bureaucratic policy making at local, state and national levels, with emphasis on the relationship between governmental bureaucracies and political system in the United States.

Integrated Emergency Management | PA 404

Through a case/scenario driven approach, learners deal with scenario related threat events of increasing complexity, urgency, and intensity. Participants develop emergency policies, plans, and procedures to ensure an effective response. Preparedness and Response, Recovery and Mitigation, Public and Media Relations, and Political/Public Policy issues are integrated through the case/scenario.

Prerequisite: PA 306.

Cases in Public Administration | PA 430

A concentrated study of the techniques of public administration, including the public budgeting process, law enforcement administration, recreation administration, and the administration of other public services.

Prerequisite: PA 364.

Public Budgeting Process | PA 440

Areas studied include budget planning, formulation, execution, and auditing; the sharing of taxing and spending power between the executive and legislative branches; the agency role of advocacy in budget preparation; budgets as a reflection of public policy.

Administrative Law | PA 445

Areas explored include bureaucracy and the regulatory process; judicial review of administrative action, the Administrative Procedures Act of 1946; delegation, standing, exhaustion, sovereign immunity, rulemaking, tort liability, evidence, discretion, investigation and enforcement.

POLITICAL SCIENCE

US Government | PS 100

A survey of the basic constitutional principles, political institutions and public policies of American national government. Meets the social science requirement.

State and Local Government | PS 230

A survey of the basic principles, organizations and functions of government on state, county, municipal, township and district levels. Meets the social science requirement.

PSYCHOLOGY

Human Growth, Development and Guidance | PSY 142

Same as EDU 142

General Psychology | PSY 190

An introduction to the scientific study of behavior and mental processes, including major approaches and methodologies. The course samples a broad range of topics, including biological foundations, development, learning, cognition, personality, abnormal psychology and social behavior. Meets the social science requirement.

Conflict Resolution | PSY 240

An overview of conflict resolution and the mediation process as an alternative dispute resolution mechanism. Learning activities-conceptual and experimental in nature- are designed to promote an integration in the areas of problem solving behavior, skill development and personal awareness. Prerequisite: PSY 190. Meets the social science requirement.

Substance Abuse | PSY 302

The effects of psychoactive drugs are studied in this course, as well as the origins of substance abuse, characteristics of substance abusers, and consequences for the individual, family and society. Approaches to substance abuse treatment are discussed.

Prerequisite: SOC 110 or PSY 190.

Cognition | PSY 323

An analysis of cognitive processes, including attention, perception, concept formation, language, memory, problem solving and decision making.

Prerequisite: PSY 190.

Motivation | PSY 338

A review of the major theories that attempt to explain motivated behavior from a physiological, cognitive, social, environmental and/or learning point of view. Application of motivation theories to organizations, education, sports and daily life.

Prerequisite: PSY 190.

Abnormal Psychology | PSY 360

A survey of the major classifications of psychopathology, including conceptual approaches to the understanding of psychopathology, etiology and treatment.

Prerequisite: PSY 190.

Research Methods | PSY 373

This course explores the development of skills essential to critical evaluation of behavioral research. The emphasis is on understanding scientific method, research, methodologies and statistical analysis.

Prerequisites: SOC 110 or PSY 190 and MATH 220.

Human Behavior in the Social Environment | PSY 383

An analysis of individual, group and cultural influences on human behavior. The emphasis is on contrasting levels of analysis and application to a variety of environmental settings. NOTE: Some background in both psychology and sociology is strongly recommended. Same as SOC 383.

Prerequisite: SOC 110 or PSY 190.

Social Gerontology | PSY 397

This course focuses on personal, interpersonal and societal factors in the human aging process. Emphasis is on family, community and governmental responsibility in defining and resolving problems of the aged in a modern industrial society.

Prerequisite: SOC 110 or PSY 190.

Personality | PSY 432

A survey of the major theories of the nature and development of personality.

Prerequisite: PSY 190.

Issues and Ethics in the Helping Professions | PSY 454

An analysis of issues and ethical problems involved in the helping professions and programs.

Prerequisite: PSY 190.

RELIGION

Introduction to World Religion | REL 120

An investigation of the phenomenon of religion with special emphasis on systems of belief, codes of conduct, use of ritual and notions of the sacred. Several religious traditions (e.g., Hinduism, Buddhism, Taoism, Judaism, Christianity, Islam) will be examined and compared with reference to these issues. Meets the humanities requirement.

SOCIOLOGY

Principles of Sociology | SOC 110

A basic introduction to sociology as a scientific analysis of the social relations and practices of human beings. Specific attention is given to social psychology, various forms of social stratification and inequality, social institutions and social change. Meets the social science requirement.

Social Problems | SOC 220

A critical investigation of selected social problems; their causes, development and the alternative social policies that address these problems. Topics will include: substance abuse, the problems of family life, poverty and its relation to different forms of social inequality. Meets the social science requirement.

Diversity in the United States | SOC 240

This course provides sociological perspectives for recognizing the diversity within our society and for analyzing the development and current position of complex subcultures within the structure of modern America. Meets firstly the cultures requirement or secondly the social science requirement, but not both.

Social Welfare Programs and Policies | SOC 384

An analysis of social policies in the United states, with emphasis on the dimensions of choice and alternative policies, along with assessment of contemporary social welfare issues, programs and legislation.

Prerequisites: SOC 110

College Studies | Religious Studies

Undergraduate Religious Studies | What They Offer

NOTE: This list includes both accredited and unaccredited schools.
Accredited schools are highlighted.

SCHOOL	DIPLOMA / CERTIFICATE OF COMPLETION	FOR COLLEGE CREDITS	ASSOCIATE'S DEGREE	BACHELOR'S DEGREE
	✓	✓		
	✓	✓		✓
CHRISTIAN BIBLE COLLEGE & SEMINARY		✓	✓	✓
CHRISTIAN LEADERSHIP UNIVERSITY	✓	✓	✓	✓
FREEDOM BIBLE COLLEGE & SEMINARY	✓	✓	✓	✓
	✓	✓	✓	✓
	✓	✓	✓	
INTERNATIONAL CHRISTIAN COLLEGE & SEMINARY	✓	✓		
	✓	✓		
ST. PETERSBURG SEMINARY & YESHIVA	✓		✓	✓
VISION INTERNATIONAL UNIVERSITY	✓	✓	✓	✓
WESLEYAN CHURCH	✓			

Arlington Baptist College

3001 West Division
Arlington, Texas 76012
(817) 461-8741
www.arlingtonbaptistcollege.edu/content/distance-education
kmarvin@arlingtonbaptistcollege.edu

Arlington Baptist College offers a variety of religious study options, including certificates, diplomas, and degrees. However, a significant number of credits would need to be transferred into the school to meet degree requirements.

Accreditation: Association for Biblical Higher Education, Commission on Accreditation

AVAILABLE TO PRISONERS

Bible Certificate

Bible Institute Diploma

A variety of for-credit courses and degree options

Tuition Rates:	**$150 per credit**
	(Most courses will cost $450 each.)
	$350 per non-credit course
Payment Plan:	None
Textbook Fees:	Not included in tuition
Additional Fees:	**Application fee: $25; Registration fee: $50**
Transfer/Exam Options:	Case-by-case basis
Time Limits:	4 months per course
Proctor required?	Yes, for degree options

Arlington Baptist College
Available Courses

It is suggested that courses be taken in listed order. Each course is worth two credits.

New Testament Survey
(dbi-1202-3) - each book of the new testament is studied with regard to its chief events, characters and teachings. The significance of the historical, cultural and political background is considered.

Old Testament Survey
(dbi-1201-3) - an overview of each old testament book is given. The historical, geographical and cultural back- grounds are explored, as well as the purpose of each old testament book.

Bible Study Methods
(dbi-1205-3) - an introduction to the various tools of bible study, the methodical and inductive approach to the study of scripture and the principles of interpretation

Evangelism
(dcm-1210-3) - evangelism is defined and methods of evangelism are examined from their scriptural and historical foundations. Principles are sought which will make the students more effective in their witnessing. This course requires pastoral approval.

Pentateuch - Genesis
(dbi-2203-3) - a chapter by chapter study of genesis emphasizes the foundations of civilization, religion and the nation of israel. The beginnings of god's plan of redemption receives attention.

Bible Doctrine
(dth-2201-3) - an introduction to bible doctrine is offered, emphasizing definition of terms and the ten major doctrines of the bible.

Ecclesiology
(dth-2210-3) - the student is involved in a detailed study of the church including: its nature and function; its officers, its ordinances, and its place in god's plan. Various views of the nature of the church are given and the local church view is supported. The means of carrying out the church's mission are surveyed. Articles 13 and 14 of the statement of faith are explained.

Acts: Life of Paul
(dbi-3201-3)- an analysis of the acts of the apostles as revealed in the book of acts., this course considers background information regarding the historical setting, cultural setting and missionary activities of the early church. The ministry of paul receives special attention.

Romans: Foundations of the Faith
(dbi-3202a-3) - an in-depth study of the book of romans with a focus on paul's logical five-step progression in his presentation of the foundational truths of the christian faith.

Cults & World Views
(dcm-3201) - an examination of the teachings of major pseudo-christian cults is given against the backdrop of a christian world view. Several other significant world views are also examined in an attempt to better prepare the student for witnessing and defending their faith in an increasingly secular society. In examining the cults, emphasis is placed on the history, development, and erroneous teachings of these belief systems as well as the unexamined presuppositions which underlie these systems.

Theology I
(DTH-3205-3) - Based on the definitions studies in Bible Doctrine, the relationship of doctrines to each other is treated here. The course begins by considering how man comes to know God and continues to explore the revelation of God to man through Scripture, the works of God, man and his sin, salvation, and the end things. Study is made to show how one doctrine gives rise to another. Prerequisite: DTH 2201-3.

Theology II
(DTH-3206-3) - Continues Theology I. Prerequisite DTH 2201-3

Hermeneutics
(DBI-3201) - This course is an introduction to the general and special principles of Biblical interpretation. The importance, history, and methods of interpretation will be investigated. Prerequisite: Junior rank. Recommended: Theology I & II.

Catholic Distance University

115 West Congress Street
Charlestown, West Virginia 25414
www.cdu.edu   cdu@cdu.edu

Catholic Distance University is the only school approved by the Vatican to offer the Catechetical Diploma through correspondence. CDU's courses have helped prisoners to become chaplains' assistants who evangelize and minister to their fellow prisoners when priest and chaplains were unavailable, as well as to develop ministry careers beyond prison walls.

CDU also offers degree options, although one online course is required for degree options. Accredited only by DEAC.

Accreditation: Distance Education Accrediting Commission (DEAC)

AVAILABLE TO PRISONERS

Advanced Catechist Certificate

Bachelor of Arts in Theology

A few non-credit courses

Tuition Rates:	**$305 per credit**
	(Most course will cost $915 per each.)
	Advanced Catechist Certificate: $165
	Non-credit course: $10 each
Payment Plan:	Monthly payment plan available, but will require an additional $30 per course
Textbook Fees:	Not included in tuition, approximately $100 per course. Included in non-credit course
Additional Fees:	**Application fee: $50**
Transfer/Exam Options:	90 credit per bachelor degree (recommended)
Time Limits:	5 years per degree
Proctor required?	Yes

Catholic Distance University
Available Non-Credit Courses

Students wishing to take these courses are required to provide a brief explanation of how you plan to use your education in theology to grow in faith, as a letter from your chaplain stating your genuine interest and ability to complete college-level work in religious studies. Catechism will be sent with the first course, which should be retained for all four courses.

Christian Prayer | RELED N024

Students completing these lessons will be given new understandings to help them adapt their own way of prayer so that it transforms their relationship with God. They will be able to relate prayer to living the Christian life; to explain the revelation of prayer in the old and new testaments; to trace the development of prayer in the Christian tradition; to identify was of overcoming obstacles to prayer, and finally to summarize the main truths that are contained in the Our Father.

Profession of Faith | RHLED N021

Explores the deeper meaning behind the words of the Nicene Creed and the Apostle's Creed, which represent the profession of faith of traditional Christianity, as well as how and why these creeds were written. Upon completion, students should be able to explain the historical and dogmatic development of the creed, and to relate the heretical fads of the early Church with similar heresies still in existence today.

The Ten Commandments: Part A (THEO N060) & Part B (THEO N061)

Examines the sources of Christian Morality and the moral responsibilities required by the Ten Commandments and the teachings of the Church.

Catholic Distance University
Advanced Catechist Certificate

This program trains catechist to explain and effectively communicate the essential and fundamental content of Catholic Doctrine: profession of faith, liturgy and sacrament, moral teachings, and the nature of prayer for communion with God and with others.

REQUIRED COURSES:

Introduction to the Catechism | RELED N020 (2 CEUs)
The Profession of Faith | RELED N021 (2 CEUs)
The Celebration of the Christian Mystery | RELED N022 (3 CEUs)
Life in Christ | RELED N023 (3 CEUs)
Christian Prayer | RELED N024 (2 CEUs)
Catechetical Foundations: Part One | RELED N141 (3.5 CEUs)
Catechetical Foundations: Part Two | RELED N144 (3.5 CEUs)
Introduction to the Bible: Part One | SCRPT N001 (2.5 CEUs)
Introduction to the Bible: Part Two | SCRPT N002 (3 CEUs)
Mary: Mother of the Redeemer, Mother of the Church | THEO N135 (2 CEUs)

ONE OF THE FOLLOWING ELECTIVE COURSES:

Wisdom: A Journey with God to God | SCRPT N157 (3.5 CEUs)
Catechetical Foundations: Part Two | RELED N142 (3.5 credits)

Catholic Distance University
Bachelor of Arts in Theology

This program is designed for students who have not yet earned a bachelor's degree, but who have earned a minimum of 88 undergraduate credits (or who have an associate's degree) including general education requirements. This theology will help students expand their knowledge of the Catholic Faith and develop skills needed to demonstrate competency in explaining the essential teachings of the Catholic Church using Sacred Scripture, Sacred Tradition and Magisterial documents, with emphasis on the Catechism of the Catholic Church and the Documents of the Vatican II.

REQUIRED COURSES:

God, Man & the Universe | THEO312 (3 credits)
Jesus Christ: God, Man and Savior | THEO331 (3 credits)
Theology of the Sacraments, Part One | THEO451 (3 credits)
Theology of the Sacraments, Part Two | THEO452 (3 credits)
Catholic Fundamental Moral Theology, Part A | THEO361 (3 credits)
Catholic Fundamental Moral Theology, Part B | THEO362 (3 credits)
Introduction to Sacred Scripture | SCRPT301 (3 credits)
Early & Medieval Church History | CHIST319 (3 credits)
Fundamentals of Catholic Doctrine | THEO302 (3 credits)

NINE CREDITS OF ELECTIVE COURSES:

The Liturgy Today | THEO457 (1 credit)
Survey of Catholic Spirituality | SPIR304 (3 credits)
Divine Revelation: Scripture & Tradition According to the Vatican II | SCRPT302 (1 credits)
An Introduction to the Church According to the Documents of the Vatican II | THEO346 (1 credit)
Catholic Apologetics | THEO442 (3 credits)
Madonna: Mary in the Catholic Tradition | THEO335 (3 credits)
Historical Development of Marriage in the Church | THEO358 (3 credits)
General Catechetics: Methods & Materials | RELED301 (3 credits)

Global University | School of Bible & Theology

1211 South Glenstone Avenue
Springfield, Missouri 65804-0315
(800) 443-1083, (417) 862-9533
www.globaluniversity.edu   *info@globaluniversity.edu*

Global University offers four levels of study: free foundational Bible education (see *Personal Enrichment Studies* sections): fee-based ministerial training (see *Vocational Studies* section) and college-level education offering undergraduate and graduate degrees (see *Graduate Studies* section). They are a fully accredited school whose credits will likely transfer to other schools and they will accept credit transfers.

Accreditation: North Central Association of Colleges and Schools, The Higher Learning Commission; Distance Education Accrediting Commission

AVAILABLE TO PRISONERS

Certificate programs in:
Bible & Theology; Bible Interpreter; Christian Mission; Christian Communicator; and General Studies

Diploma in:
Bible & Theology; and Ministry

Associate of Arts in:
Christian Education; Church Ministries; and Bible & Theology

Bachelor of Arts in:
Bible & Theology; Intercultural Studies; and Christian Education

Tuition Rates:	**$104.80 per credit for undergraduate studies (after 20% prisoner discount)**
	(Most courses will cost $314.40 each.)
Payment Plan:	None
Textbook Fees:	Not included in tuition
Additional Fees:	**Application fee: $50 for undergraduate studies**
Transfer/Exam Options:	96 credits per bachelor degree program; 9 credits per Master of Arts degree program; 21 credits per Master of Divinity program
Time Limits:	6 months; $65 for a 6-month undergraduate/graduate degree programs; $20 for Berean-level courses
Proctor required?	Yes

Global University
Available Courses

BIBLE DIVISION

The Life of Christ in the Synoptic Gospels | BIB1032 (2 credits)

This course is A study of the life of Christ from the viewpoint of the Synoptic Gospels-Mathew, Mark, and Luke. The Life of Christ in the Synoptic Gospels helps the student grasp the chronological progression and the spiritual significance of important events in Christ's life. It also stresses His message and His method, including His parables and miracles. Organized around three themes-the world, the Man, and the message-this study helps students integrate their understanding of His life and work with a clear commitment to live by the principles He taught and the values He demonstrated. They are enabled to preach and teach about Christ with greater understanding and effectiveness.

The Life of Christ in the Synoptic Gospels | BIB1033 (3 credits)

See description of BIB1032 The Life of Christ in the Synoptic Gospels.

The Gospel of John | BIB1042 (2 credits)

This course presents an analytical study of the Gospel of John. Special attention is given to the structure of the Gospel and the progressive development of its main themes of belief in Jesus Christ and unbelief, and the resultant conflict between the two. The life, character, and redemptive ministry of Jesus Christ are examined in their historical context and from a divine perspective as portrayed by john the Evangelist.

The Gospel of John | BIB1043 (3 credits)

See description of BIB1042 The Gospel of John.

Acts | BIB1053 (3 credits)

Acts deals with the continuing ministry of the resurrected Christ in the world through the Holy Spirit. The author analyzes and examines questions concerning the growth of the church, both historical and contemporary. Using the principles of divine guidance illustrated in Acts, the course shows how apparent defeats and setbacks actually became victories and advances for the gospel. The Study Guide suggests practical applications to help the student face similar problems today. (BIB3073 The Book of Acts parallels this course. Students may enroll in either course, but not both.)

Paul's Salvation Letters: Galatians and Romans | BIB1072 (2 credits)

Paul's Salvation Letters: Galatians and Romans gives the student a deep appreciation of the apostle Paul. In the midst of church planting, he explains the gospel, confronts false teachers, distinguishes between law and grace, and show how the gospel is rooted in Old Testament Scripture. His systematic explanation of gospel to the Romans gives the student insight into the major doctrines of sin, salvation, and sanctification. The student also learns how union with Christ and the indwelling Holy Spirit enable him or her to mature spiritually and live victoriously.

Paul's Salvation letters: Galatians and Romans | BIB 1073

See description of BIB1072 Paul's Salvation Letters: Galatians and Romans above.

Paul's Letters to Pastors | BIB 2022 (2 credits)

Paul's letters to Pastors is a basic study of the Epistles of 1 and 2 Timothy and Titus that describe God's strategy for a healthy church. The student will learn about the personal life and duties of a pastor in finding and preparing leaders for service in the church. The student will study the various subgroups within a congregation and how to recognize and deal with error. Finally, the student will consider the essential nature of the gospel of Jesus Christ.

A Study in the Book of Hebrews | BIB2032 (2 credits)

A Study in the Book of Hebrews uses both analytical and topical studies to develop the main themes in the Epistle to the Hebrews. An introductory study of the structure of the book helps the student see more clearly its relationship to the Old Testament and the pattern of its development. Historical information on the background of the book gives an understanding of its warnings and exhortations. Numerous charts and outlines emphasize the main truths of the Epistle and are of great value to those who want to preach or teach from Hebrews.

A Study in the Book of Hebrews | BIB2033 (3 credits)

See description of BIB2032 A Study in the Book of Hebrews above.

Principles of Biblical Interpretation | BIB2042 (2 credits)

This course is divided into four units. The first unit presents fundamental truths that must be accepted before beginning a study of the Bible. The second unit deals with general principles of interpretation that are applicable to any type of literature. Specific rules that apply to special types of literature are overviewed in the third unit. In the final unit, the student is given sample passages of scripture to which he or she will apply the guidelines of interpretation that have been learned.

Principles of Biblical Interpretation | BIB2043 (3 credits)
See description of BIB2042 Principles of Biblical Interpretation.

The Corinthian Letters | BIB2062 (2 credits)
This course covers the study of 1 and 2 Corinthians and gives the student a view of the life in the city of Corinth and the problems these Epistles were written to correct. Since these are in some ways the most self-revealing of Paul's letters, the course provides deeper insight into the apostle's character and ministry. Throughout The Corinthian Letters, the author emphasizes the practical application of Paul's teachings for today. The great doctrines of the Bible in these Epistles apply to contemporary Christian life and ministry. (BIB4053 Corinthians parallels this course. Students may enroll in either course, but not both.)

Prison Epistles | BIB2102 (2 credits)
This course focuses on letters written to believers by Paul the apostle while he was imprisoned in Rome. Students will gain an understanding of the historical and literary backgrounds of each Prison Epistle and be able to distinguish their major theological themes. Paul's teachings will be examined to equip students to apply them to contemporary life and to identify heresy. Students also will learn traditional Pentecostal views on passages that address such issues as election and security of the believer.

Genesis | BIB3012 (2 credits)
How did the world come into existence? What is humanity? Why do we exist? How did evil come into the world? Paul Hoff discusses these and many other difficult questions in the interpretive Study Guide Genesis. He includes spiritual types and practical applications. He traces the thread of God's plan of redemption from its beginning promise in Eden to the formation of God's chosen people through whom this plan would be realized.

Genesis | BIB3013 (3 credits)
See description of BIB3012 Genesis.

Pentateuch | BIB3022 (2 credits)
Pentateuch considers the origin of both the earth and humankind. From Genesis to Deuteronomy, the course helps the student trace the nation of Israel from its beginnings until its entrance into the Promised Land. Included in the course are studies on the Creation theories, the Flood, and the concept of holiness as presented in the book of Leviticus.

Pentateuch | BIB3023 (3 credits)
See description on BIB3022 Pentateuch.

Old Testament Historical Books | BIB3033 (3 credits)
This interpretive survey covers the historical books of the Old Testament-the books of Joshua through Esther. The books deal with the period of about one thousand years from the entrance of the nation of Israel into the Promised Land until its return after the exile. The course especially emphasizes Israel's messianic mission first described in God's covenant with Abraham, father of the Hebrew nation. It examines the background, structure, and content of each book to provide an understanding of the times and their relationship to God's purpose in redeeming the world through Jesus Christ.

Themes from the Major Prophets | BIB3052 (2 credits)
Students gain and understanding of the major prophets Isaiah, Jeremiah, and Ezekiel, who these men were, why God called them to be His messengers, what their messages were, and how to apply these messages.

Themes from the Minor Prophets | BIB3062 (2 credits)
This study covers the contributions of the minor prophets as seen in the light of their times and ours, the doctrines they preached, and the meanings and fulfillment of their prophecies.

The Book of Acts | BIB3073 (3 credits)
Students will learn and be able to defend evidences for the traditional dating and authorship of Acts as well as explain why these are important to the book's historical reliability and spiritual authority. The will gain new appreciation for the work of the Holy Spirit and the foundations from which Pentecostal theology and practice developed.

Hebrew I | BIB4034 (4 credits)
Study of the Semitic language of the ancient Hebrews. The author stresses the fundamentals of Hebrew, paying special attention to the use of these skills in translation. Audio CDs accompany this course.

Hebrew II | BIB4044 (4 credits)
This course continues the study of Hebrew vocabulary, grammar, and syntax. It enables the student to read, understand, and translate the easier passages of narrative prose in the Hebrew Bible. Audio CDs accompany this course.

Corinthians | BIB4053 (3 credits)

An in-depth study of the Corinthian letters, beginning with exegesis, teaching students how to use this method of Bible study to understand the problems faced by first-century Corinthian believers, with solutions that can be applied today.

Daniel & Revelation | BIB4072 (2 credits)

This course covers passages of other Old and New Testament books in addition to Daniel and Revelation when such passages help promote a better understanding of biblical prophecy. The unit titles point out the progression of events during the end time. In the final unit, biblical prophecy moves beyond time into eternity. Christ's second coming is the theme of this course.

Wisdom Literature | BIB4132 (2 credits)

This course introduces the student to the ancient pursuit of wisdom, both in Israel and among her neighbors, and the genre, content, and social context of the wisdom writings. The course examines both Old Testament wisdom books and wisdom writings produced in the period between the Testaments. Particular attention is given to themes that run throughout the wisdom tradition and the ways these themes develop and change in successive wisdom writings.

Undergraduate Greek I | BIB4143 (3 credits)

This course presents a study of Koine Greek grammar and syntax with emphasis on reading and understanding the Greek text of both the New Testament and extra biblical Koine literature. This course requires supervised examinations that include translation of selected New Testament and/or extra biblical passages.

Undergraduate Greek II | BIB4153 (3 credits)

This course presents the ongoing study of Koine Greek that includes recognition and use of Koine Greek grammar and syntax that are necessary to translation and exegesis of the Greek text of the New Testament and extra biblical teachings. This course also requires supervised examinations that include translation of selected New Testament and/or extra biblical passages.

Old Testament Literature: His Story | LIT1212 (2 credits)

This course is the study of beginnings. It shows how the ancient, inspired Hebrew writers expressed in narrative form a record of God's saving deeds from the beginning of God's work with all humankind. Concepts like covenant, priesthood, law, trust, faithfulness, and righteousness come from the Old Testament. Students learn to tell God's story from the record of the Old Testament and be equipped to pass it on to their generation and those to follow.

Old Testament Literature: His Story | LIT1213 (3 credits)

See description of LIT1212. This course is the same, except that a CRA must be completed.

The New Testament as Literature | LIT1312 (2 credits)

This course is intentionally a literary approach to understanding the New Testament, not as a survey course. More attention is given to understanding literature with an overarching goal to prepare students to appreciate and understand the New Testament more fully in its divinely ordained original context.

The New Testament as Literature | LIT1313 (3 credits)

See description of LIT1313. This course is the same, except that a CRA must be completed.

THEOLOGY DIVISION

Pneumatology | THE1012 (2 credits)

The person, works, and ministry of the Holy Spirit are the topics examined in this biblical study. Among the questions discussed from both the Old and New Testaments include: Who is the Holy Spirit? What is the baptism of the Holy Spirit? How do I liv a Spirit-filled life? Students are encouraged to apply these and other biblical teachings to their own teaching and preaching ministries.

Pneumatology | THE1013 (3 credits)

See description of THE1012. This course is the same, except that a CRA must be completed.

Gods & Angels | THE1032 (2 credits)

This independent-study textbook attempts to present a broad biblical view to help better students understanding of nature of God and angels. The course teaches that biblical theology clearly includes all people in God's plan of redemption and the unbeliever will be redeemed when they believe and accept God's plan of salvation.

Gods & Angels | THE1033 (3 credits)

See description of THE1032. This course is the same, except that a CRA must be completed.

Man & Sin | THE1042 (2 credits)

Introductory study of the biblical doctrines of the origin and nature of humankind and of the problem of sin and its effects. Students learn to appreciate these subjects from a biblical, systematic, and, to a lesser extent, historical perspective. The course emphasizes biblical interpretation from the view of evangelical Christians, but this positions is understood against the backdrop of predominant non-Christian worldviews.

Man & Sin | THE1043 (3 credits)
See description of THE1042. This course is the same, except that a CRA must be completed.

Biblical Theology & Prayer | THE1053 (3 credits)
Study of the great prayers of the Bible and the lessons we can learn from prayer ministry today. Stresses the importance and impact of prayer in contemporary life and encourages students to pray regularly and fervently.

The Bible & the Church | THE2012 (2 credits)
A basic study of bibliology and ecclesiology in which the student investigates the nature and authority of the Scriptures. In the second half, the author considers the biblical basis for the church, its Old Testament antecedents, and its beginning, nature, and purpose.

The Bible & the Church | THE2013 (3 credits)
See description of THE2012. This course is the same, except that a CRA must be completed.

Soteriology | THE2022 (2 credits)
The doctrine of salvation – the work of Christ in bringing lost humanity into fellowship with God – is the focus of Soteriology. The study includes the doctrines of repentance, faith, conversion, regeneration, justification, adoption, sanctification, and prayer in the life of a Christian. The twelve lessons stress applying salvation truths personally and sharing them with others.

Soteriology | THE2023 (3 credits)
See description of THE2022. This course is the same, except that a CRA must be completed.

Eschatology | THE2032 (2 credits)
Eschatology is the study in the area of biblical teaching that concerns last things – the final outcome of the present order. The author addresses these teachings and gives a biblical picture of events. The second coming of Christ, the Tribulation, and the nature of predictive prophecy are among the topics discussed. The student also considers and analyzes a number of current eschatological systems.

Eschatology | THE2033
See description of THE2032. This course is the same, except that a CRA must be completed.

Christology | THE2043 (3 credits)
Introduces the student to Old Testament typology as well as to the prophesied concerning Christ's present and future work. Presents certain controversial historical and contemporary views of Jesus and relates them to the Word of God.

Apologetics | THE3013 (3 credits)
Faith and knowing are the two consistent themes of this course. It examines and explains the relationship between them, helping the student persuade others that there is no better way to follow than that of faith in, and obedience to, the God of the Christian Scriptures.

Old Testament Biblical Theology | THE4013 (3 credits)
Traces the development of major Old Testament doctrines. It deals with what the Old Testament teaches about God, creation, humanity, sin, the Messiah, revelation, inspiration, angels, Satan, the various testaments and covenants, judgment, and life after death. It provides a wealth of material for preaching and teaching from the Old Testament.

CHURCH MINISTRIES DIVISION

The Work of the Pastor | MIN1052 (2 credits)
Focuses on the pastor's call to and preparation for Christian ministry. Examines the relationships vital to successful ministry and reviews the pastor's primary responsibilities. Based on the books of 1 and 2 Timothy and Titus, this course enables students to recognize and apply biblical principles to different situations they face in a local congregation. Specific principles treated relate to the selection of church leadership, the discipline of church members, and guidelines for church worship.

The Work & the Pastor | MIN1053 (3 credits)
See description of MIN1052. This course is the same, except that a CRA must be completed.

Ministerial Ethics | MIN1062 (2 credits)

Traces the development and history of the ethical thought of the Israelite leaders and of the Ten Commandments, through the era of John the Baptist, the twentieth-century Holiness Movement. Current moral/ethical issues and the ethical aspects of major Pentecostal doctrines are outlines. Guidelines for proper relationships with the congregation and with fellow ministers are highlighted. It concludes with the practical application of ethics to the minister's home life and ministry.

Ministerial Ethics | MIN1063

See description of MIN1062. This course is the same, except that a CRA must be completed.

Introduction to Pastoral Counseling | MIN1092 (2 credits)

Examines different perspectives from which pastoral counseling may be seen. It emphasizes the necessary steps in preparing to become a pastoral counselor and gives attention to legal and practical ramifications of counseling. It also examines some of the issues faced by the pastoral counselor, seeking to find balance between the clinical and the spiritual, with the Bible as the final authority. It also investigates some of the current approaches to counseling and sets guidelines for counseling settings and sessions.

Introduction to Pastoral Counseling | MIN1102

See description of MIN1092. This course is the same, except that a CRA must be completed.

Great Commission Strategies | MIN1102 (2 credits)

This course establishes a biblical theology of the Great Commission. It presents and in-depth study of evangelism and discipleship principles that are universal in their application. Important elements of Great Commission Strategies include the nature of the gospel message, the biblical definition of discipleship, and the methodology of Jesus. Challenges facing the church in multiple facets are also explored. Finally, the course integrates evangelism and discipleship, presenting then as two sides of a single task.

Human Relations | MIN2012 (2 credits)

Examines the agape concept thoroughly and applies it to every kind of human relationship. Based on a biblical model, this course focuses on practical applications for individuals in all their relationships: with God, with others, and with themselves.

Christian Counseling | MIN2022 (2 credits)

Examines the agape theory approach to counseling. This helps students follow Christ's command to love one another. This course is not a theological approach; rather, it is a means to practical Christian counseling.

Christian Counseling | MIN2023 (3 credits)

See description of MIN2022. This course is the same, except that a CRA must be completed.

Expository Preaching | MIN2032 (2 credits)

Emphasizes the step-by-step process of constructing expository sermons. Includes a brief treatment of basic types of sermons, the analysis and exposition of Scripture passages, the use of multiple sermonic processes in expository preaching, and the building of a teaching program.

The Biblical Role of Women | MIN2052 (2 credits)

Written by the Assemblies of God women – ordained ministers and scholars – this course uses exegetical and hermeneutical approach to study what the Scripture says about women in life, family, and ministry. Study of this course helps students learn how God related to women in the Old Testament and identify roles women played in the first-century church.

Introduction to Church Music | MIN3012 (2 credits)

This course begins with a study of the basic purposes of church music, forming the foundation of biblical philosophy that can guide to its proper use. Much of the course material deals with the function of music in church outreach, as well as the organization of instrumental and choral ensembles. Discusses the challenge of evaluating church, music and considers the responsibilities and concerns of church music leadership.

Introduction to Church Music | MIN3013 (3 credits)

Introduction to Church Music | MIN3013 (3 credits)

Preparing & Preaching Biblical Messages | MIN3042 (2 credits)

The intention of this course is to give a clear understanding of the basic principles of Christian preaching. It stresses the prime place of biblical exposition in authoritatively communicating the Christian message. It deals with practical matters such as the preparation of sermons, sources of materials, construction of sermon components, variety of sermon types, and delivery of sermons.

Preparing & Preaching Bible Messages | MIN3043 (3 credits)

See description of MIN3042. This course is the same, except that a CRA must be completed.

Worship of God | MIN3052 (2 credits)
This course is designed to give a clear understanding of Christian worship as it is directed by the Holy Spirit. It discusses the necessity, value, and results of worship and presents biblical models of worship as guidelines for both individual and corporate worship. It gives practical instruction in leading group worship by following biblical guidelines. It also encourages personal development and growth in devotional worship.

Worship of God | MIN3053 (3 credits)
See description of MIN3052. This course is the same, except that a CRA must be completed. The Church's Educational Task | MON3062 (2 credits)

The Church's Educational Task | MIN3062 (2 credits)
Examines what the Bible has to say about such concepts as teaching, training, and religious instruction. In general, the course discusses the church's role and responsibility to train and instruct its members and families in the Word of God.

The Church's Educational Task | MIN3063 (3 credits)
See description of MIN3062. This course is the same, except that a CRA must be completed.

A Strategy for Church Growth | MIN4033 (2 credits)
Designed to acquaint students with the importance of the Great Commission in relation to world evangelization and church planting. Students will learn to identify the principles that underlie the growth of the church and to make a diagnostic study of a local church. The will also learn to identify reasons for growth or lack of it.

INTERCULTURAL STUDIES DIVISION

Cross-Cultural Communications | COM3103 (3 credits)
Dedicated to helping the student become sent one to present Christ and his Kingdom in an environment other than their own. To do this, the course addresses how communication and culture relate, how to reach people where they are, how differently people think and express ideas across cultures and subcultures, and how the thoughts and expressions of people affect their behavior. American Church History | HIS 3103 (3 credits)

Assemblies of God History, Missions, & Governance | HIS3123 (3 credits)
Study of the historical development of the Assemblies of God, the history of the missions' movement in the Assemblies of God, and the ecclesiastical governance of the Fellowship. Attention is given to the General Council Constitution and Bylaws in relation to credentialed ministers, local churches, and district councils.

Introduction to Assemblies of God Missions | MIN1012 (2 credits)
This is an introductory course in the science of missions. It is a survey of the theology, history, and methods, of Christian missions in general and within the Assemblies of God in particular. Emphasis is placed on recent developments, crucial issues, current trends, and missions as they are carried out through national and local churches.

Introduction to Assemblies of God Missions | MIS1013 (3 credits)
This course is the same as MIS1012, except that a CRA must be completed.

Introduction to Missions | MIS1022 (2 credits)
Two international and biblical themes are treated through this course: those of the redeemed people of God and Christ's strategy of missions. A former missionary writes from his own years of experience.

Introduction to Missions | MIS1023 (3 credits)
This course is the same as MIS1023, except that a CRA must be completed.

The Bible & Missions | MIS2012 (3 credits)
This course is a biblical study about the missionary tasks of the church, with a focus on world evangelism and discipleship. It emphasizes the lost condition of humankind and God's plan for redemption and introduces the student to the spiritual resources available to the church for the task of reaching the world with the gospel.

The Bible & Missions | MIS2013 (3 credits)
This course is the same as MIS2013, except that a CRA must be completed.

Marriage Counseling: A Cross-Cultural Approach | MIS2062 (2 credits)
Attempts to address the void of pastoral training in marriage counseling. It begins with a look at a model of lasting change based on biblical theology and examines key biblical passages to establish a clear understanding of God's purpose for Christian marriage and presents a biblical-practical-motive model of marriage counseling.

Marriage Counseling: A Cross-Cultural Approach (3 credits)

This course is the same as MIS2062, except that a CRA must be completed.

Introduction to Islam | MIS3022 (2 credits)

This course is an introductory study of Islam, including its beliefs, practices, and present status as a world religion. The history of Islam is summarized, and key terms defined. In the final unit, the author contrasts key beliefs of Islam with Christianity and offers practical guidelines for effective Christian witness to Muslims.

Introduction to Islam | MIS3023 (3 credits)

This course is the same as MIS3022, except that a CRA must be completed.

Women in Islam | MIS3042 (2 credits)

This course is designed to introduce the student to the spiritual, private, and public worlds of Muslim women as a prelude to reaching them with the message of life. Investigates the barrier preventing the spread of the gospel among Muslim women. Emphasizing the need to be well acquainted with the world of Muslim women to minister effectively, this course presents biblical models of witness that build trust and community in which the gospel can be heard and received.

Women of Islam | MIS3043 (3 credits)

This course is the same as MIS2042, except that a CRA must be completed.

Christian Ministry in a Muslim Context | MIS4012 (2 credits)

Trains Christians to understand how to relate to the Muslim culture. Students are introduced to the significantly different Islamic culture, worldview, and practices and the adjustments a Christian must make to appreciate, communicate, and relate to Muslims. Objectives include how to contextualize an individual's lifestyle to facilitate relevant ministry and how to prepare a contextualized message for sharing the gospel with Muslims.

Christian Ministry in a Muslim Context | MIS4013 (3 credits)

This course is the same as MIS4012, except that a CRA must be completed.

Approaches to Muslims | MIS4022 (2 credits)

Examines seven approaches to sharing the gospel of Jesus with Muslims. The goal of this course is to enable the student to share the truths of the gospel in a sensitive and meaningful way with the sons of Ishmael.

Approaches to Muslims | MIS4023 (3 credits)

This course is the same as MIS4022, except that a CRA must be completed.

Philosophy of Missions | MIS4053 (3 credits)

This course is composed of individualized special readings and/or research techniques to define a philosophy of missions. Any student desiring to complete this directed reading must submit a proposal to the Dean of the Undergraduate School of Bible and Theology.

Cross-Cultural Counseling | MIS4102 (2 credits)

This course provides a biblical perspective on cross-cultural relationships. It is designed to help the student understand cultural differences and to identify biblically appropriate ways to respond to inequality and difference. The challenge is to become aware of personal cultural programming, to gain knowledge of a variety of minority groups, and to develop skills for effective ministry across cultural barriers to promote the unity of the body of Christ.

Cross-Cultural Counseling | MIS4103 (3 credits)

This course is the same as MIS4102, except that a CRA must be completed.

GENERAL EDUCATION DIVISION

Church Business | BUS2102 (2 credits)

Church Business is an introductory study of many of the Principles, procedures, and techniques used in today's business world as they apply to the local church and its leadership. In this IST, pastors, church business administrators, and other church leaders will find the problem-solving approach to these subjects of practical value. The course first introduces the student to the organizing and staffing functions of the church that enable it to operate effectively. The student then learns practical methods of raising money for the church's expenses. Other emphases include the importance of keeping good records and ideas on better management of the church's money, facilities, and equipment.

How to Speak in Public | COM1012 (2 credits)

This course is designed to increase the Student's awareness of the importance of speech in all areas of life and human cultures. Its main emphasis is on the values of Christian ministry through speech. The units of the course deal successively with speech and the speaker, the speaker and his or her audience, and intercultural aspects of speech.

How to Speak in Public | COM1013 (3 credits)

This course is the same as COM1012, except that a CRA must be completed.

Introduction to Computers | CSC1023 (3 credits)

This course covers the essential knowledge necessary to begin using computers as tools in personal ministry and within the church. It introduces the value of computer technology and shows the relationship between the various components of typical computer system, describing the basic operation of computers and important software programs. Students are encouraged to consider how they might use computers to enhance their effectiveness in ministry, whether in the church or in other areas. Finally, the course discusses the impact of rapidly changing technology on society and culture.

Principles of Teaching | EDU3102 (2 credits)

This course presents a Christian philosophy of education based on the concepts implied in Luke 2:52: "Jesus grew in wisdom and stature, and in favor with God and men." The first unit deals primarily with the characteristics and needs of students at different ages and considers ways Christian teachers can meet these needs. The second unit looks into the fundamental responsibilities of the teacher and how to fulfill them, and the third unit provides practical help in the use of contemporary educational methods. The last unit presents the steps in preparing, presenting, and evaluating lessons.

Principles of Teaching | EDU3103 (3 credits)

This course is the same as EDU3102, except that a CRA must be completed.

Competency and Proficiency in Teaching | EDU3112 (2 credits)

Competency and Proficiency in Teaching provides practical instruction on effective teaching techniques. The course begins by emphasizing the need for transformational teaching-teaching in which students actually live what they have learned. In this course the student will learn what transformational teaching is and how it differs from traditional methods. The student will discover how the brain learns and the strategies needed to help students not only retain information but also use it in their everyday lives. The course takes the student step-by-step through the process of writing learning objectives, course descriptions, lesson plans, and syllabi. Then it helps the student use those tools in the classroom.

Competency and Proficiency in Teaching | EDU3113 (3 credits)

This course is the same as EDU3112, except that a CRA must be completed.

Foundations of Educational Psychology | EDU3212 (2 credits)

This course deals with the application of psychological principles to the design and guidance of educational experiences. It is intended to provide teachers with tools to make the teaching-learning process effective and rewarding. The course examines similarities and differences among learners, various teaching methods, the basics of classroom management, motivation theory, and how to use and construct tests. Wherever possible, applications of psychological principles to Christian education are described.

Foundations of Educational Psychology | EDU3213 (3 credits)

This course is the same as EDU3212, except that a CRA must be completed.

Instructional Media | EDU3613 (3 credits)

This course is designed to help students explore ways to incorporate instructional media into their teaching and preaching ministries. It covers layout and design principles, production of projected and non-projected visuals, use of computers and the internet, and the latest social media tools. The goal is to help students find ways to use all of the tools available to enhance teaching and learning. A collateral writing assignment (CWA) is required in order to complete the course. This course includes a CD with a PowerPoint presentation on writing syllabus.

Christian Adult Education in Cultural Context | EDU4132 (2 credits)

Through this course the student will be enabled to help others become effective teachers of adults. The course is designed to quicken the student to understand and apply the principles of Christian adult education to a program of church leadership training appropriate to his or her cultural context. It combines a study of theory, history, and practical application with a variety of anecdotes to illustrate the concepts. The focus is primarily on education and training for church leadership and ministry, although the principles can apply to other programs. The course also emphasizes the recognition of individual, cultural, environmental, and occupational demands that inform the shaping of a contextualized educational program. It is intended to provide the tools to enable educators to teach Christian adults with excellence.

Christian Adult Education in Cultural Context | EDU4133 (3 credits)

This course is the same as EDU4132, except that a CRA must be completed.

Introductory Writing | ENG1023 (3 credits)

Introductory Writing students practice and acquire the fundamental writing principles: parts of speech; sentence structure and sentence types, from simple to compound-complex; and punctuation. The course project consists of four assigned essays, each being submitted incrementally; thus students receive individual feedback from instructors throughout the course. Additionally, the collateral writing assignment (CWA) teaches vital research skills; it requires students to develop a research question and thesis statement. Next they gather notes from scholarly sources, organize their body of research, and write an accurately documented report.

Writing Better English | ENG1102 (2 credits)

Writing Better English shows how an author's point of view and choice of language determine style and influence the meaning of written communication. The course also covers more advanced grammatical principles and the application of sentence structure to improve written communication depending on one's purpose of narration, description, explanation or persuasion. Special topics include academic outlining and an orientation to research, report, and summary writing.

Writing Better English | ENG1103 (3 credits)

This course is the same as ENG1102, except that a CRA must be completed.

Studies in Physical Science | GSC1103 (3 credits)

In this course, the knowledge of science is built from the fundamental concepts of space, time, energy, and mass. Given these concepts, the basic principles of physics and chemistry are described and applied. The course includes surveys of astronomy and geology, with special emphasis on chemical and physical principles. Attention is also given to the scientific method and to the ways science affects the life of humanity on earth.

Experiments in Physical Science: A Laboratory Manual | GSC1121 (3 credits)

This manual provides hands-on experiments in physical science. The experiments give confirmation to what was learned in the course GSC1103 Studies in Physical Science. The experiments investigate subjects in physics, chemistry, astronomy, meteorology, geology, and ecology. This laboratory manual introduces students to scientific principles as applied to their environments. Access to a computer with a CD drive is required to play the CD that accompanies this course.

Orientation to Global University Learning | GUO1002 (2 credits)

This course assists new students in understanding the process and expectations of studying with Global University in the distance learning setting. It provides an overview of academic policies and guide students in developing skills in library usage, creative and critical thinking, reading and writing, study and note taking, and time management. Students identify personal learning styles to increase effective study practices and learn to make connections between personal views and other worldviews. They are introduced to how Global University courses are designed, become familiar with how to prepare assignments, and learn what to expect from three credit courses.

The Church: From Pentecost to the Reformation | HIS2202 (3 credits)

The Church: From Pentecost to the Reformation is an introductory study of Christianity from its birth to the beginnings of the Reformation. The course provides an introduction to history as a scientific discipline and emphasizes the importance of history in relation to the Christian Faith. The course deals with the apostolic church, the early church fathers, the ecumenical councils, the emergence of medieval theology and church practice, and the beginning of the renaissance in Europe. Course content includes a consideration of the contribution of major Christian theologians, the relationship of the church and state, and the rise of monasticism and missions. The twelve lessons enable the student to apply insights from the past to contemporary situations.

The Church: From Pentecost to the Reformation | HIS2203 (3 credits)

This course is the same as HIS 2202, except that a CRA must be completed

The Church: From the Reformation through the 20th Century | HIS2302

This course provides an introductory study of the history of Christianity from the sixteenth through the twentieth centuries. The student will consider renewal periods, organizational matters, theological issues, and geographic expansion. The student will also examine the lives and contributions of significant Christian preachers, leaders, and theologians, concluding with an assessment of recent trends such as the charismatic renewal and non-Western Missionary outreach. The lessons are structured to enable the student to apply insights learned from the past to contemporary situations.

The Church: From the Reformation through the 20th Century (3 credits)

This course is the same as HIS2302, except that a CRA must be completed

Civilization Past and Present 1 | HIS2503 (3 credits)

This course traces the rise of both Western and Eastern civilizations from their preliterate beginnings. Consideration is given to the development of civilization in China, India, the Greco-Roman world, Eastern Europe, and Russia. The student becomes acquainted with the rise of Islam and the beginnings of civilization in Africa, Europe, and the Americas. This foundation leads to an understanding of states and political systems. As the history of the world civilization is developed, a number of global issues are considered, including migration, religion and government, location and identity, and technological exchange. This course concludes with a review of the scientific revolution and the Enlightenment.

Civilization Past and Present II | HIS2603 (3 credits)

This course continues the study of world civilization from the time of the French political revolution and the Copernican scientific revolution. Consideration is given to the rise of Eastern and Western states and the development of modern nations. The student will witness early attempts to establish democratic governments and the formation of the bipolar world that continued through the twentieth century. Global issues include slavery, gender, world war. And international law. The course concludes with a review of world governance.

Foundations for Health | HSC2012 (2 credits)

Foundations for Health is a study of the principles of health and hygiene. With the theme of illness prevention, it examines nutritional needs, immunizations, environmental hygiene, and other methods of disease control. The course focuses on practical methods for protecting health, such as safety in the home, safe care during pregnancy and childbirth, and water purification. It also stresses how to recognize symptoms of many common ailments and how to treat these problems to prevent further sickness or complications. The course concludes with instructions on basic first aid for emergency situations. The intended audience is students who live and work or plan to live and work in a developing country that has less access to health care.

Foundations for Health | HSC 2013 (3 credits)

This course is the same as HSC2012, except that a CRA must be completed.

The Church's Response to the HIV/Aids Crisis | HSC2022 (2 credits)

This course provides in-depth and accurate information about the greatest human tragedy in the history of the world-the HIV/AIDS epidemic. The course is designed with the hope that, as pastors and Bible school students increase their knowledge of the facts about HIV/AIDS and possible interventions, they will take the lead in developing outreach ministries that will radically change the course of the disease. Moreover, the course shows that compassion extended to those infected or affected by AIDS will radically change the hearts and lives of individuals.

The Church's Response to the HIV/AIDS Crisis | HSC2022 (3 credits)

This course is the same as HSC2021, except that a CRA must be completed.

Guidelines for Leadership | LDR3012 (2 credits)

The selection and development of Christian leaders is one of the major challenges the church faces. This course provides students with a contemporary theology of Christian leadership. It discusses leadership theory, presents servant-leadership as a model for Christian leaders, discusses biblical principles of leadership, and describes the major functions of leadership.

Guidelines for Leadership | LDR3013 (3 credits)

This course is the same as LDR3012, except that a CRA must be completed.

Managing Conflict | LDR4102 (2 credits)

This course is a study of the effective managing of conflict, particularly in the church. It draws from a scriptural foundation with input from contemporary Christian and leadership literature.

Managing Conflict | LDR4103 (3 credits)

This course is the same as LDR4102, except that a CRA must be completed.

Introduction to World Literature | LIT1022 (2 credits)

This course is designed to cultivate the student's understanding and appreciation for literature from traditions around the world and from classical works into the modern era.

Introduction to World Literature | LIT1023 (3 credits)

This course is the same as LIT1022, except that a CRA must be completed.

Business Mathematics | MTH1103 (3 credits)

This course is designed to develop the mathematical skills necessary to maintain banking records, figure percentages as they apply to sales and property, calculate merchandise markups and discounts, simple and compound interest, determine depreciation, and understand business statistics.

College Algebra | MTH2503 (3 credits)

Addresses properties of numbers, absolute values, factoring, functions, linear and nonlinear equations, inequalities, exponentials and logarithms.

Statistical Techniques | MTH3303 (3 credits)

This course is a storehouse of methods for using the techniques of statistics.

Fundamentals of Music | MUS1012 (2 credits)

Study of the value and function of music as the avenue of human expression. This course develops basic concepts of melody, musical style systems, major and minor tonality, rhythm and harmony, along with the system of musical notation.

Introduction to Philosophy | PHL2013 (3 credits)

This introductory study of philosophy provides students with a basic understanding of the nature and aims of philosophy. It acquaints them with some representative philosophical problems and current philosophical issues.

Introduction to Psychology: A Christian Perspective | PSY3013 (3 credits)

This course traces the development of the science of psychology to the beginning of the 21st century. Students learn the basic scientific principles and methodologies of psychology from a Christian perspective.

People & Their Beliefs | REL2012 (2 credits)

Surveys ten of the prominent living religions of the world: Hinduism, Sikhism, Taoism, Confucianism, Buddhism, Shintoism, Judaism, Christianity and Islam. The course concludes with an analysis of the departure of heretical sects from orthodox Christian principles.

People & Their Beliefs | REL2013 (3 credits)

This course is the same as REL2012, except that a CRA must be completed.

Introduction to Sociology | SOC2012 (2 credits)

This course is a general survey course about the nature and scope of sociology, including basic sociological methods and concepts.

Introduction to Sociology | SOC2013 (2 credits)

This course is the same as SOC2012, except that a CRA must be completed

Hobe Sound Bible College

PO Box 1065
Hobe Sound, Florida 33475
(772) 546-5534
www.hsbc.edu www.hobeonline.edu dalbertwalker@hsbc.edu

Hobe Sound Bible College offers a number of basic evangelism and discipleship certificate courses and degrees. They regularly work with prisoners, providing discounts to prisoner-students. They are fully accredited.

Accreditation: Association for Biblical Higher Education, Commission on Accreditation

AVAILABLE TO PRISONERS

Non-credit Certificate programs in:
Bible (I and II); Christian Studies; General Education

Associate of Arts in:
Biblical Studies; Ministry; Counseling; Intercultural Studies; Pre-Professional Studies

Bachelor of Arts in:
General Christian Studies (with concentrations in Education; Counseling; Ministerial Studies, and Intercultural Studies)

Tuition Rates:	**$25 per credit (for prisoners)**
	(Most courses will cost $75 each.)
	Associate's degree: $1,650
	Bachelor's degree: $2,300 (approximately)
	$405 per course for non-prisoners
Payment Plan:	None
Textbook Fees:	Included in tuition (for prisoners only)
Additional Fees:	None for prisoners
Transfer/Exam Options:	All but the final 30 credits can be transferred
Time Limits:	6 months; Free 2-month extension
Proctor required?	Yes

Hobe Sound Bible College
Course Options

The following courses all award three (3) credits each unless marked otherwise.

BIBLE COURSES

Principles of Biblical Interpretations | BI1210
Old Testament Survey | BI1110
New Testament Survey | BI1130
Gospels | BI2220
Gospels of John | BI3220
Acts: The New Testament Church | BI2120
Corinthian Letters | BI2210
Romans | BI4120
Pastoral Epistles | BI3420
Hebrews | BI4210
Daniel & revelation | BI3120
Genesis | BI3630
Pentateuch | BI2330
Old Testament Historical Books | BI2320
Wisdom Literature & Psalms | BI4130
Major Prophets | BI2410
Minor Prophets | BI3520
Music in the Bible | BI4540
Archeology & the Middle East | ANTH1150

BUSINESS

Introduction to Business | GEB1011
Financial Accounting | BS2110
Managerial Accounting | BS2120
Business Communications | GEB2220
Church Business | MN4330
Basic Business Economics | BS2520

CHURCH HISTORY

Church History I: Ancient & Medieval | CH2210
Modern Church History II | CH2220
History of Missions | MI2120
History of the Holiness Movement | CH3230
American Church History | CH3231
History of the Bible | BI4540
History of Revival

History of Methodism

COUNSELING

Introduction to Counseling | PCO3005
Pastoral Counseling | CN3210
Couples & Marriage Counseling | PCO3252
Family Counseling | PCO3253
Addictions Intervention Counseling | PCO4310
Crisis Intervention | MHS4470
Group Counseling | PCO4320
Psychological Measurement | CN4420
Assessment in Counseling | PCO3315
Issues in Counseling | CN3310
Human Growth & Development | MHS2055
Child Development | SS2210
Human Sexuality & Counseling | MHS4470
Adolescent Psychology |
Early Childhood Education
Child Guidance |
Nutrition/Safety |
Child Curriculum |
Family/School/Community |
Introduction to Special Education |
Child Capstone |
Pre-School Program Planning & Administration |
Early Language Arts |
Introduction to Exceptional Child |

EDUCATION

Foundations of Education | ED2110
Fundamentals of Education I | EDG2323
School Administration | EDG2203
Materials & Methods | EDE4269
Educational Psychology | EDP4005
Teaching Bible | ED3610
Audio Visual | ED3630
Student Teaching | ED4610 (6 credits)
Phonics | ED 3430

Teaching Language Arts in Elementary School | EDE3306
Teaching Health & Physical Education | ED3210
Teaching Music in Elementary School | ED3220
Teaching Arithmetic in Elementary School | ED3320
Teaching Reading | EDE3307
Teaching Arts & Crafts in Elementary School | EDE4224
Teaching Social Studies in Elementary School | EDE4430
Teaching Science in Elementary School | EDE4410
Children's Literature | ED3720
Teaching in Secondary School | ED4561
Teaching Math in Secondary School | ED4510
Teaching English in Secondary School | ED4520
Teaching History in Secondary School | ED4530
Teaching Social Studies in Secondary School | ED4550
Teaching Biological Science in Secondary School | ED4560
Teaching Physical Science in Secondary School | ED4570
Technology in the Classroom | ED4200
Sports Injury Management |

ENGLISH

English Composition | ENC1101
Rhetoric & Research | ENC1134
Public Speaking | SPC1320
Introduction to Literature | EN2110
Sacred Classics | EN2162
Journalism | EN4233
Creative Writing | EN3140
American Literature | EN2210
English Literature | EN 3210
Adolescent Literature | EN3730
Introduction to Poetry | EN3120
World Literature | EN4210
Shakespeare |
Homer & the Ancient Poets |
Advanced Grammar & Composition | ENG4064

HISTORY

History of Western Civilization I | EUH1110
History of Western Civilization II | EUH1120
American History I | HI2010
American History II | HI2020
Ancient Egypt | HI3310
Archeology of the Middle East | HI150
Introduction to Archeology | HI2230
History of Judaism | HI3120
Colonial America |
Ancient Rome |
Ancient Greece |

HEALTH SCIENCE

Nutrition | HSC3011
Principles of Physical Fitness | HSC3021
Community Health | HSC3041
Health & Wellness I or III | SS2730
Anatomy & Physiology | BSC3031
Sports Injury Management |

MATHEMATICS

Foundations of College Math | MA1210
Business Math | MAT1220
College Algebra | MAT2120

MINISTERIAL

Homiletics | MN3130
Expository Preaching | MN3120
Hermeneutics | MN4120
Principles of Administration | MN4310
Human Relations | MN2220
Pastoral Ministries | MN3110
Christian Leadership | MN4320
Church Management | MN4332
Church Business | MN4333
Personal Evangelism | MN3420
Child Evangelism | MN3425
Ministerial Internship | MN4610
Youth Ministry Internship | YMN4610 (6 credits)
Children's Ministry Internship | CMN4610 (6 credits)

MISSIONS

Introduction to Missions | MI1110
History of Missions | MI2120
Principles of Missions | MI3210
Church Planting & Growing | MI3220
Perspectives on World Evangelism | MI3420
Cross-Cultural Communications | MI3310
World Religion Systems | MI4220
Introduction to Islam | MI4240
Missions Internship | MI4510

MUSIC

Fundamentals of Music | MUT1011
Music History I | MUH2111
Music History II | MUH2112
Foundations of Music Ministry | MU2350
Music in the Bible | BI1170

PHILOSOPHY

Introduction to Philosophy | PHI2710

SCIENCE

Physical Science Survey I | PSC2330
Physical Science Survey II | PSC234
Biological Science Survey I | BSC2320L
Biological Science Survey II | BSC2321L
Anatomy & Physiology | BSC3031
Physics I | PSC3130
Physics II | PSC3131
Meteorology | MET2331
Chemistry I | SC2340
Chemistry II | SC2341
Astronomy | AST2332
Oceanography | OSC2220
Geology | PSC2333
Marine Biology | BSC3420
Ecology | BSC2312
Botany | BSC2341
Animal Behavior | BSC2311
Wildlife Conservation | BSC2313
Environmental Science | BSC2314
Zoology | BSC2322
Microbiology | BSC2323
Introduction to Origins | BSC3110

Creation Conservation |

SOCIAL SCIENCE

Health & Wellness I or III | SS2730
Human Growth & Development | SS2120
Child Development | SS2210
General Psychology | PSY1015
Introduction to Sociology | SS2110
World Geography | SS1410
Introductory Humanities | SS2130
Survey of Art History | SS2140
Political Science | SC2340
Basic Economics | BS2520
Archeology of the Middle East | HI1150
Cultural Anthropology | SS4540
Conflict Management | SS3410
Introduction to Sociology | SS2110
Social Problems |
American Government |

TESOL (TEACHING ENGLISH TO SPEAKERS OF OTHER LANGUAGES)

Cross-Cultural Communications | MI3310
Methods in TESOL | TSL2340
Linguistics | TSL3240
TESOL Curriculum & Materials | TS3410
TESOL Testing | TS4410
TESOL Theory | TS2330
Practicum in TESOL | TS4320
Language I |
Language II |

THEOLOGY

Foundations of Faith | TH1110
Christian Theology I (Systematic) | TH3310
Christian Theology II (Systematic) | TH3320
Theology of Holiness | TH2210
Hermeneutics | MN4120
Apologetics | TH2410
Christian Beliefs | TH1010
College Studies | Accredited

Moody Bible Institute

MOODY DISTANCE LEARNING

820 North LaSalle Boulevard
Chicago, Illinois 60610
(800) 588-8344, (312) 329-4000
www.moodydlc.edu   mdlc@moody.edu

Moody Bible Institute offers quality religious education in a limited amount of certificate and for-credit college-level courses. Degree programs require online access, but students can earn credits that are transferable to most other colleges.

NOTE: Only 18 credits can be earned by non-degree students. After 18 credits, students are required to enroll as a degree-seeking student. Since degree programs are only available online, most prisoner-students will only be able to earn the 18-credit limit.

Accreditation: North Central Association of Colleges and Schools, The Higher Learning Commission; Association for Biblical Higher Education, Commission on Accreditation

AVAILABLE TO PRISONERS

Variety religious for-credit courses

Tuition Rates:	**$300 per credit**
	(Most courses will cost $900 each.)
Payment Plan:	25% down and 3 to 5 payments
Textbook Fees:	Not included in tuition
Additional Fees:	**Application fee: $35**
	Shipping: $12 per course
Transfer/Exam Options:	Not applicable
Time Limits:	6 months
Proctor required?	No

Moody Bible Institute
Course Listing
The following courses earn three (3) credits each unless marked otherwise.

BIBLE STUDIES

Old Testament Survey | BI 1111 (4 credits)
New Testament Survey | BI 1112 (4 credits)
Elements of Bible Study | BI 1120
John | BI 2211
Acts | BI 2214
Bible Introduction | BI 2230
Hermeneutics/Bible Study Methods | BI 2280
Major Prophets I | BI 3316
Pauline Epistles I | BI 3325
Hebrews | BI 3333
Romans | BI 4410

GENERAL STUDIES

Introduction to Psychology | GSU 2210
Introduction to Philosophy | GSU 2250

MINISTRY STUDIES

Principles of Discipleship | EV 2210
Christian Missions | MS 1103
Christian Worship | MU 2267
Pastoral Ethics | PS 2262
Communication of Biblical Truth | PS 3330

THEOLOGICAL STUDIES

The Church & Its Doctrines | TH 1110
Survey of Bible Doctrine I | TH 2225
Survey of Bible Doctrine II | TH 2226

College Studies | Unaccredited

The following schools provide college-level education. However, none of these schools are accredited by accrediting agencies that are recognized by either the U.S. Department of Education or the Council for Higher Education Accreditation (CHEA).

Basically speaking, you cannot go wrong if you choose a school that is accredited by a recognized accrediting agency. You CAN go wrong by choosing a school that is not accredited. HOWEVER, just because a school is non-accredited doesn't mean that they do not provide quality educational opportunities. It simply means that you'll want to exercise caution and evaluate your education goals.

Some reasons why you may not decide to learn from an unaccredited school:

° If you are interested in pursuing a college degree from an accredited school in the future, the "credits" you earn from an unaccredited school will NOT be accepted by the accredited school.

° The reason why some unaccredited schools are not accredited is because they do not provide the quality education required to meet an accrediting agencies standards. While we try to avoid listing any school that will not provide a quality education, we can't know for certainty why a school does not have accreditation.

Some reasons you may decide to learn from an unaccredited school:

° If you are not planning on pursuing further education, many of these schools provide quality education that will sufficiently help you reach your scholastic goals. This is especially true when it comes to religious-based schools that simply do not seek accreditation for religious reasons.

° Unaccredited schools are typically considerably cheaper that accredited ones. If the school provides the education you are seeking, this may be a more economical way to accomplish your goal.

° Unaccredited schools typically offer a faster path to a degree while providing a lot more flexibility. For prisoners, this can be a valuable asset.

° If you are contemplating potentially furthering your education through accredited schools, you may still be able to use what your newfound knowledge gained from the unaccredited school to take and succeed at credit-by-examination courses from the accredited school at a fraction of what taking the course from that school would have cost.

° For those pursuing religious degrees, religious organizations often do not require the student to have gained their education from an accredited school for purposes of ordination or ministerial licensure. It's the knowledge that is important, not the accreditation.

If you are considering an unaccredited school, it would be wise to first decide what you want out of an education. If you are just learning for the sake of learning or to gain knowledge towards a potential job path not overly specialized in nature that you intend to pursue upon release, an unaccredited school may be more than adequate for you. If you do consider enrolling in one of these schools, you may wish to request materials from them that you can use to evaluate whether they will work for your education purposes.

American Institute of Holistic Theology

2112 11th Avenue South, Suite 520
Birmingham, Alabama 35205
(800) 650-4325
www.aiht.edu   admiss@aiht.edu

The *American Institute of Holistic Theology* offers a variety of religious study courses from an interfaith perspective. They offer a number of degrees (see Graduate Studies section for more degree options) with courses covering the world of religion, parapsychology, metaphysics, and holistic health and ministries. AIHT also offers an ordination as an interfaith minister program.

Accreditation: None

AVAILABLE TO PRISONERS

Ministerial Bachelor's Degree

Ordination

A variety of courses with certificates of completion

Tuition Rates:	**$495 per course**
	$4950 per Ministerial Bachelor's Degree
	$990 Ordination
Payment Plan:	10% down ($495), plus monthly installments
Textbook Fees:	Included in tuition
Additional Fees:	None
Transfer/Exam Options:	None
Time Limits:	5 years
Proctor required?	

Christian Bible College & Seminary

605 Southwest U.S. Highway 40 #336
Blue Springs, Missouri 64014
(800) 543-3720, (816) 228-3720
www.cbcs-degree.com   *cbcs-degree@msn.com*

Christian Bible College & Seminary (CBCS) offers a number of associate and bachelor degree options, as well as Graduate degrees (See *Graduate Studies* section). They have a unique and especially useful payment policy for prisoners (see below).

Accreditation: They claim accreditation by Accrediting Commission International, but this agency is not recognized by the U.S. Department of Education or CHEA.

<u>Available for Prisoners:</u>

Associate of:
Bible Studies I; Christian Ministry I; Theological Studies I; Religious Education; Christian Education; and Pastoral Ministry (for licensed or ordained clergy only)

Bachelor of:
Bible Studies II; Christian Ministry II; Theological Studies II; Religious Education; Biblical Counseling; Christian Education; Pastoral Ministry (for licensed or ordained clergy only)

Tuition:	**$1,700 per associate degree** **$1,900 per bachelor degree** **NOTE: 20% discount if paid in full**
Payment Plans:	**$50 up front for each of the first two textbooks ($100, plus the $50 Application fee = $150 total).** **The remainder of the tuition can be deferred until you are employed outside of prison, which you can then pay back through payments.** **Degree will not be awarded until full payment is made, but they will provide a letter of completion to assist with getting a job.** Otherwise, tuition payments may be made in equal monthly payments for the term of study until paid in full.
Cancellation Policy:	Full refund within two weeks after enrollment; 80%refund within 30 days; 50%within 60 days; 30% within 90 days.
Textbooks:	Not included in tuition, range from $17 to $41
Additional Fees:	**Application fee: $50**
Transfer Credits:	Up to 45 credits per associate degree; up to 30 credits per bachelor's degree CEUs, outside certificates, diplomas, military experience, experiential learning

Christian Bible College & Seminary
Available Courses

BIBLE STUDIES

Intro to the Old Testament | BS201
Intro to New Testament | BS202
Spirit-Led Preaching | BS203
Bible Study (Books of Old Testament) | BS204 – BS222 (Genesis thru Malachi)
Bible Study (Books of New Testament) | BS223 – BS241(Matthew thru Revelation)
Life of Christ | BS342
From God to Us | BS343
Revelation Prophecy Commentaries | BS344
Creative Bible Study Methods | BS347
The Final Countdown | BS 356
Beginners Guideline to Crossing Cultures | BS362
Learn New Testament Greek | BS363
Know What You Believe | BS369
Know Why You Believe | BS370
Interpreting the Pauline Epistles | BS385

BIBLICAL COUNSELING

Creative Bible Study Methods | BS347
Biblical Concepts for Christian Counseling | BC348
Every Father's Business: Christian Home | BC371

CHRISTIAN MINISTRY

Church History in Plain Language | CM345
The Seven Laws of the Learners | CM346
Worship in Spirit and Truth | CM350
How to Prepare Sermons | CM351
Preaching from the Prophets | CM352
Life in the Father's House | CM353
Spiritual Discipleship | CM357
Christian Foundations | CM358
The Doctrines that Divide | CM359
The New Freedom of Forgiveness | CM364
How to Worship Jesus Christ | CM365
Spiritual Leadership | CM366
Compassionate Ministry | CM373
Balancing the Christian Life | CM375
An Introduction to Biblical Hermeneutics | CM376
Revival: God's Plan for His People | CM377
God is Great, God is Good | CM378
Pastor to Pastor | CM379
Powerful Evangelism for the Powerless | CM380
Evangelism Explosion | CM381
The Disciple-Making Pastor | CM383
Basic Christianity | CM386
Why I am a Christian | CM388
The Attributes of God: Volume I (A Journey into the Father's Heart) | CM389

The Pursuit of God | CM390
Christian Mission in the Modern World | CM391

RELIGIOUS EDUCATION

Foundations of Ministry | RE400
The Christian Educator's Handbook on Teaching | RE401
Exploring Christian Education | RE402
The Christian Educator's Handbook on Family Life Education | RE403
The God bearing Life | RE404
Christian Education in the Small Membership Church | RE405
Creative Teaching Methods | RE406
Christian Education Leadership... | RE407
Christian Education Handbook | RE408
Teaching to Change Lives | RE409
Effective Bible Teaching | RE410
Handbook of Youth Ministry | RE411
Childhood Education in the Church I & II | RE412
Christian Education I & II | RE413
Contemporary Approaches to Christian Education | RE414
Theologies of Religious Education | RE415
Joining Children on the Spiritual Journey | RE416
Handbook of Planning Religious Education | RE417
Handbook of Young Adult Religious Education | RE418
The Youth Worker's Guide to Helping Teenagers in Crisis | RE419
Introducing Christian Education – Foundations for the 21st Century | RE420
Religious Education Volunteers | RE421
The Christian Educator's Handbook on Children's Ministry | RE422
The Christian Educator's Handbook on Spiritual Formation | RE423

THEOLOGICAL STUDIES

Science & the Bible | TS349
Spiritual Maturity | TS354
Christian Apologetics | TS355
How to be Born Again | TS360
So What's the Difference | TS361
The Adversary | TS367
Overcoming the Adversary | TS368
The Knowledge of the Holy | TS382
A Basic Guide to Eschatology | TS384
Concise Theology | TH387
Christian Evidences | TS392

Christian Leadership University

3792 Broadway Street
Cheektowaga, New York 14227 - 1123
(800) 466-6961, (716) 681-4896
www.cluonline.com   clu@cluonline.com

Christian Leadership University offers a wide variety of religious degrees and courses. They offer discounted tuition to prisoners, as well as a course "audit" option.

Accreditation: None

AVAILABLE TO PRISONERS

Associate's and *Bachelor's* degrees in the following:

Biblical Studies; Christian Arts; Christian Counseling; Christian Entrepreneurship; Christian Leadership; Divine Healing; Intercession; Ministry; Missions & Evangelism; Prophetic Ministry; Theology; Worship Ministry; Youth Ministry

A varied selection of courses

Tuition Rates:	**$50 per credit** **(Most courses will cost either $150 or $200)** **Audit only: $25 per course**
Payment Plan:	None available
Textbook Fees:	$5 to $50 per course
Additional Fees:	**Shipping fee: $10 per course** **Syllabus: $3 per course**
Transfer/Exam Options:	Up to 90 credits per bachelor degree
Time Limits:	3 to 6 months depending on course
Proctor Required?	No

Christian Leadership University
Available Courses

The following courses are all awarded with 3 credits unless marked otherwise.

ART

Creative Writing | ART220
Creative Writing II | ART221
Creative Writing III | ART341 (2 credits)

BIBLE

Understanding the Bible | BIB100 (1 credit)
Pentateuch | BIB101
History I – United Kingdom | BIB102
History II – Divided Kingdom | BIB103
Poetry Books | BIB104
Major Prophets | BIB105
Life of Christ | BIB106

Acts & Epistles | BIB107
Epistles & Revelations | BIB108
Principles of the Kingdom | BIB310
Isaiah | BIB322
Gospel of John | BIB375
Romans | BIB377
Ephesians & Colossians | BIB380
Pastoral Epistles | BIB382
Bible Research Methods | BIB390

BUSINESS

Fulfill Your Final Destiny | BUS102
Money by Design | BUS105
Business is Ministry | BUS201
Kingdom Entrepreneurs | BUS209
Start & Succeed in Your Own Business | BUS301
Anatomy of a Business Plan | BUS302
Recordkeeping for the Small Business | BUS310
Ethical MLM | BUS312
New Trends in Management | BUS320

COUNSELING

Counseled by God | COU202
Cornerstones of Communication | COU203
Prayers That Heal the Heart | COU301 (4 credits)
Parenting by Grace | COU305

EVANGELISM

Personal Evangelism | EVA210
Miracle Evangelism | EVA215 (1 credit)
Cultural Studies | EVA315

GOVERNMENT

The Constitution & Constitutional Law | GOV 202 (4 credits)

HEALING

Take Charge of Your Health | HEA102
Authority of the Believer | HEA201
God's Provision for Healing | HEA315

INTERCESSION

Introduction to Intercession | INT201

Prophetic Intercession | INT301

LEARNING

Gifted to Succeed | LEA103
Creating Your Mission Statement | LEA205
Developing the Leader Within You | LEA303
Apprenticed to Leadership | LEA 310
Visionary Leadership | LEA321

MINISTRY

Five Fold Ministry Gifts | MIN210 (2 credits)
Building Dynamic Teams | MIN211 (1 credit)
Experiencing God in the Small Group | MIN310
Your Theology & Youth Ministry | MIN325
Becoming a Youth Specialist | MIN330 (4 credits)
Anointed Preaching | MIN415

PROPHECY

Releasing Spiritual Gifts | PRO201
Introduction to the Prophetic | PRO301
Communion with God | REN103
Father Heart of God | REN105
Naturally Supernatural | REN204
Increasing the Anointing | REN206
Healing Anointing | REN207
War in the Spirit | REN208
Wisdom Through Dream Interpretation | REN310

SCIENCE

Catastrophism & Evidences for the Flood | SCI301 (4 credits)

THEOLOGY

The Basics of Christianity | THE101
Foundational Studies About Christian Faith | THE103
Foundational Experiences | THE120
The Law & the Spirit | THE121
God's Release of Women | THE207

The Church Triumphant | THE208
Names & Attributes of God | THE301
(4 credits)
Discovering the Blood Covenant |
THE302
Feasts of Jehovah | THE303
The Bible Speaks to Contemporary
Issues | THE310
House Church | THE331

Leadershiop – Servanthood in the
Church | THE332

WORSHIP

Believer's Worship I | WOR101
Theology of Worship | WOR201
Theology of Music | WOR202
Church: Place of Worship Assessment
for Safety & Security | WOR 202
Prayers that Heal the Heart | COU201

Freedom Bible College & Seminary

1270 Highway 412 W, Suite K
Siloam Springs, Arkansas 72761
(800) 494-7497, (479) 373-6420
www.freedombiblecollege.org   *admissions@freedomministries.com*

Freedom Bible College & Seminary (FBCS) offers a number of religious certificate and Christian-based degree options. They also offer a certificate course for the visually impaired.

Accreditation: FBCS is unaccredited by choice. Regarding accreditation, they state, "Since we believe in the separation of church and state, we have not applied for accreditation to the U.S. Department of Education or any state or federal agency."

Available for Prisoners:

Variety of for-credit courses

Certificates in:
Biblical Studies; Christian Workers; Pastoral; Teaching

Associate degrees in:
Christian Liberal Studies; Ministry

Bachelor degrees in:
Liberal Christian Studies; Biblical Studies; Christian Education; Church History; Evangelism; Ministry (with Emphasis options in Church Leadership; Church Management; Prison & Hospital Chaplaincy; Rudiments of Abuse Counseling; Rudiments of Family & Emotional Counseling; Rudiments of General Counseling; Youth Ministry); Theology; and World Missions

	$326 per course; $250 per noncredit course
	Christian Education Teaching Certificate: $675
Tuition:	**Certificate Programs: $2,321**
	Associate Degree: $2,677
	Bachelor Degree: $3,326
	(10% discount with full payment upon enrollment)
Payment Plan:	Associate/Bachelor degree program: $100 per month, plus books
Textbooks:	Not included in tuition. Ranges on average from $20 to $80 each.
Cancellation Policy:	Full refund within two weeks of enrollment, less processing fee; 70% refund up to 30 days after enrollment; 40% refund up to 60 days after enrollment; None thereafter.
Transfer credit:	Credit for life experience is evaluated for degree programs through the Master Degree level. Military service personnel will receive three (3) credits per year of honorable service, up to 12 credits.

Freedom Bible College & Seminary
Certificate Programs

These certificate programs are designed to meet the needs of students who are interested in a specific professional specialization, and which may be helpful toward parole board consideration and reentry planning.

These are groups of courses that provide a concentration in a particular study area, without the need to take the general education courses of degree programs. They are more economical options than a full degree track.

Once completed, each of the following certificate earns college credit as marked, which can be used towards future learning.

BIBLICAL STUDIES CERTIFICATE

For students who want to expand their knowledge of the Bible and improve their effectiveness in ministry, this program helps students to gain a practical knowledge of Biblical interpretation, doctrine, evangelism, and discipleship.

Course	credits
Prayer Essentials | BSC-1053	3
Old Testament Survey | BSC-2013	3
New Testament Survey | BSC-1023	3
Basic Christian Theology | BSC-1033	3
Chronology of Christ | BIB-30123	3
The Works of Jesus | BIB-30133	3
Sermon on the Mount | BIB-30143	3
Origins of the Bible | BIB-3003	3
Biblical Geography | BIB-1023	3
The Effective Minister of Education | CER-2023	3
Total credits	**30**
Total cost	**$2,321 plus fees**

CHRISTIAN WORKER'S CERTIFICATE

This is designed for potential missionaries, pastors, and lay people who desire a greater knowledge of the Bible and a better understanding of the professional challenges of ministry.

Course	credits
Prayer Essentials | BSC-1053	3
Old Testament Survey | BSC-2013	3
New Testament Survey | BSC-1023	3
Basic Christian Theology | BSC-1033	3

Holding on to your God Given Dreams | CC-33193	3
The Effective Minister of Education | CER-2023	3
Understanding World Religions | ED-15424	3
Christian Social Ministry | MIN-3213	3
Church Administration I | TH-3133	3
God's Truth | TH-3153TP	3
Total credits	30
Total cost	$2,321 plus fees

PASTORAL CERTIFICATE

Designed for lay ministers working in a variety of contexts including parishes and secular professions to develop the theological and spiritual grounding necessary to become wiser and more effective ministers and leaders.

Course	credits
Handling & Avoiding Church Debt | ADM-8013	3
Prayer Essentials | BSC-1053	3
Old Testament Survey | BSC-2013	3
New Testament Survey | BSC-1023	3
Basic Christian Theology | BSC-1033	3
Biblical Christian Counseling I | CC-3343	3
Christian Healing for Victims of Abuse | CC-33203	3
Christian Counseling for Troubled Teens | CER-2043	3
Stress Among Christian Workers | MIN-3283	3
The Effective Minister of Education | CER-2023	3
Total credits	30
Total cost	$2,321 plus fees

TEACHING CERTIFICATE

This course is an essential guide for all who teach the Bible or are considering teaching Bible Study classes at any level. It combines the wisdom of experience with insights gleaned from interviews with leading master level Bible teachers. It is filled with advice that will help the bible teachers at all level of experience. (See course descriptions below.)

Course	credits
The Bible Teacher | ED-1013	3
Beginning Biblical College Classroom Instruction | ED-1023	3
Advance College Classroom Instruction | ED-1033	3
Elements of Biblical Teaching | ED-3403	3

	Total credits	12
	Total cost	$675 plus fees

Freedom Bible College & Seminary
Teaching Certificate Course Descriptions

The Bible Teacher | ED-1013

This course is an essential guide for all who teach the Bible or are considering teaching Bible study classes at any level. It combines the wisdom of experience with insights gleaned from interviews with leading master level bible teachers. It is filled with advice that will help bible teachers at all levels of experience.

Beginning Biblical College Classroom Instruction | ED-1023

This class is full of experience-tested, research-based advice for graduate students and new teaching faculty. It provides a range of innovative and traditional strategies that work well without requiring extensive preparation or long grading sessions. What do you put on the syllabus? How do you balance lectures with group assignments or discussions? What grading system is fair and most efficient for your class? How do you get a dialogue going when the students won't participate? How do you prevent cheating, and what do you do when it occurs?

Advanced College Classroom Instruction | ED-1033

This course presents an insightful look at what makes a great teacher, based on a study of three-dozen teachers from a cross section of disciples and from medical school faculties to under graduate departments. The text concludes that the quality of teaching is measured not by whether students pass exams but whether they retain the material to such an extent that it influences their thoughts and actions.

Elements of Biblical Teaching | ED-3403

This course is a classic guide for both the minister of education and Sunday School teachers which both inspires and gives a solid base of understanding.

Freedom Bible College & Seminary
Available Courses

ASSOCIATE OF MINISTRY COURSES

This degree is designed to provide you with a working knowledge of the Bible, an intimate relationship with Christ, and a compassion for relationships with people. The heart of Ministry is reconciling people to God through a balanced life of serving both God and people.

Introduction to Missions | MIN-1013
Introduction to Youth Ministry | MIN-1023
The Ministry of Education | MIN-1033
Applied Systemic Theology | MIN-1043
Introduction to Evangelism | MIN-1053
Church Growth | MIN-1063
Expository Preaching | MIN-1073
Family Ministry | MIN-1083
Introduction to Eschatology | MIN-1093
Ministry of Bereavement | MIN-10103
The Pastor Under Fire | MIN-10113
Foundations of Christian Education | MIN-10123
Taking Special Care to Develop your Ministry | MIN-10133

BACHELOR OF BIBLICAL STUDIES COURSES

Designed to prepare students to serve as a ministry leader, staff member, lay leader or volunteer by possessing the skills to think Biblically about the issues facing Christian ministry and bringing value to your ministry team. Other opportunities include serving as a missionary, associate pastor or in other ministry capacities. Students will also be prepared to pursue a master of Divinity or other Seminary Degree Options.

Biblical Geography | BIB-1023
Origins of the Bible | BIB-3003
The Identity of Christ | BIB-3013
New Testament Background | BIB-3023
Hermeneutics | BIB-3043
Understanding the Bible | BIB-3073
Christology | BIB-3083
Introduction to the Hebrew Prophets | BIB-3093

Skills of Bible Reading | BIB-30103
Chronology of Christ I | BIB-30123
The Works of Jesus | BIB-30133
Sermon on the Mount | BIB-30143
Typology | BIB-30153
Revelation & Reality | BIB-30163
The Pentateuch | BIB-30173
Historical Books | BIB- 30183
The Four Gospels | BIB-30193
Introduction to Biblical Hermeneutics | BSC-1083
Heaven | BSC-1093

BACHELOR OF MINISTRY – CHURCH MANAGEMENT EMPHASIS COURSES

Students will gain a foundation of knowledge relating to the health and growth of the church and church organizations. Key management proficiencies are integrated with Christian studies to help gain an understanding of biblical teachings on motivation, ethics, and teamwork for effective spiritual leadership.

Personal Christian Leadership | CBM-3603
Principles of Christian Leadership | CBM-2613
Governing the Church | CBM-3623
Stress Among Christian Workers | CBM-3633
Ministering in Prospective | CBM-3643
Keeping Church Records | CBM-3653
Financial Management for Pastors & Church Leaders | CBM-3663
Ministerial Liabilities | CBM-3673
Leadership Development for the Local Church | CBM-3683
Biblical Principles of Finance | CBM-3693
Church Administration I | CBM-36102
Church Administration II | 36113
Handling & Avoiding Church Debt | CBM-36123

BACHELOR OF MINISTRY – RUDIMENTS OF ABUSE COUNSELING COURSES

Provides students with the education to provide guidance to people who are confronted with crisis, especially in the areas of abuse, whether chemical, physical or emotional. Students learn to offer support and resolution guidance through a spiritual context.

Introduction to Christian Psychology | CC-3303
Developing Christian Counseling Strategy | CC-3313
Conflict Management in the Church | CC-3323
Intrinsic Healing I | CC-3333
Basic Biblical Counseling | CC-3363
Christian Counseling I | CC-33153
Christian Counseling II | CC-33163
Overcoming the Old Nature | CC-33173
Christian Healing for Victims of Abuse | CC-33203
Recovering from the Past through Prayer | CC-33213
Healing Adult Victims of Childhood Sexual Abuse | CC-53114
Intrinsic Healing II | CC-7214
God's Healing for Damaged Emotions | CC-7224

BACHELOR OF MINISTRY – RUDIMENTS OF ABUSE COUNSELING COURSES

Provides students with the education to provide guidance to families and individuals in the areas of emotions, effective communication, and problem-solving. Students learn to offer support and resolution guidance through a spiritual context.

Introduction to Christian Psychology | CC-3303
Developing Christian Counseling Strategy | CC-3313
Christian Counseling for the Depressed | CC-3383
Christian Counseling for Self-Esteem | CC-3383
Counseling Theology | CC-3393
Short Term Christian Marriage Counseling | CC-33183
The Christian Response to Suicide | CC-33143
Basic Biblical Counseling | CC-3363
Christian Counseling I | CC-33153
Christian Counseling II | CC-33163
Recovering from the Past through Prayer | CC-33213
God's Healing for Damaged Emotions | CC-7224
Christian Counseling for Troubled Teens | CER-2043

Theology of Counseling Families | TH-31133

BACHELOR OF MINISTRY – RUDIMENTS OF GENERAL COUNSELING COURSES

Provides students with the education to provide guidance to people who are confronted with crisis or uncertainties. Students learn to offer support and resolution guidance through a spiritual context.

Introduction to Christian Psychology | CC-3303
Developing Christian Counseling Strategy | CC-3313
Conflict Management in the Church | CC-3323
Christian Counseling I | CC-33153
Christian Counseling II | CC-33163
Basic Christian Counseling I | CC-3323
Basic Christian Counseling II | CC-3343
Short Term Christian Counseling | CC-33103
Song of Solomon | CC-33223
Equipping Saints to Counsel | CC-33263
Practical Foundations | CC-33313
Case Studies in Christian Counseling | CC-5384

CERTIFIED CHRISTIAN CHAPLAINCY PROGRAM

Fundamentals of Correctional Chaplaincy II | CER-2073
Fundamentals of Correctional Chaplaincy III | CER-2083
Fundamentals of Correctional Chaplaincy IV | CER-2093
The Chaplain as Caregiver I: Ministry to Those in Hospitals & Nursing Homes | CER-20103
The Chaplain as Spiritual Caregiver II: Where id God When People Hurt? | CER-20113
Christian Social Ministry | MIN-3213

BACHELOR OF MINISTRY – CHURCH LEADERSHIP EMPHASIS COURSES

An emphasis in leadership designed to teach students to prepare for the challenges of pastoral and organizational leadership. The course will contribute to competencies that transform their understanding and practice of leadership, and thus promote the growth of healthy churches.

Church Team Leadership I | CL-4103
Ethics in Church Team Leadership I | CL-4113
Ethics in Church Team Leadership II | CL-4123
Leadership in African American Churches | CL-4143
Effective Church Leadership I | CL-4153
Leadership for Small Churches | CL-4163
Effective Church Leadership II | CL-4173
Mobilization of Church Leaders | CL-4183
Using Students in Church Leadership | CL-4193
Life-Changing Discipleships | CL-41103
The Community-Effective Church I | CL-41113
The Under Shephard | CL-41123
The Community-Effective Church II | CL-41133

BACHELOR OF MINISTRY-PRISON & HOSPITAL CHAPLAINCY EMPHASIS |

For students who desire to minister to and provide spiritual support to those who are unable to attend organized religious services because they are hospitalized or incarcerated.

Introduction to Christian Psychology | CC-3303
Christian Counseling for Self-Esteem | CC-3383
Christian Counseling Ethics | CC-5324
Crisis Counseling for Christians | CC-5344
Intrinsic Healing II, Spiritual Growth | CC-7214
Healing for Adult Victims of Childhood Sexual Abuse | CC-53114
Fundamentals of Correctional Chaplaincy I | CER-2063
Fundamentals of Correctional Chaplaincy II | CER-2073
Fundamentals of Correctional Chaplaincy III | CER-2083
Fundamentals of Correctional Chaplaincy IV | CER-2093

The Chaplain as Caregiver I: Ministry to Those in Hospitals and Nursing Homes | CER-20103
The Chaplin as Spiritual Caregiver II | CER-20113
Social Ministry | MIN-3213

TEACHING CERTIFICATE COURSES

The Bible Teacher | ED-1013
Beginning Biblical College Classroom Instruction | ED-1023
Advanced College Classroom Instruction | ED-1033

BACHELOR OF CHRISTIAN EDUCATION COURSES

Designed to prepare students to teach in a Christian School classroom. Courses emphasize philosophy and methodology of Christian education and introduces students to strategies for planning, preparing instructional materials and instruction to teach effectively in a Christian School.

Elements of Biblical Teaching | ED-3403
Ministry of Teaching-Learning to Teach | ED-3413
Church Administration 1 | ED-3423
Doctrines of Christian Faith 1 | ED-3433
History of Evangelism | ED-3443
Social Ministry | ED-3463
Effective Bible Teaching | ED-3473
Christian Education Administration | ED-3483
Adult Education for Christian Educators | ED-3493
History of Christian Education | ED-34103
God's Healing for Damaged Emotions | ED-34133
Freedom from Bondage | ED-34143
Heartfelt Preaching | MIN-5214

BACHELOR OF EVANGELISM COURSES

Equips students to impact the world for Christ through a deeper understanding of theology and evangelism history. Areas of study include inductive Bible study, church history, methods of evangelism, and theology.

Introduction to Evangelism | EV-4203

Introduction to Missions | EV-4213
History of Evangelism I | EV-4223
The Heart of Evangelism | EV-4233
Essential Skills of Preaching | EV-4253
Eschatology III | EV-4263
Exegesis – New Testament | EV-4273
Revival | EV-42103
Effective Witness | EV-42183
Advanced Evangelism I | EV-42193
Advanced Evangelism II | EV-42203
Evangelizing the Unchurched | EV-42213
History of Evangelism I | EV-42223

BACHELOR OF CHURCH HISTORY COURSES

The purpose of this degree is to acquaint the student with a broad perspective of Church History.

Church History I | HIS-4003
Church History II | HIS-4013
Documents of the Early Church I | HIS-4023
Documents of the Early Church II | HIS-4033
Study of the Ecumenical Councils | HIS-4043
Christianity – Rise to Dominance | HIS-4053
History of North American Christianity I | HIS-4063
History of North American Christianity II | HIS-4073
Non-Canonical Writings of the Early Church | HIS-4083
Backgrounds of Christianity I | HIS-4093
Backgrounds of Christianity II | HIS-40103
Christ to Constantine | HIS-40113
Denominations in the United States | HIS-40123

BACHELOR OF MINISTRY COURSES

Provides students with a biblical and practical foundation for ministry through courses in ministry leadership, congregational dynamics, and ministry practice. This degree program is ideal for you if you are actively involved in the local church and other Christian organizations.

Basics of Christian Education | MIN-3203

Christian Social Ministry | MIN-3213
Church Administration I | MIN-3223
History of Evangelism | MIN-3233
Christian Leadership Development | MIN-3243
Conquering the Christian Battlefield of the Mind | MIN-3253
Essentials of Preaching | MIN-3263
Intrinsic Health I – Nouthetic Counseling | MIN-3273
Stress Among Christian Workers | MIN-3283
Applied Homiletics | MIN-3293
Ethics in Christian Leadership | MIN-32103
Ministry for the Baby Boomers | MIN-32133
Christian Worship | MIN-32143
Cults I | MIN-32153
Cults II | MIN-32163

BACHELOR OF WORLD MISSIONS COURSES

Designed to help students communicate biblical truths effectively to people from cultural backgrounds different from their own. Students will become more aware and sensitive to cultural differences effectively reducing the likelihood of causing offense.

Biblical Missions | MIN-3523
Christian Missions | MIN-3543
Ministry in Missions I | MIN-3553
Theological Education – Worldwide | MIS-3563
Christian Anthropology I | MIS-3573
Christian Anthropology II | MIS-3583
Mission Theology | MIS-3593
Biographical Studies in Missions I | MIS-35103
Biographical Studies in Missions II | MIS-35113

BACHELOR OF THEOLOGY COURSES

Designed to challenge students to think theologically about the foundation of their faith and contemporary challenges facing the church. Prepares students to pursue careers in professional ministry or as a lay minister, including working as a non-preaching associate pastor or with church organizations.

History of Evangelism II | TH-3103
Doctrines of Christian Faith I | TH-3113
Christology | TH-3114
The Identity of Christ | TH-3123
Church Administration I | TH-3133
Hermeneutics | TH-3143
God's Truth | TH-3153
Old Testament Theology III | TH-3163
Systemic Theology I | TH-3173
Systemic Theology II | TH-3183
Christ and the Old Testament | TH-3193
Old Testament Healing | TH-31103
Theology of Counseling Families | TH-31133
Christology | TH-31143

BACHELOR OF MINISTRY – YOUTH MINISTRY EMPHASIS COURSES

Trains students for effective youth ministry within the adolescent subculture by introducing students to developmental characteristics, cultural and sociological influences, ministry philosophies and strategies, teaching methodologies, and program planning approaches that are essential to youth ministry.

Introduction to Youth Ministry | YOU-3703
Youth Group vs. Youth Ministry | YOU-3713
Effective Biblical Counseling | YOU-3723
Forming Spiritual Children | YOU-3733
Helping Youth to Make the Right Choices | YOU-3743
Screening Church Youth Workers | YOU-3753
Junior High Ministry | YOU-3763
Christian Counseling for Adolescents at War I | YOU-3773
Christian Counseling for Adolescents at War II | YOU-3783
Advanced Youth Ministry I | YOU-37113
Advanced Youth Ministry II | YOU-3

International Christian College & Seminary

PO Box 530212
Debary, Florida 32753-0212
(877) 391-3741
www.iccscampus.org   *info@iccscampus.org*

International Christian College & Seminary (ICCS) is an evangelical school with a focus on equipping students to spread the Gospel of Christ throughout the world and enrich the lives of others through continued community outreach and humanitarian efforts. They offer a number of degree opportunities as well as an Ordination program.

Accreditation: ICCS claims accreditation by the International Theological Accountability Association, but this agency is not recognized by the U.S. Department of Education or CHEA.

Available to Prisoners:

Numerous college & seminary degree options (see below)

Tuition:	**$1,425 per degree for prisoners**
	$9,497 per degree for non-prisoners
	Ordination Program: $795
Payment Plans:	Plans starting at $12.95 per month
Additional Fees:	**Application fee: $25**
Transfer Credits:	Case-by-case basis
Proctor Required?	No

International Christian College & Seminary
Degree Options

ASSOCIATE'S DEGREES

Bible Studies
Church Administration I
Christian Ministry I
Christian Counseling I
Theological Studies I
Religious Education
Christian Education
Pastoral Ministry
Church Education
Pastoral Ministry
Church Growth
Church Planting
Christian Leadership
Contemporary Christian Music
Pulpit Ministry
Crusade Evangelism Ministry

BACHELOR'S DEGREES

(Prerequisite: Associate Degree)

Biblical Studies II
Church Administration II
Christian Ministry II
Christian Counseling II
Theological Studies II
Religious Education
Biblical Counseling
Christian Education
Pastoral Ministry
Church Growth
Church Planting
Christian Leadership
Contemporary Christian Ministry
Pulpy Ministry
Crusade Evangelism Ministry

International Christian College & Seminary
Ordination Program

As an ordained minister, you will have the authority to establish a church; preach the Gospel around the world; start a Christian school; perform marriages; officiate funerals; become a missionary; an evangelist; a pastor; and/or begin your ministry.

ICCS states that their Ordination is only available to select applicants who either 1) graduate from ICCS with a degree, or 2) have a "direct and personal call from the Lord Himself." If the latter, they require students to make a "calling statement," a detailed accounting of the calling and on outline of the ministry for which the Lord has called you.

Takes approximately two years to complete and requires the passing of eight courses and two exams.

Omega Bible Institute & Seminary

PO Box 70, Swartz, LA 71281-00709
(318) 343-9800
www.omega.edu

Omega Bible Institute & Seminary offers a number of religion and spirituality-based certificate and degree options. You cannot take individual courses, but must instead enroll in and entire certificate or degree program. They also offer graduate degree programs (See Graduate Studies section.)

Accreditation: Transworld Accrediting Commission, which is not recognized by the U.S. Department of Education or CHEA

Available for Prisoners:

Certificate Programs in: *Marriage Counseling, Apologetics – Defense of Christian Faith, Alternative Religions & Cults, Foreign Missions, Christian Leadership, Spiritual Warfare, Life of Christ, Christian Counseling, Homiletics – The Art & Science of Preaching, and Christian Education*

Diploma in Biblical Studies

Associate of Arts in: *Biblical Studies*

Bachelor Degrees in: *Biblical Studies, Christian Counseling, Christian Education, Ministry and Theology*

Tuition:	**Certificate Programs:** $50 per credit ($600 per program.) **Diploma in Biblical Studies:** $35 per credit ($1,050 per diploma program) **Associate Degree Program:** $39 per credit ($2,340 per program) **Bachelor Degree Program:** $39 per credit ($4,680 per program) 10% discount if paid a full year in advance of study.
Payment Plans:	Equal payments can be made for the months of the course of study.
Cancellation Policy:	Non-refundable
Textbooks:	Included in tuition
Additional Fees:	Application Fee: NONE Postage must be paid by the student
Transfer Credits:	Experience credits of up to 6 hours for each year of services are available for preachers who have served some years in full-time ministry.

Rock of Ages Ministries | College of Biblical Studies

PO Box 4419
Dalton, GA 30719
(706) 459-3233
www.roapm.com *roacobs@gmail.com*

The Rock of Ages College of Biblical Studies and Theological Seminary has been offering religious education since 1996. In 2009, they expanded their options to include studies for doctorate degrees. They now offer three levels of study, including a variety of undergraduate and graduate degree options. The first year of studies does not require students to have a high school diploma or GED. If you are looking for a graduate degree course, see our Graduate Studies section.

They are of Baptist faith and adhere strictly to the Authorized King James Version.

Entrance/placement evaluation is required for students who have earned a degree from another institution.

Accreditation: NOT Accredited

Available for Prisoners:
Certificate of Biblical Studies (does not require HS diploma or GED)
Associate of Biblical Studies
Bachelor Degrees in the following disciplines: Bible Studies, Religious Education, or Theology

Tuition:	$15 per credit (32 credits per year = $480). 50% off for spouses of students. 10% discount if paid a full year in advance of study.
Payment Plans:	Payment must be made in full for each year of study.
Cancellation Policy:	Non-refundable
Textbooks:	Included in tuition
Additional Fees:	Application Fee: $30 Postage must be paid by the student Reinstatement Fee (if transferring from another institution): $30
Transfer Credits:	Credits are available for previous completions of the same subjects offered by Rock of Ages. Experience credits of up to 6 hours for each year of services are available for preachers who have served at least five years in full-time ministry. Evaluation fee of $100 is required.

St. Petersburg Seminary & Yeshiva

3190 Gulf to Bay Boulevard
Clearwater, Florida 33759
(727) 399-0276
www.sptseminary.edu   admin@sptseminary.edu

St. Petersburg Seminary & Yeshiva offers Christian and Messianic Judaic certificate and degree courses. NOTE: They are NOT accredited.

Accreditation: NONE

AVAILABLE TO PRISONERS

Certificate of Religious Studies

Bachelor of Arts in Religious Studies

Bachelor of Arts in Judaic Studies

Master of Arts in Judaic Studies

Master of Divinity

Master of Rabbinic Studies

Tuition Rates:	**$605 per certificate course**
	$665 per undergraduate course
	$785 per graduate course
	$ 965 per doctorate course
Payment Plan:	Monthly payment plans available
Textbook Fees:	Not included in tuition
Additional Fees:	**Application fee: $50**
Transfer/Exam Options:	Not applicable
Time Limits:	16 weeks, extensions offered
Proctor required?	No

St. Petersburg Seminary & Yeshiva
Available Courses

Biblical Hermeneutics (principles of biblical interpretation) | BIE 4/6823
The Epistles from a Jewish Perspective | BNT 3/5503
Hebrews: Its Distinctive Jewish Message | BNT 3/5513
The Gospels Against Their Jewish Background | BNT 3/5523
New Testament Survey | BNT 3/5603
The Pentateuch/Torah | BOT 4/6543
Former Prophets (Joshua through II Kings) | BOT 4/6713
Major Prophets | BOT 4/6833
Minor Prophets | BOT 4/6843
Biblical/Messianic Apologetics | BST 3/5833
Church History I and II | *CCH 3/5613 and CCH 3/5623
Jewish Practices in a Messianic Context: The Jewish Experience | CJS 3/5103
Introduction to Rabbinic Literature | *CJS 3/5343
The Basics of Synagogue Worship | CJS 3/5453
Tanakh: The Beginnings of the Jewish People (= CJS 3/5313 Jewish Roots and Foundations of Scripture, I) | CJS 3/5513
The Apostolic Writings: The Early Messianic Jewish Community | CJS 3/5523
Jewish Roots and Foundations of Scripture, II | CJS | 3/5323
Messianic Jewish Spirituality: Contributions of Jewish Spiritual Experience to Devotional Life | CJS 3/5753
The History of Judaism and the Jewish People | CJS 3/5773
The Talmud | CJS 3/5783
Sabbath and Weekday Services: Jewish Worship and Liturgy | CJS 7756
Zionism and the State of Israel | CJS 3/5853
Messianic Jewish Theology | CJS 3/5873
Congregational Growth and Development | CWM 3/5913

Vision International University

1115 D Street
Ramona, California 92065
(800) 984-7466   (760) 789-4700
www.vision.edu   info@vision.edu

Vision International University (VIU) offers a variety of certificate, diploma and degree options in religious studies. They are accustomed to working with prisoners.

Accreditation: Regarding accreditation, VIU states, "Vision International University is striving to gain recognition internationally, to provide the highest quality education possible. In 2007, we received full approval to operate from the Bureau of Private post-secondary Education (BPPE), which establishes educational and operational standards to serve as regulations for instructional quality, fiscal and administrative responsibility, and institutional stability for private post-secondary schools."

AVAILABLE TO PRISONERS

Certificate Course options

Advanced Diploma

Catechetical Diploma

Associate of Arts in Ministry

Bachelor of Arts in Christian Studies

Bachelor of Ministry

Tuition Rates:	**$100 per credit**
	Certificate course: $1,575
	Associate's degree program: $3,150
	Bachelor's degree program: $6,300
	$75 per credit for undergraduate studies
Payment Plan:	Down payment of $375 and $175 per month
Textbook Fees:	Not included in tuition; $50 to $75 per course for undergraduate studies
Additional Fees:	**Application fee: $20 (for prisoners; $50 non-prisoners)**
	Registration fee: $75
	Graduation fee: $125 for bachelor's degree
Cancellation Policy:	Full refund within 10 days of enrollment, less administration fee
Transfer/Exam Options:	Case-by-case basis
Time Limits:	None
Proctor Required?	No

Vision International University
Certificate Course Programs

Vision's Certificate programs constitute half of the courses necessary to achieve their Associate of Arts (A.A) in Ministry degree. Therefore, it is exactly half the price of this degree. If you intend to pursue an A.A. from them, you will need to take certificate Option One.

OPTION ONE

Course	Credits
English Composition	GE 103	3
Hermeneutics: Introduction to Bible Study	BI 100	3
Dynamic Christian Foundations	RS 101	3
New Testament Survey	BI 102	3
Spiritual Formation: Journey to Wholeness	RS 109	3
Christian Life	RS 102	3
Christian Character Development	RS 219	3
The Gospel of John	BI 201	3
Sociology of Marriage and Family Life	CC 101	3
Introduction to Management	GE 112	3
Total credits	**30**
Total cost	**$1,575 plus fees**

OPTION TWO

Course	Credits
The Book of Mathew	BI 109	3
New Testament Prophetic Ministry	CI 101	3
Purpose & Destiny of the Church	CI 102	3
Practicum: Servanthood	PC 100	3
Introduction to Communication: Evangelism Perspectives	RS 103	3
Principles of Power & Prayer	RS 106	3
Spiritual Warfare	RS 110	3
Kingdom Living	RS 111	3
Fruit of the Spirit	RS 121	3
New Creation	RS 122	3
Total credits	**30**
Total cost	**$1,575 plus fees**

Vision International University
Available Courses

Each of the following courses earns three (3) credits. However, they cannot be taken separately. They must be taken in a Certificate or Degree program. The program these courses apply to is noted next to each course (C = Certificate program; A = Associate degree program; B = Bachelor degree program)

THEOLOGY/RELIGIOUS STUDIES

Course	Program
Hermeneutics: Introduction to Bible Study | BI 100	C, A
Old Testament Survey | BI 101	A
New Testament Survey | BI 102	C, A
The Pentateuch | BI 103	A
The Book of Mathew | BI 109	C, A
The Gospel of John | BI 201	C, A
The Book of Acts | BI 202	A
Pauline Epistles: Romans | BI 203	A
Interpreting Signs & Symbols | BI 205	A
Corinthians | BI 220	A
Ephesians | BI 223	A
Major & Minor Prophets of the Old Testament | BI 302	A
Advanced Hermeneutics | BI 400	B
Authenticity & Authority of the Bible | BI 405	B

HUMAN BEHAVIOR

Course	Program
Sociology of Marriage & Family Life | CC 101	C, A
Introduction to Psychology: Christian Counseling Perspectives | CC 201	A
Marriage & Family II: Parenting on Purpose from a Christian Perspective | CC 218	A
Self-Concept: Studies in Biblical Inner Hearing | CC 301	A
Assessment in Christian Counseling | CC 303	A
Developing a Counseling Ministry | CC 304	A
Human Sexuality | CC 305	A
Crisis Counseling: A Christian Perspective | CC 402	B
Counseling the Dysfunctional Family | CC 404	B
Counseling & Family Violence | CC 406	B
Human Development | CC 415	B

PRACTICUM

Course	Program
Practicum: Servanthood | PC 100	C, A
Practicum: Stewards in God's House | PC 200	A
Practicum: Practical Ministry | PC 300	A

PROPHETIC

Course	Program
New Testament Prophetic Ministry | CI 101	C, A
Purpose & Destiny of the Church | CI 102	C
The Day of Saints | CI 201	A
The Gift of the Spirit | CI 202	A
Prophetic Protocols & Ministry Principle | CI 301	A

GENERAL EDUCATION

English Composition | GE 103	A
Introduction to Management | GE 112	C, A
Financial Integrity & Stewardship | GE 220	A

EDUCATION

Dynamics of Teaching | ED 101	A
Philosophy of Christian Education | ED 401	B
Classroom Management | ED 432	B

LEADERSHIP

Conflict Management & Resolution | OL 440	B
Ethics in Leadership | OL 460	B

BUSINESS

Biblical Foundations of Business | CI 420	B
Biblical Management from a Biblical Worldview | CI 422	B
Principles of Transportation in the Workplace | CI 424	B
Communications & Spirituality in the Workplace | CI 426	B
Marketing for Business & Ministry | CI 428	B

RELIGIOUS STUDIES

Dynamic Christian Foundations | RS 101	C, A
Christian Life | RS 102	C, A
Introduction to Communication: Evangelism Perspectives | RS 103	C, A
Theology of Worship | RS 105	A
Principles & Power of Prayer | RS 106	C, A

Spiritual Formation: Journey to Wholeness | RS 109	C, A
Spiritual Warfare | RS 110	C, A
Kingdom Living | RS 111	C, A
Fruit of the Spirit | RS 121	C, A
New Creation Living | RS 122	C, A
History of Civilization I: Church History Perspectives | RS 200	A
Authority of the Believer | RS 201	A
Cults & the Occult | RS 202	A
Soteriology | RS 203	A
Healing Covenant | RS 205	A
Faith Dynamics | RS 209	A
The Blood Covenant | RS 210	A
Speech & Communication: Homiletics | RS 212	A
Introduction to Charismatic Theology | RS 217	A
Christian Character Development | RS 219	A
Angelology | RS 248	A
Demonology | RS 249	A
Faith Dynamics II: Mountain Movers | RS 250	A
Pastoral Ministry | RS 301	A
Introduction to Leadership | RS 304	A
Introduction to World Missions | RS 305	A
Finding God's Will | RS 307	A
Principles of Philosophy of Church Growth | RS 314	A
Royal Priesthood | RS 349	A
Dynamics of Revival | RS 350	A
Women's Roles in the 21st Century	B

Church: A Christian Perspective | RS 403		RS 442	
History of Women in Ministry | RS 405	B	Advanced Christian Worldview Studies | RS 444	B
Women of Excellence in Home & Ministry | RS 407	B	Women's Effective Ministries | RS 445	B
Systemic Theology | RS 419	B	Disciplining the Ex-Offender | RS 447	B
Christian Theology | RS 435	B	Ministry in Correctional Institutions | RS 448	B
Ecclesiology | RS 436	B	Ministry in Juvenile Correctional Settings | RS 449	B
Christology | RS 437	B	Worship Leading | RS 451	B
Eschatology | RS 438	B	Quest for God | RS452	B
Pneumatology (The Holy Spirit) | RS 439	B	Biblical Theology of Worship | RS 453	B
The Challenge of Leadership | RS 440	B	Theology of Music: A Christian Perspective | RS 454	B
Strategic Church Administration | RS 441	B	Future Worship | RS 462	B
Church Growth & Development |	B		

Wesleyan Church
EDUCATION & CLERGY DEVELOPMENT

PO Box 50434
Indianapolis, Indiana 46250
(317) 774-3912
www.wesleyan.org   education@wesleyan.org

The *Wesleyan Church Education and Clergy Development* provides ministerial training to prisoners. They are designed to equip approved students with ministerial preparation who, due to circumstances, are unable to follow the preferred path (four years of undergraduate training) to becoming a minister. They require prospective students to be 28 years of age or older, unless with special permission from the district board of ministerial development.

Accreditation: None

Available for Prisoners:

A number of courses designed for ministerial training

Tuition:	$195 per course
Payment Plans:	None available
Textbooks:	Not included in tuition
Cancellation Policy:	Full refund within two week of registration; 50% refund within 90 days or registration.
Transfer credits:	Students may submit college/seminary transcripts for possible course credit.
	Credit-by-Portfolio option is available. Request an application.
Time Limits:	201 days, with possible 60-day extension at the discretion of the instructor
Proctor Required?	No

Wesleyan Church
Available Courses

Old Testament Introduction | Course 03

This course will enable the student to gain a clearer understanding of the Old Testament as a whole, as well as its parts. You will gain factual knowledge that you can pass along to others, so that all can better know the God of the Old Testament and share his good news with others. The student will gain knowledge about the structure, content, history and geography of the Old Testament.

New Testament Introduction | Course 04

This course will enable the student to gain a clearer understanding of the New Testament as a whole, as well as its parts. You will gain factual knowledge that you can pass along to others, so that all can better know the Jesus of the New Testament and share his good news with others. The student will gain knowledge about structure, content, history and geography of the Old Testament.

Introduction to Theology | Course 05

The field of Christian doctrine will be studied in this course. It is a study in basic beliefs and why we believe as we do. The course surveys the general field of theology. Later courses will go more into details on various doctrines.

Old Testament Covenant and Law-Pentateuch | Course 11

A special study of the first five books of the Bibl. It will give a student insight into God's dealings with primitive people, and show how these books are definitive for the rest of Scripture. Emphasis will be placed on the books of Genesis and Exodus.

Testament Poetry | Course 12

The purpose of this course is to study the books of Job, Psalms, Proverbs, Ecclesiastes, and the Canticles (Song of Solomon); to note the comparable literature of the surrounding cultures; to study the form and function of Hebrew poetry; to develop skills in the interpretation and utilization of poetic literature; to study the characteristics of wisdom literature, noting its contribution on the Old Testament.

Old Testament Prophets | Course 13

The student will be given insight into the message of two of the biblical prophets, Jeremiah and Amos. The study will provide guidelines in approaching the prophets both for personal study and for preaching.

Methods of Bible Study | Course 14

This course is an introduction to hermetics, the art of biblical interpretation, through the study of the principles of induction, the de elopement of skills, and the use of various reference tools which are applied to specific books of the Bible.

New Testament Church-Acts | Course 15

The study of the New Testament Church as found in the book of Acts. It relates to the redemptive ministry of Christ and His selection and training of disciples who were to become the apostles of the New Testament Church. The study will include the divine origin, purpose and plan for the church, the relationship of Christ, the Holy Spirit and the apostles in the church's growth, the composition and character of the church, the reasons for its success in a pagan world, and its relevance to the Christian church today.

Romans | Course 16

The purpose of this course is to give the student a clear understanding of the message of the Epistle to the Romans, as well as to provide experience in techniques of the inductive study of the New Testament books.

The Life of Christ | Course 18

This course will give the student a clear understanding of the message and life of Jesus Christ as well as provide experience in the discipline of engaging in practical theology leading to ongoing Bible study and lesson preparation.

Sociology | Course 21

This course provides an introduction to the basic principles and issues in the field of sociology-the study of human interaction. It will help students see the need for critical thinking about the social world, gain familiarity with basic sociological concepts, confront social change and plan for the future, and clarify their own values so they can appreciate how Christian faith is transmitted through human interaction.

Psychology | Course 22

This course is a study of the subject matter and methods of psychology as a science. The student will study human development and the physiological basis for behavior, personality, learning, sensation, perception, motivation, emotion, adjustment for mental health, abnormal behavior, and social psychology. Such a study will provide the basis for a better understanding of one's own behavior and that of others.

Christian Education | Course 23

The course is designed to provide an introduction to the educational ministry of the church. Special attention will be given to four broad topics: biblical, theological, and philosophical foundations; aspects of the teaching/learning process; the needs, abilities, and special considerations of teaching various groups of people; and the organization and design of the Christian education ministries of the local church.

General Church History | Course 25

This is a general survey of the Christian church from the New Testament to the present. The course deals with important persons, movements, and doctrinal developments. The study helps to understand the Christian Church in America and in the world today. It will help the student to understand the beliefs and the denominational expressions on modern Christianity.

Spiritual Formation | Course 26

This course is designed for the personal and spiritual growth of the minister, exploring the foundations of the spiritual life, as well as methodologies and resources for developing Christian spirituality in the lives of others in cooperation with the work of the Holy Spirit. This course should enhance the student's ability to see the relationship between spirituality and ministry, and to discover principles for the enrichment of their own spirituality and to help Christian disciples grow in their relationships with Christ.

Evangelism/Missions | Course 27

This course provides an overview of the outreach mission of the church both locally and globally, stressing biblical/theological foundations and contemporary practical issues.

Evangelism/Church Health | Course 28

The purpose of this course is to ignite a passion to share Christ's love with others. Through a series of Units, the student will actively engage in personal evangelism work, under the leading of the Holy Spirit. There will also be guided purposeful reflection on evangelism techniques and methodologies, church health and church planting.

Global and Intercultural Ministries | Course 29

This course provides an overview of the history, theology and practice of cross-cultural mission theory, including local church involvement in cross-cultural ministry.

Philosophy | Course 31

This course is designed to provide a framework to assist in the philosophy of making an ethical decision, and will provide insight into various thought processes and how segments of society arrive at their values. The course should help solidify what you believe and help you to express and defend your beliefs.

Advanced Theology | Course 32

This course gives you a chance to build on what you learn in Introduction to Theology, to dig a bit deeper into theology in Wesleyan perspective. This course should help you better grasp our theology intellectually, better know the GOD our theology describes, and better serve Him and His people. Objectives of the class are: 1. To gain a deeper understanding of God, the world he made, humanity, sin, and redemption. 2. To expand your skills of thinking about and applying theological truth. 3. To equip you to proclaim and live the truth.

Introduction to Homiletics | Course 33

This course provides a combination of theory and practice in the preparation and delivery of sermons. Analysis of sample sermons will occur with suggestions for finding and filing sermon resource material.

Pastoral Ministries | Course 34

This course will provide a survey of the tasks which accompany pastoral ministry in a local church setting. Emphasis will be placed on pastors as persons as well as the competencies needed for contemporary ministry.

Wesley History and Discipline | Course 35

This course will be an introduction to the Discipline and a survey of the historical development of The Wesleyan Church. The student will be introduced to the doctrines, standards, practices and procedures that govern the church and the theological, historical, and sociological factors which have shaped the development of the denomination.

Worship | Course 36

The course will include a study of the biblical, theological, historical, and contemporary elements of Christian worship such as Scripture, music, sacraments, liturgy, prayer, and the ministry of the Word. Students will have a chance to evaluate their own personal worship. This course should enhance the student's ability to plan, participate in, and lead acts of public worship.

Church Leadership/Management | Course 38

This course will introduce the student to basic principles of church leadership, church management, and parliamentary law. Through reading, observation and reflection, the student will be prepared to provide leadership in a local church.

Doctrine of Holiness | Course 42

This course gives you a chance better understand the Wesleyan doctrine of holiness. The course gives you a better intellectual understanding of this doctrine, for your own benefit and for the people among whom you minister. Hopefully, as you gain in understanding, God will work in you, drawing you closer to him and equipping you for more powerful service.

Expository Preaching | Course 43

This course provides tools and techniques for biblically based preaching and practice in preparing various types of expository sermons from select scripture passages.

Pastoral Counseling | Course 44

The objective of this study will be to acquaint the student with various approaches to pastoral problems and the duties of a pastor in assisting persons in need. The student should gain an understanding of ministry appropriate to proper pastoral care. It will include the work of the pastor from both a psychological and theological frame of reference.

Supervised Ministry | Course 55 (51,52,53)

This is a one-year curriculum directed by the DBMD and Education and Clergy Development. This may be taken concurrently with the correspondence courses, or after their completion. It is not necessarily a part of the two years of service requirement, but it may involve one of those years as an intensive period of supervision. Students must register for the course and complete the full curriculum in order to receive credit.

GRADUATE STUDIES

Graduate Studies | General

Graduate School Recommendations

Schools, and what you want out of them, vary in so many ways the it is impossible to make an overall recommendation. Therefore, we leave that up to the accrediting agencies. However, one common interest among all prisoners is the quality of the communication between the outside world and your cell.

When researching schools. We send requests to each one as if we are prisoners. We want to know how they respond to your requests, which is a great guide in determining how well the school will work with you should you decide to enroll.

The following schools are recommended as institutions who stood out from the rest in how well they communicated, how accommodating they were to our requests for information, how comprehensive their sent information was, and how willing they were to work with prisoners. Starred "*" listings are exceptional in meeting the above criteria, proving that they have a good understanding of the unique challenges that prisoners face.

---

* Adams State University
Global University (Religious)

Colleges | Graduate (Accredited) | What They Offer

SCHOOL	CERTIFICATE OF COMPLETION	FOR COLLEGE CREDIT	MASTER'S DOCTORATE DEGREE	NONE
ADAMS STATE UNIVERSITY		✓	✓	
AMERICAN GRADUATE UNIVERSITY	✓	✓	✓	
CALIFORNIA COAST UNIVERSITY	✓	✓	✓	
SOUTHWEST UNIVERSITY	✓	✓	✓	
UNIVERSITY OF IDAHO				✓
UNIVERSITY OF NORTHERN IOWA				✓
UNIVERSITY OF SOUTH DAKOTA				✓

Colleges | Graduate (Accredited) | 2018 Tuition Rates

(cheapest to priciest)

SCHOOL	TUITION RATES (PER CREDIT)	AVERAGE COURSE COST
UNIVERSITY OF IDAHO	$200.00	$600.00
CALIFORNIA COAST UNIVERSITY (MASTERS COURSES)	$230.00	$690.00
GLOBAL UNIVERSITY (MASTERS COURSES)	$236.00	$789.00
SOUTHWEST UNIVERSITY	$275.00	$825.00
CALIFORNIA COAST UNIVERSITY (DOCTORATE COURSES)	$290.00	$870.00
GLOBAL UNIVERSITY (DOCTORATE COURSES)	$290.00	$870.00
AMERICAN GRADUATE UNIVERSITY	$325.00	$975.00
ADAMS STATE UNIVERSITY	$350.00	$1,050.00
CATHOLIC DISTANCE UNIVERSITY	$450.00	$1,350.00

SCHOOL LISTING LAYOUT

CONTACT INFORMATION

This is the school's address and where you can go for more information on that school. There is always more information than we can provide concerning each school. We encourage you to contact every school you are interested in.

DESCRIPTION

Key details are provided about each school so that you are aware of information of note that may impact you as a prisoner-student.

ACCREDITATION

The following schools are all accredited by a variety of agencies, which are marked under each entry. As you've learned, accreditation is vital in determining the quality of a learning institution. But not all accrediting agencies are created equal. Therefore, you should exercise caution when selecting a school. (For a complete discussion on this topic, see section on *Accreditation* early in this book.)

AVAILABLE TO PRISONERS

This will keep you informed of what you can earn from this school, such as diplomas, degrees, and certificates. School offerings change regularly, which is why we update this book annually.

TUITION

This is the fee the school charges for courses, course credits, grade levels, and other programs.

PAYMENT PLANS

Many schools offer payment plans to make programs more affordable during study. Even if a payment plan is not listed, a school may be willing to work with you to develop an affordable plan that will work with your circumstances.

CREDIT TRANSFER/EXAM OPTIONS

If you have previously earned credits from another school, this section will tell you if this school may allow you to transfer those credits in. It will also let you know if they have credit-by-exam options.

TIME LIMITS

Schools generally place limits on how long you have to take a course. If you cannot complete your course in time, many schools offer extensions, often for a fee.

PROCTOR REQUIRED?

This area will tell you if a school require their examinations to be proctored (supervised by an impartial person.)

CANCELLATION POLICY

If you are unhappy with the school, or you determine that the courses you purchased are just not going to work for you, this section will tell you about the schools course refund policy.

AVAILABLE COURSES

This section provides information on the courses offered by the school, including courses available, descriptions, and prerequisites.

Adams State University

OFFICE OF EXTENDED STUDIES

208 Edgemont Boulevard, Suite 3000
Alamosa, Colorado 81101
(800) 548-6679, (719) 587-7671
www.exstudies.adams.edu   exstudies@adams.edu

Adams State University offers several levels of educational opportunities for prisoners, including a graduate degree. (See *College Studies* section for undergraduate course options.)

Accreditation: North Central Association of Colleges and Schools | The Higher Learning Commission

AVAILABLE TO PRISONERS

Master of Business Administration *(36 credit hour program)*

Tuition Rates:	$350 per credit
	(Most courses will cost $1,050 each.)
Payment Plan:	None
Textbook Fees:	Not included in tuition
Additional Fees:	None for prisoners
Transfer/Exam Options:	6 credits per graduate degree. Up to 30 the CLEP credits.
Time Limit:	12 months
Proctor Required?	Yes

Adams State University
MBA Curricula

BUS 500 - Leadership Skills for Managers (3 Credits)
This course teaches practical skills required for effective management at all levels of an organization, and is designed to increase a learner's understanding of key concepts and procedural guidelines related to organizational management, human resource, and leadership. The purpose is to be equipped to deal effectively with managerial challenges dealing with people.

BUS 505 - Creating Consumer Value (3 Credits)
This course presents learners with a comprehensive approach to creating consumer value. This includes marketing and brand management in for-profit firms as well as identifying and meeting consumer needs in non-profit and governmental organizations. Topics include segmentation and targeting of consumers; the positioning levers of product, price, promotion, and distribution; and brand management.

ECON 505 - Managerial Economics (3 Credits)

This course demonstrates how economics theory is applied to national and international managerial decision-making. The course covers topics such as demand analysis, production and cost functions, market structure, managerial understanding of public policy, and international trade finance topics.

BUS 510 - Global Business Perspectives (3 Credits)

This course deals with management of organizations that operate, directly and indirectly, in more than one country. While the major focus will be the multi- national corporation, management of smaller firms, which only export, will also be considered. The primary emphasis will be on the special management problems, which are unique to multi-national operations.

BUS 520 - Managerial Accounting (3 Credits)

This course provides a review of financial reporting standards and statements and analysis of those financial statements. Managerial accounting principles will be explored as well as budgeting, cost allocation, accumulation, cost behavior, and relevant costs; revenues are approached from a manager's perspective.

BUS 525 - Financial Analysis (3 Credits)

Students will embark on studying basic financial principles and enhance that with understanding various valuation concepts and methods. Emphasis is also placed on capital budgeting and long term financing as well as working capital management. The course will blend time-tested finance principles and the latest advancements with the practical perspective of the financial manager.

BUS 530 - Organizational Behavior (3 Credits)

This course deals with human behavior in a variety of organizations. Conceptual frameworks, case discussions, and skill-oriented activities are applied to each topic. Topics include communications, motivation, group dynamics, leadership, power, the influence of technology, and organizational design and development. Class sessions and assignments are intended to help participants acquire the skills that managers need to improve organizational relationships and performance.

BUS 540 - Strategy (3 Credits)

In this course, learners examine tools and techniques for competitive analysis, strategic planning, and strategy implementation. Learners gain knowledge of the tools and concepts needed to develop a business strategy including macro environmental scanning, industry and competitive analysis, value chain analysis, SWOT analysis, identification of critical success factors and driving forces, and development of strategic alternatives and recommendations.

BUS 545 - Leading Entrepreneurial Organizations (3 Credits)

Successful organizations emphasize learning to sustain their competitive advantage. This course will study entrepreneurship and intrapreneurship. Areas of emphasis include uncovering the methodologies and characteristics that foster innovation and achieve meaningful change in business that lead to the creation and implementation of profitable business opportunities.

BUS 550 - Technology and Innovation (3 Credits)

This course adopts the perspective of a general manager - an individual charged with diagnosing complex situations and resolving them in ways that enhance organizational performance. The course emphasizes how general management decisions contribute to the creation and appropriation of economic value through innovation.

BUS 555 - Leading for Results (3 Credits)

This course focuses on how leaders mobilize others within their organization to get extraordinary things done. You will analyze what characteristics you need to develop to achieve your own professional goals and reflect on ways you can develop your competencies as a leader.

BUS 560 - Leadership Capstone (3 Credits)

This capstone course integrates knowledge gained in the previous graduate business courses. It centers on the theme that organizations achieve sustained success when their managers have astute, timely, strategic game plans, and they implement these plans with proficiency. This class incorporates the "big picture" and cuts across the whole spectrum of business and leadership.

American Graduate University

733 North Dodsworth Avenue
Covina, California 91724
(877) 351-9060, (626) 966-4576
www.agu.edu *info@agu.edu*

American Graduate University offers a variety of Master's degrees and certificates in several management disciplines. This is one of the few schools where prisoners can earn an accredited MBA and other quality business-oriented graduate degrees.
AGU has one of the best refund policies of any of the listed schools. They are accustomed to working with prisoner-students.

Accreditation: Distance Education Accrediting Commission

AVAILABLE TO PRISONERS

Master's Degree Programs:

Master of: *Acquisition Management; Contract Management; Leadership and Management; Project Management; Supply Chain Management*

Master of Business Administration *(MBA)* in: *General Management; Acquisition and Contract Management; Project Management; Supply Chain Management*

Master's Certificate Programs in: *Acquisition and Contracting; Project/Program Management; Supply Chain Management; Financial Management and Pricing; Management*

Tuition Rates:	**$325 per credit (Most courses will cost $975 each.)** **$11,700 per Master's degree** **$15,600 per MBA** **$5,850 per certificate program** (requires successful completion of 6 courses.)
Payment Plan:	Three equal monthly payments
Textbook Fees:	Not included in tuition
Additional Fees:	**Application fee: $50; Course Challenge fee: $325; Re-Enrollment fee: $325**
Credit Transfer Options	Up to 6 credits per Master's program; 9 per MBA program. Test-Out/Course Challenge option available for up to two courses (6 credits): $325 per course.
Time Limit:	5 months; one free 30-day extension, $100 for second extension
Proctor Required?	Yes
Cancellation Policy:	Full refund up to 10 days after registration, after 10 days and up to 7½ months student is refunded all but $195. No refunds beyond 7½ months.

American Graduate University
Available Courses

The following courses earn three (3) credits each.

Certificate programs require six (6) courses; Master's degree courses require twelve (12) courses; MBA's require sixteen (16) courses.

ACQUISITION AND CONTRACTING COURSES

This program provides knowledge of the acquisition and procurement processes and how this interrelates with standard business management processes.

Federal Government Contracting
Government Contract Law
Pricing and Financial Management
Business Development and Proposal Preparation
Contract Management and Administration
Negotiation -- Principles and Practices
Source Selection and Contract Award

PROJECT/PROGRAM MANAGEMENT COURSES

This program provides knowledge of the organizational, human, business and technical processes for successfully managing projects and programs.

Program Management
Managing Projects
Mastering IT Project Management
Technical Program Management
Building and Managing Project Teams
Contracting and Procurement for Project Managers
Risk Analysis and Management
Earned Value Management Systems
Project Quality Management
Negotiation for Project Managers

SUPPLY CHAIN MANAGEMENT COURSES

This program provides knowledge of the practices and procedures of the supply chain management function with a focus on supply chain management approaches.

Supply Management
Logistics Management in Government Acquisition
Supply Chain Management
Global Logistics Management
Price and Cost Analysis
Applications in Supply Chain Management

LEADERSHIP COURSES

Leading Creativity and Innovation
Cross-Cultural Management

Critical Thinking and Decision Analysis
Organizational Theory, Design and Change
Strategic Leadership
Advanced Approaches in Leadership

GENERAL MANAGEMENT COURSES

This program provides a structured, yet varied knowledge of the practice and principles of business management.

Essentials of Management
Marketing
Communication and Ethics
Law and Contracts
International Business Operations
Operations Management
Leadership - Principles and Practices
Business Research Methods
Management Accounting and Control
Organizational Behavior and Human Resources
Financial Management
Management Economics
Strategy and Business Policy
Management Information Systems

California Coast University

925 North Spurgeon Street
Santa Ana, California 92701
(888) 228-8648, (714) 547-9625
www.calcoast.edu   *admissions@calcoast.edu*

California Coast University provides quality distance education that is widely respected by employers, including the U.S. government, the military, and civilian corporations. They have extensive paper-based course offerings at a reasonable tuition rate, including various MBA options.

Accreditation: Distance Education Accrediting Commission

AVAILABLE TO PRISONERS

Master of Science in: *Criminal Justice; Management; Psychology*

Master of Arts in: *Organizational Leadership*

Master of Business Administration in: *Business Marketing; Health Care Management; Human Resource Management; Management*

Master of Education in: *Administration; Curriculum and Instruction*

Doctor of Education in: *Educational Administration; Educational Psychology; Organizational Leadership*

Certificate Programs: *Business Administration; Curriculum and Instruction; Educational Administration; Health Care Management; Human Resource Management; Management Studies; Marketing Studies; Organizational Leadership; Psychology Studies*

Tuition Rates:	**Master's courses: $230 per credit (Most courses cost $690 each. $8,280 to $8,970 per degree)**
	Doctoral courses: $290 per credit (Most courses cost $870 each. $19,140 per degree)
	Certificate programs = $1,800
	No single course enrollment
Payment Plan:	Monthly payment plans available: $500 down, $100 per month
Textbook Fees:	Not included in tuition. Textbook rental program available ($25 per book for 120 days)
Additional Fees:	**$75 Application fee**
Transfer/Exam Options:	6 credits per master degree
Time Limit:	5 years per degree
Proctor Required?	Yes

California Coast University
Available Courses

The following courses earn three (3) credits each, unless otherwise marked.

Certificate programs require twelve (12) credits; Master's programs require 36 to 39 credits; Doctoral programs require 66 credits.

BUSINESS ADMINISTRATION COURSES

Human Relations | BAM 501
Management Information Systems | BAM 509
Human Resource Management | BAM 510
Marketing Management | BAM 511
Financial Management | BAM 513
International Business Management | BAM 514
Organizational Behavior | BAM 515
Business Law | BAM 521
Business Ethics | BAM 530
Strategic Management | BAM 560
Modern Management | BAM 562
E-Commerce Management | BAM 570

HEALTH CARE ADMINISTRATION COURSES

Health Care in America | HCA 501
Ethical and Legal Issues for Health Care Professionals | HCA 503
Multicultural Health Care | HCA 505
Organizational Behavior in Health Care | HCA 507

MARKETING COURSES

Sales Marketing | MKT 512
Global Marketing | MKT 542
Value Marketing | MKT 552
Retail Marketing | MKT 555

PSYCHOLOGY COURSES

Developmental Psychology | PSY 501
Human Sexuality | PSY 503
Psychopathology | PSY 505
Theories of Marriage and Family | PSY 509
Professional Ethics and the Law | PSY 511
Alcohol and Chemical Substance Abuse | PSY 517
Counseling Systems and Techniques | PSY 525
Assessment Techniques | PSY 527
Psychology of Aging | PSY 530
Physiological Psychology | PSY 540
Group Psychotherapy | PSY 550
Clinical Psychology | PSY 560

CRIMINAL JUSTICE COURSES

Criminology Theory | BCJ 501
Drugs, Justice and Society | BCJ 510
Criminal Justice Administration | BCJ 515
Multicultural Issues in Law Enforcement | BCJ 530
Computer Crime | BCJ 545
Supervision in Law Enforcement | BCJ553
Police Administration and Management | BCJ 562
Criminal Justice Policy | BCJ 563
Deviant Behavior | BCJ 565
Terrorism and Homeland Security | BCJ 575
Correctional Counseling | BCJ 582

EDUCATIONAL COURSES

Integrating Technology into Teaching | EDU 501
Cultural Issues in Education | EDU 507
Models of Teaching | EDU 510
Leadership and Organizational Behavior | EDU 520
Psychology Applied to Teaching | EDU 521
Strategic Issues Management | EDU 523
Curriculum Design and Instruction | EDU 524
Supervision of Instruction | EDU 526
Educational Personnel Management | EDU 529
School -- Community Relations | EDU 532
Career Development | EDU 540
Leadership and Technology | EDU 545
Public Policy | EDU 546
Legal Aspects of Education | EDU 547
Global Perspectives in Curriculum | EDU 548
Public Policy | EDU 591
Legal Aspects of Education | EDU 592
Philosophical Foundations of Education | EDU 602 (4 credits)
Learning Theory | EDU 610 (4 credits)
History of Education | EDU 614 (4 credits)
Analysis of Current Issues in Education | EDU 618 (4 credits)
Organizational Behavior and Adaptive Leadership | EDU 621 (4 credits)
Group Dynamics | EDU 624 (4 credits)
Foundations in Leadership | EDU 625 (4 credits)
Managing Human Resources | EDU 627 (4 credits)
Diversity in Global and Multicultural Organizations | EDU 629 (4 credits)
Educational Finance | EDU 630 (4 credits)
Motivation and Learning | EDU 640 (4 credits)
Managing Conflict in Organizations | EDU 642 (4 credits)
Advanced Curriculum Development | EDU 645 (4 credits)
Educational Measurement | EDU 646 (4 credits)
Educational Standards and Accountability | EDU 647 (4 credits)
Advanced Educational Psychology | EDU 649 (4 credits)
Leading Through and by Change | EDU 650 (4 credits)
Educational Research | EDU 652 (4 credits)
Quantitative Methods in Educational Research | EDU 653 (4 credits)

Huntington College of Health Sciences

117 Legacy View Way
Knoxville, Tennessee 37918
(800) 290-4226, (865) 524-8079
www.hchs.edu   studentservices@hchs.edu

Huntington College of Health Sciences specializing in providing correspondence education in diet, nutrition, and health management. They offer several diplomas where students can comprehensively learn a specialty, while gaining college credit, without having to take full degree programs. They also offer graduate diploma and degree options (see *Graduate Studies* section)

Accreditation: Distance Education Accrediting Commission (DEAC)

AVAILABLE TO PRISONERS

Master of Science in Nutrition

Doctor of Science in Healthcare

Tuition Rates:	$368 per credit $19,616 to $22,448 per program
Payment Plan:	Limited payment options (2 payments over 2 months)
Textbook Fees:	$2,700 estimated cost per degree program
Additional Fees:	**Application fee: $75** **Enrollment fee: $200 per graduate degree program; $50 per individual course**
Cancellation Policy:	Full refund within 5 days of enrollment; full refund, less $75, for cancellation 5 days to prior to beginning of course assignments, other percentages based on percentage of course completion.
Transfer/Exam Options:	18 credits per bachelor program
Time Limit:	4 months per course; $50 for a 3-month extension
Proctor Required?	Yes

Huntington College of Health Sciences
Available Courses

Biological Sciences

Cellular & Molecular Biology | BIO720 (3 credits)

Reviews the important concepts of molecular biology such as the relationship between the molecular structure and function, the dynamic character of cellular organelles, the use of chemical energy in running cellular activism macromolecular biosynthesis, the diversity at the macromolecular and cellular levels and the mechanisms that regulate cellular activities.

Business Administration

Management of a CAM Practice | BUS601 (3 credits)

Explores the procedures used by CAM practitioners for establishing and managing their own businesses. Students will examine start-up issues, marketing, legal aspects, finances and strategies for maintaining a successful practice.

Chemistry

Advanced Biochemistry | BIO510 (3 credits)

Exploration of the biochemical processes essential in disease prevention and treatment with an emphasis on nutrition.
Prerequisite: Organic & Biochemistry

Health Sciences

Complementary & Alternative Medicine | HEA610 (3 credits)

Designed to provide current and future clinical nutritionists, other healthcare practitioners, students in other healthcare fields, clinical nutrition researchers, and faculty with the tools for appraising and selecting among complementary and alternative medicine (CAM) therapeutics currently in use. Students will formulate treatment protocols integrating principles and materials from CAM modalities that enhance treatment outcomes and lower treatment costs.

Research in Complementary & Alternative Medicine | HEA620 (3 credits)

Explores standards of quality in clinical research on complementary and alternative medicine and therapy. Reviews various research methodologies, as well as special issues as they apply to herbal medicine, homeopathy, acupuncture, massage, prayer, and other therapies with a goal of assessing the quality of evidence to determine best options for patient care.

Capstone Project | HEA730 (12 credits)

The Capstone Project is the culminating experience of the DHS in Integrative Healthcare degree for both areas of concentration. Challenges doctoral students to apply the knowledge and skills they've acquired throughout the program to their professional careers. Completely individualized, this project encourages students to select a work-related project that will result in professional growth and career development. Dissertation and formal presentation required.

Nutritional Sciences

Advanced Nutrition | NUT520 (4 credits)

This course is an assessment of in-depth study of macro- and micro-nutrition digestion, including absorption, metabolism, excretion, inter-relationships, and requirements in normal individuals.

Prerequisite: Understanding Nutrition I, Anatomy & Physiology, Organic, and Biochemistry.

Integrative Nutrition | NUT525 (4 credits)

Explores the foundations of integrative nutrition and dietary recommendations from a scientific perspective. The structure of nutrients, related metabolic processes, energy balance, and requirements throughout the life cycle are explored.

Prerequisite: Understanding Nutrition I, Anatomy & Physiology, Organic and Biochemistry.

Nutrition Assessment | NUT530 (4 credits)

This course is an assessment of nutritional status of individuals in various stages of the life cycle using dietary, anthropometric, biochemical and clinical assessment. Identification of psychosocial, behavioral and cultural factors influencing food choices is studied.

Prerequisite: Advanced Nutrition

Advanced Clinical Nutrition | NUT540 (4 credits)

Explores the role of medical nutrition therapy in the maintenance of health and treatment of symptoms associated with diet-related diseases, including application and integration of basic nutrition principles and assessment.

Prerequisite: Advanced Nutrition.

Nutrition Research | NUT550 (4 credits)

Explores the scientific method of inquiry for conducting research. A variety of research designs and statistical tools are reviewed to answer research questions and test hypotheses. A critical review of current scholarly literature, ethical issues in research, and selection of appropriate descriptive, inferential, parametric, and nonparametric statistics are reviewed and applied.

Prerequisite: Statistics

Research in Integrative Nutrition | NUT555 (4 credits)

A synthesis of conventional and integrative approaches to nutrition developed in a critical review of current scholarly literature. Students develop a three-chapter proposal on a specific topic in integrative nutrition.

Prerequisite: Statistics

Current Trends in Nutrition | NUT560 (3 credits)

Identifies, examines, and discusses current nutrition issues. A critical objective analysis of selected peer-reviewed nutrition research that provides scientific evidence to take position on issues is included.

Prerequisite: Advanced Nutrition

Current Trends in Integrative Nutrition | NUT565 (3 credits)

Explores the current state and projected future state of trends of studies on nutrition in light of integrative approaches to health and wellness. Students will establish and defend their positions using evidence-based sources.

Prerequisite: Advanced Nutrition

Life-Span Nutrition | NUT572 (3 credits)

Study of factors influencing nutrient requirements and metabolism in individuals from birth through old age.

Prerequisite: Understanding Nutrition I

Advanced Community Nutrition | NUT574 (3 credits)

Conduct needs assessment in communities and plan and implement nutrition intervention programs and evaluate their effectiveness. Disseminate nutrition information using effective and appropriate education strategies to promote positive health behaviors in ethnically diverse communities.

Food & Culture | NUT576 (3 credits)

An in-depth study of the dietary habits and behaviors of different cultures with specific focus on vegetarian nutrition. It explores factors that influence food selection, the effects of food habits, and the nutritional status and problems unique to specific ethnic groups.

Herbal Therapies & Alternative Healing | (3 credits)

Examines identification and critical analyses of medicinal herbs, including their active components, bio-availability, mode of action, effective doses, and safety. Evaluation of health claims associated with herbal supplements.

Capstone Project | NUT630 (3 credits)

The Capstone Project allows students to apply the knowledge and skills they've acquired throughout the program to their professional careers. Completely individualized, this project encourages students to select a work-related project that will result in professional growth hand career development.

Functional Medicine & Nutrition | NUT650 (3 credits)

Creates a new roadmap for improving patient outcomes across a wide range of chronic health conditions. The approaches to disease management and prevention here represent the evolution of the functional medicine model over more than 20 years, through the voices of leading clinicians and scientists.

Advanced Nutrition with Clinical Applications | NUT702 (3 credits)

Presents an overview of the use of food and supplements to support health and well-being. Focuses on how traditional diets from many cultures promote well-being and how adoption of modern eating patterns often leads to the development of chronic disease. Student is required to complete in-depth research assignments that will reinforce the important concepts and enhance writing and research skills.

Antioxidants | NUT703 (3 credits)

Summarizes a current knowledge of biochemical and clinical aspects of antioxidant molecules and free radicals, highlighting the effects of antioxidants o the aging process and in prevention and/or fighting the progression of diseases associated with oxidative stress such as arteriosclerosis, cancer, skin, eye, and neurological disease. Emphasizes the value and importance of antioxidants in daily diet.

Nutritional Medicine I | NUT710 (3 credits)

Designed to provide all healthcare practitioners with scientific evidence for the use of diet, vitamins, minerals, amino acids, essential fatty foods, and other significant natural metabolites in the management and treatment of chronic and acute health conditions.

Prerequisite: Nutrition Assessment.

Nutritional Medicine II | NUT711 (3 credits)

Designed to provide all healthcare practitioners with scientific evidence for the use of diet, vitamins, minerals, amino acids, essential fatty foods, and other significant natural metabolites in the management and treatment of chronic and acute health conditions. This course is a continuum of Fundamentals of Nutritional Medicine.

Prerequisite: Nutritional Medicine I.

Nutritional Medicine III | NUT712 (3 credits)

Designed to provide all healthcare practitioners with scientific evidence for the use of diet, vitamins, minerals, amino acids, essential fatty foods, and other significant natural metabolites in the management and treatment of chronic and acute health conditions. This course is a continuum of Nutritional Medicine III.

Prerequisite: Nutritional Medicine II.

Nutrigenomics | NUT720 (3 credits)

Examines the role of nutrients in gene expression and the interactions between the diet and genes. Presents a comprehensive science-based approach to the beneficial effects of dietary compounds on diseases. Advanced analytical techniques applied to current challenges and their solutions are reviewed.

Prerequisite: Functional Medicine & Nutrition.

Nutraceuticals & Functional Foods | NUT730 (3 credits)

Nutraceuticals & functional foods are an essential component of integrative medicine and modern health care. This course provides a scientific approach to critically analyze health claims and apply current research when making recommendations as a health practitioner.

Perelandra College

8697-C La Mesa Boulevard
La Mesa, California 91942
(619) 335-0441
www.perelandra.edu   ken@perelandra.edu

Perelandra College has recently begun working with prisoner-students to provide paper-based courses. They currently offer only a limited number of courses, all in the writing. NOTE: They are not accredited.

Accreditation: NONE

AVAILABLE TO PRISONERS

Graduate-level Certificate in Creative Writing

Tuition Rates:	
Payment Plan:	Monthly payment plans are available
Textbook Fees:	Not included in tuition
Additional Fees:	None
Transfer/Exam Options:	Not applicable
Time Limits:	None
Proctor required?	No

(watermark overlay: No longer offers print courses. Online only. They would like you to write and let them know. If interested in their courses, they will add you their mailing list for future updates on correspondence opportunities.)

Creative Writing
Available Online Courses

Story Basics (Writing 501, 3 credits)

asks students to read seminal books on creating stories and to submit assignments that relate to the texts as well as to a story or stories of their own. They are required to write and submit for critique around 7500 words of original fiction or dramatic non-fiction and to revise following the critique. They gain the skills and confidence to begin writing and revising stories. They learn to describe the structure of dramatic stories, to summarize stories by giving the action-idea, to define the purposes and goals they intend for their writing to achieve, and to demonstrate in their writing the principles of clear, concise and compelling prose.

Poetry Basics (Writing 502, 3 credits)

approaches poetry emphasizing ways to use the language more effectively in all modes of writing. The course includes readings from exemplary poetic and critical works and the writing and revising of poems. By the end of the course, students will demonstrate, through their poetry and by analysis of their own work as well as that of established poets, their familiarity with a variety of poetic forms and techniques. In addition, they will exhibit competence in writing concise, rhythmically sound poems that surprise and perhaps delight.

Screenwriting (Writing 507, 3 credits)

introduces the key elements in writing a feature length screenplay: screenplay structure, plot development, scene development, characterization, and dialog. Books on craft, the professor's guidance, and several writing assignments require students to master the basics while they conceptualize their feature length script. At the conclusion of the course students will have a short film script, a beat sheet or treatment for their full-length screenplay, and the first act of their   screenplay.

Article Basics (Writing 508, 3 credits)

is an introduction to modern journalism. Students outline articles, interview sources and research background information. Required reading includes examples of both traditional news features and literary journalism. Required writing includes a journal of responses to the readings and assigned articles. By the end of the course, students will have at least one article suitable for sale to a magazine.

Genres (Writing 509, 3 credits)

offers insights into a particular genre, stressing the differences and similarities between that genre and general fiction. Students read excellent work in the genre as well as at least one instructional text, and submit for critiques original stories or parts of books they are creating.

Bible as Stories (Literature 551, 3 credits)

approaches the stories of the Old and New Testaments as archetypal models for contemporary fiction and asks students to write one short, short story and one longer short story using these models. Students will create complex characters and interesting plot lines and conflicts, and gain strong organizational and editing skills.

Advanced Story (Writing 601, 3 credits)

requires that students refine both their craft and their attitudes toward their work. Reading assignments explore the structure of dramatic fiction and encourage students to find, refine, or expand their artistic vision. Writing assignments require them to examine what they discovered and to put their discoveries to use. By the end of the course, students will express with clarity why they write and who their target audience is. They will also prove in both the final exam and through their stories that they have grasped the structure of dramatic fiction.

Prerequisite: Writing 501

The Novel (Writing 602, 3 credits)

is an in-depth study of the structural and other elements of novels of various types. Required reading includes two novels and two critical works on the form. Required writing includes outlines, a synopsis, and 10,000 words of a novel's beginning. Students gain the theoretical skills required to structure a compelling novel. They learn that different genres present different expectations and that a variety of different methods of structuring the novel can be equally viable. Through the structural analysis of two novels by masters of the form, they learn to outline in at least two ways. They write the beginning of a novel using one of the outlines. Their grasp of the knowledge the course offers will be proven by exercises and their novel beginning.

Prerequisite: Writing 501

Advanced Poetry (Writing 603, 3 credits)

assumes previous study of poetry. It places its primary focus on the variety of poetic forms (e.g., free verse, the sonnet, villanelle, and other forms). Key attention is given to writing poetry that "surprises." Students read poems, and write, have critiqued, and revise, poems in which they demonstrate skill at using several forms and at creating images and exposing ideas with deft and precise use of language.

Prerequisite: Writing 502

Independent Study in Literature (Literature 610, 1-6 credits)

is a student/faculty designed course in which the student, advised by a faculty member, designs a reading list in a genre in which the student's interest lies or in which the faculty member determines the student can benefit from reading. After reading each of the works assigned, students analyze from a writer's point of view and in doing so determine elements they can apply to their own   work. Evaluation of student work in the course is based upon the depth and clarity of the student's analysis.

Prerequisite: 12 credits of graduate study in writing or literature

Thesis Tutorial, (Writing 611, 1-6 credits)

is the course in which the student receives critical feedback from a faculty member about the thesis project in whole or in part and responds by revising. The grade in the course will be the grade awarded the completed thesis project, as judged by two faculty members. The thesis must be of publishable length (as a rule at least 150 manuscript pages for prose or 60 manuscript pages for poetry) and of such quality that two faculty members consider it publishable by a commercial press.

Southwest University

2200 Veterans Boulevard
Kenner, Louisiana 70062
(504) 468-2900
www.southwest.edu   southwest@southwest.edu

Southwest University offers a wide selection of paper-based business-related degrees and certificates. They are only accredited by the DEAC, which may hinder credit-transfer options if the student chooses further education beyond SU.

Accreditation: Distance Education Accrediting Commission

AVAILABLE TO PRISONERS

Master of Arts *in Management*

Master of Business
(emphasis: Business Administration; Management; Organizational Management)

Master of Science *in Criminal Justice*

Graduate Certificate Programs in *Business Administration, Criminal Justice, Leadership & Management, Management, and Organizational Management*

Tuition Rates:	**$275 per credit (Most courses will cost $825 each.)**
	Individual courses: $460 per credit (Most courses will cost $1,380 each.)
	Certificate Program: $5,520
	$250 per credit for DANTES qualified students
Payment Plans:	Certificate programs: $3,725 down payment, $2,070 within 10 weeks
	Degree programs: $1,025 down payment, 24 equal monthly payments for the remainder due.
Textbooks:	Not included in tuition
Additional Fees:	Application fee: $75; Registration fee: $200; Graduation/Certificate of Completion fee: $125; Shipping fee: $70; Handling fee: $16.50; Study guide: $90; Library fee: $25
Transfer/Exam Options:	9 credits per Masters degree. **Experiential credit:** up to 6 credits/masters' degree. **Credit-by-Exam:** up to 25% of credit required for degree.
Proctor required?	No
Cancellation Policy:	Full refund within 5 days of enrollment; 80% refunded up to first course; Other percentages based on the percentage of courses completed.

Southwest University
Graduate Certificate Programs

These certificate programs are designed to meet the needs of graduate students who are interested in a specific professional specialization. These certificate programs are open to applicants with a Bachelor's Degree.

These are groups of courses that provide a concentration in a particular study area, without the need to take the general education courses of degree programs. They are more economical options than a full degree track. (See *Tuition* above.)

Once completed, each of the following certificate earns 12 college credits, which can be used towards future learning, as well as a Southwest University Certificate of Completion.

(see course descriptions on the following pages)

BUSINESS ADMINISTRATION CERTIFICATE

SELECT ANY FOUR COURSES:

Marketing Management | MKT 630
Organizational Behavioral Management | MGT 637
Financial Management | FIN 655
Human Resources Strategic Issues | HRM 657
Legal Environment of Business | MBA 670
Strategic Management | MGT 672
Managerial Decision Process | DSC 680

LEADERSHIP & MANAGEMENT CERTIFICATE

SELECT ANY FOUR COURSES:

Organizational Behavior Management | MGT 637
Issues in Human Relations | HR 638
Management & Leadership | MGT 651
Supervision of a Diverse Workforce & Teams | MGT 661
Effective Human Resource Management | HRM 663
Strategic Management | MGT 672
Managerial Decision Processes | DSC 680

MANAGEMENT CERTIFICATE

SELECT ANY FOUR COURSES:

Developing Management Competencies | MAM 605
Marketing Management | MKT 630
Organizational Behavioral Management | MGT 637
Management & Leadership | MGT 651
Human Resource Management for Managers | MAM 668
Managing Change in Organizations | MAM 674
Designing & Executing Strategy | MAM 676

ORGANIZATIONAL MANAGEMENT CERTIFICATE

SELECT ANY FOUR COURSES:

Organizational Behavioral Management | ORG 637
Issues in Human Relations | HR 638
Organizational Theory & Design | ORG 645
Management & Leadership | MGT 651
Human Resources Strategic Issues | HRM 657
Supervision of a Diverse Workforce | MGT 661
Effective Human Resource Management | HRM 663

CRIMINAL JUSTICE CERTIFICATE

SELECT ANY FOUR COURSES:

Justice Administration | CJ 604
Organizational Theory & Management | CJ 605
Juvenile Justice | CJ 612
Criminal Investigation | CJ 630
Deviant Behavior | CJ 650
Perspectives in Criminology | CJ 655
Negotiations: Crisis & Hostage | CJ 674

Southwest University
Available Courses

ACCOUNTING

Managerial Accounting | ACC 620

This course contains a rich variety of problem material ranging from simple to challenging. Some areas covered are: essentials of cost and managerial accounting, cost definitions, cost behavior and cost estimates. Also includes capital budgeting income tax effects on capital budgets as well as quantitative methods for managers.

CRIMINAL JUSTICE

Police Administration & Management | CJ 600

Complete coverage and comprehensive study course in police administration and other aspects of police work. Major subjects are addressed in the text such as police professionalization, politics and administration.

Justice Administration | CJ 604

A comprehensive study that encompasses all three components of the Criminal Justice system: police, courts and corrections and also other contemporary administrative issues. It also includes a look at the challenges of the future.

Organizational Theory and Management | CJ 605

This course presents an analysis of criminal justice administration. It introduces a combination of theory and research. This course was designed with the active criminal justice professional in mind. Its purpose is to increase the effectiveness and productivity of criminal justice organizations.

Juvenile Justice | CJ 612

A study course that presents a comprehensive overview of the juvenile justice philosophy and procedure in a no nonsense forum. Presents the Uniform Juvenile Court Act, the Gault, the Kent and the Windship decisions in their entirety.

Comparative Criminal Justice System | CJ 622

This course discusses how countries around the world have organized their police, courts and correctional agencies. The course presents a rationale for studying other systems of justice and crime as a world problem. This course allows students to reach a better understanding of comparative and international issues.

Criminal Investigation Restructuring the Past | CJ 630

Provides sound methods for reconstructing a past event based on three major sources of information: people, physical evidence and records. Introduces newer technological advances in the field.

Administration of Corrections | CJ 640

Discusses the practical application of acceptable principles and procedures in the correctional setting. Includes: inmate processing and culture.

Deviant Behavior | CJ 650

A study of deviant behavior as an inescapable feature of modern, complex society. Incorporates contemporary issues with theories of deviant behavior. Case information included.

Perspectives in Criminology | CJ 655

Discusses the traditional areas of criminology and addresses popular topics such as policy debate, deterrence and incapacitation, race and social class, rights of the accused.

Criminal Behavior | CJ 660

A complete study course on criminal justice and social psychological analysis as applicable to the criminal justice profession. Major issues addressed include theoretical issues, social psychology and the law, the offender's decision and the victim's decision to report crime and much more.

Research Methods | CJ 665

Presents a survey of research methods including research design, measurement, experimental and data collection and analysis. Emphasis is on interpreting and critically evaluating research in Criminal Justice.

Negotiations: Crisis and Hostage | CJ 674

Combines principles and applications from criminal justice, psychology, communications, business and other into a framework for hostage negotiations.

Special Topics in Criminal Justice | CJ 680

Subject to faculty approval. A project or an independent paper that will demonstrate knowledge and understanding of a specific subject.

DECISION PROCESSES

Managerial Decision Processes | DSC 680

The primary focus of this course is on strategic decision making made by middle and upper level of management, particularly in a multi-disciplinary context. The curriculum provides a collection of theories that apply to both public and private enterprise. Strategic decisions made by top management, including determinants for successful strategic choices are examined.

ECONOMICS

Managerial Economics | ECO 642

This course explores the use of economic analysis in making business decisions involving the use of and organization's scarce resources. It explains that managerial economics can predict how external economic changes can cause internal economic changes in business organizations.

FINANCE

Financial Management | FIN 655

This course presents practical information for corporate financial management. It defines objectives of financial decision-making and the tactics and strategies for achieving them.

HUMAN RELATIONS

Issues in Human Relations | HR 638

This course offers a comprehensive treatment of human relations in the workplace. Students will gain an understanding of what it takes to become a successful employee and manager. Focus is on quality, teamwork, diversity, productivity and ethics.

HUMAN RESOURCE MANAGEMENT

Human Resources Strategic Issues | HRM 657

This course provides information on strategic issues that challenge human resource managers. It enlarges on the basic knowledge students will have already learned and integrates new challenges for the human resources professional.

MANAGING FOR MANAGERS

Developing Management Competencies | MAM 605

This course focuses on the essential skills all managers should possess in order to be successful and improve competency in a managerial role. It provides the opportunity for students to complete assessments of their skills to better manage life and relationships and to continually improve competencies. This course assists students in developing and enlarging management skills and how to foster productive growth-producing relationships with others in the work setting.

Accounting for Business Systems | MAM 628

This course provides an array of accounting terms, concepts and applications used to develop financial information which can be used in both external and internal reports. It provides students a working knowledge of financial and managerial decision processes. Its focus is on accounting reports which will aid managers in how to interpret information related to planning, evaluating performances, and making decisions.

Global Management | MAM 648

This course explores the dynamic global environment of business management by exploring the political, legal, restructuring and downsizing, reengineering and network structure. It includes current research, events and global developments. Students are exposed to recent trends that are affecting international business managers in today's hyper-competitive global environment.

Management for Quality and Excellence | MAM 665

This course focuses on the fundamental principles and historical foundation of total quality. There is a strong emphasis on high-performance management practices. Students will be exposed to the Malcolm Bridge Award, ISO 9000, Six Sigma, strategic leadership, strategic work system design, and workforce engagement.

Human Resource Management for Managers | MAM 668

This course investigates and assesses selected critical human resource issues, functions, and approaches that practicing managers' use. The course focuses on strong organizing themes including areas of planning, recruitment, legal compliance, performance appraisal, training/development, and mentoring/empowerment. An organizing structure which emphasizes the HR Triad is presented throughout the course.

Managing Change in Organizations | MAM 674

This course offers students and professionals a variety of change approaches. It introduces reflective questions for change managers to consider when handling issues. This course will build critical thinking skills that will enable the business person to adapt to changing demands and skills in managing changes.

Designing & Executing Strategy | MAM 676

This course examines core concepts and analytical tools of strategic management. It highlights strategy-related development which penetrates many industries and the world economy. Areas include evaluating a company's competitive position, strategies for competing in foreign markets, diversification, corporate culture and leadership, social responsibility and environmental sustainability.

Special Topics in Management | MAM 682

A project or an independent paper that will demonstrate knowledge and understanding of a specific subject.

MANAGEMENT

Information Management in Business | MGT 610

This course discusses the changing demands in today's fast-paced organizations by relating management information systems to management and the organization. Its focus is understanding from a business viewpoint.

Organizational Behavior Management | MGT 637

This course provides future and current managers with information about people and their behavior within the context of the business environment. Provides students up-to-date information on current trends to business and issues affecting businesses today. Some areas of focus are: employee support policies, reward systems, procedural justice, high-performance teams, and goal framing effects.

Management & Leadership | MGT 651

This course presents comprehensive information on major theories and research on leadership and managerial effectiveness in formal organizations. It also provides advice and practical suggestions for business leaders to improve leadership skills.

Management in the 21st Century | MGT 659

This course combines management and organizational behavior. It presents an effective integration of theory and application and offers students a more accurate reflection of the responsibilities faced by today's managers. It introduces a new management paradigm and builds managerial competencies by focusing on knowledge areas, including, planning and monitoring systems, organizing tasks, people and culture, and leading and empowering people.

Supervision of a Diverse Workforce & Teams | MHT 661

This course provides outstanding information on supervision techniques as it explores principles of management, planning, staffing, organizing, leading, and controlling people and operations, with a strong emphasis on real-world situations.

Strategic Management | MGT 672

This course focuses on skill building in all major areas of strategy formulation. It offers three themes: global factors, information technology, and preserving the natural environment.

MARKETING MANAGEMENT

Marketing Management | MKT 630

This course focuses on business-level marketing strategy and utilizes four key dimensions to broaden the understanding of marketing management including customer satisfaction and market strategies planning. Students will analyze markets and the marketing environment, as well as develop marketing strategies.

MBA

Business Ethics & Responsibilities | MBA 635

This course focuses in ethical issues, obligations and responsibilities in the business arena. Moral concepts related to practical ethical decision making are discussed as are obligations of business to society and community.

Legal Environment of Business | MBA 670

Describes areas of law that seem to be of greatest importance to business managers, legal environment topics that mangers frequently deal with, as well as the basic core of business law topics.

ORGANIZATIONAL MANAGEMENT

Organizational Behavioral Management | ORG 637

This course provides future managers and current managers with information about people and their behavior within the context of the business environment. Provides up-to-date information on current trends in business and issues effecting business today. Focus areas are employee support policies, reward systems, procedural justice, high-performance teams, and goal-framing effects.

Organizational Theory & Design | ORG 645

This course presents comprehensive, current learning information of theoretical advances in organizational theory, restructuring and downsizing, reengineering, and network structure. The student is provided in-depth coverage of advanced information technologies and the effects on organizational structure.

College Graduate Studies | Religious

Catholic Distance University

115 W. Congress Street
Charles Town, West Virginia 25414
www.cdu.edu   admissions@cdu.edu

Catholic Distance University offers one graduate study course in addition to several undergraduate options (see *College Studies* section).

CDU's courses have helped prisoners to become chaplains' assistants who evangelize and minister to their fellow prisoners when priest and chaplains were unavailable, as well as to develop ministry careers beyond prison walls.

Accreditation: Distance Education Accrediting Commission

AVAILABLE TO PRISONERS

Master of Arts in Theology

Tuition Rates:	**$450 per credit (Most courses will cost $1,350 each.)**
Payment Plan:	Monthly payment plan available, but will require an additional $30 per course
Textbook Fees:	Not included in tuition, approximately $100 per course. Included in non-credit course
Additional Fees:	**Application fee: $50**
Transfer/Exam Options:	Transfer credits are accepted
Time Limits:	5 years per degree
Proctor required?	Yes

Catholic Distance University
Available Courses

MASTER OF ARTS IN THEOLOGY

Program provides serious study of dogmatic, moral, and sacramental theology, philosophy, spirituality and Church history. Students choose the MA solely as a way to increase their knowledge of the Catholic faith, as well as to bring their knowledge to their families, careers, or individual lives. Program requires a bachelor's degree.

REQUIRED COURSES:

God, Man and the Universe | THEO-513 (3 credits)
Jesus Christ: God, Man and Savior | THEO532 (3 credits)
Theology of the Sacraments, Part One | THEO561 (3 credits)
Theology of the Sacraments, Part Two | THEO562 (3 credits)
Catholic Fundamental Moral Theology, Part A | THEO561 (3 credits)
Catholic Fundamental Moral Theology, Part B | THEO562 (3 credits)
Introduction to Sacred Scripture | SCRPT502 (3 credits)
Church History | CHIST-561 (3 credits)
Catholic Apologetics | THEO-512 (3 credits)
Introduction to Church's Social Teaching (Ecclesiology) | THEO-581 (3 credits)
Philosophy for Theology | PHIL-301 (3 credits)

NINE CREDITS OF ELECTIVE COURSES:

Madonna: Mary in the Catholic Tradition | THEO-535 (3 credits)
The Vocation & Mission of the Laity | THEO-644 (3 credits)
General Catechetics: Methods & Materials | RELED-501 (3 credits)
The Historical Development of Marriage | THEO-558 (3 credits)
Survey of Catholic Spirituality | SPIR-504 (3 credits)
The Gospel of Life in Health & Medicine | THEO-676 (3 credits)
Introduction to the Church's Social Teaching | THEO-581 (3 credits)
Catholic Martyrs of the Twentieth Century | CHIST-554 (3 credits)

Global University | Graduate School of Theology

1211 South Glenstone Avenue
Springfield, Missouri 65804-0315
(800) 443-1083, (417) 862-9533
www.globaluniversity.edu   *gradenroll@globaluniversity.edu*

Global University offers four levels of study: free foundational Bible education (see *Personal Enrichment Studies* sections): fee-based ministerial training (see *Vocational Studies* section) and college-level education offering undergraduate (see *College Studies* section) and graduate degrees. They are a fully accredited school whose credits will likely transfer to other schools and they will accept credit transfers.

Accreditation: North Central Association of Colleges and Schools, The Higher Learning Commission; Distance Education Accrediting Commission

AVAILABLE TO PRISONERS

Master of Arts in the following:

Biblical Studies; and Ministerial Studies

Master of Divinity

Graduate Certificate Programs

Tuition Rates:	**$263 per credit for graduate studies (after 25% prisoner discount)** **(Most course will cost $789 each.)**
Payment Plan:	None
Textbook Fees:	Not included in tuition
Additional Fees:	Application fee: $75
Transfer/Exam Options:	9 credits per Master of Arts degree program; 21 credits per Master of Divinity program
Time Limits:	6 months; $65 for a 6-month undergraduate/graduate degree programs
Proctor required?	Yes

Global University Graduate School of Theology
Graduate Certificate Programs

The following certificate programs allow students to focus on a specialized area without having to complete a full graduate degree program. It should be noted, however, that completion of these certificates does not constitute a degree or a professional certification. Each of the following courses earn three (3) credits for a total of 18 credits per certificate program. For descriptions of courses, see the following pages.

GRADUATE STUDIES CERTIFICATE IN NEW TESTAMENT STUDIES

CHOOSE ANY SIX OF THE FOLLOWING:

Colossians and Philippians | BNT5053
Letter to the Galatians | BNT5093
Letter to the Hebrews | BNT5103
Acts as History and Theology | BNT5183
Graduate Greek I | BNT5573
Graduate Greek II | BNT5583
Pneumatology in Lucan Literature | BNT6043
Backgrounds in the New Testament: Cultural and Historical Concepts | BNT6203
The Gospels | BNT6303
Intermediate Greek (Graduate Greek III) | BNT6673
Greek Exegesis of the Letter to the Hebrews | BNT7103
Romans: An Exegetical Analysis | BNT7503

Total Credits: 18
Total Cost: $4,740

GRADUATE STUDIES CERTIFICATE IN EDUCATION

CHOOSE ANY SIX OF THE FOLLOWING:

Educational Measurement | EDU5023
Education in the Bible | EDU5043
Bible School Administration | EDU5053
Curriculum and Instructional Design | EDU5063
Teaching Strategies: Facilitating Adult Education | EDU 6073
Educational Psychology | EDU6203
Practicum: Education | EDU6903

Total Credits: 18
Total Cost: $4,740

GRADUATE STUDIES CERTIFICATE IN INTERCULTURAL STUDIES

CHOOSE ANY SIX OF THE FOLLOWING:

The Biblical Theology of Missions | MIS5013
Cultural Anthropology | MIS5033
Missions from the Two-Thirds Worlds | MIS5053
Trends and Current Issues in Missions | MIS5093
Paradigms for Pentecostal Missions | MIS5103
Strategies for Cross-Cultural Ministry | MIS6023
History of the Expansion of Christianity | MIS6043
Islam and Animism: A Christian Perspective | MIS6073

Total Credits: 18
Total Cost: $4,740

GRADUATE STUDIES CERTIFICATE IN LEADERSHIP

CHOOSE ANY SIX OF THE FOLLOWING:

Foundations for Christian Leadership | LDR5013
Leadership Emergence Patterns | LDR5023
Conflict Management | LDR5043
Leadership Training Models | LDR5053
Leadership Research | LDR5063
Dynamics of Christian Organizations | LDR6033
Practicum: Leadership | LDR6903

Total Credits: 18
Total Cost: $4,740

Global University Graduate School of Theology
Course Listing

The following courses each earn three (3) credits unless marked otherwise.

BIBLE | BIBLICAL STUDIES DIVISION

Historical Approach to Hermeneutics | BIB5013
The Bible as Literature: Theory and Methodology | BIB5033
Foundations of Biblical Language | BIB5543
Hermeneutics: God's Message and It's Meaning | BIB6293
Practicum: Biblical Studies | BIB6903
Thesis: Biblical Studies | BIB6926 (6 credits)

BIBLE NEW TESTAMENT | BIBLICAL STUDIES DIVISION

Colossians and Philippians | BNT5053
Letter to the Galatians | BNT5093
Letter to the Hebrews | BNT5103
Acts as History and Theology | BNT5183
Graduate Greek I | BNT5573
Graduate Greek II | BNT5583
Pneumatology in Lucan Literature | BNT6043

Backgrounds to the New Testament: Cultural & Historical Contexts | BNT6203
The Gospels | BNT6303
Pauline Prison Epistles | BNT6403
Intermediate Greek (Graduate Greek III) | BNT6673
Advanced Greek Language and Exegesis (Graduate Greek IV) | BNT6683
Practicum: New Testament Studies | BNT6903
These: New Testament Studies | BNT6926 (6 credits)
Greek Exegesis of the Letter to the Hebrews | BNT7103
Romans: An Exegetical Analysis | BNT7503
1 Corinthians: An Exegetical Analysis | BNT7513
Dissertation Writing & Defense: New Testament Studies | BNT8966

BIBLE OLD TESTAMENT | BIBLICAL STUDIES DIVISION

Science and the Bible | BOT5113
Isaiah: Major Themes | BOT5143

Hosea & Amos | BOT5153
Poetry & Proverb: The Psalms and Wisdom of Literature | BOT5173
Origins: Christian Faith and Natural Science | BOT5333
The Pentateuch: Critical Issues | BOT6233
Practicum | Old Testament Studies | BOT6903
Thesis: Old Testament Studies | BOT6926 (6 credits)
Dissertation Writing & Defense: Old Testament Studies | BOT8966

EDUCATION | MINISTERIAL STUDIES DIVISION

Educational Measurement | EDU 5023
Education in the Bibles | EDU 5043
Bible School Administration | EDU5053
Curriculum & Instructional Design | EDU5063
Teaching Strategies: Facilitating Adult Education | EDU6073
Educational Psychology | EDU6203
Practicum: Education | EDU6903
Thesis: Education | EDU6926 (6 credits)
Dissertation Writing & Defense: Education | EDU8966 (6 credits)

LEADERSHIP | MINISTERIAL STUDIES DIVISION

Foundations for Christian Leadership | LDR5013
Leadership Emergence Patterns | LDR5023
Conflict Management | LDR5043
Leadership Training Models | LDR5053
Leadership Research | LDR5063
Dynamics of Christian Organizations | LDR6033
Practicum: Leadership | LDR6903
Thesis: Leadership | LDR6926
Dissertation Writing & Defense: Leadership | LDR8966 (6 credits)

MINISTRIES | MINISTERIAL TRAINING STUDIES

Preaching to Change Lives | MIN5013
Foundations to Pastoral Theology | MIN5203
Marriage & Family Counseling | MIN5263
Developing a Christian Worldview | MIN5273
Ministerial Ethics: The Bible Confronts a Changing World | MIN6233
Relationships for a Lifetime of Ministry | MIN6503
Spiritual Formation: Principles of Christian Discipleship | MIN6513
Practicum: Ministry | MIN6903
Thesis: Ministerial Studies | MIN6926 (6 credits)
Dissertation Writing & Defense: Ministerial Studies | MIN8966 (6 credits)

MISSIONS | MINISTERIAL STUDIES DIVISION

The Biblical Theology Missions | MIS5013
Cultural Anthropology | MIS5033
Missions from the Two-Thirds World: Issues & Models for the Emergent Church | MIS5053
Trends & Current Issues in Missions | MIS5093
Paradigms for Pentecostal Missions | MIS5103
Strategies for Cross-Cultural Ministry | MIS6023
History of Expansion of Christianity | MIS6043
Islam & Animism: A Christian Perspective | MIS6073
Practicum: Missions | MIS6903
Thesis: Missions | MIS6926
Dissertation Writing & Defense: Missions | MIS8966 (6 credits)

RESEARCH | GENERAL EDUCATION DIVISION

Graduate Research & Writing |
Principles & Practice | RES5023
Practicum: Research | RES6903
Research Methodology | RES6913
Graduate Thesis & Dissertation:
Purpose, Process, and Product |
RES6926
Dissertation Writing & Defense |
RES8966 (6 credits)

THEOLOGY | BIBLICAL STUDIES DIVISION

Current Trends in International
Theology | THE5013
Contemporary Issues in Pneumatology |
THE6083
Theology of the Holy Spirit in the Old
Testament | THE6093
Theology of the Holy Spirit in the New
Testament | THE6103
Practicum: Theology | THE6903
Thesis: Theology | THE6926
Dissertation Writing & Defense:
Theology | THE8966 (6 credits)

Graduate Studies | Unaccredited | Religious

American Institute of Holistic Theology

2112 11ᵗʰ Avenue South, Suite 520
Birmingham, Alabama 35205
(800) 650-4325
www.aiht.edu   admiss@aiht.edu

The *American Institute of Holistic Theology* offers a few graduate degree programs from an interfaith perspective in Holistic Theology. (See 'College Studies | Religious' for undergraduate degrees.)

Accreditation: None

AVAILABLE TO PRISONERS

Masters, Doctor of Theology, and Doctor of Ministry in Holistic Theology

A variety of courses with certificates of completion

Tuition Rates:	**$495 per individual course**
	$5,500 Master's degree
	$6,050 Doctor of Ministry (DMin)
	$9,000 Doctoral (ThD)
Payment Plan:	10% down ($550 for Masters, $600 for Doctoral), plus monthly payments
Textbook Fees:	Included in tuition
Additional Fees:	None
Transfer/Exam Options:	None
Time Limits:	5 years
Proctor required?	Yes. ThD and PhD requires a defended dissertation through Skype call.

Christian Bible College & Seminary

605 Southwest U.S. Highway 40 #336
Blue Springs, Missouri 64014
(800) 543-3720, (816) 228-3720
www.cbcs-degree.com   cbcs-degree@msn.com

Christian Bible College & Seminary (CBCS) offers a number of associate and bachelor degree options, as well as Graduate degrees (See Graduate Studies section). They have a unique and especially useful payment policy for prisoners (see below).

NOTE: They claim accreditation by Accrediting Commission International, but this agency is not recognized by the U.S. Department of Education or CHEA.

Available for Prisoners:

Master of:
Theology; Divinity; Ministry; Exegetical Theology; Pastoral Ministry; Divinity in Christian Counseling; Ministry in Christian Counseling; Religious Education; Christian Education

Doctor of:
Theology; Divinity; Ministry; Exegetical Theology; Pastoral Ministry; Divinity in Christian Counseling; Ministry in Christian Counseling; Religious Education; Christian Education

Tuition:	**Master degree: $2,100** **Doctorate: $2,400** **Doctorate/PhD: $2,700** **20% discount if paid in full** **(Note payment plan below)**
Payment Plans:	$50 up front for each of the first two textbooks ($100, plus the $50 Application fee + $150 total). The remainder of the tuition can be deferred until you are employed outside of prison, which you can then pay back through payments. Degree will not be awarded until full payment is made, but they will provide a letter of completion to assist with getting a job.
Textbooks:	Not included in tuition, range from $17 to $50
Additional Fees:	**Application fee: $50**
Transfer credits:	CEUs, outside certificates, diplomas, military experience, experiential learning

Christian Bible College & Seminary
Graduate Course Listing

CHRISTIAN MINISTRY

Putting Your Past Behind You | CM502
The Effective Pastor | CM510
Christian Ethics, Contemporary Issues, & Options | CM512
The Master Plan of Evangelism | CM516
Introducing World Missions | CM517
Church Administration Handbook | CM522
The Holy Spirit & You | CM523
Purpose Driven Youth Ministry | CM524
Praying the Names of Jesus | CM525
The Purpose Driven Church | CM528
Leadership Handbook of Management & Administration | CM529
Handbook of Christian Apologetics | CM530
The Complete Evangelism Guide Book | CM531
Epistemology | CM622
Courageous Leadership | CM624
The Purpose Driven Life | CM628
Completing the Task (Reaching the World for Christ) | CM631

EXEGETICAL THEOLOGY

Jesus Christ our Lord | ET508
Classic Christianity: A Systemic Theology | ET511
Jesus According to Scripture | ET626

PASTORAL MINISTRY

Shepherding God's Flock I & II | PM501
Starting a New Church (The Church Planter's Guide to Success) | PM513
Renovation of the Heart | PM621
Pastors at Greater Risk | PM627

THEOLOGICAL STUDIES

New Horizons in Hermeneutics | TH503
The Doctrine of the Knowledge of God | TH504
Interpreting the Prophetic Word | TH506
Christian Theology I & II | TH507
The Integration of Psychology & Theology | TH509
God the Father Almighty | TH514
Introducing Christian Doctrine | TH515
Using New Testament Greek in Ministry | TH518
The Jesus we Missed | TH519
Knowing Scripture | TH520
Knowing God | TH521
New Testament Theology | TH526
Basic Theology | TH527

Introduction to Philosophy | TH620
A Praying Life | TS623
Why Believe? | TS625
Christianity at the Religious Roundtable | TS629
When Skeptics Ask | TS630

Christian Leadership University

3792 Broadway Street
Buffalo, New York 14227
(716) 681-4896
www.cluonline.com   *clu@cluonline.com*

Christian Leadership University offers a wide variety of religious education options, including certificates and degrees. However, they are not accredited.

Accreditation: None

AVAILABLE TO PRISONERS

Certificates of Completion, Master and Doctoral degrees in the following:

Biblical Studies; Christian Arts; Christian Counseling; Christian Entrepreneurship; Christian Leadership; Divine Healing; Intercession; Ministry; Missions & Evangelism; Prophetic Ministry; Theology; Worship Ministry; Youth Ministry

Tuition Rates:	**$50 per credit (Most course will cost $200 or $250 each.)**
Payment Plan:	None available
Textbook Fees:	$17 to $57 per course
Additional Fees:	**Shipping fee: $10 per course**
	Syllabus: $3 per course
Transfer/Exam Options:	Up to 25% can be transferred credits; up to 25% can be from life experience, although life experience must have come through a Christian college.
Time Limits:	3 to 6 months
Proctor required?	No

Christian Leadership University
Graduate Course Listing
The following courses are all awarded with 4 credits unless marked otherwise.

BUSINESS
Fulfill Your Financial Destiny | BUS502

COUNSELING
Prayers that Heal the Heart | COU501 (2 credits)

MINISTRY
Experiencing God in a Small Group | MIN510
Communion with God | REN503
Wisdom Through Dream interpretation | REN510

THEOLOGY
Names & Attributes of God | THE501
Discovering the Blood Covenant | THE502
Feasts of Jehovah | THE503 (5 credits)
House – Church | THE531
Leadership – Servanthood in the Church | THE532
Place of Worship: Assessment for Safety & Security | THE501 (5 credits)

Freedom Bible College & Seminary

1270 Highway 412 West, Suite K
Siloam Springs, Arkansas 72761
(479) 373-6420
www.freedom.edu   admissions@freedom.edu

Freedom Bible College & Seminary (FBCS) offers a number of religious certificate and degree options.

Accreditation: FBCS is unaccredited by choice. Regarding accreditation, they state, "Since we believe in the separation of church and state, we have not applied for accreditation to the U.S. Department of Education or any state or federal agency."

Available to Prisoners:

Master's degrees in:
Christian Education; Christian Church Leadership; Divinity; Ministry (with emphasis options in Counseling); Theology

Doctorate degrees in:
Christian Education; Ministry (with emphasis options in Counseling); Religious Research; Theology

Tuition:	**$326 per course** **$250 per course for class audit** **Graduate Certificate program: $2,321** **Teaching program: $675** **Master of Divinity: $4,302** **Master Degree (other): $3,977** **Doctorate Degree: $4,760** **Doctorate of Religious Research: $7,578** (10% discount with full payment upon enrollment)
Payment Plan:	Master degree program: $125 per month plus books; Doctorate Degree: $150 per month plus books
Additional Fees:	Application fee: $100
Textbooks:	Not included in tuition. Ranges on average from $20 to $80 each.
Cancellation Policy:	Full refund within two weeks of enrollment, less processing fee; 70% refund up to 30 days after enrollment; 40% refund up to 60 days after enrollment; None thereafter.
Transfer credit:	Credit for life experience is evaluated for degree programs through the Master Degree level. Military service personnel will receive three (3) credits per year of honorable service, up to 12 credits.

Freedom Bible College & Seminary
Graduate Certificate Programs

The following certificate programs require a Bachelor Degree, General Ministerial License or Ordination prior to enrollment. These programs are designed to meet the needs of students who are interested in a specific professional specialization, and which may be helpful toward parole board consideration and reentry planning.

These are groups of courses that provide a concentration in a particular study area, without the need to take the general education courses of degree programs. They are more economical options than a full degree track.

Once completed, each of the following certificate earns college credit as marked, which can be used towards future learning.

CERTIFIED CHRISTIAN CHAPLAINCY PROGRAM

This course provides an overview for psychologists, psychiatrists, social workers, clergy, corrections professional, and volunteers of the role that chaplains play in assisting in the rehabilitation of offenders in addition to the ministerial and administrative responsibilities.

Course	credits
New Testament Survey | BSC-1023	3
Prayer Essentials | BSC-1053	3
Christian Counseling Ethics | CC-5324	3
Crisis Counseling for Christians | CC-5344	3
Intrinsic Healing II: Spiritual Growth | CC-7214	3
Fundamentals of Correctional Chaplaincy I | CER-2063	3
Fundamentals of Correctional Chaplaincy II | CER-2073	3
Fundamentals of Correctional Chaplaincy III | CER-2083	3
Fundamentals of Correctional Chaplaincy IV | CER-2093	3
The Chaplain as Spiritual Caregiver I | CER-20103	3
The Chaplain as Spiritual Caregiver I | CER-20113	3
Social Ministry | MIN-3213-1	3
Total credits	**36**
Total cost	**$2,321 plus fees**

CHRISTIAN EDUCATION TEACHING CERTIFICATE

This program requires an additional six hours of coursework beyond a Bachelor degree with Christian Education emphasis. After completion of the additional study, a test will be administered by a proctor.

Total cost	$675.00

Freedom Bible College & Seminary
Graduate Course Listing

MASTER OF CHRISTIAN CHURCH LEADERSHIP COURSES

Church Leadership Assessment | CL-5504
Church Team Leadership II | CL-5514
Spiritual Leadership | CL-5524
Leadership in the Old Testament | CL-5534
Hearing God's Voice | CL-5544
Fairness in Church Leadership | CL-5554
Jesus, the Model of Leadership I | CL-5564
Jesus, the Model of Leadership II | CL-5574
Transforming Church | CL-5584

MASTER OF MINISTRY – COUNSELING EMPHASIS

Techniques of Christian Counseling | CC-5314
Christian Counseling Ethics | CC-5324
Crisis Counseling for Children | CC-5344
Christian Counseling for Substance Abuse & Addiction | CC-5354
Biblical Counseling & Prayer | CC-5374
Case Studies in Christian Counseling | CC-5384
Case Studies in Christian Counseling for Youth | CC-5394
Christian Marriage Counseling | CC-53104
Healing Adult Victims of Childhood Sexual Abuse from a Christian Perspective | CC-53114
Bereavement Ministry | CC-53124

DOCTORATE OF MINISTRY – COUNSELING EMPHASIS COURSES

Intrinsic Healing II, Spiritual Growth | CC-7214
Healing for Damaged Emotions | CC-7224
Christian Counseling Concepts | CC-7234
Christian Marital Counseling | CC-7244
Supervision of Pastoral Care | CC-7254
Family Ministry | CC-7294
Dissertations (Phase I, II, III) | CC-7264, 7274, 7284

MASTER OF THEOLOGY COURSES

Old Testament Theology I | TH-5114
Doctrines of Christian Faith II | TH-5134
Integrative Theology I | TH-5164
Integrative Theology II | TH-5174
Integrative Theology III | TH-5184
Applied Systemic Theology | TH-51104
Old Testament Revisited | TH-51114
Eschatology III | TH-51134

DOCTORATE OF THEOLOGY COURSES

Eschatology I | TH-7004
Historic Christianity | TH-7014
Evangelistic Theology | TH-7044
Old Testament Theology II | TH-7054
Eschatology II | TH-7094

MASTER OF CHRISTIAN EDUCATION

Teaching Ministry in the Church | ED-5414
Church Administration II | ED-5434
Communication Techniques | ED-5474
Woman in Ministry | ED-5494
Basics of Christian Education | ED-54104
Discipleship | ED-54114
Understanding World Religions | ED-54124
Pastoral Supervision | ED-54134

DOCTORATE OF CHRISTIAN EDUCATION COURSES

Teaching for Results in Christian Education | ED-7314
Developing Christian Counseling Strategy | ED-7334
The Effective Minister of Education | ED-7344
Directing Christian Education | ED-7394
Progressive Christian Leadership | ED-73104
Women's Ministry | ED-8013

MASTER OF MINISTRY COURSES

Exegesis – New Testament | MIN-5204
Heartfelt Preaching | MIN-5214
Christian Conflict Management | MIN-5224
Seniors Ministry | MIN-5234
Revival | MIN-5274
Ministry in Missions | MIN-52104
Old Testament Revisited | MIN-52114
Apologetics I | MIN-52124

DOCTORATE OF MINISTRIES COURSES

Supervision of Ministries | MIN-7194
Advanced Homiletics | MIN-7124
Intrinsic Healing II: Spiritual Growth | MIN-7134

Salvation in the Old Testament | MIN-7144
Principles of Church Evangelism | MIN-7154
Apologetics II | MIN-71104

DOCTORATE OF RELIGIOUS RESEARCH COURSES

Advanced Apologetics | DRR-9004
A Study of the Church Fathers | DRR-9014
Self-Directed Research Study | DRR-9024
Christian Philosophy 1 | DRR-9034
Christian Philosophy II | DRR-9044

Assigned Research-The First Counsel of Nicaea | DRR-9054
Self-Directed Research Study | DRR-9074
Assigned Research-Early Christianity in America | DRR-9084
Self-Directed Research Study | DRR-90114
Dissertation Phase 1 | DRR-90124
Dissertation Phase II | DRR-90134
Dissertation Phase III | DRR-90144
Major Field Reading | DRR-90164
Assigned Research-The History and Development of the Bible | DRR-90-174
Major Field Reading | DRR-90204

Omega Bible Institute & Seminary

PO Box 70, Swartz, LA 71281-00709
(318) 343-9800
www.omega.edu

Omega Bible Institute & Seminary offers a number of religion and spirituality-based certificate and degree options. You cannot take individual courses, but must instead enroll in and entire certificate or degree program. They also offer undergraduate degree programs. (See College Studies section.)

Accreditation: Transworld Accrediting Commission, which is not recognized by the U.S. Department of Education or CHEA

Available for Prisoners:

Master of Arts in Biblical Studies

Master of: *Christian Counseling, Divinity, Christian Education, Ministry, and Theology*

Doctor of: *Christian Counseling, Theology, Christian Education, Ministry, and Philosophy*

Tuition:	**Masters: $45 per credit** **Master of Arts: $2,700** **Master of Christian Counseling: $2,025** **Master of Christian Education: $2,160** **Master of Divinity: $3,150** **Master of Ministry: $2,250** **Master of Theology: $2,250** **Doctor of: $50 per credit** **Doctor of Christian Counseling or Theology: $2,500** **Doctor of Christian Education or Ministry: $2,250** **Doctor of Philosophy: $3,900** 10% discount if paid a full year in advance of study.
Payment Plans:	Equal payments can be made for the months of the course of study.
Cancellation Policy:	Non-refundable
Textbooks:	Included in tuition
Additional Fees:	Application Fee: NONE Postage must be paid by the student
Transfer Credits:	Experience credits of up to 6 hours for each year of services are available for preachers who have served some years in full-time ministry.

Rock of Ages Ministries | College of Biblical Studies

PO Box 4419
Dalton, GA 30719
(706) 459-3233
www.roapm.com   roacobs@gmail.com

The *Rock of Ages College of Biblical Studies and Theological Seminary* has been offering religious education since 1996. In 2009, they expanded their options to include studies for doctorate degrees. They now offer three levels of study, including a variety of undergraduate and graduate degree options.

They are of Baptist faith and adhere strictly to the Authorized King James Version.

Accreditation: NOT Accredited

Available for Prisoners:

Master Degree in the following disciplines: *Bible Studies, Religious Education, or Theology*

Doctorates in the following disciplines: *Biblical Studies, Religious Education, Ministry, or Theology*

Tuition:	**Master Degree Program: $25 per credit (36 credits per year = $900)** **Doctorate Program: $40 per credit (36 credits per year = $1,440. Doctor of Theology requires 4 additional credit hours.)** **50% off for spouses of students. 10% discount if paid a full year in advance of study.**
Payment Plans:	Payment must be made in full for each year of study.
Cancellation Policy:	Non-refundable
Textbooks:	Included in tuition
Additional Fees:	Application Fee: $30 Postage must be paid by the student Reinstatement Fee (if transferring from another institution): $30
Transfer Credits:	Credits are available for previous completions of the same subjects offered by Rock of Ages. Experience credits of up to 6 hours for each year of services are available for preachers who have served at least five years in full-time ministry. Evaluation fee of $100 is required.

Vision International University

1115 D Street
Ramona, California 92065
(800) 984-7466   (760) 789-4700
www.vision.edu   info@vision.edu

Vision International University (VIU) offers a variety of graduate degree options in religious studies.

Accreditation: Regarding accreditation, VIU states, "Vision International University is striving to gain recognition internationally, to provide the highest quality education possible. In 2007, we received full approval to operate from the Bureau of Private post-secondary Education (BPPE), which establishes educational and operational standards to serve as regulations for instructional quality, fiscal and administrative responsibility, and institutional stability for private post-secondary schools."

AVAILABLE TO PRISONERS

Master of Arts in: *Christian Counseling; Christian Education; Leadership*

Master of Theological Studies

Master of Divinity

Doctor of Ministry

Tuition Rates:	**$150 per credit (Master's program: $2,394; Doctorate program: $2,660)**
Payment Plan:	$525 down payment and $165 per month per Master's degree program; $825 down payment and $200 per month per Doctorate degree program
Textbook Fees:	Not included in tuition; $75 to $150 per course for graduate studies
Additional Fees:	**Application fee: $20 for prisoners ($50 for non-prisoners)** **Graduation fee: $150 for master's degree, $200 for doctorate**
Cancellation Policy:	Full refund within 10 days of enrollment, less administration fee
Transfer/Exam Options:	Case-by-case basis
Time Limits:	None
Proctor required?	No

Vision International University
Graduate Course Listing

Each of the following courses earns three (3) credits. However, they cannot be taken separately. They must be taken in a graduate degree program.

The program these courses apply to is noted next to each course (M = Master degree program; D = Doctoral degree program)

CHRISTIAN COUNSELING

Course	Program
Psychology & Theology	CO500	M
Human Development	CO510	M
Counseling Theories & Strategy	CO530	M
Crisis Counseling	CO540	M
Marriage & Family Counseling	CO550	M
Assessment & Diagnosis	CO560	M
Group Dynamics	CO610	M
Addiction Counseling	CO620	M
Cross-Cultural Counseling	CO630	M
Ethics & Law	CO640	M
Pastoral Care of the Elderly	CO680	M
Human Sexuality	CO710	M
Clinical Applications of Counseling in the Church	CC840	D
Psychopathology, Sin & Demonic Influence	CC850	D
Psychotherapy, Pastoral Counseling & Inner Healing	CC860	D
Psychology & Theology: A Personal Integration	CC870	D
Personality Theory, Therapy: A Christian Worldview	CC880	D

CHRISTIAN EDUCATION

Course	Program
Philosophy of Christian Education	ED500	M
Primary Christian Education	ED600	M
Secondary Christian Education	ED620	M
Curriculum Development in Christian Education	ED650	M
Teaching Methodology	ED750	M
Conflict Resolution in Educational Leadership	ED810	D
Human Behavior	ED820	D
Psychology of Learning in Education	ED830	D
Philosophy of Educational Leadership	ED840	D
Educational Leadership for Private School & Church	ED850	D

CHURCH HISTORY

Course	Program
Survey of Church History	CH505	M
The History of Church & the Reformation	CH506	M
The History of the Church Since the Reformation	CH507	M
A History of the Charismatic Movements	CH510	M

DOCTORAL MINISTRY

Course	Program
Leadership in Pastoral Care	DM800	D
Church Growth & Leadership		D

DM801	
Cross Cultural Perspectives in Pastoral Leadership | DM803	D
The Media, Leadership, and the Church | DM804	D
Spiritual Development of the Pastor, Church & Community | DM805	D
Ethics & the Church in Today's Culture: Pastoral Perspective | DM806	D
Conflict Management & Resolution of Church Life | DM807	D
Women in Ministry: The Controversy Over the Ordination of Women | DM809	D
Leadership Principles Applied to Pastoral Ministry & Church Extension | DM810	D
Missions of the 21st Century | DM811	D
The New Apostolic Reformation: Paradigms & Procedures | DM812	D
Psychology & Theology: Conflicting or Contemporary | DM813	D
Contemporary Theology & Evangelical Belief | DM814	
Renewal Ministry from a Historical Church Perspective | DM816	D
Revival & Church Planting | DM817	D
Preaching: It's Place & Purpose in Contemporary Culture | DM818	D
Doctoral Project | DM899 (10 credits)	D

LEADERSHIP STUDIES

Church Administration &	M

Leadership | CE501	
Interpersonal Communications & Conflict Management | CE502	M
Advanced Leadership & Administration | CE503	M
Adult Ministries in the Church | CE504	M
Effective Administrative Leadership | CE505	M
Introduction to Leadership & Leaders | LE501	M
Ministry Leadership Foundations | LE502	M
Dynamics of Effective Leaders & Followers | LE503	M
Spirituality & Leadership | LE504	M
Contemporary Issues in Leadership | LE505	M
Leader Development | LE506	M
Leadership Practicum | LE511	M

MINISTRY STUDIES

Spiritual Formations | MT501	M
The Role of Women in Ministry | MT502	M
Evangelism in the Local Church | MT504	M

NEW TESTAMENT

The Sermon on the Mount | NT501	M
The Pastoral Epistles | NT502	M
NT Survey: The Gospels/Life of Christ | NT504	M
The Epistles & Revelation | NT508	M
Fundamentals of New Testament Greek | NT509	M
The Christian & New Testament Theology | NT511	

OLD TESTAMENT

The Book of Psalms | OT505	M
Understanding the Old Testament | OT506	M
The Christian & Old Testament Theology | OT509	M

PHILOSOPHICAL & SYSTEMATIC THEOLOGY

Christian Ethics | PT501	M
Christian Worldview | PT504	M
Contemporary Theology I | ST503	M
The Doctrines of Man & Sin | ST504	M
The Doctrine of Salvation | ST505	M
The Doctrine of the Trinity | ST506	M
Contemporary Theology II | ST507	M

WORLD MISSIONS

Introduction to World Missions | WM501	M
The History of Missions | WM502	M
Urban Mission & Ministry | WM503	M

RELIGIOUS LITERATURE

Religious Newsletters & Periodical

FREE Newsletters & Periodicals

BUDDHIST

DHARMA FRIENDS | COMPASSION WORKS FOR ALL

PO Box 7708, Little Rock, AR 72217-7708
Monthly Newsletter.

DHARMA GARDEN

1 Fairtown Lane, Taneytown, MD 21787
www.facebook.com/DharmaGardenSangha
dharmagardensangha@gmail.com
Quarterly newsletter.

GASSHO | ATLANTA ZOTOT ZEN CENTER

1167-C Zonolite Pl., Atlanta, GA 30306
www.aszc.org
Bi-monthly newsletter.

GAY BUDDHIST FELLOWSHIP

PMPB 456, 2215-R Market St., San Francisco, CA 94114
www.gaybuddhist.org
Bi-monthly newsletter.

INSIGHT | INSIGHT MEDITATION SOCIETY

1230 Pleasant St., Barre, MA 01005
www.dharma.org
Bi-monthly newsletter.

IBMC | INTERNATIONAL BUDDHIST MEDITATION CENTER

928 S. New Hampshire Ave., Los Angeles, CA 90006
www.ibmc.info
Bi-monthly newsletter.

LIBERATION MAGAZINE | LIBERATION PRISON PROJECT

PO Box 31527, San Francisco, CA 94131
www.liberationprisonproject.org
Bi-monthly newsletter.

PURPLE LOTUS JOURNAL

636 San Mateo Ave., San Bruno, CA 94066
www.purplelotus.com
Annual magazine.

SNOW LION

PO Box 6483, Ithaca, NY 14851-6483
www.snowlionpub.com
Bi-monthly newsletter.

TRICYCLE MAGAZINE | THE BUDDHIST REVIEW

1115 Broadway, Suite 1113, New York, NY 10010
Quarterly magazine. Note: Tricycle is a FEE-based magazine, but they will send back issues for FREE.

CATHOLIC

MY PEOPLE | PRESENTATION MINISTRIES

3230 McHenry Ave., Cincinnati, OH 45211
Monthly newsletter.

VOICE OF PROVIDENCE, THE | PIOUS UNION OF ST. JOSEPH

953 E. Michigan Ave., Grass Lake, MI 49240
www.pusj.org
Bi-monthly magazine.

CHRISTIAN (NON-DENOMINATIONAL)

A LITTLE GOOD NEWS | HUMAN KINDNESS FOUNDATION

PO Box 61619, Durham, NC 27715
www.humankindness.com
Quarterly newsletter.

CONVERSATIONS | THE CONVERSATIONS WITH GOD FOUNDATION

PMB 1150m 1257 Siskiyou Blvd., Ashland, OR 97520
www.cwg.org
Bi-monthly newsletter.

CROSSROADS JOURNAL OF THE ARTS

PO Box 900, Grand Rapids, MI 49509
Bi-monthly newsletter.

FISHER OF MEN PRISON MINISTRIES

5403 N. Second St., Loves Park, IL 61111
(815) 633-7508
www.prisonministry.net/fompm
Monthly newsletter.

HEART OF AMERICA

PO Box 1685. Independence, MO 64055
www.heartmin.org
Monthly newsletter.

INSIDE JOURNAL | PRISON FELLOWSHIP

PO Box 17500, Washington, D.C. 20041
www.prisonfellowship.org   *insidejournal@pfm.org*
Bi-monthly newsletter.

JOY WRITERS GOOD-NEWS LETTER

2001 Liberty Square Dr., Cartersville, GA 30121
Bi-monthly newsletter.

OUR DAILY BREAD

PO Box 270, Grand Rapids, MI 49501-0270
www.obd.org
Monthly devotional booklet.

PRESENT TRUTH

PO Box 315, Kansas City, OK 74347
(304) 633-5411
www.presenttruth.info   *newsletter@presenttruth.info*
Monthly newsletter.

REFLECTIONS | LOVED ONES OF PRISONERS

PO Box 14953, Odessa, TX 79768
www.loopsministries.com
Monthly newsletter.

TOMORROW'S WORLD

PO Box 3810, Charlotte, NC 28227-8010
www.tomorrowsworld.org
Bi-monthly magazine.

YARD OUT | PRISONERS FOR CHRIST

PO Box 1530, Woodinville, WA 98072
www.pfcom.org
Three times annually newsletter.

HINDU

HEART TO HEART | THE AMERICAN GITA SOCIETY

515 Lowell Place, Fremont, CA 94536
www.gita-society.com
Bi-monthly newsletter.

JEHOVAH'S WITNESSES

WATCHTOWER & AWAKE

Watchtower Bible & Tract Society, 1000 Red Mills Rd., Walkill, NY 12589-3299
www.jw.org
Bi-monthly magazines.

KRISHNA

IPM FREEDOM NEWSLETTER | ISHKON PRISON MINISTRY

1400 Cherry St., Denver, CO 80220
Bi-monthly newsletter.

MESSIANIC JEWISH

MESSIANIC TIMES

PO Box 2190, Niagara Falls, NY 14302
www.messianictimes.com
Bi-monthly magazine.

NATIVE AMERICAN

NATIVE PRIDE | NATIVE AMERICAN PRIDE COM.

33 Bay Shore Dr., Bay City, MI 48706
Bi-monthly newsletter.

RED WARRIOR | RED HEART WARRIOR'S SOCIETY

PO Box 4362, Allentown, PA 18105
Quarterly newsletter.

OTHER

MEDITATION MONTHLY INTERNATIONAL | WHITE MOUNTAIN EDUCATION ASSOCIATION

543 Eastwood Dr., Prescott, AZ 86303
www.wmea.org
Bi-monthly newsletter.

Fee-Based Religious Periodicals

BUDDHIST

BUDDHADHARMA

Features on Buddhist traditions and disciplines, Eastern history, politics. More. 8 issues/year.

SHAMBHALA SUN

Buddhist magazine. Everything Buddhist. 12 issues/year.

TRICYCLE

Features on the independent voice of Buddhism in western culture. 10 issues/year.

TURNING WHEEL JOURNAL

Features a variety of information on the Buddhist faith. 4 issues/year.

CATHOLIC

AMERICA

Catholic weekly magazine. 52 issues/year.

CATECHIST MAGAZINE

Features article for catechists, DREs and religion teachers working with student's pre-school aged to adults. 7 issues/year.

CATHOLIC ANSWER, THE

Easy to read magazine on the teachings of the Catholic faith. 6 issues/year.

CATHOLIC DIGEST

Editorials of inspiration, information, and human interest stories. 12 issues/year.

LIGUORIAN

Catholic guidance, counsel, and moral education for Catholics of all ages. 10 issues/year.

OUR SUNDAY VISITOR

Coverage of important national and international news. 52 issues/year.

PRIEST, THE

For and about the priesthood. 11 issues/year.

SOJOURNERS

A Christian voice that preaches not political correctness but compassion. 10 issues/year.

TAKE OUT-FAMILY FAITH ON GO

Written for today's busy Catholic family. A mini-mag alternative of *Our Sunday Visitor*. 10 issues/year.

CHRISTIAN (NON-DENOMINATIONAL)

ANGELS ON EARTH

Stories of angels and the messages they deliver, filled with profound mystery and faith-affirming hope. 6 issues/year.

BIBLE STUDY MAGAZINE

Tools and methods for bible study and insights. 6 issues/year.

CHARISMA

For the contemporary Christians. 12 issues/year.

CHRISTIAN CENTURY

An ecumenical journal of opinion and news. 26 issues/year.

CHRISTIANITY TODAY

Features on evangelical conviction. Theory. 12 issues/year.

CHURCH EXECUTIVE

For senior pastors and church administrators. Ideas and strategies that address church issues. 12 issues/year.

HOPE TODAY

Editorial on life challenges and opportunities on an inspirational level. 12 issues/year.

KINDRED SPIRIT

Global guide to positive change. 10 issues/year.

MEN OF INTEGRITY

Daily devotionals for the unique challenges men face. 6 issues/year.

MESSAGE MAGAZINE

Features addressing African American issues. 6 issues/year.

MINISTRY TODAY

Hands on magazine for Christian leaders. 6 issues/year.

MY DAILY VISITOR

Pocket sized magazines offering scripture-of-the-day references. 6 issues/year.

RELEVANT

For forward thinking, spiritually passionate people, challenging all people to go beyond the traditional teachings. 6 issues/year.

SPORT'S SPECTRUM

Christian sport's magazine containing exclusive interviews with Christian athletes. 8 issues/year.

TODAY IN THE WORD

High-quality monthly Christian instruction and inspirational magazine of approximately 40 pages. 12 issues/year.

HINDU

HINDUISM TODAY

Interviews with spiritual leaders, news, and issues. 8 issues/year.

JEWISH

MINDSTREAM

Focuses on all issues concerning Judaism and Zionism. 6 issues/year.

MOMENT magazine

Features on the Jewish community. 6 issues/year.

MUSLIM

PRISONWORLD MAGAZINE | DAWAH INTERNATIONAL

PO Box 380, Powder Springs, GA 30127

(678) 233-8286
www.prisonworldmagazine.com

Bi-monthly Muslim-based tabloid featuring entertainment news. Proceeds go towards prison outreach programs. 6 issues/year. $5/issue (or 12 stamps.)

TAO

EMPTY VESSEL

Dedicated to the exploration and dissemination of non-religious Taoist philosophy. 4 issues/year.

OTHER

LIVING SPIRIT

Features material on all aspects of life, with a focus on teaching people to research and learn for themselves. 4 issues/year.

PARABOLA

Explores human question. 4 issues/year.

SACRED HOOP

Explores ancient sacred traditions around the world. 6 issues/year.

SCIENCE OF MIND

Offers a spiritual perspective on world events. 12 issues/year.

SEDONA JOURNAL OF EMERGENCE

Features on self and spiritual awakenings. 12 issues/year.

TATHAASTU

Features on happy and healthy life. 6 issues/year.

VIBRANT LIFE

Features on physical health, mental clarity and spiritual balance. 6 issues/year.

Part 5   Find Resources

Every prisoner requires good sources of information for whatever their ambition. Gaining an education is no exception.

This part will help you find any education-related resource you might need, and much more that will assist you in other positive directions.

Don't forget: *Prison Lives* is your one-stop source for all of your prisoner resource needs. There are a wealth of places out there that are waiting to assist you with any wish you may have, and our *Prison Lives Almanac: Prisoner Resource Guide* is just the resource you need to help you locate them.

Educational Organizations?

Prisoner Services?

Textbook Sellers?

Educational Coordinators?

EDUCATION ORGANIZATIONS

Look at the following resource listings as a treasure map.

Many of the resources will lead you right to the treasure you seek. Others will require more digging. When you contact a listing, always be sure to ask about other organizations that may provide something more in line with what you are seeking.

Don't get discouraged. The treasure you seek is out there!

These are not the only resources!

You can find numerous additional listings in specifically themed chapters throughout this guide.

ACCESS

PO Box 10253, Chicago, IL 60610
(864) 379-6669
www.accessed.org
ACCESS is a network of support for distance education faculty of Christian schools.

AMERICAN COUNCIL ON EDUCATION

One Dupont Cir. NW, Suite 250, Washington, D.C. 20036-1193
(800) 626-9433
www.aenet.edu *www.gedtest.org*
ACE regulates and provides information on GED testing and ACE credits, credits earned through supervised exams used as transfer credits to various colleges. Write for more information.

COLLEGE LEVEL EXAM BOARDS

45 Columbus Ave., New York, NY 10023
(212) 713-8000
www.collegeboard.org
Regulates and provides information on *CLEPs* (College Level Exam Programs), online testing to assess potential student's knowledge for placement in college or transfer credits.

COLLEGE GUILD

PO Box 6448, Brunswick, ME 04011
www.collegeguild.org *collegeguild@gmail.com*
The *College Guild* offers a variety of free un-accredited, non-credit, print-based college-level studies for prisoners. Their courses are designed to be thought-provoking and fun, to encourage objectivity and creativity, and to provide an opportunity to spend time constructively. Courses are developed and administered by volunteer teachers.

They offer a wide variety of subjects, including Art of the Masters, Biography, Creative Language, Drama Club, Drawing from the Inside Out, Environmental Issues, Families, Gardening, Greek Mythology, Health, Histories, Journalism Club, Logic & Puzzles, Marine Biology, Philosophy, Poetry Club, Precision Drawing, Science, Short Story Club, and Sports.

They generally have a waiting list in the range of 6-8 months.

CORRECTIONAL EDUCATION ASSOCIATION

8182 Lark Brown Rd., Suite 202, Elkridge, MD 21075
(800) 783-1232
www.ceanational.org
CEA is a professional organization of educators and administrators who provide legislative support and awareness for prison education efforts around the U.S. They typically will not work directly with prisoners, but they will work with those who support prisoner education efforts. They publish *The Journal of Correctional Education*.

DISTANCE EDUCATION ACCREDITING COMMISSION (DEAC)

1101 17th St. NW, Suite 808, Washington, DC 20036
(202) 234-5100
www.deac.org *info@deac.org* *(Corrlinks registered)*
Formerly known as the DETC, DEAC is an accrediting agency that specializes in schools that offer correspondence courses. They provide prisoners with a FREE list of current correspondence schools that are accredited by them. NOTE: There are many correspondence schools and other programs that are not listed by the DEAC.

EXCELSIOR

7 Columbia Cir., Albany, NY 12203
Provides information on Excelsior exams, formerly Regents exams, an entrance exam service used to provide schools an accurate assessment of a potential student's knowledge for placement or transfer credit.

Federal Student Aid Information Center

PO Box 84, Washington, D.C. 20044
(800) 433-3243
www.studentaid.ed.gov
FSAIC provides information on federal student aid and recent Pell grant considerations.

Inside-Out Center

Suite 331, MB 66-10, 1810 Liacouras Walk, Temple University, Philadelphia, PA 19122
(215) 204-5163
www.insideoutcenter.org insideout@temple.edu
Inside-Out Prison Exchange Program is an international education initiative to bring transformative education opportunities to prisoners through collaboration with colleges and universities around the globe. They currently offer programs in over 100 countries, have hosted over 600 courses of study and have helped over 27,000 prisoner-students. Write for programs in your area.

International Association of Bible College & Seminaries

6171 Gateway Rd., X, Columbus, GA 31909
www.iabcs.org
Provides support to religious schools and seminaries.

National College Studies

675 Blue Mountain Rd., Saugerties, NY 12477
NCS provides information on Experiential credits, college credits granted for life experience. Write for a copy of the Experiential Learning Guidebook.

Prison Entrepreneurship Program

PO Box 926274, Houston, TX 77292-6274
www.prisonentrepreneurship.org
PEP is an education program that connects prisoners with successful business people to teach them professional and entrepreneurial skills, including a 5-month business concepts and theory, and presentation and networking course. Through a thorough application process and intensive study requirements, they ensure that those involved in the program are determined and willing to improve their circumstances. You must be within three years of release, have a clean disciplinary record, and have no gang affiliations or history of sexual convictions.

Prison Scholar Fund

1752 NW Market St., #953, Seattle, WA 98107
www.prisonscholars.org
The Prison Scholar Fund works to build partnerships and find investors to supply assistance and funds for educational grants for prisoners. Prisoners are funded for a single class, with consideration for further education upon successful completion of that class. Write with a summary of your education goals and the classes you are interested in.

Scholarship Academy

50 Hurt Plaza, Suite 860, Atlanta, GA 30303
(470) 355-1732
www.scholarshipacademy.org
inquiries@scholarshipacademy.org
The Scholarship Academy is a comprehensive scholarship prepatory program that teaches low-income, first generation college students to navigate the maze of financial aid in order to fund their college education.

U.S. Department of Education

400 Maryland Ave., Washington, D.C. 20002
www.ed.gov
The U.S. Department of Education sets and maintains all education policy for schools in the U.S. They can provide general information on education options in the U.S., including accreditation, current financial aid information and answer other education-related inquiries.

Post Prison Education

Transitioning from a prison environment can be daunting. Fortunately, schools and organizations are beginning to recognize the importance of assisting students in education opportunities even after release from prison.

If you are a student-prisoner and are reentering society in one of the states that happens to contain one of the following organizations, contacting them may vastly improve your odds at continuing your education beyond bars. Generally, the following organizations provide ex-offender support through scholarship opportunities, academic advising and career counsel, advocacy, and mentoring.

CALIFORNIA

PROJECT REBOUND

Project Rebound assists formerly incarcerated students seeking to enroll in CalState, San Francisco State, or Fresno State University. They encourage and provide support to ex-offender students wishing to attend school full-time towards a bachelor degree.

PROJECT REBOUND | CALIFORNIA STATE UNIVERSITY

Fullerton: 800 N. State College Blvd., Fullerton, CA 92831
(657) 278-7859
www.fullerton.edu   rebound@fullerton.edu

Los Angeles: 5151 State University Dr., Los Angeles, CA 90032
(323) 343-3000
www.calstatela.edu

PROJECT REBOUND | FRESNO STATE UNIVERSITY

5150 N. Maple Ave., McLane Hall, H Wing, Room 187, Fresno, CA 93740-8026
(559) 278-2313
www.fresnostate.edu/studentaffairs/projectrebound

PROJECT REBOUND | SAN FRANCISCO STATE UNIVERSITY

Cesar Chavez Student Center, 1650 Holloway Ave., T-138, San Francisco, CA 94132-1722
(415) 405-0954
www.asisfu.org/rebound

UNDERGROUND SCHOLARS INITIATIVE

The *Underground Scholars Initiative* is a grassroots effort created by UC Berkeley students who have been impacted by the Prison Industrial Complex, including those formerly incarcerated or with incarcerated family members. They create a pathway for ex-offenders and system impacted individuals to gain a higher education at UC Berkeley.

They also offer a correspondence program for currently incarcerated individuals to help them reach their academic goals. This includes transcript analysis, and connecting them with Ambassadors at their local community colleges once released.

UNDERGROUND SCHOLARS INITIATIVE | UC BERKELEY

2495 Bancroft Way, Berkeley, CA 94704
(510) 643-2226
www.callink.berkeley.edu/organizations/usi

WASHINGTON

POST-PRISON EDUCATION PROGRAM

The *Post-Prison Education Program* is the only Washington state program that offers wrap-around services to releasing prisoners and their families in conjunction with providing them, access, support, and the resources to attain post-secondary education. The program focuses its efforts on uneducated communities, low income communities, and communities of color. The Program works within prisons and in partnership with a state-wide network of community and governmental organizations to recruit students, fund the students' educational needs, and connect students to existing community services.

POST-PRISON EDUCATION PROGRAM

810 Third Ave., Suite 180, Seattle, WA 98104
(206) 524-3333
www.postprisonedu.org

Online Education (FREE)

Academic Earth

1001 McKinney St., Suite 650, Houston, TX 77002
(281) 846-3073
www.academicearth.org
Academic Earth was among the earliest developers of FREE online education. They provide listings of the best educational opportunities that are available across the web, as well as hosts the Open Education Database (http://oedb.org/open), which offers a collection of over 10,000 FREE online courses.

Carnegie Mellon University | Open Learning Initiative

www.oli.cmu.edu
Carnegie Mellon's Open Learning Initiative provides many of the same courses taught in universities around the world. You will gain the education, however, they do not provide certificates of completion nor any verification of learning.

Coursera

www.coursera.org
Coursera partners with top universities and organizations worldwide to provide access to world-class educational opportunities in almost any subject. They currently offer over a thousand courses through more than 100 partner schools.

EdX

141 Portland St., 9th Floor, Cambridge, MA 02139
www.edx.org
EdX is a FREE online education initiative created through a partnership between Harvard and MIT, established to offer classes and MOOCs (see glossary) from the world's best universities, including MIT, Harvard, Berkeley, University of Texas, and many others. Classes in a wide range of subjects cover many of the same curriculums in these prestigious and otherwise expensive schools.

Free Video Lectures

www.freevideolectures.com/free-college-courses-online
Free video lectures offer a collection of over 1000 FREE lectures in more than 25 subjects from Ivy League universities and the best colleges around the U.S., including MIT, Yale, Harvard, Stanford, McGill, as well as independent schools such as the Khan Academy. Several of their courses even offer certificates of completion or course credit.

Harvard University | Harvard Extension

51 Brattle St., Cambridge, MA 02138
(617) 495-4024
www.extension.harvard.edu/open-learning-initiative
Harvard Extension offers a variety of online courses that are also taught through traditional Harvard classes. Many of their courses are FREE, but some courses have fees. Fee-based courses typically offer college credit.

MIT | OpenCourseWare

77 Massachusetts Ave., Cambridge, MA 02139-4307
(617) 253-1000
http://ocw.mit.edu
MIT's OpenCourseWare provides nearly all of MIT's course materials, over 2,200 in all, online for FREE to anyone who would like to use them for self-paced study. No credit or certificates are awarded.

Open University

44 (845) 300-60-90
www.open.edu
Open University is the first and largest online university in the UK. They offer thousands of FREE courses and provide FREE access to over 15,000 research publications.

Tufts University | OpenCourseWare

Medford, MA 02155
(617) 628-5000
http://ocw.tufts.edu
Tufts OpenCourseWare, established by MIT, provides Tufts University course materials online for FREE, and offers feedback on courses taken.

Udacity

2465 Latham St., 3rd Floor, Mountain View, CA 94040
www.udacity.com
Udacity offers a variety of courses that were developed and taught by leaders in the tech community. Classes involve hands-on projects, lectures, and expert feedback and offer credentials upon completion.

University of the People

http://uopeople.edu
University of the People is the world's first non-profit completely FREE accredited online university, (accredited by Distance Education Accrediting Council – DEAC). They offer tuition-free associate and bachelor's degree programs in Business Administration and Computer Science.

PRISONER SERVICES

Booksellers

AK PRESS

674-A 23rd St., Oakland, CA 94612
www.akpress.org
Wide variety of titles, with many anarchy listings. 30% discount to prisoners. Thousands of titles. FREE catalog.

AMERICAN CORRECTIONAL ASSOCIATION | PUBLICATIONS DEPARTMENT

206 N. Washington St., Suite 200, Alexandria, VA 22314
www.aca.org
300+ titles on various topics. Many self-help options. FREE catalog.

B.B.P.D.

PO Box 248, Compton, MD 20627
www.bookstoinmates.com
500+ titles on various topics (see below). $3.95 shipping for the entire order. FREE catalog.

BBPD Book categories include:
- Street Life
- African/Indigenous
- Antebellum
- Business/Economics
- Civil Rights/Black Liberation
- Classical African Civilization
- Health/Nutrition
- Islam
- Languages
- Law
- Espanol
- Magazines
- Masonry/Secret Societies
- Modern Black/Religious Thought
- Political Issues
- Prison Life-experience
- Psychology/Education
- Religious Anthropology
- Sociology/Family/Love
- Spiritual Philosophy

BLACK MEDIA FAMILY

PO Box 27514, Lansing, MI 48909-7514
blackmediafamily@gmail.com
Write for a current listing of publications. Catalog features mostly urban/street titles.

BOOKS 'N THINGS WAREHOUSE

PO Box 7330, Shrewsbury, NJ 07702-7330
(800) 681-2740
www.mybntw.com
Books' N Things Warehouse sells a wide variety of books of every genre, as well as calendars, journals, toys, and more. Write for a FREE catalog.

BOOKRAK

PO Box 104720, Jefferson City, MO 65110-4720
(800) 456-1774
www.bookrak.com

All paperback books, in all genres, but are limited in non-fiction. Shipping cost can add up to as high as $4.70 per order. FREE catalog as frequently as monthly.

BUD PLANT'S BOOKS

PO Box 1689, Grass Valley, CA 95945
www.budplant.com
Bud Plant's offers a comprehensive listing of contemporary art and photography titles, comic book related titles, nude and female from books and many others. Send for a FREE catalog.

CLEIS PRESS

101 Hudson St., 37th Floor, Suite 3705, Jersey City, NJ 07302
(646) 257-4343
www.cleispress.com
Cleis Press publishes books for the LGBT community, as well as BDSM, romance, and erotic collections. Write for a catalog.

EDEN PRESS

PO Box 8410, Fountain Valley, CA 92728
www.edenpress.com
Wide variety of topics. Catalog features extensive listing of how-to titles. FREE catalog.

EDWARD R. HAMILTON BOOKSELLERS

PO Box 15, Falls Village, CT 06031-0015
www.hamiltonbooks.com   www.erhb.com
Great option for prisoners. FREE comprehensive color catalogs with thousands of titles. All topics. Once you place an order with them, you will continue to receive their comprehensive catalogs for years. They are accustomed to dealing with prison-specific issues, although you should be aware of what your prison system allows before placing an order. $3.50 shipping for entire order.

GRADUATE GROUP

PO Box 370351, West Hartford, CT 06137
www.graduategroup.com
Catalog contains mostly prisoner help and reentry titles. Send SASE for current listings.

GROUNDWORK BOOKS

10323 Student Center, La Jolla, CA 92037
(858) 452-9625
groundwork@libertad.ucsd.edu
Specializes in geography, political science, social civics, criminal justice, and history. 40% discount to prisoners. May send up to two FREE books to prisoners who are indigent. Stamp donations are appreciated.

HAYMARKET BOOKS

PO Box 180165, Chicago, IL 60618

(773) 538-7884
www.haymarketbooks.org
Haymarket books publishes and distributes radical-themed titles reflecting the values of social justice reform activists. Discounts are offered to prisoners. Write for a catalog.

HIT POINTE

540 N. Lapeer Rd., Suite 255, Orion Township, MI 48362
(248) 845-8229
www.hitpointe.com services@hitpointe.com
Hit Pointe offers a wide selection of fantasy and roll-playing game-related books, such as D&D, Pathfinder, etc., as well as board games and trading cards. Some used books are available. Write for FREE catalog.

HONEY BEAR BOOKS

PO Box 422, Fort George Station, New York, NY, 10040
Honey Bear Books distributes spicy magazines, trading cards, and calendars, magazines: $7.95; Calendars:$12.95; Trading cards: $6/set of 12. Send SASE for more info.

IMAILTOPRISON.COM   *New Listing*

1115 FM 517 Road East, Dickinson, TX, 77539-8644
(281) 534-370
www.imailtoprison.com
IMailtoPrison.com offers a wide variety of books and magazines. Send SASE for more info.

INTELLIGENT SOLUTIONS

4-831 Kuhio Highway, Suite 438-333, Kapaa, HI 96746
(800) 770-8802
www.toolsforfreedom.com
Mostly 'get-rich-quick' and infomercial related titles. Features over 700 titles. FREE catalog.

JAGUAR BOOKS

6881 Stanton Ave., #F, Buena Park, CA 90621
Variety of genres, English and Spanish. Send $1 or 3 stamps for catalog.

KILL SHOT KING

PO Box 81074, Corpus Christi, TX 78468
www.killshotking.com
Kill Shot Kings (KSK) sells a variety of discounted popular new and used books. They provide additional discounts for large orders (of 9 or more). All prices include tax, shipping, tracking, and insurance. Send SASE for FREE current sample catalog or $2.50 (10 FCS) for full catalog of over 1,000 book titles. They will also provide price quotes on any book: 5 quotes for 2 FCSs and a SASE. (2 FCSs for each additional 5 quotes.)

They also sell a large variety of intimate girl pictures, as well as intimate calendars, and "unbound books."

ACE LANFRANCO PUBLICATIONS

5447 Van Fleet Ave., Richmond, CA 94804-5929

ACE Lanfranco Publications offers publication and ad-sheets, such as the Bay Area Advertiser. Write for current list of publications.

LEFT BANK BOOKS

92 Pike St., Box A, Seattle, WA 98101
www.leftbankbooks.com

Small family-owned website specializing in small publishers. Catalog must be printed from their website. Accepts stamps for payment.

LOCKDOWN BOOKSTORE, THE

PO Box 215, Moorpark, CA 93020
(888) 858-2676

Limited titles, mostly erotica. Send $1 and SASE for current catalog.

NATIONAL LAWYERS GUILD

132 Nassau St., Suite 922, New York, NY 10038
www.nlg.org
FREE book list. Mostly legal titles.

NOTES & NOVELS

12436 FM 1960 West, PMB 177, Houston, TX 77065
(281) 890-8911
www.notesandnovels.com

Offers a wide variety of topics and thousands of titles. Send $9 or 30 FCS for 95-page catalog containing thousands of books, calendars, journals, magazines, and stationary.

OPEN, INC.

PO Box 472223, Garland, TX 75047
www.openinc.org
FREE book list. Limited selections.

OXFORD UNIVERSITY PRESS

198 Madison Ave., New York, NY 10016
(816) 445-8685
www.oup.com

FREE Oxford University/Oceana book list. Specializes in legal and reference titles.

PAPERBACK SWAP 'N SHOP

1115 FM 517 Road East, Dickinson, TX 77539
(281) 534-3370
www.imailtoprison.com

The Paperback Swap 'n Shop offers 'grab bag' used book specials, such as a three foot stack of books for $30 to $54. They also offer magazine subscriptions. Write for current offerings.

PATHFINDER PRESS

PO Box 167767, Atlanta, GA 30321-2767
(404) 669-0600
www.pathfinderpress.com

Specializes in the "works of revolutionary and world class leaders" in all major languages, as well as Swedish, Farsi, and Indonesian. $3 for entire order. Orders must be placed online. 50% discount for prisoners. FREE catalog.

PM PRESS

Po Box 23912, Oakland, CA 94623
(510) 658-3906
www.pmpress.org

Features mostly counter-culture and anti-incarceration titles. 50% off for prisoners. FREE catalog.

PRISON PUBLICATIONS

PO Box 174, Thompson, CT, 06277
www.prisonpublication.com   info@prisonpublications.com

Prison Publications offer books, including new and used options, and some magazine subscriptions. Send SASE for more info

SOUTH END PRESS

PO Box 382132, Cambridge, MA 02238
(718) 955-4841
www.southendpress.org

Specializes in radical topics. 50% discount for prisoners. Free catalog.

SPECIAL NEEDS X-PRESS

3128 Villa Ave., Bronx, NY 10468
(718) 220-3786
www.shopsnx.com

Special Needs X-Press specializes in ordering books and magazines. However, orders must be placed through their website. If you have the ability to receive these items through primary distributors, such as Amazon, you will likely have better results. They also offer gift options. See separate listing.

NOTE: Reviews are currently mixed on this new listing. Come back to our Fall Prisoner Entertainment Guide for a full review.

SURESHOT BOOKS PUBLISHING

PO Box 924, Nyack, NY 10960
(845) 675-7505
www.sureshotbooks.com

They have a wide variety of subjects, including books, magazines and newspapers. Catalog costs $12.95 (which can be purchased with 2 books of FCS – catalog only, not books). Note: They accept email through most prison providers.

TEXAS PRISON BOOKSTORE

1301 DuPont Cir, Orange, TX, 77630
www.texasprisonbookstore.com

Texas Prison Bookstore offers a wide variety of discounted books. Many for as low as $3.99, as well as magazine and writing supplies. Request catalog.

VALLEY MERCHANDISERS

1134 Outer Dr., Hagerstown, MD 21742

Specialize in hard-to-find and out of print books. They will do searches for books and sell them at discounted prices to prisoners and families.

VENTURA BOOKS

7928 Oak St., Los Molinos, CA 96055

Limited variety, specializing in erotica titles. Send SASE for current catalog.

WHOA BOOKS — New Listing

PO Box 226, Bloomfield, NJ, 07003

www.whoabooks.com   *whoabooks1@gmail.com*

Whoa Books carries many urban themed books and magazines. Send SASE for more info.

FREE Books

Keep in Mind...

Most FREE-books-to prisoners programs are sparsely staffed donor-supported organizations. They are generally established out of the kindness of individuals who wish they had the ability to fill all requests as specifically and as quickly as the requestor would like them filled. Therefore, please be patient with them, and keep the following in mind.

They are typically not a library or bookstore, and likely will not have specific titles.

Keep requests generalized, as in 'Dictionary', beginner Spanish, thriller novels, etc. Do not ask for a specific title or author and expect to get it.

Send backup requests, 2nd, 3rd, and 4th options.

If you are looking for education books, specify what grade level, as in High school, college, professional, etc.

Write neatly and be sure to provide you name, prison ID, and address.

Mention any restriction your prison may have, as in paperback only, maximum number allowed per order, whether used is okay, or if an invoice is required.

Take note of the states serviced in the listing.

Above all, BE PATIENT. And, oh yeah, did we mention 'be patient'?

FREE BOOK Topics

Most of the following book providers ask that you request books by topic instead of title. This makes their process much simpler. Unless otherwise noted, the following topic index can be used when requesting books from these providers. Not every book provider will have books on every topic below, so give plenty of options in your request.

addiction	biology	dreams
Africa	brain science	economics
African American	business	education
AIDS/HIV	career	engineering
alternative technology	Caribbean	exercise
anthropology	chemistry	fantasy
archeology	comics	feminism
architecture	computers	film
art/drawing	cookbooks/food	foreign language (specify)
Asia/Pacific	death/dying	games/puzzles
astrology	dictionaries	gardening
astronomy	disease (specify)	geology
biography/Memoir	drama	global warming

graphic novels
health
historical fiction
history (specify time or locale)
humor
incarceration
large-print
Latino/Chicano
LGBT/gender studies
literature/classics
mathematics
Middle East
music
mysteries/crime
mythology
National Geographic mags
occult

parenting
philosophy
photography
physics
poetry
political science
Prison Legal News mags
psychology
racism
radical 'zines
reading
reference
religion (specify)
research
romance
science fiction
sexual abuse

self-help
shamanism
short stories
sociology
South America
Spanish (books in)
spirituality
sports
statistics
travel/outdoor
UFO/conspiracy
war
westerns
Wicca
women's health
writing/grammar
yoga

AMERICAN CORRECTIONAL ASSOCIATION

8025 Laurel Lakes, Laurel, MD 20707-5075
Serves: All states except Oregon. No religious or legal books.

ANTIOCH COLLEGE BOOKS TO PRISONERS PROJECT

One Morgan Place, Yellow Springs, OH 45387
Serves: ALL states.

APPALACHIAN PRISON BOOK PROJECT

PO Box 601, Morgantown, WV 26507
Aprisonbookproject.wordpress.com
appalachianbp@gmail.com
Serves: KY, MD, OH, TN, VA, and WV.

BEEHIVE BOOKS BEHIND BARS | WELLER BOOK WORKS

607 Trolley Square, Salt Lake City, UT 84102
(801) 319-5051
www.beehivebooksbehindbars.com
Serves: AZ, CA, CO, ID, MT, NM, NV, OR, UT, WA, and WY.

BOOK 'EM

PO Box 7137, Pittsburgh, PA 12513
(412) 251-7302
Serves: Pennsylvania only. Primarily supplies educational and non-fiction books and magazines.

BOOKS THROUGH BARS | NEW SOCIETY PUBLISHERS

4722 Baltimore Ave., Philadelphia, PA 19143
(215) 727-8170
www.booksthroughbars.org
Serves: DE, MD, NJ, NY, PA, VA, and WV.

BOOKS THROUGH BARS NYC | BLUESTOCKINGS BOOKSTORE

172 Allen St., New York, NY 10002
www.booksthroughbarsnyc.com
Serves: ALL states except AL, FL, LA, MA, MI, MS, NC, PA, and OH. Priority is given to NY prisoners. They specialize in history and political books, with some literary fiction and educational books. No religious books.

BOOKS THROUGH BARS ITHACA | AUTUMN LEAVES BOOKSTORE

115 The Commons, 2nd Floor, Ithaca, NY 14850
(607) 645-0250
prisonactivist@gmail.com
Serves: CA, FL, NY, PA, TX, and others. Write to see if your sate is included.

BOOKS TO OREGON PRISONERS

PO Box 11222, Portland, OR 97211
www.bookstooregonprisoners.org
Serves: Oregon only.

BOOKS TO PRISONERS | JOINT EFFORT

PO Box 78005, Vancouver, BC, Canada V5N 5W1
Serves: Canadian prisoners only.

BOOKS TO PRISONERS | LEFT BANK BOOKS

92 Pike St., Box A, Seattle, WA 98101
(206) 442-2013
www.bookstoprisoners.net
Serves: ALL states except CA or states that require first class postage or new books. No religious or legal books. Stamps or donations are appreciated

BRAILLE INSTITUTE LIBRARY SERVICE

741 N. Vermont Ave., Los Angeles, CA 90029

FREE Braille books to prisoners who are legally blind.

CHICAGO BOOKS TO WOMEN IN PRISON

PO Box 14778, Chicago, IL 60614
www.chicagobwp.org   chicagobwp@gmail.com
Serves: Women prisoners in all states.

CLAREMONT PRISON LIBRARY PROJECT

PMB 128, 915-C W. Foothill Blvd., Claremont, CA 91711
Serves: ALL states. Specializes in self-help personal, and spiritual growth publications. No legal, technical, or GED.

CLEVELAND BOOKS TO PRISONERS

PO Box 602440, Cleveland, OH 44102
Serves: ALL states. They give priority to Ohio prisoners.

DC BOOKS TO PRISONS PROJECT

PO Box 34190, Washington, DC 20043-4190
www.dcbookstoprisoners.org   btodc@gmail.com
Serves: ALL states EXCEPT CT, IL, MA, ME, NH, NJ, NY, OH, OR, PA, RI, VT, WA, and WV. They will ship two books per request, one request allowed every 6-month period.

EAST BAY PRISONER SUPPORT

PO Box 22449, Oakland, CA 94609
www.eastbayprisonersupport.wordpress.com
Serves: CA, AZ, NM, TX, UT, and NV. They primarily provide anarchist titles. They will send magazines to LGBT prisoners and women in any state. Write for a catalog.

GROUNDWORK BOOKS

0323 Student Center, La Jolla, CA 92037
(858) 452-9625
groundwork@libertad.ucsd.edu
Serves: ALL states. Specializes in geography, political science, social civics, criminal justice, and history. May send up to two FREE books to prisoners who are indigent. Stamp donations are appreciated. Note: Thy also sell books at a 40% discount to prisoners.

INSIDE BOOKS PROJECT | 12TH STREET BOOKS

827 W. 12th St., Austin, TX 78701
(512) 655-3121
www.insidebooksproject.org
contact@insidebooksproject.org
Serves: Texas only, except Del Valle. No hardcover books, bibles, pulp fiction, or pornography.

INTERNATIONAL PRISON BOOK COLLECTIVE | INTERNATIONALIST BOOKS

405 W. Franklin St., Chapel Hill, NC 27516
www.prisonbooks.info
Serves: AL, MS, and some NC prisons.

LOUISIANA BOOKS TO PRISONERS

1631 Elysian Fields, #117, New Orleans, LA 70117
lab2p@wordpress.com   books2prisoners@gmail.com
Serves: Al, AR, FL, GA, KY, LA, MS, NC, SC, TN, VA, and WV. They give priority to women and Louisiana prisoners. No legal books or almanacs.

MAOIST INTERNATIONAL MINISTRY OF PRISONS (MIM)

PO Box 40799, San Francisco, CA 94140
www.prisoncensorship.info   mim@prisoncensorship.info
Serves: ALL states. MIM specializes in political, legal, and historical books, as well as some dictionaries and other reference books. They expect work in exchange for books, such as writing articles for their newsletter, sharing literature, leading campaigns and other advocacy. Stamps are appreciated.

MIDWEST BOOKS TO PRISONERS | QUIMBY BOOKSTORE

1321 N. Milwaukee Ave., PMB. #460, Chicago, IL 60622
(312) 842-7390
www.midwestb2p.com
Serves: IA, IL, IN, KS, MI, MN, ND, MO, NE, OH, SD and WI.

MIDWEST PAGES TO PRISONERS PROJECT | BOXCAR BOOKS AND COMMUNITY CENTER

PO Box 1384, Bloomington, IN 47402
(812) 727-0155
www.pagestoprisoners.org
Serves: AZ, AR, FL, IA, IN, KS, KY, MN, MO, ND, OH, OK, SD, TN, and WI.

OPEN BOOKS PRISON BOOK PROJECT

1040 N. Guillemard St. Pensacola, FL 32501
(850) 453-6774
www.openbookspcola.org
Serves: Florida only.

PRISON BOOK PROGRAM | ASHEVILLE

67 N. Lexington Ave., Asheville, NC 28801
www.main.nc.us/prisonbooks   prisonbooks31@hotmail.com
Serves: GA, NC, SC, and TN. If your institution requires prior approval, you must include approval with your book request. Stamps appreciated.

PRISON BOOK PROGRAM | THE READERS CORNER

31 Montford Ave., Asheville, NC 28801
www.main.nc.us/prisonbooks   prisonbooks31@hotmail.com
Serves: NC, SC, GA, and TN only.

PRISON BOOK PROGRAM QUINCY | LUCY PARSONS BOOKSTORE

1306 Hancock St., Suite 100, Quincy, MA 02169
www.prisonbookprogram.org info@prisonbookprogram.org
Serves: ALL states EXCEPT CA, IL, MD, MI, NV, and TX.

Note: Allows two free book shipments per year. They also offer a 6-page National Prisoner Resource List and an LGBTQ resource list, FREE to prisoners.

PRISON BOOK PROJECT

PO Box 396, Amherst, MA 01004
(413) 584-8975
www.prisonbooks.org prisonbookproject@riseup.net
Serves: CT, MA, ME, NH, RI, TX, and VT.

PRISON LIBRARY PROJECT

915-C W. Foothill Blvd., PMB 128, Claremont, CA 91711-3356
(909) 626-3066
www.cprisonlibraryproject.org
Serves: ALL states EXCEPT HI, MA, MI, MS, NE, NV, PA, VA, and WI. PLP specializes in self-help, personal and spiritual growth, wellness, and metaphysical books. No law or technical books.

PRISONER'S LITERATURE PROJECT | BOUND TOGETHER BOOKS

1369 Haight St., San Francisco, CA 94117
(415) 672-7858
www.prisonersliteratureproject.com prisonlit@gmail.com
Serves: ALL states EXCEPT OR and TX. No thrillers, westerns, or romance books. Stamp donations appreciated.

PROVIDENCE BOOKS THROUGH BARS | MYOPIC BOOKS

42 Lenex Ave., Providence, RI 02907-1910
(401) 356-0388
www.providencebtb.org info@providencebtb.org
Serves: ALL states.

READ BETWEEN THE BARS | DAILY PLANET PUBLISHING

PO Box 1589, Tucson, AZ 85072-1589
www.readbetweenthebars.com
readbetweenthebars@gmail.com
Serves: Arizona only.

UC BOOKS TO PRISONERS

PO Box 515, Urbana, IL 61803
(708) 782-4608
www.books2prisoners.org
Serves: Illinois only.

WISCONSIN BOOKS TO PRISONERS

426 W. Gilman St., Madison, WI 53703
(608) 262-9026
Serves: Wisconsin and LGBT prisoners nationwide.

WOMEN'S PRISON BOOK PROJECT | BONESHAKER BOOKS

2002 23rd Ave. South, Minneapolis, MN 55404
www.wpbp.com womensprisonbookproject@gmail.com
Serves: Women and transgender prisoners in ALL states EXCEPT CA, FL, IL, IN, MA, MI, MS, OH, OR, and PA.

Office Services / Personal Assistants

4EVER CONNECTED

PO Box 47898, Tulsa, OK, 74147
changeiscoming2016@gmail.com
4ever Connected offers a variety of prisoner assistance services including email, social media monitoring, sports betting, messaging, calling plans and more. Send SASE for more info.

A BOOK YOU WANT

PO Box 16141, Rumford, RI 02916
zling13@comcast.net
A Book You Want provides ordering services, including, books, gifts, and more. They will also do internet searches, print out lyrics, etc. Accepts stamps as payment.

ACADIA IMAGING SERVICES BUREAU

2040 Westlake Ave. N, #307, Seattle, WA 98109
Acadia offers document, slide and photo scanning services. They will scan handwritten or printed documents into digital form for 10 cents/page (b&w) or 17 cents/page (color). Great for prison writers.

ACE SERVICES ORGANIZATION

PO Box 1799, Patterson, NJ 07509-17799
aorganization3@aol.com
Ace Services Organization offers general prisoner assistance services such as email, internet research, social media, phone number setup, mail and banking services, typing, copies and more. Send SASE for more information and pricing.

AMBLER DOCUMENTS

PO Box 938, Norwalk, CT 06852
(203) 849-0708
www.protypeexpress.com
Ambler Documents provides typing and layout services. They accept handwritten documents, but not legal paperwork. Prices start at $2 per double-spaced page.

COMPUTERZ FOR CONVICTZ

104 Rolling Rock Rd., Tempe, GA 30179-3656
Computerz for Convictz provides computer services for prisoners, including internet research , social media set up, and more. Write for more information.

CYBER HUT DESIGNS

PO Box 541, North Dighton, MA 02764
www.freebirdpublishers.com
Cyber Hut Designs offers web and graphic design services, including web pages, book covers, brochures and more. Write for list of current services.

ELITE PARALEGAL AND PRISONER SERVICES (EPS)

PO Box 1717, Appleton, WI 54912-1717
(920) 749-1060
www.eliteparalegalservices.us
EPS provides a variety of services with a focus on paralegal assistance. Stamps accepted. Send SASE for more information.

FOR THE SCOOP

PO Box 90594, San Antonio, TX 78209
www.forthescoop.com   info@forthescoop.com
For the Scoop provides email news service, including world, U.S., and sports news, and TV schedules, direct to *TruLincs* accounts. $2/month. *TruLincs* users only.

FULL HOUSE TYPING & EDITING

New Listing

PO Box 361402, Decatur, GA, 30036
Full House Typing & Editing offers document and manuscript typing, editing and copyrighting. Pricing begins at $1.50 per page. Send SASE for more info.

NOTE: They will not allow writings containing witchcraft or satanic themes or gratuitous pornegraphic content.

HAWKEYE EDITING

PO Box 16405, St. Paul, MN 55116
Hawkeye Editing provides manuscript typing and editing services. Services are available through *CorrLinks*. Send SASE for more information.

HELP FROM BEYOND THE WALLS

PO Box 185, Springvale, ME 04083
helpfrombeyondethewalls@gmail.com
Help From Beyond the Walls provides prisoner assistance services, including copies, email services, *Facebook* setup, internet research, pen pal registry, stamp buying and more. Send SASE for brochure.

HELPING HANDS

PO Box 1793, Gastonia, NC 28054
Helping Hands provides prisoner publishing services, including editing, formatting, cover design, social media setup and more. Payment plans available. Send SASE for more information.

HELP FROM OUTSIDE

2620 Bellevue Way NE, #200, Bellevue, WA 98004
(206) 486-6042
www.helpfromoutside.com   info@helpfromoutside.com
Help From Outside provides a wide range of prisoner assistance services, including administrative, paralegal,

internet researching, purchases, email, publishing, and banking services. $200 initial deposit, $25 application fee. $30/hour for most services, charged in 15-minute increments ($7.50). Send for FREE brochure.

INFO LINES

PO Box 644, Shady Cove, OR, 97539
(541) 878-2600
www.infolines.com
Info Lines offers a variety of prisoner assistance services, including photo forwarding, gift purchasing and info services such as stock quotes, daily sports lines and news.

IN SCAN DOCUMENT SERVICES

401 Wilshire Blvd., 12th Floor, Santa Monica, CA 90401
(800) 470-5338
www.inscan.com
In Scan offers document scanning services. Send you documents, which they will scan, store, and send back your originals to you. One-time storage fee of $59.99, plus the price of scanning, ($0.30/page, up to 500 pages; $0.25/per page, over 500 pages.)

INMATE AID

PO Box 2451, Forrest City, AR 72336

6803 Lake Worth Rd, Suite 200, Greenacres, FL, 33467-2980
(866) 966-7100
www.inmateaid.com
Inmate Aid offers a variety of prisoner info services, including latest state and federal law changes, prison reforms appellate decisions, etc. They will also assist with discount calling plans, money transfers, mail services and an online social network for prisoners/friends/family. Send SASE for more info.

INMATE CONCIERGE SERVICES

450 W. Hanes Mill Rd., Suite 226, Winston-Salem, NC 27105
(336) 926-0079
inmateconciergeservices@gmail.com
Inmate Concierge Services offers a wide range of prisoner assistance services, including photocopies, internet research, book and catalog orders and more. Send SASE for pricing and more information.

INMATE LOVE LINK

4001 Inglewood Ave., Suite 144, Redondo Beach, CA 90278
www.inmatelovelink.com *support@inmatelovelink.com*
Inmate Love Link offers a variety of basic prisoner assistant services, including photocopies, email, and pen pal services (see separate listing.)

INMATE PHOTO PROVIDER | IPP

PO Box 2451, Forrest City, AR 72336

(870) 317-7561
www.inmatephotoprovider.com
socialmedia@inmatephotoprovider.com (CorrLinks)
IPP offers a number social media/dating site set up and monitoring services. For a flat fee ($15/site) they will set up your profile on the your choice of the most popular sites, such as Facebook, Twitter, Plenty of Fish, Instagram, among others. Provide your site of choice along with a 200-word bio and up to 4 photos. They will provide you with a copy of your page and log-on information. They can also upload photos to existing accounts ($7.50 for up to 10), and monitor your existing profiles ($21 to $60/month, depending on your package of choice).

IPP also specializes in providing quick and easy photo delivery services. [See our Photo Service Providers section] and gift options [See our Gift section.]

Send SASE for complete information on services offered.

Money Gram accepted: Richardett Edwards, same address, email: Jonese531@yahoo.com

INMATE SCRIBES

PO Box 818, Appleton, WI 54912
Inmate Scribes offers a number of individual and packaged services, including email, social media, research, friend finding, photos, personal gifts and more.

INMATE SERVICES

PO Box 535547, Grand Prairie, TX 75053
(214) 298-2603
J161jones@yahoo.com

INMATE SERVICES CORP.

PO Box 25851, Honolulu, HI 96830
iscEyeCandy.com *iscFeedbackForum@gmail.com*
Inmate Services Corp. offers a variety of services geared towards CorrLinks users, such as texting services, sports lines, market updates, and photo forwarding. But the also offer gifts, social media setup and monitoring, and the Eye Candy magazine.

Eye Candy launched it's inaugural edition in May 2017. It is a bi-monthly 96-page full-color magazine featuring mostly scantily-clad women (BOP friendly) and a few articles on varied topics. (single issues: $8.99 + $3.75 s/h; one year: $29.99.) Send SASE for more info.

IT'S GORGEOUS SECRETARIAL SERVICES

PO Box 41454, Washington, DC 20018
(202) 582-9924
www.itsGorgeousLLC.com *lgsecservices@gmail.com*
It's Gorgeous LLC offers some prisoner services, specializing in social media setup and monitoring. They also offer gift-buying services and photo printing. Send SASE for more info.

J&J SERVICES

PO Box 200261, Arlington, TX 76006

J&J Services provides pen pal sing-up assistance. They will advertise multiple site listing sign-ups for a one-time $30 fee.

LeNoir Publications

350 Bay St., Suite 100-361, San Francisco, CA 94133
(877) 786-4290
www.lenoirpublications.com
services@lenoirpublications.com

Lenoir Publications provides prisoner publishing services, including editing, typing, printing, and distribution. Send for FREE information.

Let Me Write It For You

PO Box 156, Clarksville, TN, 37041
(931) 269-9718
www.letmewriteitforyou.org
LetMeWriteItForYou@gmail.com

Let Me Write It For You provides professional writing services, specializing in resumes. Send SASE for welcome kit.

Let My Fingers Do Your Typing

c/o Sandra Z. Thomas, PO Box 4178, Winter Park, FL 21793-4178
(407) 579-5563

Let My Fingers Do Your Typing provides typing, printing, and copy services for prisoners.

Midnight Express Books

PO Box 69, Berryville, AR 72616
(870) 210-3772
mebooks1@yahoo.com

Midnight Express Books provides prisoner book publishing services, including editing, formatting, cover design, and more. They also offer web design, social media posting, book/magazine search/purchase, and more. Send SASE for more information.

MSent

www.msent.com

MSent let's users instantly send letters and photos to loved ones in prison.

On Demand Inmate Services

PO Box 81, Cheltenham, PA 19012
(318) 277-9712
ondemandis@yahoo.com

On Demand provides general prisoner assistance, including posting personal bios online, intimate photos, gift shopping and more. Send $2, or 4 stamps for catalog and services.

Prisoner Inmate Family Service

PO Box 1852, Pismo Beach, CA 93448
www.PrisonerInmateFamilyService.com
FamilyInmateSev@aol.com

Prisoner Inmate Family Service provides a variety of personal assistant services, including internet research, mail services, gift packages, and stamp purchasing ($7.50/new book of Forever stamps, $0.25 for singles). Send SASE for more information.

Prisoner Promotions

691 S. Green Bay Rd., #212, Neenah, WI 54956

Prisoner Promotions provides prisoner social media assistance, including email and social media posting. They also offer catalog ordering, photocopying, photo services and a prisoner store for prisoners to sell creations. Send SASE for brochure.

Prison Legendary Service (LS)

PO Box 686, Eustace, TX 75124
www.PrisonLS.com

Prison LS provides a number of prisoner services, including magazine/book/gift ordering, printing, web research, investigative and Parole Pack services. They also offer social media/pen pal signup and monitoring, website setup and photo-selling (see separate listing).They also offer a number of other prisoner services, as well as photo-selling (see separate listings). Stamps are accepted as payment (at roughly 65% of face value – 3 Forever stamps for $1). Send SASE for complete information.

Website Building: Basic personal website containing your own named domain, bio and pictures: $100/year. Marketing of your site: $150/year (in addition to web page build). They will send you a quote for more complex website needs.

Social Media: Account setup on free sites (i.e., Facebook, Tagged, Tinder) with 5 photos, profile and 150-word first post: $20 Sign-up on paid services is available for $40 plus site fees (includes 3 months of basic monitoring.)

SGDI products

PO Box 502, Dalzell, SC, 29040
(803) 840-7579
sgdiproducts@gmail.com

SGDI Products offer basic prison assistance services including online purchases, gift buying and clerical services.

They also offer a magazine list. Send SASE for info. Stamps Accepted.

SPECIAL MIRACLES

New Listing

PO Box 46884, Cincinnati, CA, 45246
www.specialmiraclesllc.com   info@specialmiracles.com
Special mMracles offers a wide range of prisoner assistance services, including legal and reentry assistance, messaging, photoshopping, copying, gift purchasing and more. Send SASE with 3 FCS for catalog.

SURE PLEASURES PROMOTIONS/INMATE DIGITAL

PO Box 552201, Opa Locka, FL, 33055
www.inmatedigitalservices.com

New Listing

Sure Pleasures Promotions offers digital services to Corrlinks users, including texting and news downloads. Sign up through their email address: Inmate digital services@Gmail.com

TEXT TO WRITE.COM

New Listing

PO Box 531038, Orlando, FL, 32853-1038
(818) 538-8371
www.texttowrite.com   contact@texttowrite.com
Text to Write offers friends/family a Text-to-letter service. Messages and photos can be emailed or Texted, which will be converted to physical form and mailed to prisoners.

TFL

77 Old Glenham Rd, #117
(860) 484-3835
www.tflservices.com   tfldoesit@gmail.com
TFL offers a variety of services, including gift purchases, internet assistance and other services. They also offer a pen pal ad forwarding service. If you have a pen pal ad out there already, they will re-list your ad through other providers. Service fee of $15.

ULTIMATE INMATE ASSISTANTS (UIA)

PO Box 62, Warrenville, SC, 29851
(804) 504-1236
www.ultimateinmateassistants.com
ultimateinmateassistants@gmail.com

New Listing

Ultimate Inmate Assistants offers a wide variety of assistance services, including internet research, shopping, social media, exotica and transsexual photo printing. Send SASE and request brochure, gift catalog, or photo catalogs. Info available online.

VOICE FREEDOM CALLS

2620 Bellevue Way NE, Box 175, Bellevue, WA 98004
www.voicefreedomcalls.com
Voice Freedom Calls offers voicemail and texting solutions for prisoners. They assign you a phone number which you and your friends and family can use as a drop box for messages. They claim that it works will all prison phone providers, subject to prison restrictions. It can not be used from federal facilities.

WEBLIFE SERVICES

New Listing

PO Box 14245, Raleigh, NC, 27620
(252) 220-5500
weblifeservices@Gmail.com
Weblife Services offers a variety of prisoner assistance services, including social media setup, website and social media management, photo services (printing and gifts), and location services. Send SASE for more info.

PRISONER ASSISTANCE SERVICES BY PRISON LIVES

PO Box 842, Exeter, CA 93221
www.prisonLives.com   info@prisonlives.com (CorrLinks registered)

Our *Prisoner Assistance Services* are designed to directly help you **accomplish anything** you hope to do from prison, despite your confines.

We understand how difficult it con be to get even the simplest tasks done. So we provide a range of reliable services at reasonable rates to help you keep moving forward towards your goals.

Minimum deposit of $100 is required to open an account.

Online Shopping Service:
Books, gifts, care *packages and all other orders*. $5 for one item, $3.99 per item for multiple items, this in addition to purchase price.

Typing:
5 pages $7.50 per page, 5+ to 200 pages $5 per page, 200+ pages $4 per page. Includes proofing and formatting.(per typed page of 350 words)

Scanning:
$ 0.15 per page up to 500 pages.
500+ pages $ 0.10 per page. Output PDF.
Printed output additional $0.10per page.

Printing:
$0.10 per page.

Book publishing:
Packages as low as $100 for a publish-ready book with cover, which includes:
- Publishers and free ad space for one year.
- ISBN assigned to Prison Lives.
- ISBN with your own name as publisher: $125

Research, Graphic & Web Design, and any other services not listed are charged based on the time worked.

Rates: $30 per hour.

No Monthly Account Fees!

EDUCATION BOOKS

GENERAL INFORMATION

HOW TO EARN A COLLEGE DEGREE WITHOUT GOING TO COLLEGE

by James P. Duffy

A detailed guide on how to obtain an external degree through life experience, independent study, examinations and correspondence courses.

$18.35

COLLEGE IN PRISON: READING IN AN AGE OF MASS INCARCERATION

by Daniel Karpowitz

Demonstrates how the liberal arts can alter the landscape inside prisons by expanding access to the tranformative power of American higher education. It tells the story of the Bard Prison Initiative, by Bard College, from a small pilot program to a nationwide network.

$19.95

COLLEGE IN PRISON: INFORMATION AND RESOURCES FOR INCARCERATED STUDENTS

by Bruce Michaels

An incarcerated student shares his experiences with gaining a formal education while behind bars.

$14.95

PRISON EDUCATION GUIDE

by Christopher Zoukis

Prisoner-student provides step-by-step information on gaining a formal education while behind bars. Includes some prisoner-friendly school information and other correspondence opportunities available to prisoners. 2016. 280 pages.

$49.95

WHAT TO STUDY

BOOK OF MAJORS 2017

by The College Board

Helps students decide what to study, where to study, and jobs associated with the chosen field of study. This is the most comprehensive and most current guide to college majors, containing in-depth descriptions of 200 of the most popular majors and courses involved.

$28.99

GETTING A COLLEGE DEGREE, A GUIDE FOR THE OLDER STUDENT

by Dr. Robert G. Wilkerson

Shows more mature students how to choose the right college, the right major, pay for education, develop good study habits and test-taking skills, and more.

$5.38

MONEY FOR SCHOOL

GETTING FINANCIAL AID 2018

by The College Board

Covers the latest financial opportunities for students, including information on scholarships, grants, loans, jobs and more.

$23.99

HOW TO GET MONEY FOR COLLEGE: 2018

by Peterson's

Comprehensive directory of information on current need-based and non-need gift aid, loans, work study and other awards available to students.

$29.95

THE ULTIMATE SCHOLARSHIP BOOK 2018: BILLIONS OF DOLLARS IN SCHOLARSHIPS, GRANTS AND PRIZES.

By Gen and Kelly Tenabe

Current information on 1.5 million scholarship, grant, and prizes opportunities indexed by career goals, school major, ethnicity, religion and more. Contains eligibility info and how to obtain the necessary applications.

$28.99

EXAM STUDY AIDS

GED Preparation

CRACKING THE GED TEST – 2017 EDITION

by Princeton Review

Get the help you need to ace the current GED testing with this content review study aid and TWO full-length practice tests.

$18.99

Career Specialty Exams Preparation

ACE PERSONAL TRAINER STUDY MANUAL: ACE PERSONAL TRAINING PREP BOOK AND PRACTICE TEST QUESTIONS

by ACE Personal Trainer Study Guide Team

A detailed overview of the information needed in preparation for the American Council on Exercise Personal Trainer Certification.

$42.99

CDL – COMMERCIAL DRIVER'S LICENSE EXAMINATIONS

by Editors of REA and Matt Mosher

Commercial drivers are always in need across the country. This book helps prepare for the CDL exam, increasing odds at landing the commercial driving jobs out there.

$19.95

CERTIFIED REHABILITATION COUNSELOR EXAMINATION PREPARATION: A CONCISE GUIDE TO THE REHABILITATION COUNSELOR TEST-TAKING

by Fong Chan PhD

Helps students hoping to enter the field of rehabilitation counseling to prepare for the CRC examination. Provides complete and detailed review of the most recent CRC exam.

$59.00

COMPTIA SECURITY+: GET CERTIFIED GET AHEAD: SYO-401 STUDY GUIDE

by Darril Gibson

For those looking to enter the field of computer security/internet technologies, the SYO-401 may be a necessary step. This study guide will help readers pass the exam on the first try.

$39.99

MEDICAL ASSISTANT EXAM STRATEGIES, PRACTICE AND REVIEW, WITH PRACTICE TEST-TAKING

by Kaplan

Provides targeted review and practice for the Certified Medical Assistant and Registered Medical Assistant exams, as well as a guide to the certification process.

$39.99

NURSING SCHOOL ENTRANCE EXAMS

by Kaplan

Comprehensive review of all tested material on major nursing school entance assessments, including the TEAS, HESI, PAX-RN, Kaplan, and PSB-RN exams. It includes a quick-reference guide of common mistakes to avoid and important formulas to remember.

$24.99

SPANISH STUDY AIDS

GED

PREPARACION PARA EL EXAMEN DE GED (SPANISH EDITITON)

by McGraw-Hill Education Editors

Preparation of the GED for Spanish-speaking students, covering all subjects.

$22.00

Citizenship

U.S. CITIZENSHIP TEST: 100 PREGUNTAS Y RESPUESTAS DEL EXAMEN DE LA CIUDADANIA

by J.S. Aaron

Ests libro le ayadara a preparse para la prueba de ciudadania de los Estados Unidos.

$7.95

BIENVENIDOS A LOS ESTADOS UNIDOS DE AMERICA: GUIA PARA IMMIGRANTES NEUVOS

by U.S. Citizenship & Immigration Services and USCIS.

Su adaptacion a una vida nueva en los Estados Unidos de America le tomara alguin tiempo. Esta guia contiene informacion basica que le ayudara a establecerse en el pais y encontrar lo que usted y su familia necesitan para su vida diaria.

$12.95

CORRECTIONAL EDUCATION COORDINATORS | STATE-BY-STATE

The following state listings can be used to communicate directly with your prison system's education coordinator.

Correctional education coordinators are your first stop to getting an education while in prison. They are the prison's education policy-makers and advisors for prisoners who would like to learn. You will want to contact them before beginning any formal educational path to determine the rules and regulations pertaining to your education wishes.

They can also inform you of current educational programs that are being offered in your facility, classes offered in coordination with local schools, as well as future offerings that may be more economical than paying for the tuition rates of outside schools.

FEDERAL

Federal Bureau of Prisons
Central Office Education Administrator
Washington, DC 20534
www.bop.gov

ALABAMA

J.F. INGRAM STATE TECHNICAL COLLEGE

PO Box 220350, Deatsville, AL 36022-0350
(334) 285-5177
www.ingram.cc.al.us

ALASKA

ALASKA DEPARTMENT OF CORRECTIONS | INMATE PROGRAMS

550 West Seventh Ave., Anchorage, AK 99501
(907) 269-7434
www.correct.state.ak.us/corrections

ARIZONA

ARIZONA DEPARTMENT OF CORRECTIONS | CORRECTIONAL EDUCATION DIVISION

1601 W. Jefferson, Third Floor, Phoenix, AZ 85007
(602) 542-5497

www.azcorrections.gov

ARKANSAS

ARKANSAS CORRECTIONAL SCHOOL

8000 Corrections Cir., Pine Bluff, AR 71603
(870) 267-6725
arkcs.arkansas.gov

CALIFORNIA

CALIFORNIA DEPARTMENT OF CORRECTIONS & REHABILITATION | DIVISION OF JUVENILE JUSTICE

PO Box 588501, Elk Grove, CA 95758-8501
(916) 683-7460
www.cdcr.ca.gov/juvenile_justice

COLORADO

COLORADO DEPARTMENT OF CORRECTIONS | EDUCATION DIVISION

2862 South Circle Dr., Colorado Springs, CO 80906-4195
(719) 579-9580
www.doc.state.co.us

CONNECTICUT

CONNECTICUT DEPARTMENT OF CORRECTIONS | UNIFIED SCHOOL DISTRICT #1

24 Wolcott Hill Rd., Wethersfield, CT 06109-1152
(860) 692-7536
www.ct.gov/doc/cwp

DELAWARE

DELAWARE DEPARTMENT OF CORRECTIONS | BUREAU OF PRISONS

245 McKee Rd., Dover, DE 19904
(302) 857-5276
www.doc.delaware.gov

DISTRICT OF COLUMBIA

(See Federal listing)

FLORIDA

FLORIDA DEPARTMENT OF CORRECTIONS | OFFICE OF EDUCATION & INITIATIVES

Building B, Room 300, 2601 Blair Stone Rd., Tallahassee, FL 32399-2500
(850) 922-3621
www.dc.state.fl.us

GEORGIA

GEORGIA DEPARTMENT OF CORRECTIONS | OPERATIONS, PLANNING AND TRAINING DIVISION

2 Martin Luther King Jr. Dr., Suite 852 East Tower, Atlanta, GA 30334
(404) 656-9181
www.dcor.state.ga.us

HAWAII

HAWAII DEPARTMENT OF PUBLIC SAFETY

919 Ala Moana Blvd., Room 405, Honolulu, HI 96814
(808) 587-1279
www.hawaii.gov/psd/corrections

IDAHO

IDAHO DEPARTMENT OF CORRECTIONS

1299 N. Orchard St., Suite 110, Boise, ID 83706
(208) 658-2066
www.idoc.idaho.gov

ILLINOIS

ILLINOIS DEPARTMENT OF CORRECTIONS | OFFICE OF ADULT AND VOCATIONAL EDUCATION

1301 Concordia Ct., Springfield, IL 62794
(217) 558-2200
www.idoc.state.il.us

INDIANA

INDIANA DEPARTMENT OF CORRECTIONS

E334 Indiana Government Center South, 302 W. Washington St., Indianapolis, IN 46204
(317) 233-3111
www.in.gov/idoc

IOWA

IOWA DEPARTMENT OF CORRECTIONS

510 East 12th St., Suite 4, Des Moines, IA 50319
(515) 725-5728
www.doc.state.ia.us

KANSAS

KANSAS DEPARTMENT OF CORRECTIONS

714 SW Jackson, Suite 300, Topeka, KS 66603
(888) 317-8204, (785) 296-0460
www.dc.state.ks.us

KENTUCKY

KENTUCKY DEPARTMENT OF CORRECTIONS

Health Services Building, 275 E. Main St., PO Box 2400, Frankfort, KY 40602-2400
(502) 564-4795
www.corrections.ky.gov

LOUISIANA

LOUISIANA DEPARTMENT OF PUBLIC SAFETY AND CORRECTIONS SERVICES

PO Box 44314, Baton Rouge, LA 70804-4314
(225) 342-6633
www.doc.louisiana.gov

MAINE

MAINE DEPARTMENT OF CORRECTIONS

25 Tyson Dr., Third Floor, State House Station #111, Augusta, ME 04333-0111
(207) 287-4342
www.state.me.us/corrections

MARYLAND

MARYLAND DEPARTMENT OF CORRECTIONS | JUVENILE SERVICES EDUCATION PROGRAM

200 W. Baltimore St., Baltimore, MD 21201
(410) 767-6284
www.marylandpublicschools.org/MSDE/divisions/careertech/juvenileservices

MASSACHUSETTS

MASSACHUSETTS DEPARTMENT OF CORRECTIONS | CENTRAL HEADQUARTERS

50 Maple St., Suite 3, Milford, MA 01757
(508) 422-4300
www.state.ma.us/doc

MICHIGAN

MICHIGAN DEPARTMENT OF CORRECTIONS | PRISONER EDUCATION PROGRAMS

206 E. Michigan Ave., Grandview Plaza, PO Box 30003, Lansing, MI 48909
(517) 335-1388
www.michigan.gov/corrections

MINNESOTA

MINNESOTA DEPARTMENT OF CORRECTIONS | FACILITY SERVICES DIVISION – EDUCATION

1450 Energy Park Dr., Suite 200, St. Paul, MN 55108-5210
(651) 361-7244
www.doc.state.mn.us/org.facilityserv/education.html

MISSISSIPPI

MISSISSIPPI DEPARTMENT OF CORRECTIONS

723 N. President St., Jackson, MS 39202
(601) 359-5304
www.mdoc.state.ms.us

MISSOURI

MISSOURI DEPARTMENT OF CORRECTIONS | DIVISION OF OFFENDER REHABILITATIVE SERVICES

1717 Industrial Dr., PO Box 236, Jefferson City, MO 65102
(573) 526-6534
www.doc.mo.gov/division.rehab/edu.htm

MONTANA

MONTANA DEPARTMENT OF CORRECTIONS

1539 11th Ave., PO Box 201301, Helena, MT 59620-1301
(406) 444-3930
www.cor.mt.gov

NEBRASKA

NEBRASKA DEPARTMENT OF CORRECTIONS

PO Box 94661, Lincoln, NE 68509
(402) 479-5723
www.corrections.nebraska.gov

NEVADA

NEVADA DEPARTMENT OF CORRECTIONS | EDUCATION AND VOCATIONAL TRAINING

Building 17, 5500 Snyder Ave., Carson City, NV 89701
(775) 887-3237
www.doc.nv.gov/programs/education.php

NEW HAMPSHIRE

NEW HAMPSHIRE DEPARTMENT OF CORRECTIONS | CORRECTIONS SPECIAL SCHOOL DISTRICT

PO Box 14, Concord, NH 03302-0014
(603) 271-1855
www.state.nh.us/nhdoc

NEW JERSEY

NEW JERSEY DEPARTMENT OF CORRECTIONS

Whittlesey Rd., Trenton, NJ 23219
(609) 292-8054
www.state.nj.us/corrections

NEW MEXICO

NEW MEXICO DEPARTMENT OF CORRECTIONS | ADULT CORRECTIONAL EDUCATION

PO Box 27116, Santa Fe, NM 87502-0116
(505) 827-8645
www.corrections.state.nm.us/programs/education.html

NEW YORK

NEW YORK DEPARTMENT OF CORRECTIONS

Harriman State Campus Building Two, 1220 Washington Ave., Albany, NY 12226-2050
(518) 457-8142
www.docs.state.ny.us

NORTH CAROLINA

NORTH CAROLINA DEPARTMENT OF CORRECTIONS | DIVISION OF PRISONS

831 W. Morgan St., 4264 MSC, Raleigh, NC 27669
(919) 838-3642
www.doc.state.nc.us/dop/education

NORTH DAKOTA

NORTH DAKOTA DEPARTMENT OF CORRECTIONS | STATE PENITENTIARY – ADULT SERVICES DIVISION

PO Box 5521, 3100 Railroad Ave., Bismarck, ND 58506-5521
(701) 328-6100
www.nd.gov/docr

OHIO

OHIO DEPARTMENT OF CORRECTIONS | OHIO CENTRAL SCHOOL SYSTEM

PO Box 779, London, OH 43140
(740) 845-3240
www.drc.ohio.gov

OKLAHOMA

OKLAHOMA DEPARTMENT OF CORRECTIONS

2901 N. Classen, Oklahoma City, OK 73106
(405) 962-6149
www.doc.state.ok.us

OREGON

OREGON DEPARTMENT OF CORRECTIONS | WORKFORCE DEVELOPMENT DIVISION

2575 Center St. NE, Salem, OR 97301
(503) 945-9090
www.doc.state.or.us/doc/trans

PENNSYLVANIA

PENNSYLVANIA DEPARTMENT OF CORRECTIONS | BUREAU OF CORRECTION EDUCATION

1920 Technology Parkway, Mechanicsburg, PA 17050
(717) 728-2573
www.cor.state.pa.us

RHODE ISLAND

RHODE ISLAND DEPARTMENT OF CORRECTIONS | EDUCATIONAL SERVICES

18 Wilma Schesler Lane, Cranston, RI 02920
(401) 462-2507
www.doc.ri.gov/rehabilitative/educational
education@doc.ri.gov

SOUTH CAROLINA

SOUTH CAROLINA DEPARTMENT OF CORRECTIONS | PALMETTO UNIFIED SCHOOL DISTRICT #1

444 Broad River R, PO Box 21787, Columbia, SC 29221-1787
(803) 896-8500
www.doc.state.sc.us

SOUTH DAKOTA

SOUTH DAKOTA DEPARTMENT OF CORRECTIONS

3200 East Highway 34, Pierre, SD 57501
(605) 773-3478
www.state.sd.us/corrections

TENNESSEE

TENNESSEE DEPARTMENT OF CORRECTIONS

Rachel Jackson Building, Fifth Floor, 320 Sixth Ave. N, Nashville, TN 37243-0465
(615) 741-1000
www.state.tn.us/corrections

TEXAS

TEXAS DEPARTMENT OF CRIMINAL JUSTICE | WINDHAM SCHOOL DISTRICT

PO Box 40, Huntsville, TX 77320
(936) 291-5307
www.wsdtx.org

UTAH

UTAH DEPARTMENT OF CORRECTIONS | SOUTH OFFICE OF EDUCATION

250 East 500 South, PO Box 144200, Salt Lake City, UT 84114-4200
(801) 538-7989
www.usoe.k12.ut.us

VERMONT

VERMONT DEPARTMENT OF CORRECTIONS | COMMUNITY HIGH SCHOOL OF VERMONT | WORKFORCE DEVELOPMENT PARTNERSHIP

103 S. Main St., Waterbury, VT 05761-1001
(802) 241-2273
www.chsvt.org/wdp.html

VIRGINIA

VIRGINIA DEPARTMENT OF CORRECTIONAL EDUCATION

James Monroe Building, Seventh Floor, 101 N. 14th St., Richmond, VA 23219-3678
(804) 225-3314
www.dce.state.va.us

WASHINGTON

WASHINGTON DEPARTMENT OF CORRECTIONS | EDUCATIONAL SERVICES DIVISION

7345 Linderson Way, MS 41129, Tumwater, WA 98501
(360) 725-8211
www.doc.wa.gov

WEST VIRGINIA

WEST VIRGINIA DEPARTMENT OF EDUCATION | OFFICE OF INSTITUTIONAL EDUCATION PROGRAMS

Building Six, Room 728, 1900 Kanawha Blvd. E, Charleston, WV 25305-0330

www.wvde.state.wv.us/institutional

WISCONSIN

WISCONSIN DEPARTMENT OF CORRECTIONS | OFFICE OF PROGRAM SERVICES – EDUCATION

PO Box 7925, 3099 E. Washington Ave., Madison, WI 53707-7925
(608) 240-5000
www.wi-doc.com

WYOMING

WYOMING DEPARTMENT OF CORRECTIONS | CORRECTIONAL EDUCATION DIVISION

1934 Wyott Dr., Cheyenne, WY 82002
(307) 777-7846
www.doc.state.wy.us/services/education.html

GED ADMINISTRATIVE OFFICES |
STATE-BY-STATE

The following state listings can be used to obtain copies of your GED exam results for your own records or for school admissions requirements.

NOTE: If you have taken your GED from prison, you can get a copy of your transcript by sending a written request to the following address with a prison check for $15:

GED Testing Service
7249 North Via Pasea del Sur #515, PMB 403
Scottsdale, AZ 85258
(877) 392-6433
www.ged.com

When writing for copies of your transcripts, remember to include the following information in your request:

- ☐ Your full legal name, including middle name of initial and the name you used on the test, if different
- ☐ Date of Birth
- ☐ Social Security Number (SSN) or Tax Identification Number (TIN)
- ☐ A copy of your correctional identification, or other state-issued ID
- ☐ Year GED earned (date test completed, if known)
- ☐ City test taken in (Testing Center name, if known)
- ☐ Your current contact information, including mailing address and outside phone and/or email, if available
- ☐ Signature and date of request
- ☐ The name of the document you're wanting to receive from them, (i.e., GED transcript, duplicate diploma, or letter verification.)
- ☐ The appropriate fee (listed with each below). Fees are generally per copy. If you want more than one copy, multiply the fee.

NOTE: Money orders and certified bank checks are always accepted. Some, but not many, accept credit cards and personal checks.

ALABAMA

ALABAMA DEPARTMENT OF POST-SECONDARY EDUCATION

PO Box 302130, Montgomery, AL 36130
(800) 392-8086, (334) 293-4500
www.accs.com
Fee: $10

ALASKA

ALASKA DEPARTMENT OF LABOR AND WORKFORCE DEVELOPMENT

1111 West 8th St., PO Box 115509, Juneau, AK 99811
(907) 465-4685
www.ajcn.state.ak.us/abe/ged.htm   ged@alaska.gov
Fee: $10. No charge for a GED transcript.

ARIZONA

ARIZONA DEPARTMENT OF EDUCATION

1535 W. Jefferson St., Phoenix, AZ 85007
(602) 658-2410
www.azed.gov/adultedservices   phxged@azed.gov
Fee: $10; $15 per microfiche record search

ARKANSAS

ARKANSAS DEPARTMENT OF CAREER EDUCATION

Three Capitol Mall, Little Rock, AR 72201
(501) 682-1500
ace.arkansas.gov/adulteducation/programs/GED
Fee: FREE

CALIFORNIA

EDUCATIONAL TESTING SERVICE (ETS) | GED RECORDS SEARCH

PO Box 4005, Concord, CA 94524-4005
(866) 370-4740
www.cee.ca.gov/ta/tg/gd
Fee: $20

COLORADO

DIPLOMA SENDER SERVICE CENTER

PO Box 722050, Norman, OK 73070-8557
(855) 313-5799
www.diplomacenter.com
Fee: $18; Add $6 for telephone orders.

CONNECTICUT

CONNECTICUT STATE DEPARTMENT OF EDUCATION | GED OFFICE

25 Industrial Park Rd., Middletown, CT 06457
(860) 807-2111
www.sde.ct.gov/sde/cwp/view
Fee: FREE (GED transcript). NOTE: Duplicate GED certificates will not be issued.

DELAWARE

DELAWARE DEPARTMENT OF EDUCATION

35 Commerce Way, Suite 1, Dover DE 11904
(302) 857-3342
www.doe.k12.de.us
Fee: $5. No charge for official GED transcript.

DISTRICT OF COLUMBIA

UNIVERSITY OF THE DISTRICT OF COLUMBIA | ADULT EDUCATION AGENCY

441 4th St. NW, Suite 350-N, Washington DC 20001
(202) 274-7173
Fee: FREE

FLORIDA

FLORIDA DEPARTMENT OF EDUCATION | BUREAU OF PROGRAM PLANNING AND DEVELOPMENT

(866) 895-8860, (888) 662-0449
ged.fldoe.org/diploma.asp
Currently, no written requests are processed. Outside sources must use online options.

GEORGIA

TECHNICAL COLLEGE SYSTEM OF GEORGIA | GED TESTING PROGRAM

1800 Century Place NE, Suite 300B, Atlanta, GA 30345

(800) 946-9433, (404) 679-1645
www.tcsg.edu/ged_trans_req.php
Fee: $8 per transcript; $15 for diploma

HAWAII

HAWAII DEPARTMENT OF EDUCATION | COMMUNITY EDUCATION SECTION

475 22nd Ave., Room 202, Honolulu, HI 96816
(808) 203-5511
www.hawaiipublicschools.org
Fee: $2

IDAHO

DIPLOMA SENDER SERVICE CENTER

PO Box 722050, Norman, OK 73070-8557
(855) 313-5799
www.diplomacenter.com
Fee: $15; Add $6 for telephone orders.

ILLINOIS

ILLINOIS COMMUNITY COLLEGE BOARD

401 E. Capitol Ave., Springfield, IL 62701
(217) 558-5668
www.passged.com/il-ged-testing.php
NOTE: Must obtain GED information from the regional office covering the location where you tested. Write the address above with your test location for the regional address you need.

Indiana

DIPLOMA SENDER SERVICE CENTER

PO Box 722050, Norman, OK 73070-8557
(855) 313-5799
www.diplomacenter.com
Fee: $15; Add $5 for postal mailing and $6 for telephone orders.

IOWA

DIPLOMA SENDER SERVICE CENTER

PO Box 722050, Norman, OK 73070-8557
(855) 313-5799
www.diplomacenter.com
Fee: $10; Add $6 for telephone orders.

KANSAS

DIPLOMA SENDER SERVICE CENTER

PO Box 722050, Norman, OK 73070-8557
(855) 313-5799
www.diplomacenter.com
Fee: $15; Add $6 for telephone orders.

KENTUCKY

KENTUCKY COUNCIL ON POST-SECONDARY EDUCATION

1024 Capital Center Dr., Suite 250, Frankfort, KY 40601
(800) 928-7323, (502) 573-5114
www.ged.ky.gov
Fee: $10 per transcript; $25 per diploma

LOUISIANA

LOUISIANA COMMUNITY AND TECHNICAL COLLEGE SYSTEM

265 S. Foster Dr., Baron Rouge, LA 70806
(225) 308-4394
www.lctcs.edu
Fee: FREE

MAINE

DIPLOMA SENDER SERVICE CENTER

PO Box 722050, Norman, OK 73070-8557
(855) 313-5799
www.diplomacenter.com
Fee: $15. Add $6 for telephone orders.

MARYLAND

MARYLAND DEPARTMENT OF LABOR, LICENSE AND REGULATION

1100 N. Eutaw St., Baltimore, MD 21201
(410) 767-0069
www.dllr.maryland.gov/gedmd
Fee: $5

MASSACHUSETTS

MASSACHUSETTS DEPARTMENT OF ELEMENTARY AND SECONDARY EDUCATION

75 Pleasant St., Malden, MA 02148
(781) 338-3000

www.doe.mass.edu/hse
Fee: $8; $2 for letter verification.

MICHIGAN

MICHIGAN DEPARTMENT OF ENERGY, LABOR, AND ECONOMIC GROWTH

201 N. Washington Square, 2nd Floor, Lansing, MI 48913
(517) 335-3461
www.passged.com/mi-ged-testing.php
gedprogram@michigan.gov
Fee: FREE (GED transcript). NOTE: Duplicate GED certificates will not be issued.

MINNESOTA

MINNESOTA DEPARTMENT OF EDUCATION

1500 Highway 36 West, Roseville, MN 55113
(651) 582-8445
www.education.state.mn.us/mde/stusuc/adulted
Fee: FREE

MISSISSIPPI

STATE BOARD OF COMMUNITY AND JUNIOR COLLEGES

3825 Ridgewood Rd., Jackson, MS 39211
(601) 432-6338
www.passged.com/ms-ged-testing.php
Fee: $5

MISSOURI

STATE DEPARTMENT OF ELEMENTARY AND SECONDARY EDUCATION

PO Box 480, Jefferson City, MO 65102
(573) 751-3504
www.hse.mo.gov
Fee: $16 per certificate. Transcript requests will only be accepted online.

MONTANA

MONTANA OFFICE OF PUBLIC INSTRUCTION | GED PROGRAM

1300 11th Ave., Box 202501, Helena, MT 59620
(406) 444-4438
www.opi.mt.gov/programs/ctae

Fee: FREE

NEBRASKA

NEBRASKA DEPARTMENT OF EDUCATION | DIVISION OF ADULT EDUCATION

301 Centennial Mall South, PO Box 94987, Lincoln, NE 68509
(402) 471-2295
www.education.ne.gov/aded
Fee: $2

NEVADA

DIPLOMA SENDER SERVICE CENTER

PO Box 722050, Norman, OK 73070-8557
(855) 313-5799
www.diplomacenter.com
Fee: $15; Add $6 for telephone orders.

NEW HAMPSHIRE

NEW HAMPSHIRE DEPARTMENT OF EDUCATION | BUREAU OF ADULT EDUCATION

21 S. Fruit St., Suite 20, Concord, NH 03301
(603) 271-6699
www.nhadulted.org/programs/hiset/transcript
Fee: FREE (for prisoners), $10 all others

NEW JERSEY

NEW JERSEY DEPARTMENT OF EDUCATION

PO Box 500, Trenton, NJ 08625
(609) 341-3071
www.passged.com/nj-ged-testing.php
Fee: FREE (GED transcript). NOTE: Duplicate GED certificates will not be issued.

NEW MEXICO

DIPLOMA SENDER SERVICE CENTER

PO Box 722050, Norman, OK 73070-8557
(855) 313-5799
www.diplomacenter.com
Fee: $18; Add $6 for telephone orders.

NEW YORK

New York State Education Department | GED Testing Office

PO Box 7348, Albany, NY 12224-0348
(518) 474-5906
www.acces.nysed.gov/hse
Fee: $10 diploma; $4 transcript

NORTH CAROLINA

North Carolina Community College System | GED Records Office

5016 Mail Service Center, Raleigh, NC 27699
(919) 807-7172
www.nccommunitycolleges.edu/
Fee: FREE (GED transcript). NOTE: Duplicate GED certificates will not be issued.

NORTH DAKOTA

North Dakota Department of Public Instruction | Adult Education and Literacy

State Capitol Building, 600 East Boulevard Ave., Bismarck, ND 58505-0440
(701) 328-4138
www.nd.gov/dpi
Fee: $10 diploma; $2 transcript

OHIO

Ohio Department of Education

25 S. Front St., 1st Floor, Mailstop 22, Columbus, OH 43215-4183
(877) 644-6338, (614) 466-1577
www.education.ohio.gov/topics/testing/ohio-options-for-adult-diploma/GED
Fee: $15 for transcripts of those who took test prior to July 5, 2014. For tests taken on or after July 5, 2014, requests (and $15) should be sent to the *GED Testing Service* address at the beginning of this section.

OKLAHOMA

Diploma Sender Service Center

PO Box 722050, Norman, OK 73070-8557
(855) 313-5799
www.diplomacenter.com
Fee: $17. Add $6 for telephone orders.

OREGON

GED Testing Service

7349 North Via Pasea del Sur, #515, PMB 403, Scottsdale, AZ 85258
(888) 906-4031, (877) 392-6433
www.ged.com
Fee: $15

PENNSYLVANIA

Pennsylvania Department of Education | Commonwealth Diploma Program

333 Market St., 12th Floor, Harrisburg, PA 17126
(717) 783-6788
www.ged.ed.state.pa.us/gedonline/
Fee: $3. Duplicate GED diplomas will not be issued.

PUERTO RICO

Puerto Rico Department of Education | Examinations, Diplomas, & Certificates Unit

PO Box 190759, San Juan, PR 00919
(787) 773-4881

RHODE ISLAND

Department of Elementary and Secondary Education

255 Westminster St., Providence, RI 02903
(401) 222-8949
www.ride.ri.gov
Fee: $5

SOUTH CAROLINA

South Carolina Department of Education

1429 Senate St., Suite 402, Columbia, SC 29201
(800) 277-7323, (803) 734-8347
www.ed.sc.gov/tests/adults
Fee: $10

SOUTH DAKOTA

South Dakota Department of Labor | Adult Education and Literacy

700 Governors Dr., Pierre, SD 57501
(605) 773-5017
www.ged.com
Fee: $10 per transcript; $15 per diploma

TENNESSEE

Diploma Sender Service Center

PO Box 722050, Norman, OK 73070-8557
(855) 313-5799
www.diplomacenter.com
Fee: $15. Add $6 for telephone orders.

TEXAS

Texas Department of Education

1701 N. Congress Ave., CC350, Austin, TX 78701-1494
(512) 463-9290
www.tea.state.tx.us
Fee: FREE, but requires outside assistance to order online.

UTAH

Utah State Office of Education

250 East 500 South, PO Box 144200, Salt Lake City, UT 84114-4200
(801) 538-7882
www.utah.schools.gov/ged
Fee: FREE

VERMONT

Vermont Department of Education

120 State St., Montpelier, VT 05620
(802) 479-1296
www.education.vermont.gov/adult-education/general-educational-development
Fee: $15

VIRGINIA

Virginia Office of Adult Education and Literacy | GED Services

101 N. 14th St., PO Box 2120, Richmond, VA 23218
(804) 371-2333
www.doe.virginia.gov/instructioNot applicabledulted/ged
Fee: $5 per transcript; $10 per certificate

WASHINGTON

State Board of Community and Technical Colleges

1300 Quince St. SE, PO Box 42495, Olympia, WA 98504-2495
(360) 704-4372
www.gedverify.org   gedcenter@sbctc.edu
Fee: FREE

WEST VIRGINIA

Diploma Sender Service Center

PO Box 722050, Norman, OK 73070-8557
(855) 313-5799
www.diplomacenter.com
Fee: $15. Add $6 for telephone orders.

WISCONSIN

Wisconsin Department of Public Instruction

125 S. Webster St., PO Box 7841, Madison, WI 53707-7841
(800) 768-8886, (608) 267-9245
www.dpi.wi.gov/ged/transcripts
Fee: $5 for first copy, $2 for each additional copy for prisoners; $15 for all others

WYOMING

Diploma Sender Service Center

PO Box 722050, Norman, OK 73070-8557
(855) 313-5799
www.diplomacenter.com
Fee: $15. Add $6 for telephone orders.

HIGHER EDUCATION AGENCIES | STATE-BY-STATE

Higher Education Agencies provide information on educational programs within each state, including colleges and universities, financial aid assistance programs, grant programs, scholarships, and continuing education programs.

ALABAMA

ALABAMA COMMISSION ON HIGHER EDUCATION

PO Box 302000, Montgomery, AL 36130
(334) 242-1998
www.ache.Alabama.gov

ALASKA

ALASKA COMMISSION ON POST-SECONDARY EDUCATION

PO Box 110505, Juneau, AK 99811
(907) 465-2969
Alaskaadvantage.state.ak.us

ARIZONA

ARIZONA COMMISSION ON POST-SECONDARY EDUCATION

2020 North Central Ave., Suite 650, Phoenix, AZ 85004
(603) 258-2435

ARKANSAS

ARKANSAS DEPARTMENT OF HIGHER EDUCATION

423 Main St., Suite 400, Little Rock, AR 72201
(501) 371-2000
www.adhe.edu

CALIFORNIA

CALIFORNIA STUDENT AID COMMISSION

PO Box 419027, Ranch Cordova, CA 95741
(916) 526-7590
www.csac.ca.gov

COLORADO

COLORADO DEPARTMENT OF HIGHER EDUCATION

1560 Broadway, Suite 160, Denver, CO 80202
(303) 866-2723
www.highered.colorado.gov

CONNECTICUT

CONNECTICUT DEPARTMENT OF EDUCATION

61 Woodland St., Hartford, CT 06105
(860) 947-1800
www.ctdhe.org

DELAWARE

DELAWARE HIGHER EDUCATION COMMISSION

820 N. French St., 5th Floor, Wilmington, De 19801
(302) 577-5240
www.doe.k12.de.us/dhec

DISTRICT OF COLUMBIA

OFFICE OF THE STATE SUPERINTENDENT OF EDUCATION | STATE BOARD OF EDUCATION

441 Fourth St NW, Suite 350 N, Washington, DC 20001
(202) 727-6436
asse.dc.gov

FLORIDA

FLORIDA OFFICE OF STUDENT FINANCIAL ASSISTANCE

1940 N. Monroe St., Suite 70, Tallahassee, FL 32303
(850) 410-5180
www.floridastudentfinancialaid.org

GEORGIA

GEORGIA STUDENT FINANCE COMMISSION

2082 E. Exchange Place, Tucker, GA 30084
(770) 724-9000
www.gsfc.org

HAWAII

HAWAII POST-SECONDARY EDUCATION COMMISSION

2444 Dole St., Room 209, Honolulu, HI 96822
(808) 956-8213
www.hawaii.edu/offices/bor

IDAHO

IDAHO STATE BOARD OF EDUCATION

650 W. State St., PO Box 83720, Boise, ID 83720
(208) 334-2270
www.boardofed.idaho.gov

ILLINOIS

ILLINOIS STATE ASSISTANCE COMMISSION

1755 Lake Cook Rd., Deerfield, IL 60015
(847) 948-8500
www.collegezone.com

INDIANA

INDIANA COMMISSION FOR HIGHER EDUCATION

101 W. Ohio St., Suite 550, Indianapolis, IN 46204
(317) 464-4400
www.che.in.gov

State Student Assistance Commission of Indiana

150 W. Market St., Suite 500, Indianapolis, IN 46204
(317) 232-2350
www.ssaci.in.gov

IOWA

IOWA COLLEGE STUDENT AID COMMISSION

603 East 12th St., 5th Floor, Des Moines, IA 50319
(515) 725-3400
www.iowacollegeaid.gov

KANSAS

KANSAS BOARD OF REGENTS

1000 SW Jackson St., Suite 520, Topeka, KS 66612
(785) 296-3421
www.kansasregents.org

KENTUCKY

KENTUCKY HIGHER EDUCATION ASSISTANCE AUTHORITY

PO Box 798, Frankfort, KY 40602
(502) 696-7200
www.kheaa.com

LOUISIANA

LOUISIANA OFFICE OF STUDENT FEDERAL ASSISTANCE

PO Box 91202, Baton Rouge, LA 70821
(225) 933-1012
www.osfa.la.gov

MAINE

FINANCE AUTHORITY OF MAINE

PO Box 949, Augusta, ME 04332
(207) 623-0095

MARYLAND

MARYLAND HIGHER EDUCATION COMMISSION

839 Bestgate Rd., Suite 400, Annapolis, MD 21401
(410) 260-4500
www.mhec.state.md.us

MASSACHUSETTS

MASSACHUSETTS DEPARTMENT OF HIGHER EDUCATION

One Ashburton Place, Room 1401, Boston, MA 02108
(617) 994-6950
www.mass.edu

TERI College Planning Center | Boston Public Library

700 Boylston St., Concourse Level, Boston, MA 02116
(617) 536-0200
www.tericollegeplanning.org

MICHIGAN

MICHIGAN STUDENT FINANCIAL SERVICES BUREAU

430 W. Allegan, 3rd Floor, PO Box 30047, Lansing, MI 48909
(800) 642-5626
www.michigan.gov/studentaid

MINNESOTA

MINNESOTA OFFICE OF HIGHER EDUCATION

1450 Energy Park Dr., Suite 350, St. Paul, MN 55108
(651) 642-0567
www.ohe.state.mn.us

MISSISSIPPI

MISSISSIPPI INSTITUTIONS OF HIGHER LEARNING

3825 Ridgewood Rd., Jackson, MS 39211
(601) 432-6623
www.ihl.state.ms.us

MISSOURI

MISSOURI DEPARTMENT OF HIGHER EDUCATION

205 Jefferson St., PO Box 1469, Jefferson City, MO 65109
(573) 751-2361
www.dhe.mo.gov

MONTANA

MONTANA UNIVERSITY SYSTEM

2500 Broadway, PO Box 203201, Helena, MT 59620
(406) 444-6570
www.mus.edu

NEBRASKA

COORDINATING COMMISSION OF POST-SECONDARY EDUCATION

140 N. Eighth St, Suite 300, PO Box 95005, Lincoln, NE 68509
(402) 471-2847
www.ccpe.state.ne.us

NEVADA

Nevada does not currently list a higher education office.

NEW HAMPSHIRE

NEW HAMPSHIRE POST-SECONDARY EDUCATION COMMISSION

3 Barrell Ct., Suite 300, Concord, NH 03301
(603) 271-2555
www.state.nh.us/post-secondary

NEW JERSEY

HIGHER EDUCATION STUDENT ASSISTANCE AUTHORITY

PO Box 540, Trenton, NJ 08625
(609) 588-3226
www.hesaa.org

New Jersey Commission on Higher Education
20 W. State St., PO Box 542, Trenton, NJ 08625
(609) 292-4310
www.state.nj.us/highereducation

NEW MEXICO

NEW MEXICO HIGHER EDUCATION DEPARTMENT

1068 Cerrillas Rd., Santa Fe, NM 87505
(505) 476-8400
www.hed.state.nm.us

NEW YORK

NEW YORK STATE HIGHER EDUCATION SERVICES CORPORATION

99 Washington Ave., Albany, NY 12255
(518) 473-1574
www.hesc.org

North Carolina

NORTH CAROLINA STATE EDUCATION ASSISTANCE AUTHORITY

PO Box 13663, Research Triangle Park, NC 27709
(919) 549-8614
www.cfnc.org

NORTH DAKOTA

NORTH DAKOTA STUDENT FINANCIAL ASSISTANCE PROGRAM

600 E. Boulevard Ave., Suite 215, Bismarck, ND 58505
(701) 328-4114
www.ndus.edu

OHIO

OHIO BOARD OF REGENTS

25 S. Front St., Columbus, OH 43215
(614) 466-6000
www.ohiohighered.org

OKLAHOMA

OKLAHOMA STATE REGENTS FOR HIGHER EDUCATION

655 Research Pkwy., Suite 200, Oklahoma City, OK 73104
(405) 225-9100
www.okhighered.org

OREGON

OREGON STUDENT ASSISTANCE COMMISSION

1500 Valley River Dr., Suite 100, Eugene, OR 97401
(541) 687-7400
www.osac.state.or.us

Oregon University System
PO Box 3175, Eugene, OR 97403
(541) 346-5700

PENNSYLVANIA

OFFICE OF POST-SECONDARY AND HIGHER EDUCATION | STATE DEPARTMENT OF EDUCATION

333 Market St., 12th Floor, Harrisburg, PA 17126
(717) 787-5041

Pennsylvania Higher Education Assistance Agency
1200 N. Seventh St., Harrisburg, PA 17102
(717) 720-2800
www.pheaa.org

PUERTO RICO

COUNCIL ON EDUCATION OF PUERTO RICO

PO Box 19900, Avenue Ponce de Leon 268, Edificio Hato Rey Center Piso 15, Hato Rey, PR 00918
(787) 641-7100
www.ce.pr.gov

RHODE ISLAND

RHODE ISLAND HIGHER EDUCATION ASSISTANCE AUTHORITY

560 Jefferson Blvd., Suite 100, Warwick, RI 02886
(401) 736-1100
www.riheea.org

Rhode Island Office of Higher Education
74 West Rd., Cranston, RI 02920
(401) 462-9300
www.ribghe.org

SOUTH CAROLINA

SOUTH CAROLINA COMMISSION ON HIGHER EDUCATION

1333 Main St., Suite 200, Columbia, SC 29201
(803) 737-2260
www.che.sc.gov

SOUTH DAKOTA

SOUTH DAKOTA BOARD OF REGENTS

306 E. Capitol Ave., Suite 200, Pierre, SD 57501
(605) 773-3455
www.sdbor.edu

TENNESSEE

TENNESSEE HIGHER EDUCATION COMMISSION

404 James Robertson Pkwy., Suite 1900, Nashville, TN 37243
(615) 741-3605
www.state.tn.us/thec

TEXAS

TEXAS HIGHER EDUCATION COORDINATING BOARD

1200 E. Anderson Lane, Austin, TX 78711
(512) 427-6101
www.thecb.state.tx.us

UTAH

UTAH SYSTEM OF HIGHER EDUCATION | STATE BOARD OF REGENTS

60 South 400 West, Salt Lake City, UT 84101
(801) 321-7103
www.utahsbr.edu

VERMONT

VERMONT STUDENT ASSISTANCE CORPORATION

10 E. Allen St., PO Box 2000, Winooski, VT 05404
(802) 655-9602
www.vsac.org

VIRGINIA

STATE COUNCIL ON HIGHER EDUCATION FOR VIRGINIA

101 N. 14th St., 9th Floor, Richmond, VA 23219
(804) 225-2600
www.schev.edu

WASHINGTON

WASHINGTON HIGHER EDUCATION COORDINATING BOARD

917 Lakeridge Way, PO Box 43430, Olympia, WA 98504
(360) 753-7800
www.hecb.wa.gov

WEST VIRGINIA

WEST VIRGINIA HIGHER EDUCATION POLICY COMMISSION

1018 Kanawha Blvd. East, Suite 700, Charleston, WV 25301
(304) 558-0699
www.hepc.wvnet.edu

WISCONSIN

WISCONSIN HIGHER EDUCATION AID BOARD

131 W. Wilson St., Suite 902, Madison, WI 53707
(608) 267-2206
www.heab.state.wi.us

WYOMING

WYOMING COMMUNITY COLLEGE COMMISSION

2020 Carey Ave., 8th Floor, Cheyenne, WY 82002
(307) 777-7762
www.commission.wcc.edu

ACCREDITING AGENCIES

The following accreditation agencies can be written to determine specifics as to whether a school you are interested in is accredited by that agency, and if so, the school's accreditation history. For more information on accreditation and to learn which accrediting agencies are legitimate or otherwise, see *Accreditation: What Does That Mean?*

U.S. DEPARTMENT OF EDUCATION (USDE) | ACCREDITING AGENCY EVALUATION BRANCH

1990 K Street NW, Washington, D.C. 20006
(202) 502-7765
www.ed.gov
USDE's Accrediting Agency Evaluation Branch is the government authority for education institution accreditation in the U.S. They can provide information on other accrediting agencies, as well as provide listings of accredited schools across the nation.

COUNCIL FOR HIGHER EDUCATION ACCREDITATION (CHEA)

One Dupont Circle NW, Suite 510, Washington, D.C. 20036-1136
(202) 955-6126
www.chea.org chea@chea.org

CHEA works closely with the government, specifically the USDE, to ensure the integrity and quality of educational institutions and the agencies that accredit them.

NATIONAL ASSOCIATION OF PROFESSIONAL BACKGROUND SCREENERS

110 Horizon Dr., Suite 210, Raleigh, NC 27615
www.napbs.com
Accreditation screening company.

NATIONAL ACCREDITING AGENCIES

ACCREDITING COMMISSION OF CAREER SCHOOLS AND COLLEGES (ACCSC)

2101 Wilson Blvd., Suite 302, Arlington, VA 22201
(703) 247-4212
www.accsc.org info@accsc.org

ACCSC provides accreditation to vocational and technical career schools.

ACCREDITING COUNCIL FOR INDEPENDENT COLLEGES AND SCHOOLS (ACICS)

750 First St. NE, Suite 980, Washington, D.C. 20002
(202) 336-6780
www.acis.org
ACICS provides accreditation to career and vocational school across the nation.

COUNCIL ON OCCUPATIONAL EDUCATION

41 Perimeter Center East NE, Suite 640, Atlanta, GA 30346
(770) 396-3898
www.council.org   info@council.org
Council on Occupational Education provides accreditation to vocational and technical career schools and programs.

DISTANCE EDUCATION ACCREDITING COMMISSION (DEAC)

1101 17th St. NW, Suite 808, Washington, DC 20036
(202) 234-5100
www.deac.org   info@deac.org (Corrlinks registered)
Formerly known as the DETC, DEAC is an accrediting agency that specializes in schools that offer correspondence courses.

NATIONAL ASSOCIATION FOR THE LEGAL SUPPORT OF ALTERNATIVE SCHOOLS

18520 NW 67th Ave.#188, Miami, FL 33015
(800) 456-7784
www.nalsas.org   educate@nalsas.org
Accredits home-schooling programs.

NEW ENGLAND ASSOCIATION OF SCHOOLS AND COLLEGES | COMMISSION ON TECHNICAL AND CAREER INSTITUTIONS (CTCI-NEASC)

209 Burlington Rd., Suite 201, Bedford, MA 01730-1433
(781) 541-5416
www.ctci.neasc.org   ctci@neasc.org

REGIONAL ACCREDITING AGENCIES

The following are regional accrediting agencies whose accreditations are recognized by USDE and CHEA. You will find their acronyms mentioned frequently throughout our school listings.

MIDDLE STATES ASSOCIATION OF COLLEGES AND SCHOOLS | COMMISSION ON HIGHER EDUCATION (MSCHE)

3624 Market St., 2nd Floor Annex, Philadelphia, PA 19104
(267) 284-5000
www.msche.org   info@msche.org
MSCHE provides accreditation for schools in: Delaware, District of Columbia, Maryland, New Jersey, New York, Pennsylvania, Puerto Rico, and the Virgin Islands.

NEW ENGLAND ASSOCIATION OF SCHOOLS AND COLLEGES | COMMISSION ON INSTITUTIONS OF HIGHER EDUCATION (NEASC-CIHE)

209 Burlington Rd., Bedford, MA 01730
(781) 271-0022
www.neasc.org   info@neasc.org
NEASC provides accreditation for schools in: Connecticut, Massachusetts, New Hampshire, Rhode Island, and Vermont.

NORTH CENTRAL ASSOCIATION OF COLLEGES AND SCHOOLS | THE HIGHER LEARNING (NCA-HLC)

30 N. LaSalle St., Suite 2400, Chicago, IL 60602
(312) 263-0456
www.ncahigherlearningcommission.org
info@hlcommission.org
Provides accreditation for schools in: Arizona, Arkansas, Colorado, Illinois, Indiana, Iowa, Kansas, Michigan, Minnesota, Missouri, Nebraska, New Mexico, North Dakota, Ohio, Oklahoma, South Dakota, West Virginia, Wisconsin, and Wyoming.

NORTHWEST COMMISSION ON COLLEGES AND UNIVERSITIES (NWCCU)

8060 165th Ave. NE, Suite 100, Redmond, WA 98052
(425) 558-4224
www.nwccu.org   info@nwccu.org
NWCCU provides accreditation for schools in: Alaska, Idaho, Montana, Nevada, Oregon, Utah, and Washington.

SOUTHERN ASSOCIATION OF COLLEGES AND SCHOOLS | COMMISSION ON COLLEGES (SACS-COC)

1866 Southern Lane, Decatur, GA 30033
(404) 679-4500
www.sacscoc.org   info@sacscoc.org
SACS-COC provides accreditation for schools in: Alabama, Florida, Kentucky, Louisiana, Mississippi, North Carolina, South Carolina, Tennessee, Texas, and Virginia.

WESTERN ASSOCIATION OF SCHOOLS AND COLLEGES | ACCREDITING COMMISSION FOR SENIOR COLLEGES AND UNIVERSITIES (WASC-ACSCU)

985 Atlantic Ave., Suite 100, Alameda, CA 94501
(510) 748-9001
www.wascweb.org wascr@wascsenior.org
WASC-ACSCU provides accreditation to schools that offer more than two-year programs, beginning at the junior level, in western states, including California, Hawaii, Guam, American Samoa, Northern Mariana Islands, Palau, Micronesia, and the Marshall Islands.

WESTERN ASSOCIATION OF SCHOOLS AND COLLEGES | ACCREDITING COMMISSION FOR COMMUNITY AND JUNIOR COLLEGES (WASC-ACCJC)

10 Commercial Blvd., Novato, CA 94949
(415) 506-0234
www.accjc.org accjc@accjc.org
ACCJC provides accreditation to schools that offer more than two-year programs, beginning at the freshman year, in western states, including California, Hawaii, Guam, American Samoa, Northern Mariana Islands, Palau, Micronesia, and the Marshall Islands.

SPECIALIZED ACCREDITING AGENCIES

> The following are a selection of a few of the specialized accrediting agencies that prisoners may require more frequently.

ART & DESIGN

NATIONAL ASSOCIATION OF SCHOOLS OF ART AND DESIGN (NASAD) | COMMISSION ON ACCREDITATION

11250 Roger Bacon Dr., Suite 21, Reston, VA 20190
(703) 437-0700
www.arts-accredit.org info@arts-accredit.org
NASAD's Commission on Accreditation provides accreditation to art and design institutions and art and design programs within institutions.

BUSINESS

ACCREDITING COUNCIL FOR INDEPENDENT COLLEGES AND SCHOOLS (ACICS)

750 First St. NE, Suite 980, Washington, D.C. 20002
(202) 336-6780
www.acics.org info@acics.org
ACICS Schools (ACICS) provides accreditation to independent business schools.

ASSOCIATION OF COLLEGIATE BUSINESS SCHOOLS AND PROGRAMS (ACBSP)

7007 College Blvd., Suite 420, Overland Park, KS 66211
(913) 339-9356
www.acbsp.org info@acbsp.org
ASBSP provides accreditation to business schools and business programs in other education institutions.

INTERNATIONAL ASSOCIATION OF MANAGEMENT EDUCATION (AACSP)

777 S. Harbour Blvd., Suite 750, Tampa, FL 33602-5730
(613) 769-6540
www.aacsb.edu info@aacsb.edu
AACSB provides accreditation to business management schools.

CONSTRUCTION

AMERICAN COUNCIL FOR CONSTRUCTION EDUCATION (ACCE)

1717 North Loop, 1604 East, Suite 320, San Antonio, TX 78232
(210) 495-6161
www.acce-hq.org ace@acce-hq.org
ACCE provides accreditation to programs that specialize in construction education.

DIABETES

AMERICAN DIABETIC ASSOCIATION | COMMISSION ON ACCREDITATION OF DIABETICS EDUCATION (CADE-ADA)

120 S. Riverside Plaza, Suite 2000, Chicago, IL 60606
(800) 877-1600 ext. 5400
www.eatright.org/cade cade@eatright.org
CADE-ADA provides accreditation to diabetes education programs.

LAW

AMERICAN BAR ASSOCIATION | LEGAL EDUCATION AND ADMISSIONS TO THE BAR

321 N. Clark St., Chicago, IL 60610
(321) 988-5000
www.abanet.org   askaba@abanet.org
ABA provides accreditation to institutions and programs that specialize in law education.

MUSIC

NATIONAL ASSOCIATION OF SCHOOLS OF MUSIC (NASM) | COMMISSION ON ACCREDITATION

11250 Roger Bacon Dr., Suite 21, Reston, VA 20190
(703) 437-0700
www.arts-accredit.org   info@arts-accredit.org
NASM provides accreditation to institutions and programs that specialize in music education.

PSYCHOLOGY

AMERICAN PSYCHOLOGICAL ASSOCIATION (APA)

750 First St. NE, Washington, D.C. 20002
(202) 336-5979
www.apa.org/ed/accreditation   apaaccred@apa.org
APA provides accreditation to programs that specialize in psychology education.

AMERICAN ASSOCIATION FOR MARRIAGE AND FAMILY THERAPY (AAMFT)

112 S. Alfred St., Alexandria, VA 22314-3061
(703) 838-9808
www.aamft.org   central@aamft.org
AAMFT provides accreditation to programs that specialize in family psychology education.

REHABILITATION

COUNCIL ON REHABILITATION EDUCATION (CORE)

1835 Rohlwing Rd., Suite E, Rolling Meadows, IL 60008
(847) 394-1785
www.core-rehab.org
CORE provides accreditation to programs that specialize in rehabilitation, including Rehabilitation Counselor Education (RCE) and Rehabilitation and Disability Studies (RDS).

RELIGION

ASSOCIATION FOR BIBLICAL HIGHER EDUCATION (ABHE) | COMMISSION ON ACCREDITATION

5575 S. Semoran Blvd., Orlando, FL 32822
(407) 207-0808
www.abhe.org   info@abhe.org
ABHE provides accreditation to institutions and programs that specialize in religious education.

ASSOCIATION OF CLINICAL PASTORAL EDUCATION (ACPE)

1549 Clairmont Rd., Suite 103, Decatur, GA 30033-4611
(404) 320-1472
www.acpe.edu
ACPE provides accreditation to institutions and programs that specialize in religious education, with an emphasis on pastoral programs.

ASSOCIATION OF ADVANCED RABBINICAL AND TALMUDIC SCHOOLS

11 Broadway, Suite 405, New York, NY 10004
(212) 477-0950
Association of Advanced Rabbinical and Talmudic Schools provides accreditation to institutions and programs that specialize in Jewish education.

ASSOCIATION OF THEOLOGICAL SCHOOLS IN THE U.S. AND CANADA (ATS) | COMMISSION ON ACCREDITING

10 Summit Park Dr., Pittsburgh, PA 15275
(412) 788-6505
www.ats.org   ats@ats.org
ATS provides accreditation to institutions and programs that specialize in religious education.

TRANSNATIONAL ASSOCIATION OF CHRISTIAN COLLEGES AND SCHOOLS (TRACS) | ACCREDITATION COMMISSION

15935 Forest Rd., PO Box 328, Forest, VA 24551
(434) 525-9539
www.tracs.org   info@tracs.org
TRACS provides accreditation to institutions and programs that specialize in Christian education.

Appendix

GLOSSARY

A

ACADEMIC ADVISOR

School faculty who works with students to plan courses of study to meet their education goals and degree requirements.

ACADEMIC YEAR

The period of formal education, typically occurring within a one-year period broken into two or three semesters.

ACCREDITATION

Recognition that an institution meets a specific set of standards, according to an independent private organization.

ACCREDITING AGENCY

A private organization that establishes a set of standards and verifies whether an educational institution meets those standards. There are more than 100, accrediting agencies, the most quality of which are recognized by the U.S. Department of Education and/or the CHEA.

ACE

The American Council on Education, an influential non-government association in Washington.

ACT

American College Testing program, administrators of aptitude and achievement tests.

ADMISSIONS

Department within the school that handles student enrollment.

ADVANCED PLACEMENT (AP) EXAMS

Examinations offered through high schools in cooperation with the College Board to determine if the exam-taker qualifies for college credit at participating colleges.

ALMA MATER

The school from which one has graduated.

ALUMNI

Graduates of a school. Technically refers to males only; females are alumnae.

AMERICAN COLLEGE TESTING (ACT) EXAMS

College admissions tests given to students at the high school level.

ASSOCIATE'S DEGREE

Degree typically awarded after completion of 60 to 64 credits and traditionally earned in two years.

AUDIT COURSES

Some schools allow students to take classes simply for the sake of learning WITHOUT course credit. These courses will typically be deeply discounted from the regular per credit tuition cost of the class chosen. It is a good way to take classes if you have limited resources. Since students will be learning the courses chosen, they may be able to use that knowledge to "test out" of the class at other schools through credit-by-examination options, which do earn college credit toward a degree.

B

BACHELOR'S DEGREE

Degree typically awarded after completion of 120 to 128 credits and traditionally earned in four years.

BIBLICAL STUDIES

Studies that provide a Biblical foundation of study for all Christians and especially for those desiring to better understand Biblical principles. These studies are designed to provide the fundamentals to the field of Bible study for the seminary student.

BURSAR

School official or department that handles tuition and payments.

C

CAMPUS

The main facility of a school, typically comprising buildings, grounds, dormitories, etc., or the office center of correspondence schools.

CEU

Continuing Education Unit, typically given by schools that offer training courses, usually awarded at the rate of one for every ten hours of work. They are, however, rarely considered equivalent to college credit. CEUs are maintained by the

International Association for Continuing Education and Training.

CERTIFICATE

Credential awarded upon completion of a non-degree study program, typically focused on a specific topic.

CERTIFICATION

Professional credential awarded for passing a competency examination in a specialized field, typically for employment licensure.

CHEA

The Council on Higher Education Accreditation, which recognizes U.S. accrediting agencies.

CLEP

The College-Level Examination Program (CLEP) is a national program sponsored by the College Board that provides a series of equivalency examinations that can be taken for college credit. The program no longer offers paper versions of their exams, making it difficult for prisoners to participate.

COLLEGE

Institutions offering courses of study that lead to Associate's, Bachelor's, and higher degrees. The term is often used interchangeably with university, although traditionally a university consists of a collection of colleges.

COLLEGE BOARD, THE

A membership organization that provides educational services, such as testing, to U.S. students.

COMMUNITY COLLEGE

A two-year school that offers noncredit and for-credit programs. Noncredit studies are typically used for vocational education while for-credit studies are used to achieve an Associate's degree.

CONTINUING EDUCATION CREDIT

See CEU

CORRESPONDENCE COURSE

A course offered through by mail and completed in-cell or at home, typically including proctored examinations.

COURSE

A unit of instruction that students take in order to learn a given subject.

COURSE DESCRIPTION

Explanation of what a given course consists of, as can be found throughout this publication. This is an essential tool for students considering a school and for portfolio assessments.

CREDIT

A unit of measure used to record completion of courses taken, typically representing the number of hours spent on studies each week. College courses are generally one to six credits each, with three credits being the most common value.

CREDIT-BY-EXAMINATION

A method students can use to receive college credit for what they already know without having to take the typical course work.

CURRICULUM

A set of courses that must be taken in order to meet degree-program requirements.

D

DANTES

Defense Activity for Non-traditional Educational Support. See DSST

DEGREE

A title given by a school to represent the completion of a degree program.

DEPARTMENT OF EDUCATION

The U.S. federal agency that governs educational matters across the nation including accrediting distance-learning programs.

DIPLOMA

Certificate awarded for the completion of an educational program.

DISSERTATION

The major research project typically required in a doctorate program. They are used to demonstrate the mastery of a field of study.

DISTANCE EDUCATION ACCREDITING COMMISSION (DEAC)

Formerly DETC, this is the primary accrediting agency of distance education institutions.

DOCTORATE

The highest degree a student can earn. These include Ph.D, Ed.D, J.D., and M.D.

DSST

DANTES Subject Standardized test (DSST) is a credit-by-examination program that was developed by the U.S. military. It offers testing services to anyone, which can be used to earn college credit for knowledge already achieved without having to take courses.

E

ELECTIVE

A non-required course that may be taken to earn credits toward the total number of credits needed to earn a degree.

EQUIVALENCY EXAMINATION

An examination designed to demonstrate in a subject where the learning was acquired outside of a traditional classroom setting.

F

FINANCIAL AID

Money given to assist a student in the ability to continue their education, including grants, scholarships, loans, tuition reductions, tax incentives, among others.

FRESHMAN

A student in their first year of a traditional four-year U.S. Bachelor's degree program.

G

GRADE POINT AVERAGE (GPA)

The average score a student has earned through their classes.

GRANTS

Financial aid distributed by state and local government that is not required repayment.

GRADUATE RECORD EXAMINATION (GRE)

Standardized test of math and verbal aptitude required by many institutions for admission into graduate programs. Some schools will award undergraduate credit for passing GRE subject exams.

GRADUATE STUDY

Higher-level study taken after completion of undergraduate college study.

GUIDED STUDY

Distance learning method where the student works one-on-one with a professor to complete a course of study.

H

HONOR SYSTEM

A system in which students are trusted not to cheat on examinations when a proctor or supervisor is not present.

HONORARY DOCTORATES

A nonacademic award given by universities and colleges to honor distinguished scholars, celebrities, and donors of large sums of money. Holders of this award may, and often do, call themselves "Doctor."

J

JUNIOR

A student in their third year of a traditional four-year U.S. Bachelor's degree program.

JUNIOR COLLEGE

See community college.

L

LIBERAL ARTS

Institution or degree program that provides broad education on typical topics such as literature, art, mathematics, and science.

LIFE-EXPERIENCE PORTFOLIO

A comprehensive accounting of all of the learning experiences in a student's life. This is the document used in granting academic credit for education learned through life experience.

LSAT

The Law School Admission Test (LSAT) is a required test for law school applicants.

M

MAJOR

Primary focus of a study in a degree-granting program at the university level.

MCAT

The Medical College Admission Test is a required exam for admission to medical school.

MENTOR

Individual who serves as a teacher or model for work or educational experience.

MINOR

Secondary focus of study in a degree-granting program at the university level.

MINISTRY STUDIES

Studies that assist students to sharpen their ministry skills and think critically about theological issues confronting ministry. These studies are typically designed to give the basics of field ministry and are especially useful for those desiring to enter the pulpit ministry.

N

NONCREDIT

A course taken that does not earn college credit.

NONRESIDENT

Student enrolled in state university who resides outside of the state. Typically, schools will charge higher tuition rates to nonresidents.

O

OPEN ADMISSIONS

An admissions policy in which everyone who applies is admitted.

P

PASS/FAIL OPTION

Instead of getting a letter or number grade in a course, the student may elect, at the start of the course, a pass/fail option in which the only grades are either "pass" or "fail." Some schools allow students to elect this option on one or two of their courses each semester.

POSTGRADUATE

British word for a person or program more advanced than the Bachelor's level. Equivalent to graduate in the U.S.

PORTFOLIO ASSESSMENT

A method students can use to obtain college credit for knowledge gained through prior education, work experience, on-the-job training, extensive reading, military training and other life experience.

PREREQUISITE

A course requirement that must be completed prior to enrollment in that course.

PROCTOR

A person who supervises the taking of an examination to ensure that there is no cheating or other rule violations. In prison, these will typically be counselors or staff from the prison's education department.

PSAT

Preliminary Scholastic Aptitude Test, given annually to high school juniors.

Q

QUARTER HOURS

A unit of measure some schools use to represent the credit awarded for a given course. A quarter hour is equivalent to two-thirds of the typical credit hour. Divide quarter hours by 1.5 to convert to traditional credit hours, and vice-versa to convert to quarter hours.

R

REGIONAL ACCREDITING AGENCY

One of the six major accrediting agencies in the U.S. whose accreditation can most be trusted when considering the quality of a school.

REGISTRAR

Department or person that handles student enrollment and course registration.

REGISTRATION

Enrollment in a course and payment of tuition fees.

RELIGIOUS EDUCATION STUDIES

Studies that prepare for a professional teaching ministry, typically offered by religious institutions. The curriculum usually offers broad education in the areas of Scripture and theology, and may require a thesis. These studies are typically pursued by individuals who are interested in serving as pastors, missionaries, evangelists, youth leaders, or in other forms of church ministry.

S

SCHOLARSHIP

Financial aid given to a student by an institution to cover education expenses. Typically awarded on the basis of academic or other achievement.

SCHOLASTIC APTITUDE TEST (SAT)

Standard testing designed by the College Board typically given during high school to determine eligibility for college admissions.

SEMESTER

A school term, generally four to five months (16 weeks), during which students take and complete courses.

SEMESTER HOUR

An amount of credit earned in a course representing one classroom hour per week for a semester. A class that meets three days a week for one hour, or one day a week for three hours, would be worth three semester hours, or semester units.

SOPHOMORE

A student in their second year of a traditional four-year U.S. Bachelor's degree program.

SYLLABUS

Outline of the course including lectures, assignments and exams, usually containing a list of the material a student will need for the course.

T

THESIS

The major requirement of research needed for Master's degree candidates.

TOEFL

Test of English as a Foreign Language, required by many schools of persons for whom English is not the native language.

THEOLOGY STUDIES

The study of God or, more generally, of religious faith, practice and experience, or of spirituality. The study of the "science of things divine." This includes the study of the nature of God, religious truth and its relationship to and influence upon other beings.

TRANSCRIPT

Official record of the student's achievements, including courses, credits and grades.

TRANSFER CREDIT

Credit that is moved from one institution to another.

TUITION

Money charged for formal instruction. This can be either the course cost or all-inclusive of the fees an institution charges.

TUITION WAIVER

A form of financial assistance in which the school charges little or no tuition.

TUTOR

See mentor.

U

UNDERGRADUATE

The period of study beyond high school to the earning of a Bachelor's degree. Term is also used to refer to the person taking this course of study.

UNIVERSITY

An institution that usually comprises one or more undergraduate colleges, one or more graduate schools, and, often, one or more professional schools.

USMLE

The U.S. Medical License Exam, required of everyone who graduates from a non-U.S. Medical school and wishes to be licensed in the U.S.

Z

ZERO-LEVEL COURSES

Courses with numbering lower than 100, typically denoting that it is a noncredit course.

INDEXES

School, Resource & Subject Directory

141

CALENDARS

August 2017

Sun	Mon	Tue	Wed	Thu	Fri	Sat
		1	2	3	4	5
6	7	8	9	10	11	12
13	14	15	16	17	18	19
20	21 Total Solar Eclipse	22	23	24	25	26
27	28	29	30	31		

September 2017

Sun	Mon	Tue	Wed	Thu	Fri	Sat
					1	2
3	4 Labor Day	5	6	7	8	9
10	11	12	13	14	15	16
17	18	19	20	21	22	23
24	25	26	27	28	29	30 Yom Kippur (begins previous night)

Be sure to order your
Prison Lives Almanac: **Prisoner Entertainment Guide** – FALL Edition
(out August 15)

October 2017

Sun	Mon	Tue	Wed	Thu	Fri	Sat
1	2	3	4	5	6	7
8	9 Columbus Day	10	11	12	13	14
15	16	17	18	19	20	21
22	23	24	25	26	27	28
29	30	31				

November 2017

Sun	Mon	Tue	Wed	Thu	Fri	Sat
			1	2	3	4
5 Daylight-Saving Time Ends	6	7	8	9	10 Veterans Day (observed)	11 Veterans Day
12	13	14	15	16	17	18
19	20	21	22	23 Thanksgiving Day	24	25
26	27	28	29	30		

December 2017

Sun	Mon	Tue	Wed	Thu	Fri	Sat
					1	2
3	4	5	6	7	8	9
10	11	12 Hanukkah (begins at sundown)	13	14	15	16
17	18	19	20 Hanukkah Ends	21	22	23
24	25 Christmas Day	26	27	28	29	30
31						

January 2018

Sun	Mon	Tue	Wed	Thu	Fri	Sat
	1 New Years Day	2	3	4	5	6
7	8	9	10	11	12	13
14	15 Martin Luther King Jr. Day	16	17	18	19	20
21	22	23	24	25	26	27
28	29	30	31			

February 2018

Sun	Mon	Tue	Wed	Thu	Fri	Sat
				1	2	3
4 Super Bowl LII	5	6	7	8	9	10
11	12	13	14 Ash Wednesday	15	16	17
18	19 President's Day (Observed)	20	21	22	23	24
25	26	27	28			

March 2018

Sun	Mon	Tue	Wed	Thu	Fri	Sat
				1	2	3
4	5	6	7	8	9	10
11 Daylight-Saving Time begins	12	13	14	15	16	17
18	19	20	21	22	23	24
25	26	27	28	29	30 Good Friday	31 Passover begins

April 2018

Sun	Mon	Tue	Wed	Thu	Fri	Sat
1 Easter	2	3	4	5	6	7
8	9	10	11	12	13	14
15	16	17	18	19	20	21
22	23	24	25	26	27	28
29	30					

May 2018

Sun	Mon	Tue	Wed	Thu	Fri	Sat
		1	2	3	4	5
6	7	8	9	10	11	12
13 Mother's Day	14	15	16 Ramadan Begins	17	18	19
20	21	22	23	24	25	26
27	28 Memorial Day	29	30	31		

June 2018

Sun	Mon	Tue	Wed	Thu	Fri	Sat
					1	2
3	4	5	6	7	8	9
10	11	12	13	14	15	16
17 Father's Day	18	19	20	21	22	23
24	25	26	27	28	29	30

July 2018

Sun	Mon	Tue	Wed	Thu	Fri	Sat
1	2	3	4 Independence Day	5	6	7
8	9	10	11	12	13	14
15	16	17	18	19	20	21
22	23	24	25	26	27	28
29	30	31				

Do you want to get your next Prison Lives product FREE?!

 Become a PRISON LIVES PROMOTER!

Recommend *Prison Lives Almanacs* to your friends, neighbors, and cellies and we'll pay you in credit towards future purchases.
For EACH order we receive with your name as a referral, we'll give you **$5** in credit towards Prison Lives Almanacs.

Here's how it works:

- Step One: Talk about us! **Promote** our Almanacs to those you know.
- Step Two: Tell the ones you're promoting our products to include **your** name with their order.
- Step Three: If we receive an order that has your name as a referral, we will send you a letter to let you know that you've earned $ towards future purchases of any of our products.
- Step Four: Simply place an order with us, less the amount that you've earned through promoting. (Only referrals that we've sent you verification of are eligible.)

PRISON LIVES
PO Box 842, Exeter, California 93221
info@prisonlives.com (corrlinks-friendly)

THANK YOU

for purchasing the

Prison Lives Almanac: **Prisoner Education Guide**

2018 Edition

Prison Lives Almanac: Prisoner Education Guide is updated **every year**.

Education information and resources for prisoners are constantly changing. So that you can find the most comprehensive, up-to-date, and dependable education information you need, *Prison Lives* keeps up with these changes and refreshes our *Prisoner Education Guide* annually.

(Next edition out August 2018.)

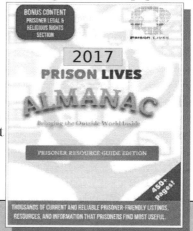

Notes

Order Form

Please indicate your choice(s) below:

Package Deals

- **Take No Prisoners**　　　**$75**
  ($15 off!) Includes 4 Almanacs: Resource Guide, Education Guide, and 2 Entertainment
- **Not Just Fun & Games Package $58**
  ($7 off!) Includes 3 Almanacs: Resource Guide and 2 Entertainment Guides
- **Enlightenment Package**　　**$45**
  ($5 off!) Includes 2 Almanacs: Resource Guide and Education Guide
- **Live & Learn Package**　　**$58**
  ($7 off!) Includes 3 Almanacs: Education Guide and 2 Entertainment Guides
- **Heaps of Fun Package**　　**$70**
  ($10 off!) Includes 4 Almanacs: An entire year's worth of Entertainment Guides!
- **Full Assault Package**　　**$130**
  ($25 off) Includes 7 Almanacs: Resource Guide, Education Guide, and a full year's worth of Entertainment Guides!

Individual Almanacs

- ➢ Resource Guide **2017 | $25**
- ➢ Entertainment Guide Winter 2017 | $20
- ➢ Entertainment Guide Spring 2018 | $20
- ➢ Education Guide 2018 | $25
- ➢ Pen Pal Starter Kit | $10

Prisoner Assistance Services

To order Prisoner Assistance Services, please complete this form and mail it together with a **detailed** explanation of the services you need on a separate piece of paper.

Include payment or request a quote.

All books and services can be ordered online.
www.PrisonLives.com

Name: _____
DOC/ID #: _____
Facility: _____
Address: _____
City: _____ State: _____ Zip Code: _____

Referred by: _____

Complete and mail with your **money order** payment to:

PRISON LIVES
PO Box 842
Exeter, CA 93221

All books are in paperback.
Guides will be shipped within approximately two weeks of receipt of payment or once published, whichever comes first.

Order Form

Please indicate your choice(s) below:

Package Deals

- **Take No Prisoners**   **$75**
  ($15 off!) Includes 4 Almanacs: Resource Guide, Education Guide, and 2 Entertainment

- **Not Just Fun & Games Package $58**
  ($7 off!) Includes 3 Almanacs: Resource Guide and 2 Entertainment Guides

- **Enlightenment Package**   **$45**
  ($5 off!) Includes 2 Almanacs: Resource Guide and Education Guide

- **Live & Learn Package**   **$58**
  ($7 off!) Includes 3 Almanacs: Education Guide and 2 Entertainment Guides

- **Heaps of Fun Package**   **$70**
  ($10 off!) Includes 4 Almanacs: An entire year's worth of Entertainment Guides!

- **Full Assault Package**   **$130**
  ($25 off) Includes 7 Almanacs: Resource Guide, Education Guide, and a full year's worth of Entertainment Guides!

Individual Almanacs

- ➢ Resource Guide | $25
- ➢ Entertainment Guide Winter 2017 | $20
- ➢ Entertainment Guide Spring 2018 | $20
- ➢ Education Guide 2018 | $25
- ➢ Pen Pal Starter Kit | $10

Prisoner Assistance Services

To order Prisoner Assistance Services, please complete this form and mail it together with a **detailed** explanation of the services you need on a separate piece of paper.

Include payment or request a quote.

f.y.i.

All books and services can be ordered online.
www.PrisonLives.com

Name: _____

DOC/ID #: _____

Facility: _____

Address: _____

City: _____ State: _____ Zip Code: _____

Referred by: _____

Complete and mail with your **money order** payment to:

PRISON LIVES
PO Box 842
Exeter, CA 93221

All books are in paperback.
Guides will be shipped within approximately two weeks of receipt of payment or once published, whichever comes first.

We want your feedback!

The *Prison Lives Almanacs* are designed to make your time in prison a more productive experience by bringing the outside world inside to you. Your input matters to us.

Please feel free to contact us anytime with your thoughts or suggestions on how we can make this an even better product. We will promptly respond to these, as well as any questions or concerns you may have.

PRISON LIVES

PO Box 842
Exeter, CA 93221

www.PrisonLives.com
info@PrisonLives.com (Corrlinks friendly)

Remember, *Prison Lives Almanac: Prisoner Education Guide* is updated every year.

Our new edition will be available in August 2018.

Reserve your copy now!

In the meantime, send your suggestions for our next guide and consider the other products in our *Prison Lives* line.

76113007R00296

Made in the USA
Columbia, SC
31 August 2017